INTRODUCTION TO QUANTITATIVE MANAGEMENT

INTRODUCTION

TO QUANTITATIVE MANAGEMENT

George J. Brabb

Professor of Management
University of Montana

HOLT, RINEHART AND WINSTON, INC.
New York / Chicago / San Francisco / Atlanta
Dallas / Montreal / Toronto / London

preface

This book is intended as a text for a course in quantitative analysis for students of business. The material has proved suitable for undergraduates at the junior and senior levels and for first-year graduate students.

The scope of quantitative analysis in business has grown substantially in recent years. It is impossible for any one book or course to cover all aspects of so broad an area. Many topics essential to a complete coverage are of necessity eliminated in the present instance. However, mastery of the materials presented will provide the reader with concepts and techniques basic to the understanding of a much broader range of quantitative tools. The level of understanding of individual techniques is developed sufficiently to aid in the intelligent interpretation of results from the application of a much wider range of quantitative techniques. The assumptions upon which particular quantitative decision models depend and the practical limitations which are placed upon the application of each model are clearly indicated. Those who wish to become sophisticated practitioners in the field will find here a solid base for the development of skill in application of quantitative techniques to business problems.

This text is unique in several respects. Statistical decision processes are developed as a unified whole which encompasses both the "classical" and the "Bayesian" approaches. The development is primarily pragmatic and intuitive rather than theoretical.

v

As the table of contents indicates, topics range from probability through expected value models, statistical inference and regression and correlation to linear programming, waiting-line models, and simulation. Although completeness of coverage of some of the topics has been sacrificed in order to include as many different quantitative techniques as possible, basic concepts are thoroughly covered in all instances.

A final unique feature of the text is the use of the same broadly structured decision problems to illustrate several different models. The reader is given an opportunity to see how the several techniques of analysis complement and supplement one another in developing complete solutions to complicated problems. The examples used are typical of real problems encountered in business organizations, but all are hypothetical and do not truly and completely reflect any real-life situations of which the author is aware. Names and places mentioned in the text are imaginary and are not intended to caricature real persons, firms, or places.

Three types of questions and problems appear at the end of each chapter. "Discussion questions" guide the student in the development of basic conceptual definitions. "Discussion problems" guide the student to the solution of problems designed to illustrate the more difficult techniques developed in the chapter. Finally, "Exercises" are designed for the student to develop alone. Answers to odd-numbered exercises are provided in Appendix A.

The author's debt to others is substantial. It is impossible to personally acknowledge all those who have influenced the development of these materials. Most of the manuscript has been subjected to critical examination in the classroom. Chapter 3 leans heavily on unpublished notes prepared by Professor William F. Sharpe of the University of Washington for a class on mathematical programming.

Professor Robert Thrall and Mr. Roger Wright of the University of Michigan contributed much to the improvement of the original manuscript by pointing out many weak and/or unfortunate statements or examples. Countless persons have made helpful comments on portions of the manuscript.

As credit lines indicate, the statistical tables in Appendix B have been reproduced from several sources. I am indebted to the Literary Executor of the late Sir Ronald A. Fisher, F. R. S., Cambridge, to Dr. Frank Yates, F. R. S., Rothamsted, and to Messrs. Oliver & Boyd Ltd., Edinburgh, for permission to reprint Tables III and VII from their book *Statistical Tables for Biological, Agricultural and Medical Research*. Appendix Tables B-1, B-7, and B-8 are taken from *Handbook of Probability and Statistics with Tables* by R. S. Burington and D. C. May, copyright © 1953,

McGraw-Hill Book Company. Used by permission of McGraw-Hill Book Company.

I am also deeply indebted to my wife, Betty, without whose unfailing and efficient assistance in typing and proofing, this work would not have been possible.

G. J. B.

OCTOBER, 1967

contents

statistical tables

section 1
introduction

1
elements of decision making

INTRODUCTION

The businessman must often deal with problems requiring a selection between alternatives. Consider the questions facing the businessman with a new product. Should the new product be placed in production and marketed? If it is to be produced, who should handle the production? a new firm or a division of an existing firm? Should the plant and equipment used to make the product be complex and costly but allow savings in labor and materials, or should an initially cheaper method with higher operating costs be adopted? Should the businessman restrict his own activity to production and leave the marketing to a firm or firms specializing in that field of operations? What form of business organization would be most successful in producing and/or marketing the product?

The selection of one action or sequence of actions from a number of alternative possible actions is known as a *decision*. A decision is based on many alternatives: it may be complex or simple to make, it may be easy or difficult to implement. Decision making in business, at the present time, is practiced more as an art than as a science. It is, however, becoming increasingly important. Increasing costs are associated with decision making. Businesses are larger; each decision involves a larger outlay of time, money, and resources. The proportion of personnel not concerned with meeting customers or with actual production is increasing. These employees are concerned either with the collection, processing, and refining of information on which decisions will be based or with using such information to make decisions. Thus, the proportion of personnel directly or indirectly concerned with the making of decisions is increasing.

Some problems in decision making can be quantified. Objective solutions optimizing particular goals can be obtained through the proper application of techniques for the analysis of quantitative data. Some of these techniques are relatively simple and nonmathematical, others involve high levels of mathematical proficiency. With the development of electronic equipment for processing data, however, these techniques are brought within the reach of most potential users. Computers provide an increasing ability to sort, collate, and organize large masses of quantitative information for use in decision making. Information on operations can be made more timely, more accurate, and more comprehensive. Finally, available information can be more completely analyzed for its basic significance as a part of routine data processing operations.

THE BASIC STEPS
IN THE DECISION-MAKING PROCESS

The most common suggestion for improving decision making is to adopt a systematic procedure or list of steps to be followed. The following list is suggested here because it is short and well suited to the use of quantitative information as the basis for decision making:

1. Define the problem.
2. Determine the assumptions and/or limitations which affect the solution.
3. Identify the possible courses of action.
4. Isolate the decision-making criterion (or criteria).
5. Determine and compare the possible outcomes and the probability of success in reaching the objective for the various courses of action.
6. Make the decision (select a course of action).
7. Implement the decision.
8. Monitor the results of the decision.

Note that decision making is recognized as a continuous, never-ending process. The reason this is so will become more apparent as the above steps are discussed more fully.

Define the Problem.   A correctly defined problem is well on the way to solution. Is the problem as stated the *actual* problem or only the apparent one? Refer again to the businessman with the new product. What is the problem? It is obviously not a simple thing. The definition of the problem requires an indication of the objective sought by any solution. Is the objective to be certain that society is not denied a desirable product or to determine if there is a market for the product which will justify its production on economic considerations alone?

Determine the Assumptions and/or Limitations Which Affect the Solution. What are the basic objectives and policies of the organization? Will any of these objectives or policies be affected by possible solutions? What are the lines of authority? Does the person studying the problem have the authority to carry out any solution decided upon? What preconceptions are held by the decision maker? How will these preconceptions (assumptions) affect the possible solution? For example, if the individual with the new product were not a successful businessman with capital and other resources available to him, he would be in no position to implement effectively any decision which required a substantial investment of capital and resources. Further along the way, a preconception (assumption) that the basic organization of the businessman's present firm is not to be changed may prevent consideration of some alternative procedures. Limitations of knowledge also can be important; the businessman may not be aware of all alternative organizational methods.

Identify the Possible Courses of Action. This step will be relatively easy if the problem has been sufficiently defined. It can, however, be extremely difficult. The new product may be economically desirable, but if the businessman has not been successful in past endeavors, some alternatives may be impossible. Courses of action can be considered possible only if they can be implemented. A list of *possible* solutions can be long. *Sometimes* an adequate list includes only the most obvious possibilities. It is important to recognize that taking no action at all is a possible solution; the results of that decision should be fully evaluated.

Isolate the Decision-Making Criterion (or Criteria). In its simplest form, this means to find how the possible decisions differ in ways which are important to the objective sought. Is there some one factor, or a small number of factors, which can be used to differentiate and choose between alternatives? At this point you are really defining the important differences among the alternatives and the characteristics which the acceptable solution must possess. For example, the objective for our inventive businessman might be to maximize the economic return from the use of resources currently available to his organization. In addition, the decision could be made to depend upon whether the desire was to maximize returns over the short run or the long run.

Determine and Compare the Possible Outcomes and the Probability of Success in Reaching the Objective for the Various Courses of Action. Once a decision has been reached as to what *can* be done (is possible) a decision is necessary as to which of the possible courses of action is *best*. What is a *best* decision? Supposedly it is that decision which maximizes the criterion (criteria) upon which the decision depends. Maybe there is not a clearly best decision in this sense. Maybe there are several equally desirable solutions. This is not likely. Human factors, overall organizational patterns, or major company policy will differentiate where other factors do not. A suggestive list of these human and organizational factors might be:

1. The number of people to be affected by the decision.
2. The size of expenditure required. Will it affect the firm's capital position?
3. The type of expenditure required. Will it entail a long-term capital outlay or only a short-term expense, size not considered?
4. The portion of the organization affected by the decision ("breadth of effect" and "depth of effect"). What departments and what levels within each department will be directly or indirectly involved?
5. The factor of risk. How likely is it that a wrong decision will lead to extensive losses? Particularly, how likely is it that a wrong decision will force the organization to go "out of business"?[1]
6. The relative amounts of subjective and objective factors involved. Can all the relevant information be objectively determined or does much of it depend upon personal judgments and opinions?

Make the Decision. It is obvious that the above process has carried us to the point where a decision is possible.

Implement the Decision. Going through the steps above and then not putting the decision into force is equivalent to not going through the process at all.

Monitor the Results of the Decision. Decision making is a continuous process, an endless process. Effective control over any organization is

---

[1] This factor can be recognized quantitatively by determining a "utility" function for the decision maker. See Schlaifer, *Introduction to Statistics for Business Decisions*, Chap. 2; and Chernoff and Moses, *Elementary Decision Theory*, Chap. 4. See also p. 210.

possible only if the effects of decisions are known. Decisions at any point in time set processes in motion which will require decisions at later points in time merely to keep the initial decision in force. For example, the decision by our inventive businessman to produce and market his new product will require continual strings of decisions concerning production and inventory levels, sales goals, selling methods, and so forth.

QUANTIFICATION IN THE DECISION-MAKING PROCESS

When one examines facts or existing information about the real world, the great complexity of these facts is undeniable. It is necessary to simplify the phenomena by ignoring all but their most elemental characteristics. Thus we arrive at hypotheses. For example, we all agree that for a given product in a specified market, at a given time, the amount of the product which can be sold is largely determined by the price charged. That is, quantity demanded is a function of price. Similarly, factors of production (men, money, machines, and land) are attracted to those pursuits in which returns from their use are highest.

The two relationships defined above could be cast in the form of mathematical equations. That is, we could express our beliefs about the relation between quantity demanded and price or about resource use and profit rates in mathematical "models." Models are widely used in quantitative decision making to predict the future behavior of some economic variable. Such models also can be used with actual data (actual prices and quantities) to test the "hypotheses" from which the models are built (see Chapters 9, 11, and 12).

Business decisions are usually determined by the "state of the world," that is, what conditions actually are which will determine the success or failure of the activity for which the decision is being made. Unfortunately, the true "state of the world" is seldom known. The decision must be made on the basis of partial information, that is, under conditions of "uncertainty."

For example, our inventive entrepreneur is uncertain as to the amount of sales which he can expect if he markets his new product. If he knew just how much of his product he might sell for each alternative course of action (strategy) and the exact net return at each of those sales levels, he could make his decision without error (with certainty). We must, of course, assume that the number of alternative strategies (courses of action) worthy of consideration would be small enough to be manageable. A few such certainty models are explained in Chapters 2 and 3. Even if the businessman cannot know for certain what will happen if he follows a particular course of action (strategy), he may be able to determine (within limits) the probable level of sales for each alternative course of action. A market survey can determine what proportion of a random sample of customers would "buy" the product. However, he still cannot *know* the "state of nature" which actually exists; he can *know* only how many persons out of the sample indicated a willingness to buy. Even if it can be assumed that this "willingness to buy" will result in an actual purchase, there is still uncertainty because only a sample was contacted. This latter uncertainty is calculable, however.

A simple example will help to illustrate the argument. Suppose you are offered a chance to play the following game: A coin is tossed (assume the coin is fair and the toss is honest). If the coin lands heads up, you *receive* ten cents; if it lands tails up, you *pay* five cents. What should *you pay* per toss, to participate in the game? five cents? more? less?

First, how often can the coin be expected to land heads up? Tails up? Since these two results exhaust the possible outcomes (by definition) and are equally likely (the coin is "fair" and the toss is "honest"), it would seem reasonable to expect that each would occur on about one half of the tosses.

What then can be expected as an *average* result? If you gain ten cents on half of the tosses and lose five cents on half of the tosses, then on the average your return would be $\frac{1}{2}(+10) + \frac{1}{2}(-5) = +5 + (-2.5) = +2.5$, or a gain of 2.5 cents per toss (this is the *expected value* of the game). The game is summarized in Table 1.1.

TABLE 1.1

RESULT OF COIN-TOSS GAME

Outcome of Toss	Result of Outcome (in cents)	Frequency of Outcome	Expected Average
Head	+10	$\frac{1}{2}$	+5
Tail	− 5	$\frac{1}{2}$	−2.5
			+2.5

If our inventive businessman can list all possible outcomes (levels of sales) and determine a probability of occurrence for each he is also in a position to determine the expected average result (expected value) of his "game" (marketing the new product).

Similarly, if the businessman can determine what proportion of his potential customers must purchase the product in order for him to receive a return sufficient to compensate for his investment and his risk in putting the product on the market, the results of the sample survey can be interpreted to indicate which decision to make. Statistical theory tells us how the results of repeated scientific samples can be expected to vary about the true value for the "population" or "universe" (the total group of elements) from which the samples are drawn. Variations of differing magnitudes have differing relative frequencies of occurrence when sampling. Knowledge concerning the nature of these relative frequencies allows us to decide whether the "probability" of an adverse outcome is too great to take the risk of marketing, that is, how likely it is that the true state of the world is unfavorable.

The technique of building a mathematical "model" of the market and using our "model" to predict behavior of the market could be used by our inventive businessman. Suppose we know from past experience that products such as the one we are considering are sold primarily to wealthy families with at least one child between the ages of eight and eighteen years. A quick estimate might be obtained if we could summarize this past experience in an equation such as:

$$S = 11 + 0.31\bar{Y} + 0.20\bar{C}$$

where

S = total sales of the product in thousands of units
$\bar{Y}$ = average income per family in the market area
$\bar{C}$ = the average number of children of proper age per family in the market area
11, 0.31, and 0.20 = constants determined from past experience.

Note that this model represents the average experience of the past, and any estimate derived from it is probably subject to error when applied to a specific instance. The distribution of this error also is calculable, but not its exact magnitude in this instance.

Note that the coin-tossing game also employed a model in that we assumed a "balanced coin and an honest toss." Without such an assumption, the probability (frequency of occurrence) of a particular outcome could not be computed.

The above discussion indicates that "models," "certainty," "risk," and "uncertainty" are important concepts in quantitative decision making. Before proceeding further, we should formally define these concepts.

Models

A model is a physical, pictorial, or symbolic representation of a system, a decision process, an organization, or an object that can be used to represent the original system, decision process, organization, or object that is the purpose of study, experimentation, or prediction.

Types of Models.   There are three basic types of models; the iconic, the analog, and the symbolic. An *iconic* model is a pictorial or physical representation of the real system, process, organization, or object. Maps, blueprints, drawings and photographs are examples of iconic models. So are model airplanes, model cars, dolls, and statues. An *analog* model represents the original properties by another set of properties which are easier to illustrate or use. An analog model is not constructed of the same materials as the original system, process, organization, or object. For example, electronic circuits made up of switches, wires transistors, capacitors, resistances, and so forth, can be used to represent the operation of physical systems such as the shock absorber and spring system on an automobile or a truck or the wings of an aircraft. The engineer's slide rule is an analog model of a computing system based upon logarithms.

The *symbolic* model is a representation of a system, process, or object by a set of symbols. Symbols may be words, letters, or arbitrary characters. The most common symbol set used in symbolic models is that of mathematics. In fact, it is not uncommon to substitute the word *mathematical* for the word symbolic in speaking of this type of model. Our major interest in this book is in symbolic (mathematical) models. The equations above are symbolic models. In fact, every equation in this book may be considered a symbolic model.

Nature of Models.   Not only do models differ in type, but they also differ as to their true purpose, intent, or nature. Some models are only *descriptive*, that is, they simply show how a process or a system operates or the characteristics that an object possesses. Descriptive mathematical models can be used to study the operation of a system or a process and even, perhaps, to predict how it will react to particular changes in its environment. A descriptive mathematical model only recreates the system or process in mathematical form. It has application only to the specific system or process and then only as to what the system or process does in operation. Prediction from such a model usually requires repeated operation many times under the same external conditions in order to learn the response characteristics of the system or process modeled. Such models underlie the simulation processes introduced in Chapter 13.

A more useful model is one which describes not just what *is* but what *should* be. Such a model is known as a *normative* model. For example, the so-called "law of demand" from economic theory is basically descriptive when stated in its simplest terms:

$$\text{quantity demanded} = f(\text{price})$$

However, even this simple "model" states a long-run tendency of the system which is *expected to hold true*. Given that the basic assumptions of economics—that is, man is an economic animal with essentially unlimited wants, but the resources for filling those wants are limited—are true assumptions, the law of demand states a relationship which *must* hold (at least in the long run). Further refined, the law of demand states that the relationship between price and quantity demanded must be inverse. An increase in price (all other things equal) leads to a fall in quantity demanded, and vice versa. When buttressed with indifference analysis (a detailed method of stating that man is an economic animal) the nature of the functional relationship between price and quantity demanded is seen (deductively) to be as postulated. It is seen that this relationship *must* be true and that the function describes what *should* be and not just what *is*. Basically, then, normative models are theoretical models which are derived from explanations of "why" things happen the way they do. Such models do not stop with just a simple description of what happens.

Models and the Real World—Abstraction. Symbolic (mathematical) models of the real world seldom can be made complex enough to cover every situation. The simple model for the law of demand shown in the previous section does not include the effects on quantity demanded of any variable other than price. There definitely are other such variables. One of the most important is income. A change in income (all other things equal) will cause a shift in the demand function. A larger (smaller) quantity will be demanded at each price when income increases (decreases). This relationship is most often of a positive nature, but it can be inverse.

The demand model could be further refined by taking into account changes in quality of the good being demanded. Another refinement might take into account the impact of a change in the price of a competing good or a change in taxation. Each change in the direction of obtaining greater reality introduces greater complexity into the model. The model rapidly becomes so complex that it surpasses our ability to obtain appropriate data and manipulate them. Also, we find that each addition returns proportionately less advantage. For example, the basic form of the demand model tells us which direction quantity demanded can be expected to change if price is changed. Only minor modifications in this relationship will usually result from the addition of each of the other variables: income, product quality, and prices of competitive goods.

The degree of abstraction appropriate to a model obviously depends upon the use to be made of it. Unfortunately, models often involve greater abstraction than we would like because of our lack of knowledge concerning relationships between variables. Usually, only the major relationships are recognized well enough to be described in the model. Effects of less important variables are often assumed to be individually minor and random in total effect. This is an assumption of the regression models of Chapter 12. When models contain a random element to represent unrecognized relationships and thus fail to explain observed behavior exactly, the models are labeled *stochastic*. Models which do not contain random elements and in which all pertinent relationships are assumed to be represented are called *deterministic*. The models studied in the next two chapters are deterministic.

Decision Models

We are primarily concerned with models used to guide decisions. For any decision problem there is a set of outcomes (returns) associated with a set of alternative strategies (or acts) and the possible states of nature. The strategies (the alternatives available) may vary in number from two to infinity. Associated with each strategy or action is a set of outcomes (returns), one for each of the possible states of nature. The possible states of nature may vary in number from one to infinity. If only one possible state of nature is recognized, then the payoff from selecting each strategy will be known. We will have a condition of decision making under conditions of *certainty* of knowledge concerning payoffs for each strategy. This is because the state of nature is known. For example, suppose our inventive businessman did have a mathematical equation describing how the volume of sales of his product will be affected by the age and income distribution of the population. If this equation has known parameters, that is, if it expresses the true relationship, he is dealing with a certainty model. Such models are discussed in Chapters 2 and 3. If, however, the parameters of the equation have been estimated from a study of sample data, the true relationship is not known and the predictions of the model are subject to error. This is a partial uncertainty model. Such a single equation model is described in Chapter 12.

Whenever the true state of nature is unknown and several states of nature are recognized as possible, the outcome resulting from the selection of a particular strategy will be *uncertain*. The degree of uncertainty involved varies along a continuum. At one end of the continuum are the decision situations where the various states of nature can be enumerated and a true *probability* of occurrence assigned to each possible state. These situations are called decision problems involving *risk*. At the other end of the uncertainty continuum are those situations where no knowledge exists concerning how likely the occurrence of each of the states of nature may be. This is the situation of *complete uncertainty*. In between the risk situation and the complete uncertainty situation fall all those situations where some knowledge of the likelihood of occurrence of each of the possible states of nature is present. This knowledge may vary from objective evidence of past experience, through informed judgment based upon long experience to subjective "guesses" based upon limited experience or no experience. Many examples of partial uncertainty and the development and use of distributions expressing the relative likelihood of occurrence of possible states of nature are found in Chapters 4, 6, 7, 9, and 10.

The statistical decision models involving sampling fall in the class of uncertainty models. The expected value models of Chapters 5–7 are more nearly risk models. The coin-tossing game discussed previously involves a true risk model. The estimation models of Chapter 8 are more nearly models involving complete uncertainty. We seldom encounter true complete-uncertainty models.

In making decisions, it is often necessary to limit the number of alternative strategies and the number of alternative states of nature which will be considered in the analysis. In deciding how many strategies to evaluate, the decision maker must consider the risks of error introduced by eliminating some strategies. The choice of states of nature to be considered is sometimes related to the choice of strategies (see Chapter 10).

Basically, quantification in decision making is used to guide us to a proper decision based on what we know about which state of the world is true. If we possessed complete information as to the state of the world, the outcome of a particular trial would no longer be uncertain; it would be known with certainty before the trial was completed. The only use to be made of quantification would be for choosing among *certain* alternatives. Even so, it may be difficult to choose the best action. For example, a custom machine shop which produces only to order and has a complement of machines and men whose operating characteristics are fully known can determine the cost of producing an available batch of jobs with a given combination of men and machines. However, it may be quite difficult to determine which combination of men and machines will lead to the lowest cost simply because many alternatives are available. For example, if there are three ways to order each job through a set of three different machines and there are 300 jobs and 20 *sets* of machines, how many different job-machine arrangements are there? (See Chapter 4.) In addition to merely counting these possibilities, suppose that the 300 jobs divide into three levels of cost of accomplishment in each one of the three machine orderings. This example is totally unrealistic because of its simplicity, but it illustrates the point that even when no uncertainty (lack of knowledge) is present, choosing the optimum alternative may be very difficult. Deterministic mathematical models are of limited usefulness in many such situations. However, mathematical simulation may prove useful.

In all cases where quantitative methods are used, a common approach exists. First, some quantifiable variable is chosen as the decision criterion. This is the *decision parameter*, the population variable whose value will determine the decision. Either through deductive logic or experimentation (for example, sample observation) or both, the value of the parameter is estimated. In most situations what we obtain is an estimate which has a certain "probability" of being within specified limits of the true value, usually an *expected value* which represents *average* experience under such conditions. In either case, the estimate computed can be expected to be subject to variation. The decision depends upon how likely it is that the "state of nature" is favorable, as judged from the estimate obtained while allowing for the variation inherent in the estimation process. In certain special circumstances, quantitative methods can choose between differing strategies for *making* the decision. This process is explained for situations involving uncertainty and the possibility of sampling in Chapters 9 and 10.

SUMMARY

Decision making is the process of choosing between alternative courses of action. The basic steps in any decision process have been defined to be:

1. Define the problem.
2. Determine the assumptions and/or limitations which affect the solution.
3. Identify the possible courses of action.
4. Isolate the decision-making criterion (or criteria).
5. Determine and compare the possible outcomes and the probability of success in reaching the objective for the various courses of action.
6. Make the decision (select a course of action).
7. Implement the decision.
8. Monitor the results of the decision.

Quantification enters the decision-making process when some quantifiable variable is chosen as the criterion for judging what alternative course of action (strategy) will be chosen by the decision process. Either through deductive logic or actual observation (sampling) the value of this decision parameter is estimated. The decision depends upon how likely it is that our estimate truly indicates that existing conditions (the state of nature) are favorable to each alternative course of action (strategy). Finally, even the decision process itself may be determined as part of the total process of making the decision in those cases where sampling is possible.

DISCUSSION QUESTIONS

1. Develop definitions in your own words for each of the following:

   (a) decision
   (b) decision-making criterion
   (c) state of nature
   (d) expected value
   (e) decision parameter
   (f) model
   (g) mathematical model

   (h) certainty model
   (i) uncertainty model
   (j) descriptive model
   (k) normative model
   (l) stochastic model
   (m) deterministic model
   (n) risk model

2. Argue that "models" of some sort underlie all our decision making. (Hint: When you think of a statistician, a teacher, a doctor, a politician, and so forth, what "attributes" and "characteristics" do you automatically "assume" him to possess? What actions and reactions do you expect of him?)

3. Do businessmen making decisions without recourse to mathematics use models?
   Hint: Do all models have to be clearly quantified? Refer to the discussion on models and the real world.

4. Differentiate *risk* and *uncertainty*. What is the importance of this distinction?
   Hint: Define the two terms carefully. How do the definitions differ? Will the difference(s) influence their use?

5. Do the following statements imply a model? If so, identify it as clearly as possible.
   (a) "There's a sucker born every minute."
   (b) "Advertising will increase sales."
   (c) The overhead rate of an organization is defined as expenses divided by the direct labor dollars.

EXERCISES

1. Suppose you are considering opening a bookstore near the university (or college) you are now attending. Consider this as a decision problem. As briefly as possible outline the elements of the decision problem. Give particular attention to the decision criterion. Assume that financing is not a problem since you have sufficient capital to establish the store.

2. Suppose you must decide between regular studying this evening (no test *scheduled* tomorrow, but a "pop" quiz possible), going out to a party, or watching a favorite one-hour television program at 9:00 P.M. Consider this as a decision problem. What are the alternatives? What is (are) the objective(s) you wish to maximize? What rule will you use to minimize the problem of competing objectives? What is your decision at this point? If you have an important test scheduled for tomorrow, how would your decision change?

section 2
decision making under certainty

2
optimization

INTRODUCTION

In the discussion of the nature of decision making in Chapter 1, we defined mathematical models as one method of guiding decisions with quantitative methods. In the present chapter some simple mathematical models are illustrated. Because one of the most useful mathematical techniques for quantitative decision making involves the use of the differential calculus, an introduction to this important tool is given in an appendix at the end of the chapter.

OPTIMAL DECISIONS FROM MODELS

Mathematical models are used in managerial analysis to *guide* decisions. The best decision is usually one which leads to the greatest profit, the least cost, or the use of the smallest number of men or machines, and so forth. This indicates that for most managerial decisions there is a variable whose value management wishes to *optimize* (maximize or minimize). We will call this variable the *object* variable. If the object variable can be expressed as dependent upon variables which management controls, the resulting model (equation or equations), can be manipulated mathematically to determine the value of the controllable variables which will lead to the optimum value of the object variable.

Incremental Analysis

Incremental analysis involves the incremental *gain* (change in the object variable) associated with a one-unit change in a controllable variable. For example, Mr. Smithson of Smithson's Party Boats is trying to decide what fee he will charge for the six-hour daytime cruise on his big paddle-wheel steamer, the *White Ghost*. The *White Ghost* can carry as many as 250 persons on the daytime cruise. Mr. Smithson knows that at $5 per person, he can fill the boat to capacity. He is convinced that raising the price will cause the loss of customers. On the average, he expects to lose one passenger for each 2.5 cent increase in the fare. Mr. Smithson's cost data indicate that it costs $275 to run the *White Ghost* on the cruise. Lunches for the passengers, extra stewards, and so forth, add a variable cost of $3 per passenger for each passenger on the boat.

Tabular Form of Incremental Analysis. One way to analyze this problem and discover the optimum fare is to compute the change in income and expense associated with each change in the fare. If Mr. Smithson increases the fare from $5.00 to $5.05 (note that the fare would not increase in 2.5 cent units), the number of passengers would fall from 250 to 248, but gross income would rise from $1250.00 (250 × $5.00) to $1252.40 (248 × $5.05). Concurrently, expenses would fall from $1025 ($275 + $3(250)) to $1019.00 ($275 + 3(248)). Net income therefore increases from $225.00 ($1250 − $1025) to $233.40 (1252.40 − $1019.00). It is apparent that each five cent rise in the fare will decrease expenses by $6.00 (2 × $3.00) since only variable costs are affected by the decrease in number of passengers. Income, on the other hand, may not increase each time the fare is raised. Eventually, the decrease in the number of paying passengers will not be offset by the increase in the fare. The change in gross income is not so easy to compute as was the change in expense. It is easier to compute incomes at each increment to the fare and adjust this with the decline in costs to arrive at the *net increment* associated with the change in fare. These computations have been carried out in Table 2.1. To keep the table within reasonable limits in size, the fare has been incremented in units of $0.25 except for the fare range between $7.00 and $7.25 where the fares of $7.10, $7.125, and $7.15 are shown to indicate the point of maximum net income.

Note that net income is little affected by the fare changes between $7.00 and $7.25. The optimum fare (analytically) is $7.125 which would attract 165 passengers. This is not a reasonable price, however, and the fare would realistically be set at either $7.00 or $7.25 to obtain 170 or 160 passengers, respectively. The final choice would probably be determined by consideration of the effects of the difference of ten passengers on the number of stewards, and so forth.

TABLE 2.1

NET EFFECTS OF FARE INCREASES FOR PARTY BOAT WHITE GHOST

Fare	No. of Passengers	Income	Variable Expense	Total Expense†	Net Income
$5.00	250	$1250.00	$750.00	$1025.00	$225.00
5.25	240	1260.00	720.00	995.00	265.00
5.50	230	1265.00	690.00	965.00	300.00
5.75	220	1265.00	660.00	935.00	330.00
6.00	210	1260.00	630.00	905.00	355.00
6.25	200	1250.00	600.00	875.00	375.00
6.50	190	1235.00	570.00	845.00	390.00
6.75	180	1215.00	540.00	815.00	400.00
7.00	170	1190.00	510.00	785.00	405.00
7.10	166	1178.60	498.00	773.00	405.60
7.125	165	1175.625	495.00	770.00	405.625
7.15	164	1172.60	492.00	767.00	405.60
7.25	160	1160.00	480.00	755.00	405.00
7.50	150	1125.00	450.00	725.00	400.00
7.75	140	1085.00	420.00	695.00	390.00

† Total Expense = Fixed Expense ($275.00) + Variable Expense

Note that the change in income associated with a rise in the fare is positive only for a small range of increase. Maximum *gross* returns are reached at a fare of $5.625. (It is left to the reader to demonstrate this.) However, the decrease in variable costs due to the decrease in number of passengers carried is greater than the decline in total revenue until the point of maximum net income. To understand this situation, one need not consider total expense. One need only observe the net effects on income and expenses. As long as the difference in these two net effects leads to an increase in net income, it pays to lower the fare. This can be seen most easily by reference to Table 2.2. Note that when the fare changes from \$7.10 to \$7.125, the net return changes from positive to negative. This change from increase to decrease is associated with a change of only one in the number of passengers carried. Note also, that both the change in income and the change in expense, if plotted against either fare or number of passengers would plot as straight lines. This is

TABLE 2.2

NET EFFECTS OF CHANGES IN FARE FOR PARTY BOAT WHITE GHOST

Fare	Number of Passengers	Effect on Net Income of Changes in Income and Expense		
		Income	Expense	Total
\$5.00	250	\$ —	\$ —	\$ —
5.25	240	+10.00	+30.00	+40.00
5.50	230	+5.00	+30.00	+35.00
5.75	220	0	+30.00	+30.00
6.00	210	−5.00	+30.00	+25.00
6.25	200	−10.00	+30.00	+20.00
6.50	190	−15.00	+30.00	+15.00
6.75	180	−20.00	+30.00	+10.00
7.00	170	−25.00	+30.00	+5.00
7.10	166	−11.40	+12.00	+0.60
7.125	165	−2.975	+3.00	+0.025
7.15	164	−3.025	+3.00	−0.025
7.25	160	−12.60	+12.00	−0.60
7.50	150	−35.00	+30.00	−5.00

due to the nature of the problem. All simple relationships (effect of fare increases on number of passengers and effect on expense of adding another passenger) are linear. This is illustrated on Figure 2.1 where the variable expense and total expense curves are seen to have constant slopes.

Algebraic Form of Incremental Analysis. If we wish to analyze Mr. Smithson's problem algebraically we can develop formulas which will allow us to compute the change in revenue and the change in costs associated with each change in the amount of the fare. The returns show:

total revenue (TR) = (fare)(number of passengers)

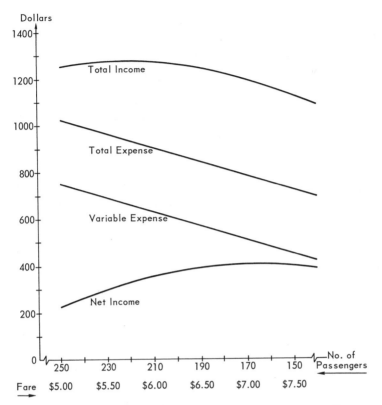

FIG. 2.1.   Effects of fare increases for party boat *White Ghost*.

Let x = number of additional passengers that could be carried on the *White Ghost*, that is, unused capacity at given fare. Then,

$$\text{number of passengers carried} = 250 - x$$
$$\text{fare} = 5.00 + 0.025x$$

Therefore,

$$TR = (5.00 + 0.025x)(250 - x)$$
$$= 1250 + 1.25x - 0.025x^2$$
$$\text{total cost } (TC) = \text{fixed cost} + \text{variable cost}$$
$$\text{fixed cost} = 275$$
$$\text{variable cost} = 3(250 - x)$$
$$= 750 - 3x$$

Then,

$$TC = 1025 - 3x$$
$$\text{net revenue } (NR) = TR - TC$$

or

$$NR = (1250 + 1.25x - 0.025x^2) - (1025 - 3x)$$
$$= -0.025x^2 + 4.25x + 225$$

The last expression is a *quadratic* equation of the general form $y = ax^2 + bx + c$. The rules of algebra tell us that the optimum values for x and y can be computed quite easily using the following formulas.[1]

2.00 $x = -\dfrac{b}{2a}$

and

2.01 $y = \dfrac{4ac - b^2}{4a}$

Substituting into 2.00,

$$x = -\frac{4.25}{2(-0.025)}$$
$$= \frac{4.25}{0.05}$$
$$= \mathbf{85}$$

Substituting into 2.01,

$$NR = \frac{4(-0.025)(225) - (4.25)^2}{4(-0.025)}$$
$$= \frac{-22.5 - 18.0625}{-0.1}$$
$$= \mathbf{\$405.625}$$

---

[1] For a derivation of these formulas for solving a quadratic see C. A. Theodore, *Applied Mathematics: An Introduction*, Homewood, Illinois: Richard D. Irwin, Inc., 1965, pp. 222–225.

Referring back to the basic problem formulation, the fare to be charged would be:

$$\text{fare} = \$5.00 + \$0.025(x)$$
$$= \$5.00 + \$0.025(85)$$
$$= \mathbf{\$7.125}$$

The number of passengers demanding tickets would be:

$$\text{number of passengers} = 250 - x$$
$$= 250 - 85$$
$$= \mathbf{165}$$

This answer agrees with the answer obtained by the tabular incremental process.

Additional Examples of Incremental Analysis. In the above example, incremental costs (costs of producing one more unit) were positive. Such costs may actually be negative under certain circumstances. For example, if a company offers a sufficiently large quantity discount. Suppose the Dry-Cell Company buys the basic raw material for the insulation in its batteries from a company which offers its product in 100 pound packages at $50 per package or $2200 per carload of 50 packages. Dry-Cell would be foolish to order just the 45 packages required for one quarter's production. Those 45 packages would cost more than the 50 packages in a carload. The total cost of the 45 packages at $50 per package (the unit-price cost) would be:

$$45(50) = \$2250$$

Actually, the incremental cost of each unit over 44 is negative. For the fiftieth package:

$$\text{incremental cost} = \text{carload price minus unit-price cost of 49 units}$$
$$= \$2200 - 49(\$50)$$
$$= \$2200 - \$2450$$
$$= \mathbf{-\$250}$$

Similarly, computer manufacturers historically rented their computers at a flat fee (say $10,000) for one shift (176 hours) per month. Considered as incremental cost, the first unit of computer use, say one hour, has as its marginal cost the shift rental ($10,000) for the total 176 hours (plus the cost of an operating crew, which might be available on an hourly, daily, weekly, or monthly basis). Additional units of computer use have a marginal cost of zero up to 176 total hours of use in one calendar month (assuming the operating crew is paid on a monthly basis). Use of one additional hour beyond 176 is possible only by paying a second shift rental (usually a percentage of the prime shift rental, say 40 percent or $4000). Thus, the one hundred and seventy-seventh hour of use involves an expenditure of $4000 for the shift rental (plus the cost of an additional operating crew for at least that one hour). Such an analysis indicates that charging internal-using departments the average cost per hour for computer use can result in less than optimum use of the computer. If any of the 176 hours goes unused, it should not be because an internal user cannot afford to pay the average cost per hour since the marginal cost of the additional use cannot exceed the direct out-of-pocket costs of operating the computer for that time. Similarly, once the decision is made to incur the cost of an extra shift, applications should be added so long as the net benefit from putting them on the computer is at least positive. The internal use charge should be set at whatever level results in full utilization of the time purchased. The appropriate charge may be either higher or lower than the average cost per hour of the total computer operation.

If the value of one variable is determined by the value of some other variable, we say that the first variable is a *function* of the second. For the example we have been using in this chapter, net income from operation of the *White Ghost* is a *function* of the number of passengers carried. If this relationship can be graphed as a straight line (usually the value of the determining variable is plotted on the horizontal axis and the value of the variable being determined is plotted on the vertical axis) the function is said to be *linear*. Such linear functions can provide a valuable control device when used in break-even analysis. Break-even analysis is an application of incremental analysis which can be used to improve operating efficiency of existing facilities, to plan for expansion of operations, and to assist in budgetary control.

Suppose, for example, that the Duravit Corporation is considering replacing their old strawberry filling and packaging lines and has developed the data shown in Table 2.3. The new line would result in lower variable unit costs and faster processing. Before approving the change, Duravit's management wants to be certain that this action will not result in a loss for the packing operation this year. While the same machinery is used for packaging other fruits, the change is being made primarily for the berry packing. Since strawberries are the most critical berry packing operation, management decides that if the new line will at least break even on strawberries, it should be installed. As indicated in Table 2.3, the company's estimate of minimum sales is 4,425,000 one pound units. Therefore, using the new line, total costs must be covered by total sales income from 4,425,000 units or less. The question is: What

TABLE 2.3

DATA ON FROZEN STRAWBERRY PRODUCTION, DURAVIT CORPORATION

	Old Line	New Line
Part A. Expected Sales and Related Data		
Minimum Expected Sales (thousand of pounds)	4425	
Expected Minimum Sales Price per One Pound Unit	$.20	
Part B. Cost Data		
1. Fixed Costs (thousands of dollars)		
Regular Factory Overhead	40	30
Other Overhead	60	60
Filling and Packaging Machines (Depreciation)	120	200
Total	220	290
2. Variable Costs (dollars per 1000 units)		
Packaging	7.00	7.00
Filler (including strawberries)	99.00	99.00
Direct Labor	2.50	.40
Other Direct Operating Costs	1.50	.40
Distribution Costs	20.00	20.00
Total	130.00	126.80

is the break-even volume? The following relationships hold whichever line is being analyzed.

(1)   sales income (SI) = sales price (p) × units sold (Q)
(2)   total costs (TC) = fixed cost (FC) + variable costs (VC)
(3)   variable costs (VC) = variable costs/units (UVC) × units sold (Q)

The break-even sales volume would be the value of Q which would satisfy the equality:

(4) $SI = TC$

expanding both sides, this becomes

(5) $p(Q) = FC + UVC(Q)$

Substituting the appropriate values from Table 2.3 for the new line, this becomes

$$0.20Q = 290,000 + 0.1268Q$$

solving for Q,

$$Q = \frac{290,000}{0.0732}$$
$$= 3,961,749$$

Substituting the break-even Q into equation (5) and solving both sides independently provides a check on the correctness of the solution.

$$0.20(3,961,749) = 290,000 + 0.1268(3,961,749)$$
$$\$792,349.80 = \$792,349.77$$

The result of the check indicates we have found a solution. The slight difference is due to rounding Q to the next larger whole number. If we had used the value of Q to one decimal place, the result of the check calculations would indicate agreement of income and expense to the nearest cent rather than to the nearest ten cents as was obtained above.

The break-even analysis carried out above is graphed in Figure 2.2. The break-even sales volumes for both the new and the old line are shown. It is left as an exercise for the reader to carry out the calculations to obtain the exact value of the breakeven sales volume for the old line.

In all of the foregoing analyses, basic relationships were assumed to be linear. The effect on costs (income) of a one-unit change in total production was assumed constant. For example, in the case of the Smithson Party Boats, each increase of $0.025 in the fare causes the number of passengers buying tickets to decrease by one person. Each time the number of passengers decreases by one person, costs are reduced by $3.00. Even so, the net revenue function turns out to be a quadratic rather than a linear function. This is not unusual. However, it is also true that there could be no maximum net revenue if the net revenue function were linear (except at an end point). It is only in break-even analysis that we have been able to find a solution utilizing only linear functions.

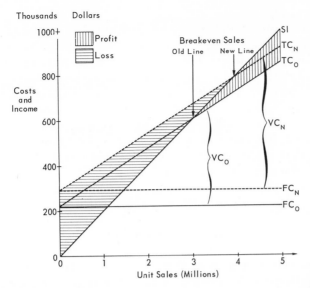

FIG. 2.2.   Breakeven analysis of old and new strawberry packaging lines of Duravit Corporation.

Note, however, that the break-even point is not a point of optimum net profit. It is merely a point where all costs are covered by revenues, the point at which positive profits *begin*.

Marginal Analysis

In the incremental analyses above, we have been dealing with *marginal analysis*. That is, the decision on whether to continue to change the decision variable was determined by an analysis of how much the contemplated change would affect costs and income. If the net effect of a contemplated change was to increase net income, the change was made. The most elementary form of incremental analysis was rather crude, assuming the nature of a trial-and-error process. The algebraic analyses were more sophisticated, allowing us to use mathematical techniques to find the optimum value directly. We stated those conditions which had to be satisfied in order to find the optimum (in the case of break-even analysis, the satisfying) point, and then solved for the value of the controllable variable which fulfilled those conditions.

In the Smithson Party Boats example, we continued to increase the fare until at the last change the net decrease in cost was just offset by the net decrease in revenue (see Table 2.2). That is, we pushed output (number of passengers carried) to the point where the *marginal cost* of carrying the last passenger was just equal to the *marginal revenue* that passenger brought in. It would seem, therefore, that the optimum number of passengers to carry could be obtained by deriving an expression for marginal revenue and an expression for marginal cost, setting the two expressions equal to each other and solving for the optimum x.

Marginal revenue is the addition to revenue associated with a one-unit change in output. In this case we are changing the number of seats left vacant on the party boat, that is, x = the number of additional passengers that could be carried on the *White Ghost*. We already have stated the total revenue function as

$$TR = 1250 + 1.25x - 0.025x^2$$

Marginal revenue (MR) at output x would be

$$MR(x) = TR(x) - TR(x - 1)$$

where

$$TR(x - 1) = (5.00 + 0.025(x - 1))(250 - (x - 1))$$
$$= 1248.725 + 1.30x - 0.025x^2$$

Substituting:

$$MR(x) = 1250 + 1.25x - 0.025x^2 - (1248.725 + 1.30x - 0.025x^2)$$
$$= 1.225 - 0.05x$$

Marginal Cost (MC) is the change in cost associated with a one-unit change in output. Each reduction by one in the number of passengers decreases variable costs by 3.00. MC is therefore constant for all x at $-\$3.00$.

The optimum level of x is that point where $MC = MR$ or where,

$$-3.00 = 1.275 - 0.05x$$
$$0.05x = 4.275$$
$$x = \mathbf{85.5}$$

This result varies by 0.5 from our previous solution. If we had defined marginal revenue as

$$MR(x + 1) = TR(x + 1) - TR(x)$$

the optimum value of x would have been calculated as 84.5. (The reader should verify this.) Our previous answer was exactly 85. Why the difference of 0.5 in each case? Because what we have just calculated is the *average* rate of change over one unit as we *approach* the point where $x = 85$. What we are really interested in is the *instantaneous rate* of change at the point where $x = 85$. The calculus must be used to obtain the instantaneous rate of change. Students without any background in differential calculus will find the appendix to this chapter helpful.

Maxima and Minima by Calculus.   In Figure 2.3 we have blown up the Net Revenue curve from Figure 2.1 in the area near the optimum. We have been attempting to find the maximum value of this function (the

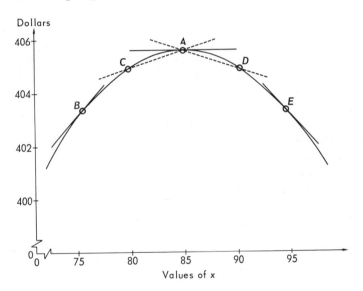

FIG. 2.3.   Total net returns from party boat *White Ghost* for selected values of x.

highest point on the curve). We know that this is the point where $MC = MR$. It must also be the point where *marginal* net revenue is zero. The maximum point is labeled as point A on Figure 2.3. It can be seen that at that point the curve has a *slope* of zero. The slope at the point A is indicated by the horizontal straight line which is *tangent* to the curve at that point.

Slope over a given range is defined as the change in the function per unit change in x over the given range. Thus, the slope of the dashed line *through* points C and A would be computed as follows:

At point C, $x = 80$ and net revenue $= \$405.000$
At point A, $x = 85$ and net revenue $= \$405.625$

$$\text{average slope} = \frac{\text{change in function}}{\text{change in } x}$$

$$= \frac{405.625 - 405.00}{85 - 80}$$

$$= \frac{0.625}{5}$$

$$= \mathbf{0.125}$$

indicating that, on the average, for every one unit change in x between 80 and 85, net revenue changes by \$0.125 in the same direction. Between $x = 85$ and $x = 90$ (line AD) the average slope would be $-\$0.125$. (The reader should confirm this.) However, this does not tell us the slope at point A. To find the slope at point A, we must take a tangent line like that at point B (or point E) which will tell us the slope at *that* point and move it along the line to point A. A general equation which describes the *slope of the function* (a general equation describing all possible tangent lines such as those at points B, A, and E) must be found.

The slope between two points on the curve is defined as the change in $f(x)$, the value of the function, over the change in x. Here

$$f(x) = -0.025x^2 + 4.25x + 225$$

If we were to increase x by some amount, say Δx, then

$$f(x + \Delta x) = -0.025(x + \Delta x)^2 + 4.25(x + \Delta x) + 225$$

and the slope of the function over the range from x to $x + \Delta x$ would be:

$$\frac{f(x + \Delta x) - f(x)}{\Delta x}$$

or

$$\frac{-0.025(x + \Delta x)^2 + 4.25(x + \Delta x) + 225 - (-0.025x^2 + 4.25x + 225)}{\Delta x}$$

which reduces to

$$\frac{-0.050x\Delta x - 0.025(\Delta x)^2 + 4.25\Delta x}{\Delta x}$$

or, the slope from x to $x + \Delta x$ equals

$$-0.05x - 0.025\Delta x + 4.25$$

If we allow Δx to approach zero, then the middle term $(-0.025\Delta x)$ drops out and the slope function at the point x (x to $x + \Delta x$ becomes x to $x + 0$ or x to x) is found to be

$$-0.05x + 4.25$$

What we have found is the *first derivative* of the net revenue function with respect to x. This would usually be symbolized as dNR/dx and verbalized as "the first of derivative of net revenue with respect to x." Thus,

$$\frac{dNR}{dx} = -0.05x + 4.25$$

We know that net revenue is a maximum at the point where the slope of the function (marginal net revenue) is equal to zero. That is, at the point where

$$\frac{dNR}{dx} = 0$$

or, substituting,

$$-0.05x + 4.25 = 0$$
$$-0.05x = -4.25$$
$$x = \mathbf{85}$$

Which says that maximum net revenue occurs at the point where $x = 85$, which agrees with our previous analysis.

The rules of calculus, as explained in the appendix to this chapter, allow us to obtain the derivative of any function being analyzed directly.

For example, suppose that the NoKut Company has calculated that its unit demand function for its Econot model is

$$p = 64 - 0.02x$$

where

p = price per unit
x = units demanded

Then the sales revenue (SR) function would be price times units sold or

$$SR = (64 - 0.02x)x$$
$$= 64x - 0.02x^2$$

Costs of production per unit for the Econot total $16.00. Therefore, the Cost (C) function is:

$$C = 16x$$

The net revenue function would be

$$NR = SR - C$$
$$= 64x - 0.02x^2 - 16x$$
$$= 48x - 0.02x^2$$

Maximum net revenue will be obtained at that sales level where marginal net revenue $\left(\dfrac{dNR}{dx}\right)$ equals zero. Utilizing Rules C.2, C.3, and C.4 from the calculus appendix,

$$\frac{dNR}{dx} = 48 - 0.04x$$

Setting $\dfrac{dNR}{dx} = 0$

$$48 - 0.04x = 0$$
$$0.04x = 48$$
$$x = \mathbf{1200}$$

NoKut should plan to produce and sell 1200 units of the Econot.

We have to be sure this is a maximum, however. As explained in the appendix on calculus, the slope of a function is zero at *any* maximum and at *any* minimum on a curve. However, at a maximum, the second derivative (the derivative of the first derivative) is generally negative (it can be zero). That is, at a maximum, the slope of the function (the marginal value) is changing from positive to negative (or to zero). Therefore, the derivative of the slope should be negative (or zero). Here:

$$\frac{dNR}{dx} = 48 - 0.04x$$

and the second derivative

$$\frac{d^2NR}{dx^2} = -0.04$$

is a negative value, indicating that $x = 1200$ is the point of maximum net revenue. In general, if the slope (first derivative) is zero and the second derivative is negative, a maximum is guaranteed.

The above examples were concerned with finding an optimum involving a *maximum* point. Calculus can also be used to find optima which occur at the *minima* of functions. For example, the Duravit Corporation is considering operating its own regional warehouses for serving Bigtown metropolitan area retailers. Duravit's management wishes to determine the minimal number of warehouses needed in the area. To do so, it must find the optimal (minimum cost) area to be served by each warehouse. Because of the special refrigeration requirements for handling frozen foods, storage costs per pound decrease as the volume handled by each warehouse increases. Conversely, the volume per warehouse is increased only by serving a larger territory which leads to increased transportation costs. Thus, the two costs associated with the warehousing function, storage costs and transportation costs, move in different directions as the size of the warehouse is changed. Increased volumes per warehouse are associated with lower storage costs per unit and larger delivery costs per unit; decreased volumes per warehouse are associated with higher unit storage costs and lower delivery costs.

In general, it is true that average cost per unit volume (per pound) for each warehouse is the sum of average storage costs, average delivery costs, and average fixed costs (fixed costs are those costs which cannot be identified as either storage or transportation costs and which do not vary with volume). That is,

(1) $C = F + S + D$

where

C = average unit cost
F = average fixed cost
S = average storage cost
D = average transportation cost

We are interested in determining the minimum cost in such a way as to make it possible to determine the minimum cost number of warehouses needed to service a given area. We need a form of the cost model which relates costs to the area served by the warehouse.

First, volume must be converted to units per unit of area. Let A stand for area in square miles and U stand for units sold per square mile.

Fixed costs are unrelated to either area or volume. Unit storage costs, however, are inversely related to volume. That is, if W equal total storage costs of a warehouse for one month, A is area and U is units sold per area, then unit storage costs (S) would be determined as,

$$(2) \quad S = \frac{W}{AU}$$

Delivery costs obviously vary directly with distance from the warehouse. If we make an assumption, common in such situations, that the area served by each warehouse is a circle with the warehouse at the center, the total area $(A) = \pi r^2$ where r is the radius of the circle (distance to the perimeter from the warehouse at the center) and π (pi) is the well-known mathematical constant (approximately equal to 3.1416). If the assumption of a circular area is valid, then the total area served by a warehouse increases proportionately with the square of the distance to the perimeter of the area served (r^2). Delivery costs per unit would change in proportion to the change in the *square root of area* served. That is,

$$(3) \quad D = k \sqrt{A}$$

where k is some constant to be determined from empirical evidence.
Substituting (2) and (3) in our original model (1), we obtain

$$(4) \quad C = F + \frac{W}{AU} + k \sqrt{A}$$

where

C = cost per unit (per pound)

F = fixed costs per quarter unassociated with volume and unclassifiable as storage or delivery costs

W = total storage costs for a quarter at one warehouse

A = area served by one warehouse (square miles)

U = units (pounds) handled by one warehouse in a quarter

k = delivery costs per unit (per pound)

(All costs are expressed in dollars.)

The minimum of the above cost function (if it has a minimum point) will be at the point where the slope (the first derivative with respect to A) is zero and the slope of the slope *at that point* (the second derivative with respect to A) is positive. The first derivative of (4) is

$$(5) \quad \frac{dC}{dA} = -\frac{W}{A^2U} + \frac{k}{2\sqrt{A}}$$

Setting (5) equal to zero and solving,

$$-\frac{W}{A^2U} + \frac{k}{2\sqrt{A}} = 0$$

$$\frac{k}{2\sqrt{A}} = \frac{W}{A^2U}$$

$$kUA^2 = 2W\sqrt{A}$$

$$kUA^{3/2} = 2W$$

$$A^{3/2} = \frac{2W}{kU}$$

$$(6) \quad A^* = \left(\frac{2W}{kU}\right)^{2/3}$$

where A^* stands for optimum value of A.

The result (6) is a general function indicating that the optimum size (square miles) of area to be served by one warehouse increases with increases in storage cost and declines with increases in delivery costs, the relationships initially postulated.

To determine if the above value of A^* is a minimum rather than a maximum, we examine the second derivative of the cost function (4).

If this second derivative (the first derivative of the first derivative (5)) is positive, this is a minimum point. Differentiating (5) (see calculus appendix for details),

$$(7) \quad \frac{d^2c}{dA^2} = \frac{2W}{A^3U} - \frac{k}{4A^{3/2}}$$

While one would expect the values of function (7) to be positive because W would be a larger value than k, it is not obvious whether all values which satisfy the above function would be positive or negative. We must evaluate the function (7) for the value of A^* we compute in any specific application.

Suppose that from accounting records for similar warehousing operations in similar metropolitan areas it is found that total direct storage costs per quarter per warehouse (W) average approximately \$7000, delivery costs per square root of area (k) are about \$0.008, and the company sells about 3500 pounds per square mile per quarter $(U = 3500)$ in similar areas. Then, by (6)

$$A^* = \left[\frac{2(7000)}{0.008(3500)} \right]^{2/3}$$

or

$$\log A^* = \frac{2}{3} \log \left(\frac{14,000}{28.0} \right)$$
$$= \frac{2}{3} \log 500$$
$$= \frac{2}{3}(2.69897)$$
$$= 1.79931$$

then

$$A^* = \textbf{63.1 square miles}$$

The minimum cost area to be served by a warehouse is 63.1 square miles *if* the value of the second derivative (7) is positive for $A = 63.1$. That is, if

$$\frac{d^2C}{dA^2} > 0$$

or

$$\frac{2(7000)}{(63.1)^3 3500} - \frac{0.008}{4(63.1)^{3/2}} > 0$$

Solving, we obtain

$$0.006281 - 0.000032 = +0.006249$$

and

$$0.006249 > 0$$

The positive value indicates that this is a minimum. The small value indicates that the slope is changing slowly at this point. Probably the cost function (4) has a relatively flat bottom at this point.

Maxima and Minima of Multivariate Functions

It is generally true that most important variables of interest to business-men will depend upon the value of more than one variable over which management has control.

In the Smithson Party Boats example, it was assumed that the number of passengers carried depended only on the price charged. Similarly, in the Duravit frozen strawberry problem (Table 2.3), it was assumed that price per pound and the number of pounds to be sold were specified by the "market" (from outside). Actually, it is well known that the variables of price and quantity interact. Further, the use of advertising can influence this interaction. Thus, the quantity sold (q) could be a function of the price per unit (p) and the amount spent on advertising (A). These latter variables are subject to manipulation by the business enterprise.

A plant superintendent for the Big Corporation wishes to determine the optimum production level for his plant. It has been established that monthly total net returns in thousands of dollars (R) can be stated as a function of total amounts in tens of thousands of dollars expended for shop labor (L) and materials (M) during the month. The function is

(1) $R = 8M + 5L + 2ML - M^2 - 2L^2 + 10$

As explained in the appendix on calculus at the end of this chapter, net returns will be maximized at a point if (1) both *partial* derivatives are equal to zero, (2) the second order partials are negative, and (3) the product of the two second partials is larger than the square of the cross-partial. We are moving to the top of the "hill" of returns in three-dimensional space. At that point, the slope of the surface of the "hill' in both directions will be *zero*. Conditions (2) and (3) on the second and cross-partials guarantee that this point is the top of the "hill," and not the bottom or only a "shoulder" of the hill.

The partial derivatives of the returns function, which are to be set equal to zero, would be:

(2) $\dfrac{\partial R}{\partial M} = 8 + 2L - 2M = 0$

(3) $\dfrac{\partial R}{\partial L} = 5 + 2M - 4L = 0$

Adding (2) and (3), we obtain:

$$13 + 0 - 2L = 0$$

so

$$2L = 13$$

(4) $L = \mathbf{6.5}$

and

$$8 + 2(6.5) - 2M = 0$$
$$2M = 21$$

(5) $M = \mathbf{10.5}$

Checking the second order partials:

$$\frac{\partial^2 R}{\partial M^2} = -2 \qquad \frac{\partial^2 R}{\partial L^2} = -4$$

The negative values indicate a maximum. The cross-partials are:

$$\frac{\partial^2 R}{\partial M \partial L} = \frac{\partial^2 R}{\partial L \partial M} = 2$$

Checking the products,

$$\left(\frac{\partial^2 R}{\partial M^2}\right)\left(\frac{\partial^2 R}{\partial L^2}\right) = 8$$
$$\left(\frac{\partial^2 R}{\partial M \partial L}\right)\left(\frac{\partial^2 R}{\partial L \partial M}\right) = \left(\frac{\partial^2 R}{\partial M \partial L}\right)^2 = 4$$

and all necessary conditions are satisfied, so that we conclude the maximum net returns are obtained where

$$L = 6.5 \qquad M = 10.5$$

That is, where the investment in shop labor is $65,000 and in materials is $105,000, total net returns would be (substituting the solution values into (1)):

$$R = 8(10.5) + 5(6.5) + 2(10.5)(6.5) - (10.5)^2 - 2(6.5)^2 + 10$$
$$= \textbf{68.25} \text{ or } \textbf{\$68,250}$$

CONSTRAINED OPTIMA

Business managers normally do not have available relatively unlimited resources with which to produce. Limits on available resources often act to restrict (constrain) the allowable solutions to this type of problem.

Solution by Substitution

Suppose, for example, that the operating budget for the plant above is set by the home office of the Big Corporation and specifies a maximum expenditure for shop labor and materials of $150,000 per month. The foregoing solution would not be possible since the optimum production level calls for a total expenditure of $105,000 + $65,000 = **$170,000**.

The constraint on total expenditure specifies that

(6) $M + L = 15$

or

(7) $M = 15 - L$

Substituting (7) into (1) from the previous section, we obtain: (the sub C on R, indicates it is a "constrained" value)

$$R_C = 8(15 - L) + 5L + 2L(15 - L) - (15 - L)^2 - 2L^2 + 10$$

or

(8) $R_C = -95 + 57L - 5L^2$

Then, applying the calculus to (8),

(9) $\dfrac{dR}{dL} = 57 - 10L = 0$

or

(10) $L = 5.7$

Since

$$\frac{d^2R}{dL^2} = -10$$

this is a maximum, and

$$R_C = -95 + 57(5.7) - 5(5.7)^2$$
$$= 67.45 \text{ or } \$67,450$$

As a check on this value, if $L = 5.7$, $M = 15 - 5.7 = 9.3$, and substitution into (1) gives

$$R_C = 8(9.3) + 5(5.7) + 2(9.3)(5.7) - (9.3)^2 - 2(5.7)^2 + 10$$
$$= 67.45 \text{ or } \$67,450$$

Unfortunately, all constraints, even though they may be equalities, are not so simple to use in restating the problem to obtain a solution. Suppose, for example, that the function had been

$$R = 8M^{-\frac{1}{3}} + 6L^{\frac{1}{2}} + 2\left(\frac{ML}{M-L}\right)^{\frac{1}{2}} - M^3 - 3L^3 + 10$$

Substitution of even so simple a relation as $M = 15 - L$ into this equation would not be easy.

Alternatively, suppose the constraint had been

$$\frac{(ML)^{\frac{1}{3}}}{M^4 + M^3L^2 + L^{\frac{1}{2}}} = K$$

The value to substitute for M would not be easily obtained nor easy to use in later manipulations. Finally, if there were more variables involved in the equation and the constraint, the problem would be more difficult for that reason.

Lagrange Multipliers

A way out of the above difficulties is available through the calculus if we bring the constraint into the function. Returning to our original constrained problem,

(1) $R_C = 8M + 2ML - M^2 - 2L^2 + 10$

subject to

(6) $M + L = 15$

If we attempt to solve for a maximum directly, we will have a set of three equations (two partial derivatives and the constraint equation) in two unknowns, an *overdefined* system without a unique solution.

We may restate (6) as

(6') $M + L - 15 = 0$

If this zero-valued expression were added to R_C, it would not change the value of R_C. Suppose we add expression (6') along with a coefficient for it, (a third variable), λ, to the equation so that the equation includes the two decision variables *and* the constraint. That is,

(11) $R_C = 8M + 2ML - M^2 - 2L^2 + 10 + \lambda(M + L - 15)$

The new variable, λ, is called a *Lagrange multiplier* after its inventor, an eighteenth century mathematician. Now if we obtain the partial derivatives of (11),

(12) $\dfrac{\partial R_C}{\partial M} = 8 + 2L - 2M + \lambda$

(13) $\dfrac{\partial R_C}{\partial L} = 5 + 2M - 4L + \lambda$

(14) $\dfrac{\partial R_C}{\partial \lambda} = L + M - 15$

We now have three equations in three unknowns, a soluble problem.

To solve the three equations:

(12) $8 + 21 - 2M + \lambda = 0$
(13) $5 + 2M - 4L + \lambda = 0$
(14) $L + M - 15 = 0$

we multiply (13) by minus one (-1) and add the result to (12), to obtain

(15) $3 - 4M + 6L = 0$

Multiplying (14) by 4 and adding the result to (15) gives

(16) $-57 + 10L = 0$

or

$$10L = 57$$
$$L = 5.7$$

and

$$3 - 4M + 6(5.7) = 0$$
$$4M = 37.2$$
$$M = 9.3$$

As a check, we substitute into (6)

$$M + L = 15$$
$$5.7 + 9.3 = 15$$
$$15 = 15$$

But, there is still some information to be obtained. The Lagrange multiplier, λ, also has a solution value.

Substituting into (12),

$$8 + 2(5.7) - 2(9.3) + \lambda = 0$$
$$\lambda = 18.6 - 19.4$$
$$= -0.8$$

What does this mean? We know that the derivative of a function is the slope of the function. The partial derivative of a function is the slope of the function with respect to the particular variable. It is the change in the *object variable* associated with a small change in the variable for which the partial is obtained. Then, $\lambda = -0.8$ indicates that for every change in the *constraint* the value of the objective changes by 0.8 units in the *opposite* direction. That is, if the constraint were to be made more binding by one unit, the maximum value of R_C would fall by 0.8 units. (See discussion problem 3.)

On the other hand, if the constraint were *relaxed* by one unit, if one more unit of money ($10,000) were made available, returns would *increase* by 0.8 units ($8000). Note that relaxing the constraint is equivalent to allowing the expression $M + L - 15$ to be equal to negative values.

Thus, we see that λ is the marginal return associated with the constraint. It is sometimes called the *shadow price* of the constraint. In the next chapter we will take up a technique for finding constrained optima and will have more to say about such shadow prices. But, it appears that if the plant superintendent can borrow funds at an interest rate of less than 0.8 it would pay to borrow funds and increase his output. Note, however, that the difference between the unconstrained optima and the constrained is only $68,250 − $67,450 = $800, while the difference in capital invested is $20,000. Obviously, this *shadow price* of 0.8 applies only at this optimum *point*, not over a wide range.

SUMMARY

A mathematical model is a symbolic representation of a system, a process, or an object which can be used to represent the system, process, or object for the purpose of study, experimentation, or prediction. Mathematical models are useful as guides to managerial decisions. In this chapter we have studied a few models of the class called deterministic *certainty* models, where all relations are assumed to be known exactly and only a single state of nature can exist.

Incremental models help us to find the *optimum* or *break-even* value of an operation if we know the effects of each change in decision variables which are under our control.

Since incremental models (trial-and-error or analytic algebra) deal with *marginal effects*, a natural extension of such analysis is to apply the calculus of derivatives to find *instantaneous rates* of change and absolute maxima or minima of functions predicting the values of the *object variable*. Calculus has the advantage of being able to deal with functions containing several variables. Also, by the use of *Lagrange multipliers* the calculus allows us to find optimal values for situations where *constraints* (restrictions on the optimum solution) expressed as equalities must be considered.

A Lagrange multiplier is sometimes called the *shadow price* for the constraint with which it is associated. It tells us how the *object variable* will be affected by changes in the constraint.

APPENDIX: ELEMENTS OF DIFFERENTIAL CALCULUS

Some Basic Definitions

In the following exposition, Δx denotes an independent variable, usually added to x and frequently very small. Similarly Δy denotes an independent variable, usually added to y and frequently small.

Let us consider the following. If

$$y = f(x)$$

and we let

$$y + \Delta y = f(x + \Delta x)$$

then, Δy is a function of the two variables x and Δx.

$$\Delta y = f(x + \Delta x) - f(x)$$

This amount, Δy, represents the change in y associated with a change of amount Δx in x.

The ratio $\Delta y/\Delta x$ is the average *rate* of change of the function $y = f(x)$. For example, for the linear function

$$y = a + bX$$

the ratio $\Delta y/\Delta x = b$, the *slope* of the straight line defined by the equation.

Differential calculus is involved with defining and measuring the slope of a function at a *point*. The limit as Δx approaches zero of the ratio, $\Delta y/\Delta x$, if it exists, we call the derivative of y with respect to x and denote it by the symbol dy/dx (or $f'(x)$). We call dy/dx the *slope* of the line $y = f(x)$ at x. The derivative of a function is thus seen to be a function providing a formula for the slope for *any* point on the curve. The derivative with respect to x of the linear function in the previous paragraph is b, the slope of the function at *all* points.

The First Derivative

Suppose we had the simple function

(1) $y = x$

What is the slope of this function? Suppose we look at the change in y associated with a change in x. Then,

$$y + \Delta y = x + \Delta x$$

Since, $y = x$, $\Delta y = \Delta x$, and dividing both sides by Δx, we get

$$\Delta y/\Delta x = 1$$

and thus the limit as Δx approaches zero is

$$dy/dx = 1$$

Next consider the function

(2) $y = x^2$

Changing x by the amount Δx,

$$y + \Delta y = (x + \Delta x)^2$$
$$= x^2 + 2x\Delta x + (\Delta x)^2$$

Since $y = x^2$,

$$\Delta y = 2x\Delta x + (\Delta x)^2$$

and, dividing both sides by Δx, we obtain

$$\frac{\Delta y}{\Delta x} = 2x + \Delta x$$

Taking the limit as $\Delta x \to 0$ (as Δx approaches 0), we find that the derivative of y with respect to x is

$$\frac{dy}{dx} = 2x$$

Suppose we differentiate the function

(3) $y = x^3 + 2$

Then, changing x by an amount Δx

$$y + \Delta y = (x + \Delta x)^3 + 2$$
$$= x^3 + 3x^2\Delta x + 3x(\Delta x)^2 + (\Delta x)^3 + 2$$

Since $y = x^3 + 2$

$$\Delta y = 3x^2\Delta x + 3x(\Delta x)^2 + (\Delta x)^3$$
$$\frac{\Delta y}{\Delta x} = 3x^2 + 3x(\Delta x) + (\Delta x)^2$$

and the limit as $\Delta x \to 0$ is the derivative,

$$\frac{dy}{dx} = 3x^2$$

As a final example consider the function

(4) $\quad y = x^3 + 3x^2 + 4x + 5$

Then,

$$Y + \Delta y = (x + \Delta x)^3 + 3(x + \Delta x)^2 + 4(x + \Delta x) + 5$$
$$= x^3 + 3x^2(\Delta x) + 3x(\Delta x)^2 + (\Delta x)^3 + 3x^2 + 6x\Delta x + 3(\Delta x)^2$$
$$+ 4x + 4\Delta x + 5$$

Subtracting the original function and dividing by Δx,

$$\frac{\Delta y}{\Delta x} = 3x^2 + 3x\Delta x + (\Delta x)^2 + 6x + 3\Delta x + 4$$

Letting $\Delta x \to 0$, the limit is found

$$\frac{dy}{dx} = 3x^2 + 6x + 4$$

Several basic rules are illustrated by the above examples:

C.1   The derivative of any *constant* with respect to any variable is always zero.

Examples (3) and (4) illustrate this rule.

C.2   For any *first-degree relationship*, $y = cx$, the derivative of y with respect to x is the coefficient of x regardless of the value of c. That is,

$$\frac{dy}{dx} = c$$

All of the above examples illustrate this rule.

C.3   For any *higher-degree relationship*,

$$y = cx^n$$
$$\frac{dy}{dx} = ncx^{n-1}$$

This rule is illustrated in all examples above. (C.2 is actually a special case of C.3)

C.4 The derivative of a *sum of several terms* is the sum of the derivatives of the individual terms. In general, if $y = y_1 + y_2$,

$$\frac{dy}{dx} = \frac{dy_1}{dx} + \frac{dy_2}{dx}$$

The third and fourth examples illustrate this rule.

Some other important rules are given without explanation other than examples of their application.

C.5 The derivative of the *product* of two expressions is the product of the first expression multiplied by the derivative of the second expression plus the second expression multiplied by the derivative of the first expression. In general, if

$$y = y_1 y_2$$
$$\frac{dy}{dx} = (y_1)\frac{dy_2}{dx} + (y_2)\frac{dy_1}{dx}$$

Example: Let $y = 6x(4x^2 + 3)$

$$\frac{dy}{dx} = 6x(8x) + (4x^2 + 3)6$$
$$= 48x^2 + 24x^2 + 18$$
$$= 72x^2 + 18$$

As a check, we obtain the product of the terms and differentiate:

$$y = 24x^3 + 18x$$
$$\frac{dy}{dx} = 72x^2 + 18$$

C.6 The derivative of a *ratio* of expressions is equal to the denominator multiplied by the derivative of the numerator minus the numerator multiplied by the derivative of the denominator all divided by the square of the denominator. In general, if

$$y = \frac{y_1}{y_2}$$
$$\frac{dy}{dx} = \frac{y_2\left(\frac{dy_1}{dx}\right) - y_1\left(\frac{dy_2}{dx}\right)}{y_2{}^2}$$

Example: Let $y = \dfrac{x^3 - 1}{2x^2}$

$$\frac{dy}{dx} = \frac{2x^2(3x^2) - (x^3 - 1)4x}{4x^4}$$

C.7 If $y = ae^{bx}$, where e = the base of the Naperian logarithms,

$$\frac{dy}{dx} = bae^{bx}$$

Examples: (1) Let $y = ae^x$,

$$\frac{dy}{dx} = ae^x = y \qquad (y \text{ is its own derivative})$$

(2) Let $y = \dfrac{e^{3x}}{x^2}$

Rewriting, $y = \left(\dfrac{1}{x^2}\right) e^{3x}$

and, remembering that $\dfrac{1}{x^2} = x^{-2}$,

$$\frac{dy}{dx} = 3x^{-2}e^{3x} - 2x^{-3}e^{3x}$$
$$= e^{3x}(3x^{-2} - 2x^{-3})$$
$$= e^{3x}\left(\frac{3x - 2}{x^3}\right)$$

C.8 If y is a *function of z*, which in turn is a *function* of still another variable, x, then the derivative of y with respect to x is the product of the derivative of y with respect to z and the derivative of z with respect to x. In general, if

$$y = f(z) \text{ and } z = f(x),$$
$$\frac{dy}{dx} = \frac{dy}{dz}\frac{dz}{dx}$$

Examples: (1) Let $y = z^3 + 2z - 3$ and $z = x^2 - 4x$

$$\frac{dy}{dx} = (3z^2 + 2)(2x - 4)$$

Substituting $z(x)$,

$$\frac{dy}{dx} = [3(x^2 - 4x)^2 + 2](2x - 4)$$
$$= 6x^5 - 60x^4 + 192x^3 - 192x^2 + 4x - 8$$

(2)   Let $y = x^4 \sqrt{x^3 + 3}$

Rewriting the function and letting $(x^3 + 3x) = u$,

$$y = (x^4)(u^{\frac{1}{2}})$$
$$\frac{dy}{dx} = x^4(\tfrac{1}{2}u^{-\frac{1}{2}})\left(\frac{du}{dx}\right) + u^{\frac{1}{2}}(4x^3)$$

Substituting $u = (x^3 + 3)$, recognizing that $\dfrac{du}{dx} = 3x^2 + 3$

$$\frac{dy}{dx} = x^4(\tfrac{1}{2} \sqrt{3x^3 + 3x})(3x^2 + 3) + \sqrt{x^3 + 3x}\,(4x^3)$$

which can be simplified if the reader wishes to do so. Note the use of u for a complicated expression in x. This *trick* can often simplify the differentiation of complicated expressions.

Second Order Derivatives

We often find it desirable to look at the *second* derivative of a function.

C.9   The *second derivative* of a function is merely the first derivative of the first derivative. In general,

$$\frac{d^2y}{dx^2} = d\left(\frac{dy}{dx}\right)\bigg/ dx$$

The reader should take special note of the way in which we write the second derivative. Examples of second derivatives are given in the section on minima and maxima below. Note that if the first derivative of a function at a point is its instantaneous rate of change, or its slope, at that point, the second derivative of the function at that point is the instantaneous rate of change of the function, or the slope of the slope.

Partial Derivatives

Partial derivatives of a function of two or more variables with respect to one of the variables are obtained by considering the remaining variables in the function as constants. One can observe the effect on the function when just one of the several variables changes by an indefinitely small amount. To uniquely identify the partial derivative and distinguish it from the simple derivative, we use the lower case Greek delta in the symbol for the partial derivative, that is,

C.10 $\dfrac{\partial y}{\partial x}$ stands for the partial derivative of y with respect to x, holding all other variables in y constant. In general, if $y = f(x, z)$

$$\frac{\partial y}{\partial x} \text{ is the derivative of } f(x, z)$$

with respect to x when z is considered to be a constant.

Examples of partial derivatives are given in the discussion of maxima and minima below.

Cross-Partial Derivatives

Second order partial derivatives are obtained in the same manner as second order simple derivatives, that is, by differentiating the first order partials with respect to one variable and then repeating the process. For example, if $y = x^2 z^3$

$$\frac{\partial y}{\partial x} = 2z^3 x \qquad \frac{\partial y}{\partial z} = 3x^2 z^2$$

$$\frac{\partial^2 y}{\partial x^2} = 2z^3 \qquad \frac{\partial^2 y}{\partial z^2} = 6x^2 z$$

but there are two other partials, the so-called *cross-partials;* which are the second order partials of each partial derivative with respect to the *other* variable. That is, $\dfrac{\partial y}{\partial x}$ can be differentiated with respect to z.

$$\frac{\partial^2 y}{\partial x \partial z} = 6z^2 x$$

Similarly, the derivative of $\dfrac{\partial y}{\partial z}$ with respect to x can be obtained.

$$\frac{\partial^2 y}{\partial z \partial x} = 6z^2 x$$

The equality of the cross-partials is not accidental and holds for all of the functions with which we deal in this text. We often speak therefore of *the* cross-partial.

Maxima and Minima of Functions of One Variable

An extreme point can exist for a function of one variable only when the tangent to the curve is horizontal. The tangent to the curve is its slope function, its first derivative. For the line to be horizontal the slope must be zero.

If we know the first derivative is zero, we realize that the curve has a point of horizontal (zero) slope. We would like to know two other things as well: Is this truly a maximum (or a minimum)? If so, which extreme is it? We would like to avoid identifying just *any* flat spot in the curve as an extreme, and we would like to avoid either identifying a maximum point as a minimum or identifying a minimum point as a maximum. To reach these goals, we must consider the second order conditions. If we are climbing over the top of a hill (passing through a maximum), the slope of the tangent (the rate of change in the first derivative) will be generally declining. This means that the second derivative cannot be positive. It must be either negative (the usual case) or zero. Consider the example, if

$$y = -x^2$$
$$\frac{dy}{dx} = -2x^2$$
$$\frac{d^2 y}{dx^2} = -4x$$

Setting dy/dx equal to zero and solving, $x = 0$ and d^2y/dx for $x = 0$ is also zero.

On the other hand, if we are passing across the inside of a bowl, the slope is changing from negative to positive as we pass the lowest point and the second derivative measuring the rate of change in the slope cannot be negative. (The reader need only consider the function $y = x^4$ to see that the second derivative can be zero at a minimum point.)

For functions of single variables we can state that,

C.11   A function in one variable will reach a *maximum* point if the first derivative is zero and the second derivative is negative, that is, if

$$y = f(x)$$

a maximum value will be found if

$$\frac{dy}{dx} = 0 \text{ and } \frac{d^2y}{dx} < 0$$

for some maximum points

$$\frac{dy}{dx} = \frac{d^2y}{dx^2} = 0$$

C.12   A function in one variable will reach a *minimum* point if the first derivative is zero and the second derivative is positive, for example, if

$$y = f(x)$$

a minimum value of y will be found if

$$\frac{dy}{dx} = 0 \text{ and } \frac{d^2y}{dx^2} > 0$$

for some minimum points

$$\frac{dy}{dx} = \frac{d^2y}{dx^2} = 0$$

Local and Global Optima

One important warning about the use of the calculus to find maxima and minima is necessary. It is possible for functions to have more than one maxima of a particular type. For example, consider the function,

$$y = x^3 + 3x^2 - 9x$$

Its derivatives are:

$$\frac{dy}{dx} = 3x^2 + 6x - 9$$

$$\frac{d^2y}{dx^2} = 6x + 6$$

Setting $dy/dx = 0$ gives the solution values,

$$x = 1 \text{ and } x = -3$$

and the second derivatives are $+12$ for $x = 1$ and -12 for $x = -3$, indicating that the function has a maximum at $x = -3$ and a minimum at $x = 1$. The graph of the function in Figure C.1 reveals that these points

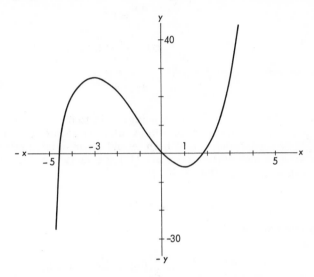

FIG. C.1. Graph of the function $y = x^3 + 3x^2 - 9x$.

are only *local* optima, the *global* optima (the highest and lowest points) are at $\pm \infty$, at the end points of the function. It often pays to graph the function to be certain that the optima defined are truly global optima (maximum optima) not just intermediate high or low points. Usually one is warned of this possibility by a multiplicity of solution values obtained when the first derivative is set equal to zero.

Maxima and Minima of Functions of Two Variables

The necessary and sufficient conditions for finding maxima and minima of functions of two variables will be stated without explanation. The reader will recognize a simple extension of the rules for functions of one variable in part of the rules given below.

C.13 For a function of two variables a point is said to be *stationary* if both first partial derivatives are equal to zero. A sufficient condition for a stationary point to be a *maximum* is that both second order simple partials are negative and the square of the *cross partial* is less than the product of the second order simple partials; that is, if

$$y = f(x, z)$$

y is a maximum if

$$\frac{\partial y}{\partial x} = \frac{\partial y}{\partial z} = 0,$$

$$\frac{\partial^2 y}{\partial x^2} < 0, \frac{\partial^2 y}{\partial z^2} < 0, \text{ and}$$

$$\left(\frac{\partial^2 y}{\partial x \partial z}\right)^2 < \frac{\partial^2 y}{\partial x^2} \cdot \frac{\partial^2 y}{\partial z^2}$$

C.14   For a function of two variables a point is said to be *stationary* if both first partial derivatives are equal to zero. A sufficient condition for a stationary point to be a *minimum* is that both second order simple partials are positive and the square of the cross partial is less than the product of the second order simple partials; that is, if

$$y = f(x, z)$$

y is a minimum where

$$\frac{\partial y}{\partial x} = \frac{\partial y}{\partial z} = 0, \frac{\partial^2 y}{\partial x^2} > 0, \frac{\partial^2 y}{\partial z^2} > 0, \text{ and}$$

$$\left(\frac{\partial^2 y}{\partial x \partial z}\right)^2 < \frac{\partial^2 y}{\partial x^2} \cdot \frac{\partial^2 y}{\partial z^2}$$

Cautions on Using Calculus to Define Extremes

Note that all but one of the extremes defined in this appendix might be only *local* extremes. That is, the maximum extreme may be only one of the points defined as a maximum. Similarly, C.14 defines *any* and all minimum points on the function, not just the minimum of the minimum points. It may even be possible that only *local* extremes exist, other than at end points, and the true extreme values of the curve (*global* optima) are not defined. It may be desirable to graph the function as a check on the calculus solution. Finally, this brief appendix is not intended as a substitute for a course in differential calculus. It is only intended to illustrate in a minimal way the usefulness of this important tool. Any reader interested in making wide use of this tool should obtain further training.

DISCUSSION QUESTIONS

1. Define the following *in your own words*. Do not use symbols or word formulas.

   (a) model
   (b) mathematical model
   (c) certainty model
   (d) descriptive model
   (e) incremental analysis
   (f) object variable
   (g) deterministic model

   (h) break-even analysis
   (i) marginal analysis
   (j) derivative
   (k) constraint
   (l) Lagrange multiplier
   (m) shadow price

2. Explain why the function, $y = f(x)$, for example, reaches its maximum at the point where $\dfrac{dy}{dx} = 0$ and $\dfrac{d^2y}{dx^2} < 0$.

3. In break-even analysis, what would be the effect of the following: (Be as specific as possible.)

   (a) a rise in overhead costs?
   (b) a rise in variable costs?
   (c) a drop in labor, materials, and/or capital requirements per unit produced?
   (d) a higher selling price?
   (e) a decrease in the number of units which can be sold at the current price?

   Hint: Refer to Figure 2.2.

DISCUSSION PROBLEMS

Show your method on all solutions.

1. The Hi-Value TV Repair Shop also sells Koloredi Colored TV sets. He expects to sell 100 of the sets over the next year with demand spread evenly over the year. He is interested in determining how many sets to order at one time. He is faced with the following costs:

   (1) Inventory carrying cost $= C(q/2)$. Where, $C = a$ constant representing interest on investment, storage costs, and so forth, involved in holding one TV set for one year, $q =$ quantity delivered per shipment. The average amount held between shipments is equal to $q/2$ if demand is evenly distributed over the period.

   (2) Reorder cost $(R) = a + b(D/q)$ where, a and b are constants related to costs of placing one order, D is the total sales expected for the year, and q is the reorder quantity.

(a) Use the calculus to obtain the optimum reorder quantity q as a general solution.

Hint: Calculate the total cost as carrying costs plus reorder costs. Then, differentiate. Remember that $1/x = x^{-1}$.

(b) If Hi-Value's books indicate that

$$D = 100 \qquad C = \$36 \qquad a = \$3 \qquad b = \$1$$

What is the optimum value of q?

2. The Lumbar Company produces unfinished chairs. The number of seconds, chairs with minor flaws, produced (S) is a function of the total good chairs produced (G) (all variables in thousands of units):

$$S = G^2 - 18G + 5$$

Determine the optimum number of chairs to produce to obtain maximum net returns if the net return on seconds is one half of the net return on good chairs.

Hints: (1) Total income = income from seconds + income from good chairs.

(2) The net return of good chairs is two times the net return of seconds.

3. Graph the problem of the Big Corporation plant superintendent, pages 39ff., including the constraint and the solution.

(a) How would you indicate a change in the constraint to $120,000?

(b) Express the change in the constraint algebraically and find the solution to the new problem.

(c) Graph the new problem and the solution.

(d) What conclusions can you draw from the above manipulations of the problem?

4. A firm has a demand function of

$$Q = a - bp$$

Where Q is quantity sold and p is the price per unit. The cost function for the firm is

$$C = F + dQ + eQ^2$$

If all the coefficients in the two functions are positive,

(a) Develop an expression for total profits of the corporation.

Hint: Profits = total earnings − total costs

(b) Develop an expression for the optimum output for maximizing total profits.

Hint: Find the first derivative and set it equal to zero.

(c) What other conditions must be met for the expression developed in (b) to be a point of maximum profit?

Hint: What are the conditions necessary to the identification of a maximum? How can they be obtained?

5. Suppose a firm has developed the following information from its accounting records:

Unit selling price: $20
Expenses of production and sale:
Fixed $50,000
Variable $5 per unit produced and sold
Overhead costs:
Fixed $50,000
Variable $2 per unit produced and sold

(a) What is the break-even production level?

Hint: *Net* return per unit times number of units must cover fixed costs.

(b) What production level is required to return $20,000 in net earnings?

Hint: Total net returns must cover fixed costs plus $20,000.

6. Suppose total revenue (R) is determined as: $R = -4x^2 + 6x$ and the cost (C) is determined as: $C = 6 + 22x$

(a) Use the calculus to obtain the marginal revenue (MR) and the marginal cost (MC) functions.

(b) Use the MR and MC functions to determine the output for which profit is a maximum.

(c) Develop the profit (P) function and use it to check the results obtained in b.

(d) What recommendations concerning output levels would you make to this producer? Explain fully.

Hint: What is the profit level at the optimum output?

EXERCISES

Show your method on all solutions.

1. Suppose a firm's total revenue (R) is determined as:

$$R = 4x - 8x^2$$

and total cost (C) is determined as:

$$C = 8 + 20x$$

(a) Use the calculus to obtain the marginal revenue (MR) and the marginal cost (MC) functions.

(b) Use the MR and MC functions to determine the output for which profit is a maximum.

(c) Check your result in (b) by developing the total profit function (P) and use it to check the accuracy of your previous calculations.

(d) What level of production do you recommend for this firm?

2. The Leadped Transport Company charges $6.50 to transport 100 pounds of merchandise 600 miles by air and only $21.50 to transport the 100 pounds across the country (3000 miles) by air. Find the function which describes how charges change as distance changes.

3. Suppose the revenue function (R) were:

$$R = 510 - 4Q^2 + 20A + 2QA - 6A^2 + 12Q$$

where

Q = quantity produced and sold
A = amount spent on advertising

(a) Find the values of Q and A which maximize revenue. Can you prove this is a maximum? Explain fully if you cannot.

(b) Suppose the above Revenue function was subject to a constraint on the availability of funds:

$$5A + 5Q = 20$$

Use Lagrange multipliers to find the optimum levels of production and advertising to provide maximum revenue.

(c) Use the algebraic substitution technique to recompute the answers as a check on your results in (b).

(d) Interpret your solutions for (b) and (c).

4. The Lessloss Company recently purchased another store building in Bigtown. Detailed analysis of the Lessloss operations indicates that earnings for such a store in the Lessloss chain would be:

$$E = 6I + 8S + IS - 2I^2 - S^2 + 8$$

where

    E = annual earnings in hundreds of thousands of dollars
    I = investment in inventory in hundreds of thousands of dollars
    S = floor space available for display in units 100 feet square

(a) What is the optimum levels of inventory investment and space used for such a store?

Funds available for the operation of the new store are limited, $500,000 has been budgeted to provide inventory and working capital. Past experience indicates that every dollar of inventory requires 40 cents of working capital. Each five square feet of floor space requires $20 in working capital for furniture, janitorial services, and so forth.

(b) What is the total requirement for working capital for any I and S?

(c) What is the maximum possible earnings if the total $500,000 is used for inventory and working capital?

5. The Theatrical Ticket Agency in Bigtown receives a ten percent commission on all tickets sold by any of the agency's three offices. Each office has an office manager receiving a salary of $6000 per year. The main office also employs one counter clerk, a telephone reception- ist and a stenographer at salaries of $4000 per year each. College students are employed on a part-time basis as needed at the rate of $2.00 per hour. Other expenses are rents and janitor services totaling $16,000 per year, and interest expense equal to three percent of the total value of tickets sold. Past experience indicates that one hour of temporary help is required for each $1000 worth of tickets sold.

(a) Determine the annual break-even sales volume.

(b) Determine the break-even sales if an outside salesman is hired and given a 0.5 percent commission on all sales plus $200 per month in place of an expense account.

6. Suppose the Zedo Company wishes to minimize the amount of tubing held in inventory for lawn sprayer production. Since the tubing used is not a widely used size, four weeks must be allowed for delivery of an order. Zedo's analysts have specified the following:

    I = number of feet of tubing on hand
    q = expected number of feet used in production each week
    D = delay between ordering date and receipt of a tubing order, in weeks
    c = inventory carrying costs per order

To minimize inventory costs, the Zedo analysts are recommending reordering when $I = qD$.

(a) Comment on the proposed policy. What are its advantages and disadvantages?

(b) If q is variable, what will be the expected result of using the policy?

(c) If Zedo were to switch to a new supplier, delivery time could be cut to one week, but the price paid would go up five percent. What would you recommend?

7. The Black Print Company is preparing a bid for a contract to print 2000 copies of a book. Each page of the book is to contain 48 square inches of printing (six inches wide, eight inches high) and have one inch margins at top and bottom and 1.5 inch margins at the sides. The book is to contain 500 pages and will be bound in a hard cover costing 40 cents per book to prepare and attach. Paper of the necessary quality costs 0.5 cents per square foot. Set up of plates for printing and running off the copies costs a total of $3.00 per page for 500 pages over 2000 copies.

(a) What is the minimum amount of paper Black can expect to use?

(b) What would be the minimum Black could afford to bid if fixed overhead and normal "profit" comprise 15 percent of direct costs?

3
objectives, constraints, and mathematical programming

In recognition of a need for strengthening the decision-making process in business, there has been an increasing application of modern scientific techniques to business problems. This new approach is characterized by a concern with operating problems and a broadened view of business organizations as single entities, as "systems" to be analyzed as units. It is also pragmatically oriented in the sense that it aims at providing a quantitative basis for making decisions about real problems. In the previous chapter we have attempted to illustrate some methods of this new "Operations Research." In this chapter we shall examine another important model in the OR arsenal of tools. It is a model for the allocation of limited resources in a manner which best meets a desired objective called *mathematical programming*. In this introduction we will restrict our exposition to the techniques applicable to the simplest linear models and make only a few comments about the nature of other programming models.

OBJECTIVES

In any decision situation, management is attempting to choose from among alternative actions, that set of actions which will attain certain

[1] This material leans heavily on unpublished class notes prepared by Professor William F. Sharpe, University of Washington.

desired goals or objectives. For example, it is commonly accepted that businessmen strive to choose that set of action alternatives which will maximize profits. This basic goal is modified, however, by the simultaneous need to satisfy other goals which conflict with the basic goal of maximum profit. For example, rational business behavior may dictate foregoing profit maximization in the immediate future in order to continue enjoying higher profits in the distant future. Also, businessmen may forego certain profit possibilities because of the danger of being guilty of antisocial behavior varying from development of "a poor public image" to being charged with violations of antitrust laws. However, as was indicated in Chapter 1, in any given situation there is some primary objective which will provide a basis for differentiating among the alternative actions available.

Decision Variables

In most decision situations faced by business managers, not all of the variables which bear on that decision are under the control of the manager. For example, in trying to determine the price to charge for his own product and the amount of that product to produce, the prices of competing brands cannot be specified as they are controlled by other businessmen. Similarly, the amount of the product which customers will purchase at a given price is not directly under the manager's control. He can control price, production, and promotional effort, but he must accept the sales volume which results. The variables which the decision maker can control in any situation are called the *decision variables* in that situation. When the influences of the decision variables on the objective sought by the decision maker are expressed analytically, the resulting expression is called an *objective function*. The variable being optimized (revenue, cost, and so forth) is called the *object variable*.

For example, Duravit Corporation packages and sells different frozen foods in competition with other firms. Duravit's management finds that it has little influence on even the prices of its products; most of its control is over variables such as volume and quality of production and promotion (sales and advertising) effort. In attempting to maximize total net revenue in any period, management might decide it could control only the amount of each product produced and its advertising outlays. The objective function for Duravit might be stated as

$$R = f(Q_1, Q_2, Q_3, \cdots, Q_n, A)$$

where

R = net revenue during the period

Q_i = quantity of product i produced during the period

A = advertising expenditure during the period

To be of analytical aid in making decisions, the exact form of this functional relationship and the coefficients (contribution) of each of the decision variables would have to be known.

Constraints on Decisions

Even if Duravit's management obtained precise and complete information for all the coefficients in the above objective function, the absolute maximum net revenue theoretically available might be unattainable. The amounts of funds available for operating expenses (labor and raw material costs) and advertising outlays are not unlimited. Productive resources available, such as plant capacity, are limited. These limitations or others (such as availability of raw products for processing) restrict the solution possibilities. These *constraints*, as we learned in the previous chapter, can limit Duravit to less than the absolutely optimal level of operation. Such constraints are usually present in business-decision situations. In Chapter 2 we saw that relatively simple objective functions subject to simple constraints (equalities) can be analyzed with the use of Lagrange multipliers. We also saw that that technique was limited. *Mathematical programming* is a set of allocation techniques which search out maximum or minimum values for an object variable in situations where at least one of the decision variables involved is subject to a constraint which is an inequality. Like any analytical mathematical tool each mathematical programming model rests on a specific set of assumptions which the user must recognize and honor if the tool is not to be misused and lead one to draw erroneous conclusions from the analysis conducted. The remainder of this chapter is devoted primarily to an introduction of the most elementary of these programming techniques, linear programming.

LINEAR PROGRAMMING

The Structure of Linear Programming Problems

The Zedo Manufacturing Company produces and sells two models of its lawn sprayer, the standard (economy) model and the deluxe model.

Profit contributions of the two models are:

$$\text{standard} = \$3.00 \text{ per unit produced and sold}$$
$$\text{deluxe} = \$5.00 \text{ per unit produced and sold}$$

A strong market exists for the company's sprayers, and the company has no plans for a price change. Costs are also expected to remain constant over the next planning period (quarter). Total profits (R) on the sprayer operation would be:

(1) $R = 3S + 5D$

Since the profit function is linear, it is possible to represent different possible levels of return as straight lines on a graph whose coordinate axes represent units of standard and deluxe sprayers produced. Figure 3.1

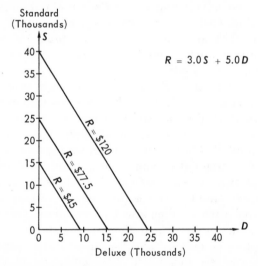

FIG. 3.1. Iso-return lines, Zedo sprayers (standard and deluxe models).

is such a graph. Each of the iso-profit (equal-profit) lines has a slope of −5/3, the ratio of the profit contributions of the two models. The reader should demonstrate to his own satisfaction that all combinations of deluxe and standard units along each iso-profit line do produce the same total profit. Note that the total profit represented by an iso-profit line increases as the iso-profit line moves away from the origin.

The iso-profit lines in Figure 3.1 can, technically, extend beyond the two axes, but negative numbers of either model of sprayer are impossible, that is, have no meaning in the real problem. The allowable combinations of models lie to the right and above the origin. The fact that decision variables cannot assume negative values forms a set of *implicit constraints* on the solution.

Manufacture of each sprayer requires a machining operation and an assembly operation. The same lathes and assembly jigs are used for both models. The deluxe model also requires painting. All units are placed

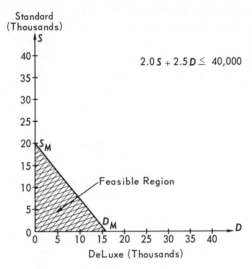

FIG. 3.2.   Machining capacity constraint.

in inventory before being sold. Each unit of the deluxe model requires two and one-half hours of machining, but each standard unit requires only two hours of machining. Zedo has set aside a machine shop with a capacity of 40,000 hours of machining time for sprayer production. Figure 3.2 indicates the possible production levels as constrained by the fact that:

(2) $2.0S + 2.5D \leq 40,000$

By using all of the machining capacity for standard units, Zedo can obtain 20,000 units without exceeding this restraint, point S_M in Figure 3.2. If the available machining capacity is used to produce only the deluxe model, 16,000 units can be produced, point D_M in Figure 3.2. In fact, any combination of the deluxe and standard models lying on the line connecting S_M and D_M or to the left and below that line can be produced without exceeding the available machining capacity. Note, however, that it does not make sense to allow either S or D to become negative. It is impossible to produce less than zero units of either model. We again encounter the *implicit* constraints. Therefore, the region within which it is *technically feasible* to produce without violating the machining capacity constraint is bounded by the line connecting S_M and D_M and the coordinate axes.

Similar restrictions on production implied by limited capacity of the other productive resources and the technical requirements of their use can be obtained from the data shown in Table 3.1. The capacity limitations implied by the limit on the amount of each resource available could be drawn on a graph like Figure 3.2. If this were done, the area lying to the left and below *all* of the constraint lines but to the right and above the origin would be the total area of technical feasibility, the *feasible region*, within which it would be possible to produce.

TABLE 3.1

TECHNICAL REQUIREMENTS AND CAPACITIES FOR PRODUCING STANDARD
AND DELUXE SPRAYERS AT THE ZEDO MANUFACTURING COMPANY

(a) RESOURCE REQUIREMENTS
Resource Requirements per Unit

Sprayer Model	Hours of Machining	Hours of Assembly	Hours of Painting	Square Feet of Warehousing
Standard	2.0	1.5	0.0	2.0
Deluxe	2.5	1.0	1.0	3.0

(b) AVAILABLE CAPACITIES

Resource	Machining Hours	Assembly Hours	Painting Hours	Warehouse Square Feet
Capacity	40,000	24,000	14,000	60,000

We see, then, that Zedo has a problem of resource allocation where the measure of success is expressed as a linear equation involving only decision variables. That is, a *linear objective function:*

(1) $\quad R = 3S + 5D$

and several *constraints* on the solution imposed by the limited capacities of available productive facilities. The constraints also can be expressed as *linear functions* of the decision variables:

(2) $2.0S + 2.5D \leq 40,000$ (Machining)
(3) $1.5S + 1.0D \leq 24,000$ (Assembly)
(4) $0.0S + 1.0D \leq 14,000$ (Painting)
(5) $2.0S + 3.0D \leq 60,000$ (Warehouse)

Also, the two decision variables substitute for one another at constant rates in each equation. Further, at least one (in this case, all) of the explicit constraints is expressed as an inequality. Finally, the decision variables (the number of units of each model to produce) cannot assume negative values. Such a problem is a linear programming problem.

Graphic Solution

When only two decision variables are involved in a linear programming problem, it is possible to obtain a solution by manipulation of the graph of the problem. Such a solution is shown for the Zedo problem in Figure 3.3. Each of the constraint equations is shown as a line on the graph. The cross-batched area bounded by the coordinate axes, the machining constraint, the assembly constraint, and the painting constraint is the *feasible region*, the total area which encompasses all combinations of the two models of sprayers which it is possible for Zedo to produce. Note that the warehouse constraint is not involved in determining the feasible region. It is "dominated" by the machining constraint. That is, at all points, the machining capacity is more constraining on output than is the warehouse capacity and the limit on warehouse capacity does not influence the possible production possibilities. It is a *redundant* constraint, the solution would be the same without it.

In order to maximize profits (R), Zedo must produce a combination of standard and deluxe units lying on the highest iso-profit line which still coincides with the feasible region at at least one point. In the present case, the iso-profit line yielding $R = \$77,500$ is the highest iso-profit line which touches the feasible region. It contacts the feasible region at the corner formed by the intersection of the machining constraint and the painting constraint. The optimum level of output is 2500 units of the standard model and 14,000 units of the deluxe model.

To illustrate the general nature both of the method by which the solution was found and of the solution itself, suppose the profit from the sale of a deluxe model were not so much larger than the profit from the sale of a standard model. Then, the iso-profit lines would not be so

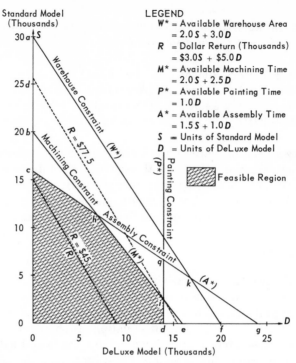

Standard Model
(Thousands)

LEGEND

W^* = Available Warehouse Area
  = $2.0S + 3.0D$
R = Dollar Return (Thousands)
  = $\$3.0S + \$5.0D$
M^* = Available Machining Time
  = $2.0S + 2.5D$
P^* = Available Painting Time
  = $1.0D$
A^* = Available Assembly Time
  = $1.5S + 1.0D$
S = Units of Standard Model
D = Units of DeLuxe Model

Feasible Region

DeLuxe Model (Thousands)

FIG. 3.3. Graphic solution, Zedo allocation problem.

steeply sloped. If the slope were $-5/4$, for example, the highest iso-profit line touching the feasible region would coincide with the machining constraint. Any combination of outputs lying along this line in the interval between the assembly constraint and the painting constraint would return the same total profit. Note, however, that two *corners* of the feasible region are included among the possible optimum solutions.

If the slope of the iso-profit lines were larger than -1, but still less than 0 ($-1 <$ slope < 0), the highest iso-profit line touching the feasible region would pass through the corner at c where the assembly constraint and the vertical axis (the *implicit* constraint line for the implicit constraint that $D \geq 0$) intersect. Note that, for all these solutions, the optimum solution *either occurs at a corner of the feasible region or includes one or more corners of the feasible region.* Note also that at *any* corner of the feasible region, the number of *nonzero* decision variables (the number of decision variables *in the solution* is equal to the number of *explicit* constraints which are *binding* (in force) at that corner.

The above relationships between the numbers of constraints and variables *in* the solution are not accidental.

3.00 *The basic theorem of linear programming:* If an optimum solution exists,
there will be one which includes a corner of the feasible region. For this
solution, the number of nonzero decision variables will not exceed the
number of effective (binding) explicit constraints.

The direct implications of this theorem are (using m for the number of
explicit constraints and n for the number of decision variables):

(1) If $n < m$, for example, the Zedo example, where $n = 2$ and $m = 4$
(one superfluous).
At most, n of the m constraints will be binding at the solution.
(2) If $n > m$, for example, suppose $n = 3$, $m = 2$.
At most, m of the n decision variables will be *in* (nonzero) at the solution, since no more than m of the m explicit constraints can possibly
be binding.

Returning to our original example and its solution (Figure 3.3), we
see that, at the solution, the painting constraint and the machining
constraint are both in force (*binding*) and both decision variables are
in the solution (being produced). Neither warehouse capacity nor assembly capacity is fully utilized, however. If the available capacities of
either of the binding constraints could be increased, profits could be
increased. Note, however, that if the painting capacity were increased
and the machining constraint remained binding, a new optimum would
be reached quickly at the point where the machining constraint meets
the D axis. At that point only the deluxe model would be produced
and profit would be little higher than at the present optimum. If the
machining constraint could be relaxed by increasing only the machining
capacity, the optimum solution would move to the corner where the
assembly constraint and the painting constraint intersect (point q).
An increase in warehousing or assembling capacity with the current
profit ratio and current machining and painting constraints would have
no effect on the solution. Profits would be affected only if this action
caused an increase in costs.

Mathematical Formulation of Linear Programming Problems

Most real-world linear programming problems involve more than two
decision variables. For three variable problems, graphic illustration is
difficult, for more than three variables, graphic analysis is impossible.
In these more usual and more interesting cases, one must resort to a
mathematical formulation of the problem and find a solution by the
application of mathematical analysis.

For example, the problem solved above could be stated in mathematical terms as follows:
Zedo wishes to *maximize* the objective function:

(1) $R = 3S + 5D$

subject to the four *explicit* constraints:

(2) $2.0S + 2.5D \leq 40,000$
(3) $1.5S + 1.0D \leq 24,000$
(4) $0.0S + 1.0D \leq 14,000$
(5) $2.0S + 3.0D \leq 60,000$

and the two implicit constraints:

(6) $S \geq 0$
(7) $D \geq 0$

In order to transform the explicit constraints from inequalities to equalities, we introduce a set of additional decision variables, called *slack variables*, each of which accounts for that amount of any productive resource allowed to remain idle. There are four explicit constraints and there are four *slack* variables to be introduced:

$$M_s = \text{unused machining capacity}$$
$$A_s = \text{unused assembly capacity}$$
$$P_s = \text{unused painting capacity}$$
$$W_s = \text{unused warehouse capacity}$$

With the four slack variables included, the four explicit constraints can be stated as equalities.

(2′) $2.0S + 2.5D + M_s = 40,000$
(3′) $1.5S + 1.0D + A_s = 24,000$
(4′) $0.0S + 1.0D + P_s = 14,000$
(5′) $2.0S + 3.0D + W_s = 60,000$

These slack variables are also covered by *implicit* constraints against negative values, for a slack could be negative only if the original constraint for the corresponding resource were violated. Note also that the contribution of each slack to the objective is zero.

With the constraint equations expressed as equalities, we have available a set of five equations in six unknowns, plus the six implicit constraints against negative values of decision variables or slack variables.

Note that for some situations a constraint could specify "at least equal to" ($\geq$) rather than "no greater than" ($\leq$) as in the sprayer example. For example, if one were attempting to find a production schedule to satisfy a given demand at minimum cost, one side condition would specify that the quantity of the good produced be sufficient to meet the given demand. Then the constraint would be of the form.

$$Q \geq k$$

Such a constraint is converted to an equality by *subtracting* the slack of Q from Q and setting the result equal to k, the limiting value. That is,

$$Q - Q_s = k$$

The slack variable (Q_s) is then interpretable as the "extra" or "unused" amount of Q (production). (We will have more to say about this in the section on minimization problems.)

Let us return to our present problem. We need to find a solution method. By a simple extension of 3.00, we can assert,

3.01   All *basic and feasible solutions* are corners of the feasible region.

We would like a method for solving the equation system of a linear programming problem which considers only these basic and feasible solutions. A general method meeting this requirement is the *simplex method:*

3.02   The *simplex method:*
   (1) Considers only basic feasible solutions. (Attention is restricted to the corners of the feasible region.)
   (2) Starting from any given corner of the feasible region, the method proceeds to a better adjacent corner. At each corner, the search for a better corner is repeated until a corner is found such that the value of the objective cannot be increased by moving to any adjacent corner.[2]

Adjacent corners are corners falling at the ends of one of the linear borders of the feasible region. Examination of Figure 3.4 makes it obvious that to move from one corner to an *adjacent* corner of the feasible region, one variable which was *in* the solution (nonzero) must leave the solution (become zero) and one variable which was *out* of the solu-

---

[2] In the case of "degeneracy" (defined in a later section), it is not possible to find a better corner at once but the simplex method still works well in practice.

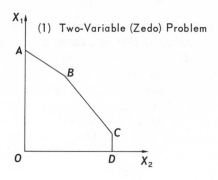

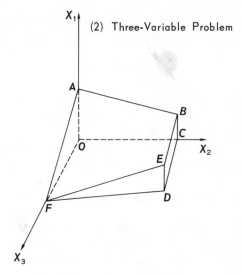

FIG. 3.4. Two feasible regions.

tion (zero) must come into the solution (become nonzero). For example, to move from corner B to corner A, decision variable X_2 must go *out* of the solution (become zero) in either the two-variable or the three-variable case. Variable X_2 would be replaced by the slack variable associated with the constraint forming line BC in the two-variable case. In the three-variable case, the slack variable associated with constraint plane $BCDE$ would replace variable X_2, would rise to its maximum possible value.

The Simplex Method

The above argument implies that if we can find one basic and feasible solution point (corner of the feasible region) and devise a systematic procedure for exchanging *in* and *out* variables so as to move to the best of any adjacent corners with higher values for the objective, we can work from corner to corner of the feasible region until an optimum solution is obtained. That is exactly what the *simplex method* does.

3.10 The *simplex method* for solving linear programming problems involves four steps:
   (1) *Choose the starting point* by finding an initial feasible solution, a corner of the feasible region.
   (2) Move to a better corner.
      (a) *Choose the variable to enter the solution.* (The variable which will add most to the value of the objective at that point.)
      (b) *Choose the variable to leave the solution.* (The variable which is driven out by bringing in the variable entering the solution.)
      (c) *Make the substitutions* of the above variables and work out the new solution.
   (3) *Check for an optimum solution.* (At the optimum, the value of the objective cannot be increased by bringing in any one of the variables which are out of the solution at that point.)
   (4) *Repeat the iterative search until an optimum is reached.* (Steps 2 and 3 are repeated as often as necessary.)

Choose the Starting Point.   Consider any linear programming problem of the form:

Maximize: $Z = z_1x_1 + \cdots + z_jx_j + \cdots + z_nx_n$

Subject to: $a_{11}x_1 + \cdots + a_{1j}x_j + \cdots + a_{1n}x_n \leq C_1$

$$a_{i1}x_1 + \cdots + a_{ij}x_j + \cdots + a_{in}x_n \leq C_i$$

$$a_{m1}x_1 + \cdots + a_{mj}x_j + \cdots + a_{mn}x_n \leq C_m$$

We have demonstrated that the addition of m slack variables, S_k ($k = 1$ to m), will convert the problem to a problem involving only equalities. The contribution of any slack variable to the objective is zero. Restating,

Maximize: $Z = z_1x_1 + \cdots z_jx_j + \cdots z_nx_n + OS_i + \cdots$
$$ + OS_i + \cdots OS_m$$

Subject to: $a_{11}x_1 + \cdots + a_{1n}x_{1n} + S_1 = C_1$

$$a_{m1}x_1 + \cdots + a_{mn}x_n + S_m = C_m$$

For any *basic* solution, exactly m of the total $n + m$ variables must be *in* the solution (nonzero). Therefore, n of the $n + m$ variables must be *out* of the solution (equal to zero). For the kind of problem we have described, such a solution is obvious, let the n decision variables be *out* of the solution and the m slack variables be *in*. (This is the cormer of the feasible region falling at the origin (see Figure 3.3) and is known as the *origin solution*.)

At any *feasible* solution, the m equalities involving the m slack variables will be satisfied. Rearranging the m equations:

$$S_1 = C_1 - a_{11}x_1 - \cdots - a_{1n}x_n$$

$$S_m = C_m - a_{m1}x_1 - \cdots - a_{mn}x_n$$

or, in general,

3.11 $S_i = C_i + a_{i1}{}^*x_1 + \cdots + a_{in}{}^*x_n$

The numbers $a_{ij}{}^*$ are called *exchange coefficients*. For the first origin solution, the exchange coefficients ($a_{ij}{}^*$) are given by the simple formula

$$a_{ij}{}^* = -a_{ij}$$

At each iteration, including the final solution, the exchange coefficients indicate, for each equation and each pair of *in* and *out* variables, the number of units of the *in* variable which must leave the solution if one unit of the *out* variable is to enter the solution. These coefficients are especially useful in analysis of the final solution as is explained in a later section.

Since all $x_j = 0$, $S_i = C_i$ for all m of the equations at the origin solution. Thus, we see that the variable on the left side of each equation is *in* the solution in the amount specified by C_i. The variables on the right side of each equation are *out* of the solution. The slack variables are equal to the C_i's, which *must be nonnegative* for the *implicit* constraints on the slack variables to be satisfied.

Choose the Variable to Enter the Solution. The simplex method obviously involves the manipulation of the real and slack variables within these equations in such a fashion that at any time, exactly m variables will be *in* the solution and the equations will be satisfied.

The solution will be *feasible* as long as all of the C_j are nonnegative (they may be zero). The *in*-variables are on the left sides of the equations and the *out*-variables are on the right sides. At each iteration (round), the variable to come into the solution should be that variable which will provide the greatest increase in the objective. However, judging the net effect of each variable on the objective may be quite complicated. Bringing in enough of one variable to move to an adjacent corner causes some other variable to go out (fall to zero). Variables other than the one going out also can change when a particular variable is brought in. For example, if we return to the Zedo sprayer example and set up the m constraint equations at the origin solution as in the previous section,

(1) $M_s = 40{,}000 - 2.0S - 2.5D$
(2) $A_s = 24{,}000 - 1.5S - 1.0D$
(3) $P_s = 14{,}000 - 0.0S - 1.0D$
(4) $W_s = 60{,}000 - 2.0S - 3.0D$

In order to bring in one unit of the standard sprayer, the exchange coefficients indicate that we must take out 2.0 hours of machining time (M_s), 1.5 hours of assembly time (A_s), and 2.0 square feet of warehouse space. Only if removing variables which, as the slack variables here, have no effect on the objective (their contribution to the objective is zero) will the net effect of the standard unit be represented by its coefficient in the objective function. In this case, the only variables affected by bringing in units of S (or D) are slack variables whose contribution to the objective is zero. In the general case the net effect (z_j^{net}) of bringing a unit of *out*-variable i into the solution would be:

3.12 $z_j^{net} = z_j^* + \sum_{i=1}^{m} a_{ij}^* z_{Ii}$

where

z_j^{net} = the net change in the objective function per unit of the jth *out*-variable brought into the solution.

z_j^* = the gross contribution to the objective of each unit of the jth *out*-variable brought into the solution (from the objective function).

z_{Ij} = the gross contribution of each unit of the ith *in*-variable to the objective (from the objective function).

a_{ij}^* = the exchange coefficient of the ith *in*-variable in the jth column (for the jth *out*-variable) at the current iteration.

Note that the $a_{ij}{}^*$ at any specific iteration need not bear any simple relationship to the original a_{ij}. Only at the beginning, origin, solution is it true that

$$a_{ij}{}^* = -a_{ij}$$

We can now define

3.13 The variable to *enter* the solution at any iteration is the *out*-variable for which $z_j{}^{net}$ is a *maximum*.

At the first change for our example, the variable to enter the solution is obviously D (deluxe model) since

$$z_S{}^{net} = z_S{}^* + (a_{m,S}{}^*)z_{M_s} + (a_{A,S}{}^*)z_{A_s} + (a_{P,S}{}^*)z_{P_s} + (a_{W,S}{}^*)z_{W_s}$$
$$z_S{}^{net} = 3 + (-2.0)(0) + (-1.5)(0) + (0)(0) + (-2.0)(0) = 3$$

and

$$z_D{}^{net} = z_D{}^* + (a_{M,D}{}^*)z_{M_s} + (a_{A,D}{}^*)z_{A_s} + (a_{P,D}{}^*)z_{P_s} + (a_{W,D}{}^*)z_{W_s}$$
$$z_D{}^{net} = 5 + (-2.5)(0) + (-1.0)(0) + (-1.0)(0) + (-3.0)(0) = 5$$

Choosing the Variable to Leave the Solution.   When some *out*-variable is brought into the solution, the m equations (3.11) must be modified to reflect this change but the proscribed equalities must still hold.

Consider the general case again and suppose we decide to bring in variable x_j. Consider the effect on the first constraint equation (in the form of 3.11),

$$S_1 = C_1 + a_{11}{}^*x_1 + \cdots + a_{1j}{}^*x_j + \cdots + a_{1n}{}^*x_n$$

In order for this equation, and all other, to remain as an equality after the introduction of a positive quantity of x_j, S_1 will have to be modified to reflect that fact. If $a_{1j}{}^*$ is positive, adding x_j will increase S_1 and no amount of x_j will cause S_1 to leave the solution (fall to zero). If $a_{1j}{}^*$ is negative, however, introducing a positive amount of x_j will cause S_1 to decrease. At the point where

$$x_j = \frac{-C_1}{a_{1j}{}^*}$$

S_1 will be driven to zero and leave the solution. If x_j is to enter the solution, the maximum amount which can enter will be equal to the minimum of the ratios

$$r_i = \frac{-C_i}{a_{ij}{}^*}$$

The variable on the left of the equation containing this *minimum* ratio will be the variable to leave the solution. That is,

3.14   The variable to *leave* the solution at any iteration is the variable on the left side of an equation for which the ratio

$$r_i = \frac{-C_i}{a_{ij}{}^*} \qquad\qquad (a_{ij}{}^* < 0)$$

is a *minimum* for variable j, the variable entering the solution.

If no $a_{ij}{}^*$ is negative, the solution is "unbounded" and an infinite profit is indicated. Since this is against the rules of economics, it cannot happen in a correctly formulated problem. Its occurrence indicates that some constraint has been overlooked.

For the Zedo sprayer example, the variable to enter the solution on the first round is D (deluxe sprayers). Referring to the original equations, the following ratios are computed:

equation (1): $r_1 = \dfrac{-40{,}000}{(-2.5)} = \mathbf{16{,}000}$

equation (2): $r_2 = \dfrac{-24{,}000}{(-1.0)} = \mathbf{24{,}000}$

equation (3): $r_3 = \dfrac{-14{,}000}{(-1.0)} = \mathbf{14{,}000}$

equation (4): $r_4 = \dfrac{-60{,}000}{(-3.0)} = \mathbf{20{,}000}$

The minimum ratio is found in equation (3), the painting constraint equation, so the slack variable P_s will go to zero (leave the solution) and 14,000 units of the deluxe model (variable D) will enter the solution. Refer to Figure 3.3 and observe that we have moved from the origin to the corner at d.

Make the Substitutions.   We have determined that 14,000 units of D should enter the solution and P_s, the painting slack, should leave the solution, but the 14,000 units of D also require the use of machining time, assembly time, and warehouse space. All of the m equations need to be adjusted to reflect the new situation. Remember that our convention is to have the *in*-variable on the left and the *out*-variable on the right of each equation. For the new solution, we rearrange the equation for the variable *leaving* the solution to reflect this state of affairs.

$$\textbf{3.15}\quad x_j{}^* = \frac{-C_i}{a_{ij}{}^*} + \left(\frac{-a_{i1}{}^*}{a_{ij}{}^*}\right)x_1 + \cdots + \left(\frac{1}{a_{ij}{}^*}\right)S_i{}^* + \cdots + \frac{-a_{in}{}^*}{a_{ij}{}^*}x_n$$

All the other equations contain an *in*-variable on the left (only $S_i{}^*$ left the solution completely unless degeneracy were present), but they also contain an *in*-variable on the right, the *out*-variable being brought in, $x_j{}^*$. Fortunately, 3.15 provides us with an expression which is equal to $x_j{}^*$ and which contains only *out*-variables. If we substitute this expression for $x_j{}^*$ in each of the remaining S_i equations, they will contain only *out*-variables on the right.

For our example, revised equation (3) is

$$(3')\quad D = \frac{-14,000}{(-1.0)} + \frac{-0}{(-1.0)}S + \frac{1}{(-1.0)}P_s$$
$$= 14,000 + 0S - P_s$$

Substituting (3') for D in (1), (2), and (4), the revised equations become:

(1') $M_s = 5000 - 2.0S + 2.5P_s$
(2') $A_s = 10,000 - 1.5S + 1.0P_s$
(3') $D = 14,000 - 0.0S - 1.0P_s$
(4') $W_s = 18,000 - 2.0S + 3.0P_s$

Check for an Optimum Solution.   We have now found a second solution, possibly an optimum solution. It was established earlier that if the new solution is an optimum solution, we could not improve the objective, Z, by bringing in any other variable (moving to an adjacent corner). We must determine if this is the case.

To determine the best variable to bring into the solution, we determined the net contribution ($z_j{}^{net}$) of each *out*-variable. It would seem that as long as the $z_j{}^{net}$ for any one of the *out*-variables is positive and nonzero, it would be possible to bring in that variable and increase the value of Z. We can then define an optimum solution.

3.16   An *optimum solution* for a maximization problem has been found when the $z_i{}^{net}$ for all remaining *out*-variables are either zero or negative.

To check the solution found for our example, we apply 3.12,

$$z_S{}^{net} = z_s{}^* + \sum_{i=1}^{m} a_{iS}{}^* z_{Ii}$$

$$= z_s{}^* + a_{M_sS}{}^* z_{M_s} + a_{A_sS}{}^* z_{A_s} + a_{DS}{}^* z_D + a_{W_sS}{}^* z_{W_s}$$
$$= 3.0 + (-2.0)(0) + (-1.5)(0) + (-0.0)(5) + (-2.0)(0)$$
$$= \mathbf{3.0}$$
$$z_{P_s}{}^{net} = 0.0 + (+2.5)(0) + (+1.0)(0) + (-1.0)(5) + (+3.0)(0)$$
$$= \mathbf{-5.0}$$

Repeat the Iterative Search until an Optimum is Reached. This second solution is not an optimum, $z_S{}^{net} = +3.0$ and Z can be increased by producing some units of the standard model.

(a) How much of S should be brought in?
and
(b) Which variable is to leave the solution?
Applying 3.14,

$$r_{1'} = \frac{-5000}{(-2.0)} = \mathbf{2500}$$

$$r_{2'} = \frac{-10,000}{(-1.5)} = \mathbf{6667}$$

$$r_{3'} = \frac{-14,000}{(-0.0)} = \mathbf{\infty}$$

$$r_{4'} = \frac{-18,000}{(-2.0)} = \mathbf{9000}$$

the limiting constraint is the machining constraint and only 2500 standard models can be produced. It is also established that M_s will be the variable to leave the solution on this iteration; 5000 units of machining time (M_s) are required to produce 2500 units of S.

Exchanging S and M_s in equation (1') by 3.15 and substituting the new expression for S, (1''), into (2'), (3'), and (4'), we obtain:

(1'') $S = 2500 - \frac{1}{2}M_s + \frac{5}{4}P_s$
(2'') $A_s = 6250 + \frac{3}{4}M_s - \frac{7}{8}P_s$
(3'') $D = 14,000 - 1.0P_s$
(4'') $W_s = 13,000 + 1.0M_s + \frac{1}{2}P_s$

Step 5. Check for an optimum by applying 3.12

$$z_{M_s}{}^{\text{net}} = -3/2 \qquad z_{P_s}{}^{\text{net}} = -5/4$$

Since all the $z_i{}^{\text{net}}$ values are negative, this is an optimum. In summary, we find that the optimum solution is:

$$S = 2500 \qquad D = 14{,}000 \qquad Z = \$77{,}500$$

Interpreting the Simplex Solution

Part of the answers obtained above are very easy to interpret: produce 2500 standard sprayers and 14,000 deluxe sprayers at a profit of $77,500. But there is other useful information in the final solution.

Variables in the Solution. We set up and maintained the set of m equations under the convention that variables *in* the solution always appear on the left side of the equation. In addition, the constant on the right side in each equation always shows the amount of the left-side variable that is *in* the solution. The total set of variables and the quantity of each *in* the solution can thus be read from the final set of equations. For example, the *in* variables and the amount of each *in* the solution are:

$$S = \text{units of standard model produced} = \textbf{2500 units}$$
$$A_s = \text{unused assembly capacity} = \textbf{6250 hours}$$
$$D = \text{units of deluxe model produced} = \textbf{14,000 units}$$
$$W_s = \text{unused warehouse space} = \textbf{13,000 square feet}$$

If an alternate use can be found for the excess assembly and warehouse capacity, profits can be enhanced.

Variables out of the Solution. Another convention we used in manipulating the simplex equations was that all variables which are *out* of the solution appear on the right-hand side of the equations. The solution equations contain only two *out* variables:

$$M_s = \text{unused machine capacity} = 0$$
$$P_s = \text{unused painting capacity} = 0$$

In other words, both of these resource capacities are fully utilized in producing the solution output. If some way could be found to increase the amounts of these resources available, profits *might* be enhanced. To determine if such action would pay, we need to know to what extent the profit would be enhanced if an additional unit of the exhausted resources were made available.

Shadow Prices. At the optimum solution, the net contribution of each *out*-variable is either zero or negative. For example, in the Zedo example, $z_{M_s}^{net}$, the net contribution of slack machining capacity to the objective is -1.5 per unit. That is, if M_s (slack machining time) is increased by one unit (to one unit), total net returns decline by $1.50. Similarly, increasing painting slack by one hour results in a decline in net returns of $1.25. Refer to Figure 3.3, and remember the binding (effective) constraints which cause these conditions are straight lines. It follows from this fact (constraint equations are linear) that an *increase* in the available capacity of one unit for a binding constraint (j) will cause the objective (net returns) to *increase* by $-z_i^{net}$ units; z_i^{net} is *negative* so $-z_i^{net}$ is *positive*. In other words, the addition of an additional hour of machining time would *add* $1.50 to net returns. Similarly, one more hour of painting capacity would increase returns by $1.25.

The value z_i^{net} is given a special name in linear programming. It is called the *shadow price* of the *out*-variable to which it applies. Shadow prices correspond to the marginal returns of economic theory. If a technique can be found for relaxing the painting constraint at a cost less than $1.25 per hour of capacity added or for relaxing the machining constraint at less than $1.50 per added hour of capacity, profits can be increased. There are some limitations on this use, however.

For example, the General Manager at Zedo has been advocating that part of the warehouse be converted to a painting booth. The cost of the renovation and the booth would average $.25 per deluxe unit over all deluxe units produced. Painting capacity would increase to 17,000 hours. Examination of Figure 3.3 indicates that the machining constraint would act to limit the production of deluxe units to 16,000. In other words, the shadow price (net addition to returns per unit) established in the solution of the problem applies only in the range from 14,000 to 16,000 unless the machining constraint is also relaxed. This example should make it obvious that while the shadow prices are one of the most useful pieces of information obtained from a linear programming solution, they must be interpreted with care. We see, then, that shadow prices are useful measures of marginal returns but their range of application is limited. Relaxing a constraint (adding to the capacity of a fully utilized resource) adds to the objective only until another constraint replaces the constraint being relaxed, that is, only until another corner of the expanded feasible region is encountered. This indicates that if we can determine how far away that corner is, we can determine the range over which the shadow price applies as a measure of returns from relaxing the constraint. We have already seen in the graphic solution for the Zedo sprayer problem that S (the units of the standard model being produced) is driven to zero first as additional hours of painting capacity are made available. This information is also available from the optimum simplex solution equations.

Adding additional units of painting capacity is equivalent to allowing P_s to assume negative values. All *in*-variables whose exchange coefficients with P_s are positive will be reduced as negative amounts of P_s are added. The exchange coefficients of the optimum solution equations are reproduced in matrix form as follows:

		M_s	P_s
S	2,500	−0.5	+1.25
A_s	6,250	+0.75	−⅞
D	14,000	0	−1
W_s	13,000	+1	+0.5
z^{net}		−1.5	−1.25

Note that the exchange coefficients of both S and W_s for P_s are positive. Adding negative amounts of P_s will cause the values for S and W_s to decline. The ratios showing the maximum amounts allowable are:

$$r_{S}' = \frac{-2500}{1.25} = \mathbf{-2000}$$

$$r_{W_s}' = \frac{-13,000}{0.5} = \mathbf{-26,000}$$

Since the minimum (absolute) ratio is 2000, the shadow price of −1.25 applies only over the range from 14,000 to 16,000 (14,000 to 14,000 + 2000) as a measure of the effect of relaxing the painting constraint.

The addition of 2000 hours of painting capacity would increase profits by $(-1.25)(-2000) = \$2500$.

A similar analysis for the machining constraint indicates that the shadow price of $1.50 holds over the range from 40,000 to 48,333.33 hours of machining capacity and profits could be increased by $12,500. (Discussion Problem 3 asks the reader to demonstrate that these latter statements are true.)

Another interpretation of the *shadow prices* provides a check on the accuracy of the final solution. This interpretation says that shadow prices are the *opportunity costs* of the productive resources used to produce the outputs of the decision variables obtained, that is, the opportunity cost that must be paid by any alternative use. The non-binding explicit constraints have implied shadow prices of zero, indicating that the resources for which excess capacity exists have an opportunity cost of zero. If some other use can be found for the unused resources, it will not require any decrease in the returns from the present use (unless the excess capacity, the available slack, is exceeded). If the shadow prices represent opportunity costs of the resources used in production, then economic theory tells us that at the optimum level of output(s) the value of the products of the shadow prices times the amounts of resources used should equal the returns from using those resources. This has been called the *exhaustion theorem*.

3.17 At the optimum solution, shadow prices are determined in such a manner that the total of the amounts of the objective function allocated to each fully utilized (exhausted) resource by its associated shadow price (sign ignored) just exhausts the total amount of the objective.

This theorem means that multiplying the amount of each exhausted resource by its associated shadow price and adding the resulting products gives the value (sign ignored) of the objective at the optimum solution. Thus, for our example, at the optimum solution

$$P = \$77,500$$

and

$$(\$1.50)(40,000) + (1.25)(14,000) = \mathbf{\$77,500}$$

The equality demonstrates that we have found the optimum solution.

Solution to Minimization Problems

In all of the preceding discussion, we have considered only a maximization problem. This was primarily a convenience during the exposition. However, despite the truth of the statement that minimization problems merely require that we reverse the signs of all coefficients in the objective function, a little more is often involved. We will now set up a minimization problem primarily to illustrate difficulties with constraint equations which are common in such cases (this problem will be solved in a later section). The same forms of constraints are sometimes encountered in maximization problems, but are most often encountered in minimization problems.

Note that changing the signs in the objective function gives a maximization problem and the variable brought in is the one with the largest positive z^{net} and the optimum solution is indicated when the z^{net} values for all *out*-variables are zero or negative.

We could solve the minimization problem without changing the signs in the objective function, but the iteration rules would have to be slightly modified. The variable to be brought into the solution at each iteration would be the variable with the smallest (largest negative) z^{net} value. Also, the optimum solution would be reached when the z^{net} values for all *out* variables are zero or positive.

The Lumbar Furniture Company has an order for 100 of its unfinished maple chairs. The chairs can be produced in two ways. One way is for Lumbar to produce the chair parts in its own shop at a cost of $2.50 per chair and use 20 minutes of Grade 3 labor to assemble each chair. Grade 3 labor is paid $1.80 per hour. The alternative method for filling the order is to purchase the parts of the chair from a competitor at a cost of $3.00 per chair and use 15 minutes of Grade 2 labor to assemble each chair. Grade 2 labor earns $2.00 per hour. The order must be filled during the next ten days. If Lumbar sends out for the parts, they must order at least 50 sets of parts (chairs). Twenty hours of each of the two grades of labor could be available at the time for assembly.

To set up Lumbar's problem as a linear programming problem, we need an objective function stated in terms of costs. If we let x_1 stand for chairs produced entirely within Lumbar and x_2 stand for chairs only assembled at Lumbar,

$$\text{costs} = 2.50x_1 + 1.80\left(\frac{20}{60}\right)x_1 + 3.00x_2 + 2.00\left(\frac{15}{60}\right)x_2$$
$$= 3.10x_1 + 3.50x_2$$

Costs are to be minimized, so our objective is,

Minimize $C = 3.10x_1 + 3.50x_2$

One constraint is specified by the fact that the order is for 100 chairs.

(D) $x_1 + x_2 = 100$

The limited supplies of labor result in two constraints. Twenty minutes ($\frac{1}{3}$ of an hour) of Grade 3 labor is used for every unit of x_1. Since only 20 hours of Grade 3 labor can be made available,

(L_3) $x_1 \leq 60$

Similarly, 15 minutes ($\frac{1}{4}$ of an hour) of Grade 2 labor is used for every unit of x_2, only 20 hours of that labor are available, and

(L_2) $x_2 \leq 80$

Since the second constraint (L_3) says that at least 40 units of x_2 (outside parts) must be used, the lot size constraint specified by the outside supplier must be considered,

(O) $x_2 \geq 50$

Summarizing, the problem in the general form is:

Minimize $Z = 3.10x_1 + 3.50x_2$

Subject to:

(D) $x_1 + x_2 = 100$
(L_3) $x_1 \leq 60$
(L_2) $x_2 \leq 80$
(O) $x_2 \geq 50$
and all $x_i \geq 0$

To restructure the constraints as equalities we must add slack variables to constraints (L_3), (L_2), and (O).

(L_3') $x_1 + S_1 = 60$
(L_2') $x_2 + S_2 = 80$
(O') $x_2 - S_3 = 50$

But, this last constraint indicates that, at the origin solution, when $x_1 = x_2 = 0$, slack variable S_3 is negative. Since the simplex method requires that the C_i in each equation must be positive if a solution is feasible, this solution cannot be feasible. Also, when (D) is set up in the simplex matrix form at the origin solution where $x_1 = x_2 = 0$, the equation says

$$0 + 0 = 100$$

To remove these difficulties, we add a purely *artificial variable* to each of these constraint equations. Then,

(D'') $x_1 + x_2 + A_1 = 100$

and

(O'') $x_2 - S_3 + A_2 = 50$

The revised (complete) objective function then becomes

$$C = 3.10x_1 + 3.50x_2 + OS_1 + OS_2 + OS_3 + MA_1 + MA_2$$

where M is a very large positive number, say 99 million.

The reason for the large value of M is to cause the artificial variables (A_i's) to be driven *out* of the solution. Their contribution to cost is too great to reach a minimum while they are *in* the solution.

By restating equations (D'') and (O'') we can see that

(D''') $A_1 = 100 - x_1 + x_2$
(O''') $A_2 = 50 - x_2 + S_3$

Substituting these values for A_1 and A_2 in the objective function and clearing, we obtain the final form of the objective function as

$$C = 150M + (3.10 - M)x_1 + (3.50 - 2M)x_2 + MS_3$$

and the expression is to be minimized. Changing the signs in the objective equation, we obtain

$$-C = -150M + (M - 3.10)x_1 + (2M - 3.50)x_2 - MS_3$$

which is to be maximized. Note that C is now negative.

The origin solution equations would be:

(1) $A_1 = 100 - x_1 - x_2$
(2) $S_1 = 60 - x_1$
(3) $S_2 = 80 - x_2$
(4) $A_2 = 50 - x_2 + S_3$

It is left as an exercise for the reader to carry through the solution by the simplex rules given earlier. (See Discussion Problem 1.) The solution is given in the next section as an illustration of the special pivoting rules given there.

PRACTICAL SOLUTION TECHNIQUES

It is obvious from following through the trivial linear programming problem solved above that manual solution of such problems by the simplex technique is a complicated and time-consuming process.

Pivoting Rules

One way in which the job can be simplified is by the adoption of mechanical pivoting rules for working through the simplex solution. One such set of rules has been developed by Baumol.[4] The steps in the process *for maximization problems only* are:

1. Set up the *origin solution* in a special table. (We will use the Zedo sprayer example, with x_1 = standard and x_2 = deluxe.)

		x_1	x_2
Z	0	+3	+5
S_1	+40,000	−2	−2.5
S_2	+24,000	−1.5	−1
S_3	+14,000	0	−1
S_4	+60,000	−2	−3

This table will be recognized as the exchange coefficients from the origin solution equations expressed in matrix form and with the original objective function added as the top row.

2. The *pivot column* is the column other than the first column with the largest positive top element.

This implies that the values in the top row are z^{net} values for the *out* variables. It will be seen that this is true at every iteration. Note that the *largest positive* top element is chosen only when one is maximizing. In the present case, the x_2 column is the pivot column (x_2 is to enter the solution).

3. The *pivot row* is determined by the *smallest* absolute quotient found by dividing each negative value in the pivot column into the corresponding constant value in the first column of that row.

[4] William J. Baumol, *Economic Theory and Operations Analysis*, 2d ed., Englewood Cliffs, N.J.: Prentice-Hall, Inc., 1965, Chapter 5.

Note that this is merely a restatement of the general simplex rule given earlier (3.14). For our example, the pivot row is the S_3 row where the ratio value is 14,000. The pivot element so identified has been circled in the initial solution matrix.

4. The *new pivot element* is the reciprocal of the old pivot element, that is, 1/(old pivot element).
5. *Other pivot row elements* are found by dividing the old element by the old pivot element and changing the sign.
6. *Other pivot column elements* are each found by dividing the old element by the old pivot element.

Performing these three steps for our example, we obtain the values shown in the partial matrix below.

		x_1	x_2
Z			-5
S_1			$+2.5$
S_2			$+1$
S_3	$+14,000$	0	-1
S_4			$+3$

Note that these coefficients can be found in the previous first iteration simplex solution.

7. *All other elements* are found by forming a rectangle with the old element and the pivot element in diagonally opposite corners and the *other* corners composed of elements in the pivot row and pivot column. The new element then equals:

$$\text{old element} - \frac{\text{product of two } other \text{ corner elements}}{\text{old } pivot \text{ element}}$$

To illustrate this rule, consider the new value for Z, the value for the first row in the first column. The corners of the rectangle are found in the origin solution matrix:

$$\begin{array}{ll} \text{(old element)} \quad 0 & 5 \text{ (pivot column corner)} \\ \text{(pivot row corner)} \quad 14{,}000 & -1 \text{ (pivot element)} \end{array}$$

and the new element is:

$$0 - \frac{5(14,000)}{(-1)} = 70,000$$

The complete solution matrix for the first iteration is:

		x_1	S_3
Z	+70,000	+3	−5
S_1	+ 5,000	Ⓔ−2	+2.5
S_2	+10,000	−1.5	+1
x_2	+14,000	0	−1
S_4	+18,000	−2	+3

Since the Z-row still contains a positive value in other than the first column, the solution is not an optimum. Carrying through the pivoting process again (the pivot element is circled), the solution matrix for the second iteration is:

		S_1	S_3
Z	+77,500	−1.5	−1.25
x_1	+ 2,500	−0.5	+1.25
S_2	+ 6,250	+0.75	−⅞
x_2	+14,000	0	−1
S_4	+13,000	+1	+0.5

Since no column other than the first has a positive top element, this is the optimum solution. Note that each shadow price is found in the first row under the *out*-variable to which it applies, the variables *in* the solution are on the left, and the amount of each *in*-variable is given in the first column. Finally, the optimum value of the objective is the top value in the first column.

As another illustration consider the Lumbar chair problem. First, we must restate the problem as defined previously in matrix form. (Using the final objective function with the changed signs as shown on page 88),

	Z	x_1	x_2 ↓	S_3
	$-150M$	$M - 3.1$	$2M - 3.5$	$-M$
A_1	100	-1	-1	0
S_1	60	-1	0	0
S_2	80	0	-1	0
A_2	50	0	⊖1	$+1$ ←

The top-row elements for x_1 and x_2 are both positive, with the element for x_2 the larger, so this is not an optimum solution. The pivot column is the x_2 column (rule 2) and the pivot row is the A_2 row (rule 3) and the pivot element thus defined has been circled. Applying rules 4, 5, 6, and 7 in turn as required, the next solution matrix is found.

	Z	x_1	A_2	S_3
	$(-175 - 50M)$	$(M - 3.10)$	$(3.5 - 2M)$	$(M - 3.5)$
A_1	50	⊖1	$+1$	-1
S_1	60	-1	$+1$	-1
S_2	30	0	$+1$	-1
x_2	50	0	-1	$+1$

The top-row element for the x_1 column is still positive so this is not an optimum and the x_1 column is the pivot column. The pivot row is the A_1 row (by rule 3) and the pivot element is the -1 lying at the intersection of that row with the pivot column (it has been circled). Again applying rules 4 to 7, we obtain the third solution matrix below.

	Z	A_1	A_2	S_3
	-330	$(3.1 - M)$	$(0.4 - M)$	-0.4
x_1	50	-1	$+1$	-1
S_1	10	$+1$	-1	$+1$
S_2	30	0	$+1$	-1
x_2	50	0	-1	$+1$

Since no top-row element is positive, this is an optimum solution. Its interpretation is straight forward: Produce and assemble 50 chairs using Lumbar parts and buy parts for 50 chairs from the outside supplier at a total cost of $330. If Lumbar could obtain parts from the outside supplier in lots of less than 50, costs could be decreased by 40 cents for each set of chair parts produced at Lumbar. However, there is a limit to this avenue of cost decrease. Only ten more units can be produced at Lumbar with the given supplies of labor for a total saving of $4.00. Without additional labor, 40 sets of chair parts would still have to come from the outside supplier.

Computer Solutions

Even with the special pivoting rules, the job of solving a linear programming problem by manual means is tedious and filled with possibilities for making errors. The most common method for finding a solution is to use a special electronic computer program. By changing the signs in the objective function, a maximization algorithm can be used to solve a minimization problem or a minimization algorithm used to solve a maximization problem.

For other than professionals in the field, emphasis should be placed on understanding where linear programming can be usefully applied and how the solutions to linear programming problems may be interpreted.

OTHER PROGRAMMING SOLUTIONS

Other Types of Programming

Mathematical programming was defined at the beginning of this chapter as a set of allocation techniques which search out optimum values for an object variable in situations where at least one of the decision variables involved is subject to a constraint which is an inequality and none of the decision variables can assume negative values. For the special case studied here, we required that all relations between variables be linear. We also had a hidden assumption that the decision variables *could* take on noninteger values (values other than whole numbers). There are cases where one or more of these restrictions prevents the use of linear programming and other forms of mathematical programming must be used.

Integer programming is frequently necessary in practice, since half of an airplane cannot fly, half of a worker cannot work, and so forth. Programming has also been extended to include quadratic objective functions (called *quadratic programming*) for guiding decisions such as what mix of common stocks gives a portfolio which best matches the risk preferences of an investor.

A technique called *dynamic programming* is available for making a series of decisions where the outcome of a subsequent decision depends upon the result from some previous decision. In these situations a decision can be truly optimum only if it takes into account its impact on the future as well as its current effects.

Finally, it is even possible to apply linear programming to problems in which either the technological coefficients in the cons raints or the coefficients of the objective function are random variables. This technique is known as *stochastic linear programming* or *linear programming under uncertainty*.

Other Programming Methods

There are solution methods other than the simplex method, some of which are very efficient for specific problems. Perhaps one of the most widely used is the *transportation algorithm*, a method used to solve a class of problems where resources available are just equal to the sum of requirements and all of the exchange coefficients are either one or zero. The technique was developed to find the minimum cost of distributing a product from a number of sources (factories or warehouses) to a number of destinations (warehouses or customers), but has application to a much wider range of problems. Its only advantage over the simplex method for these problems is its greater computational efficiency. It is merely a special case of the simplex method.

The *assignment problem* is a special case of the transportation problem in which N jobs must be assigned to N facilities with differing efficiencies.

Difficulties in Solving Programming Problems

A special technique must be used to solve a linear programming problem where *degeneracy* occurs. Degeneracy occurs whenever less than m (the number of explicit constraints) of the (decision *and* slack variables) variables are in the solution with positive values. Special procedures are necessary to obtain a solution in such a case, but the simplex method is readily modified to handle degeneration.

Occasionally one will apparently find a problem with *no optimum solution*. If the variable with the largest z^{net} value has only positive or zero exchange coefficients, there is no effective limit on the number of units of that variable which can be introduced to provide greater values of the objective. The solution is then *unbounded*. Generally, such a result occurs only because at least one of the constraints has been improperly defined or missed completely.

SUMMARY

Linear programming under certainty is a mathematical technique for solving decision problems where the *object variable* or *objective* can be expressed as a *linear function* of a set of *decision variables* subject to a set of *linear constraints*. The general method for solving such problems is the *simplex method*, a method which searches out in a systematic manner the possible solutions to the resulting set of linear equations until the *optimum solution* is found. The solution to a linear programming problem not only tells us how much of each decision variable should be included in the solution but also tells us the *opportunity cost* of resources used up in the solution. Thus, we can determine how the solution would be improved by making more of each of the used-up resources available.

The application of basic linear programming is possible only if the linearity assumptions are met, noninteger values of the decision variables are allowable, and the coefficients of the objective and constraint equations are known with certainty. The technique is also static; it cannot provide optimum solutions for problems structured as a series of interdependent decisions. Techniques exist for the solution of part of these other problems, but they have only been mentioned here.

DISCUSSION QUESTIONS

1. Identify the following in *your own* words. Use no symbols or verbal formulas.

    (a) mathematical programming
    (b) linear programming
    (c) objective function
    (d) constraint
    (e) feasible solution to a linear programming problem
    (f) basic solution to a linear programming problem
    (g) shadow price
    (h) slack variable
    (i) artificial variable
    (j) origin solution to a linear programming problem
    (k) optimal solution to a linear programming problem
    (l) feasible region
    (m) exchange coefficient

(n) iso-return line
(o) explicit constraint
(p) implicit constraint

2. Why is the origin solution normally used as the initial solution?
3. What do the coefficients within the simplex equations represent? Why is it necessary to recompute them at each iteration?
4. Why is it that, except for certain special cases, the solution to a linear programming problem lies at a corner of the feasible region?
5. Under what conditions would there be a range of optimal solutions to a linear programming problem? How should the decision maker make a final selection in such a case?
6. What would be the effect on the solution to a linear programming problem of an increase in the coefficient of one decision variable in the objective function? What would be the economic meaning of such an increase?

   Hint: Consider changes in the objective function for the Zedo sprayer problem: (1) Suppose the coefficient of S changed from 3 to 4. (2) Suppose the coefficient of D changed from 5 to 7. Now, generalize the observed effects. Would they apply to minimization problems? to decreases in coefficients?

DISCUSSION PROBLEMS

Show your method on all solutions.

1. Use the simplex rules to solve the Lumbar chair (cost) problem used in the chapter to illustrate the process of minimizing the objective.
   (a) What are the solution values?
   (b) Fully interpret your solution.
   Hints: (1) The coefficients of the artificial variables (M) do appear in the matrix.
   (2) You should need only two iterations.
2. Solve the Lumbar chair problem by graphic analysis. (Use commercial graph paper for accuracy.)
   (a) What are the graphic solution values?
   (b) What is the shape of the feasible region for this problem?
   Hint: Note that the solution to this problem is intuitively obvious given the constraints $x_1 + x_2 = 100$ and $x_2 \geq 50$ and the coefficients in the objective equation. Consider the constraint equation $x_1 + x_2 = 100$ very carefully. What feasible region does this constraint allow?

3. Demonstrate graphically and algebraically that the shadow price for the machining constraint in the Zedo sprayer problem holds over the range from 40,000 to 48,333.33 hours.

    Hint: Use commercial graph paper, expand the scales, and show only that portion of Figure 3.3 which is pertinent to the analysis.

4. The executives of Zedo Manufacturing are interested in increasing the returns from the sprayer manufacturing operation. Two specific proposals have been made:

    (1) The Production Manager has developed a plan which would expand painting capacity to 17,000 hours and machining capacity to 45,000 hours while reducing warehouse capacity to 48,000 square feet. These changes would increase unit costs of the Deluxe model 30 cents and units costs of the Standard model 15 cents.

    (2) The Marketing Manager thinks that Zedo should accept a proposal by Loware Corporation to lease warehouse space from Zedo. Loware will pay $100 rent per 1000 square feet per period. Loware will not rent less than 5000 square feet but will rent 10,000 square feet if it can be made available.

    The executives have available the results from the optimum solution to the sprayer problem given in this chapter:

    Production levels: $2500S$ $14,000D$
    Shadow prices:
    $z_{M_s}^{net} = \$-1.50$ holds from 40,000 to 48,333.33
    $z_{P_s}^{net} = \$-1.25$ holds from 14,000 to 16,000
    Excess capacities: $A_s = 6250$ $W_s = 13,000$

    Using *only* the above solution results, what action would you recommend for Zedo? Explain fully.

    Hint: Are the capacities sufficient to handle the outcome of the first proposal? How do you know? Remember, you are *not* to rework the solution.

5. A wholesale grocery firm in the Middleton area serves as a distributor of frozen fruits and vegetables to the retail grocery stores in the area. The firm attempts to rotate the frozen foods into and out of its warehouse each two weeks. On Wednesday of every other week, a supply for the next two weeks is delivered to the warehouse. The freezer space available for storing frozen fruits and vegetables measures 35 feet by 20 feet by 9 feet high. Access to all parts of the area is provided by one central aisle the length of the freezer and two cross aisles. The main aisle is six feet wide and the two side aisles are each

four feet wide. The frozen fruits and vegetables are stacked only to a height of seven feet because of the danger of crushing the bottom boxes. The firm distributes ten different frozen items. Minimum and maximum sales (in 24-package cartons measuring 12 by 12 by 6 inches) and cost and net return per carton for the next two-week period are given below. The minimum sales figures are provided by contracts with some of the grocery stores in the area. The maximum's are upper limit estimates of sales of the product during the next two weeks.

	SALES (CARTONS)		COST AND RETURN PER CARTON	
Product	Minimum	Maximum	Cost	Return
Strawberries	100	600	$4.70	$0.40
Red raspberries	80	320	4.50	0.31
Peaches	60	200	4.60	−0.08
Blueberries	50	150	4.80	0.17
Corn	150	800	4.00	0.22
Spinach	100	700	4.10	0.13
Green beans	200	1000	4.90	0.18
Carrots and peas	180	900	4.30	0.16
Peas	200	1100	4.20	0.11
Lima beans	120	500	5.10	0.19

Since this is a small, young firm, it operates primarily on a line of credit from a local bank. It has $20,000 available for investment in inventory for the next two weeks.

(a) State the above problem as a linear programming problem. Hint: Returns must be maximized subject to constraints on minimum and maximum amounts of sales, maximum investment in inventory, and maximum storage space.

(b) Set up the initial, *origin*, solution in the simplex equation form and interpret its meaning.

(c) Set up the initial, *origin*, solution in the matrix form used when applying the special pivoting rules and interpret the meaning of the matrix.

6. Suppose you were given the following problem:

Minimize: $Z = 7X_1 + 8X_2 + 5X_3 + 3X_4$
Subject to: (1) $2X_1 + 4X_2 \leq 16$
            (2) $X_2 + 3X_3 \geq 15$
            (3) $X_4 \leq 50$
            (4) $X_4 \geq 20$

(a) Identify the following:
   (1) the decision variables
   (2) the amount of slack variable 1 *in* the solution at the origin solution
   (3) the amount of slack variable 2 *out* of the solution at the origin solution
   (4) the position and amount of any artificial variables in the solution at the origin solution
(b) What is the exchange coefficient of
   (1) slack variable 1 for decision variable 1?
   (2) decision variable 1 for slack variable 1?
   (3) If you have given the same answer to parts (1) and (2) of this question, explain. If not, explain.
   Hint: Review the simplex substitution rules; what happens to the exchange coefficients when decision variables replace slack variables in the solution?
(c) State the complete origin solution to this problem.

EXERCISES

Show your method on all solutions.

1. The General Manager at Zedo has proposed that part of the warehouse be converted to a painting booth. This change would reduce the profit contribution of the Deluxe sprayer by $0.25 per sprayer. Painting capacity would increase to 17,000 hours. Rework the simplex solution to evaluate the gross return under the new set of conditions.

2. The Achey Company produces motorcycles and motorscooters. Achey is organized in three departments whose maximum weekly capacities for producing either motorcycles or motorscooters are as follows:

Department	Motorcycles	Motorscooters
	CAPACITIES	
Forming and welding	100	150
Assembly	75	125
Painting	130	90

The profit contribution of each motorcycle sold is $50. The sale of a motorscooter contributes $40 to profits. Use graphic analysis to find the optimum numbers of motorcycles and motorscooters to be produced by Achey.

3. Refer to the Achey Company problem (Exercise 2)
   (a) Express the constraints as equations if the maximum hours available in the three departments are:

Forming and welding	750
Assembly	375
Painting	234

   (b) Solve this problem by using the special pivoting rules.
   (c) Fully interpret your solution.
4. A local merchant has available a vacant lot measuring 55 by 100 feet. He regularly uses the lot for selling Christmas trees during the four weeks before Christmas. He stocks four kinds of trees: natural fir, short-needled pine, long-needled pine, and painted fir. Each tree is mounted on a simple wooden stand costing 20 cents per tree to make the stand and mount the tree. The pine trees sold by the merchant require 3 square feet of space per tree. Natural fir trees require only 2 square feet of space each but painted fir trees require 2.5 square feet each. Access aisles will consist of a center aisle 5 feet wide the length of the lot and 4 lateral aisles 3 feet wide running out each way from the main aisle. Signs, the shelter and check stand for the attendants, and so forth, will require another 100 square feet of space. Two paid attendants at $60 per week each will be needed. Lighting, heat for the shelter, signs, and so on, are expected to add another $120 to the cost. Purchase costs and selling prices for the various trees are:

Type of Tree	Purchase Cost	Selling Price
Short-needled pine	$1.30	$3.00
Long-needled pine	2.00	4.50
Natural fir	1.50	3.50
Painted fir	2.50	5.25

   From past experience, the merchant is convinced that no more than 600 of the painted fir trees and 300 of the long-needled pine can be sold from his lot. The merchant has budgeted $3500 for the Christmas tree operation and orders all his trees to be delivered in one lot at the beginning of the sale period.
   (a) Set up the above problem as a linear programming problem.
   (b) Specify and interpret the origin solution.
5. For the next quarter the Koloredi Company has decided to use a linear programming analysis to determine production levels for the three models of television sets: Supra, Prima, and Eclipse. The profit

contributions, technical resource requirements, and resource capacities are shown below. Koloredi executives feel they must produce at least 5000 units of each set each quarter in order to offer a full line and preserve their market position.

| | | TECHNICAL REQUIREMENTS BY DEPARTMENTS (*Hours*) | | |
Set	Profit Contribution	Cabinets	Electronics	Assembly
Supra	50	11	6	2.5
Prima	50	10	7	2.6
Eclipse	60	12	6.5	2.7
Total capacities (hours)		450,000	250,000	95,000

(a) What mix of the three television sets would you recommend to Koloredi? (Use linear programming to obtain the answer.)

(b) What would be optimum (maximum) level of profit?

(c) Do you have any other important information for Koloredi from your linear programming solution? Explain fully.

6. Mein Tea Company produces and sells two brands of tea, Mei and Wik. To preserve their market position, they control quality as closely as possible. Quality is primarily a combination of two characteristics, "body" and "flavor." For the Mei brand, the "flavor" index must be equal to 15 or more and the "body" index no greater than 9. For the Wik brand, the flavor index must be at least 13 and the body index should not be greater than 10. Mein Tea is developing an order for tea leaves to meet expected sales requirements of at least 20,000 pounds of the Mei brand and at least 50,000 pounds of the Wik brand at the end of the processing period. The company buys from three brokers, Mr. Loa, Mr. Hai, and Mr. Medi who have provided the following information about their available stocks:

	Loa	Hai	Medi
Body index	9	11	8
Flavor index	17	12	14
Pounds available	30,000	45,000	60,000
Cost per pound	$0.20	$0.14	$0.16

Set this up as a linear programming problem.

Hint: Let x_{ij} stand for the amount of tea from supplier i used in brand j.

7. Mr. Ira Tew runs the Tew Machine Shop Company, a job shop with two basic production lines. The cost of each shop is

$$I = \$150 \text{ per hour}$$
$$II = \$180 \text{ per hour}$$

Mr. Tew has four jobs to complete. They can each be completed on either of the two lines or split between them. Forty hours are available in each shop. The total hours required in each shop for each job are given below:

	JOBS			
Shops	1	2	3	4
I	15	15	11	6
II	12	18	10	5

Mr. Tew asks how he can minimize the cost of completing the four jobs.

(a) Set up this problem as a cost minimization linear programming problem.

Hint: There are eight decision variables.

(b) Solve the problem by application of the special pivoting rules (or a computer if one is available).

(c) Fully interpret your optimum solution.

Hint: Alternatively, students may be required only to set up the origin solution and specify what information could be obtained from the optimum solution.

(*A computer and a program for solving linear programming problems are suggested for the remaining exercises.*)

8. Obtain a simplex solution to the problem set up in Discussion Problem 4 and interpret it fully.

9. Obtain a simplex solution to the problem set up in Discussion Problem 5 and interpret it fully.

10. Obtain a simplex solution to the problem set up in Discussion Problem 6 and interpret it fully.

section 3
decision making under risk and uncertainty

4
measuring chance

INTRODUCTION

In the example of the businessman used in Chapter 1, we found a situation where the outcome (the total amount sold) was not certain. In the coin-tossing game, the result was also uncertain. In both situations it was necessary to make certain assumptions about how likely each of the several possible outcomes might be in order to arrive at an *expected* average result on which to base a decision. The chance of occurrence of a particular outcome is referred to by a variety of names. Gamblers refer to "odds." Mathematicians and statisticians refer to "probability" and "chance." All refer to basically the same thing stated in different terms or, more importantly, arising from different sources. It is the purpose of this chapter to identify the basic models from which the chance that an event will occur are derived and how the resultant probabilities are manipulated.

PROBABILITY

Classical Definition of Probability

Probability is a mathematical concept which attaches numbers to possible events to describe how likely it is that each event may occur.

105

The concept was developed originally to describe chance processes in gambling, but its use has since expanded into many other areas.

4.00 If an event may happen in A ways and fail to happen in B ways, only one of these $A + B$ ways can occur at each single opportunity for a result, and each of the $A + B$ ways is equally likely to occur, the probability of the event happening, $P(A)$, is $A/(A + B)$, the ratio of the number of ways favorable to the event to the total number of ways.

Thus, if we examine the coin-tossing situation once more, we see that the event "the coin landing heads up" can happen in only one way and can fail to happen in only one way (if the coin lands tails up). These two results exhaust the possibilities of outcomes. Further, they are mutually exclusive outcomes, that is, if one occurs the other cannot occur. Finally, the two outcomes are (by definition of "an honest coin, honestly flipped") equally likely. Applying the above rule (4.00) the probability of the coin landing heads up is $1/(1 + 1) = 1/2$.

According to the classical definition, then, probability can be conceived of as a relative frequency of occurrence. The probability of an individual event may range from 0 (zero) to 1 (one). If the event is certain to occur, then its probability of occurrence is 1. If an event is impossible of occurrence, then its probability is 0. Most events fall somewhere between these extremes and have a probability between 0 and 1.

Sources of Classical Probability Values

Classical probability values are basically derived in one of two ways: from deductive reasoning (see the coin example) and from experience. If the latter technique were to be applied to the coin example, it would be necessary to toss the coin a large number of times and compute the relative frequency of the outcome desired (heads). Probabilities derived by the application of reason are called *a priori probabilities*. Probabilities derived from experience are called *empirical probabilities*.

A priori probabilities are widely used in gambling (roulette, dice playing, card games, and so forth). They are also of importance in applied statistics. The distribution of many statistical variables (arithmetic means, proportions, and so on) from repeated random samples can be predicted through deductive (mathematical) reasoning. A large part of this book is devoted to the demonstration of the use of such *a priori* probabilities in analyzing statistical variables drawn from random samples.

Empirical probabilities are also widely used. The life expectancy tables underlying insurance rates are an excellent example of empirical probabilities. The tables are based on the mortality experiences of hundreds of thousands of persons. Fire and casualty insurance also depend upon the computation of empirical probabilities to determine the proper rates at which insurance may be sold.

Empirical probabilities are also of importance to other businessmen. In the example concerning the possible sales of the new product discussed in Chapter 1, a marketing expert might report that on the basis of sales of similar products in the past, a table could be developed to show how likely each of several alternative levels of sales would be.

These probabilities are derived from the experts' experience with similar products marketed in the same way in the same market area at a different time and perhaps should not be considered true empirical probabilities. However, even the actuarial tables do not reflect the experiences of *exactly* similar human populations living under *exactly* the same conditions. It is well known that actuarial tables possess a definite bias in favor of the insurer due to the constantly increasing longevity arising from improvements in nutrition and medical science. It therefore may seem reasonable to accept the conservative estimates of those with long experience and wide knowledge in a field as empirical probabilities. They reflect in the same manner as *a priori* probabilities a "degree of belief," a way of describing the uncertainty of knowledge.

Subjective Definition of Probability

If we admit "degree of belief" as a source of probability values, we then find two quite different kinds of belief expressed in probability form. One of these is when the probability value is a belief based on only subjective (personal) information but referring to the relative frequency of occurrence of an event over the long run. The only difference between probabilities of this type and *a priori* or empirical probabilities is the source of the values. The probability values come from personal (subjective) information only.

The second kind of belief expressed in a probability form refers not to the relative frequency of outcome in the long run but to the probability of a particular outcome for a single, unique trial.

As an example of the second of the two kinds of subjective probabilities, we have the table of possible sales levels and the probability that each will occur which the marketing expert prepares for our inventive businessman. If the businessman really has a *new* product, then it is a unique occurrence when it is offered for sale in the market place, and its acceptance by the market is impossible to specify. Consider the book publisher faced with selecting a publishable manuscript. Is he not involved in such a situation? He finds it necessary to rely on the judgment of his editors who are guided in part by the opinion of a few "reviewers," that is, outside "experts" who evaluate the book for its marketability.

When the editor accumulates experience with a particular reviewer, he tends to set a value (probability of truth?) on the opinion of that reviewer. He then is approaching the first kind of subjective probability, that involving accumulated experience with the same situation.

Thus a *subjective probability* (sometimes called a *personal probability*) can be defined in two ways.

4.01 A *subjective probability* is a value between 0 and 1 which expresses one's belief in either:
  (a) the relative frequency of occurrence of an event over a long run of trials for which it is a possible outcome, or
  (b) the possibility of an event occurring as the outcome of a single, unique trial for which it is a possible outcome.

Rules for Manipulating Probabilities

Regardless of the manner in which probabilities are obtained, the manipulation of any value between 0 and 1 which is accepted as a probability must follow the rules (axioms) of the probability calculus. First, certain characteristics of probability values are important.

4.10 The probability of any event $P(A)$ is always positive but never greater than 1. Symbolically, $0 \leq P(A) \leq 1$. If $P(A) = 0$, then the occurrence of the event (A) is considered impossible. If $P(A) = 1$, then the occurrence of the event (A) is considered to be certain.

The basic definition leads to several supportive corollaries.

4.11 $P(\chi) = P(A_1) + P(A_2) + \cdots + P(A_n) = 1$, where $A_1, A_2, \cdots, A_n$ are events only one of which can occur on a single trial. (χ is referred to as the *sample space* of the event)[1]

This corollary merely says that probabilities for all of the possible mutually exclusive events which could occur must total to 1.

Another way of stating 4.11 which is often useful in the calculation of probabilities is:

---

[1] The sample space of a chance experiment is the totality of possible outcomes, that is, the set of possible results.

4.12 $P(A) + P(\bar{A}) = 1$, where $\bar{A} = \chi - A$ or "not A."

Note that this can be written as $P(A$ or $\bar{A}) = 1$, where the *or* is inclusive, meaning either or both of the possibilities A and $\bar{A}$. Be sure you understand, however, that

4.13 $P(A$ and $\bar{A}) = 0$, that is, that A and $\bar{A}$ are mutually exclusive and cannot occur together.

Finally, 4.12 can be revised to read:

4.14 $P(A) = 1 - P(\bar{A})$

Rule 4.14 is sometimes referred to as the *complement* rule.

The ideas of probability may also be illustrated with what are called "Venn" diagrams (Joseph Venn was an English logician, 1834–1883). In Figure 4.1, the total area, A and $\bar{A}$ (not A), is equivalent to the

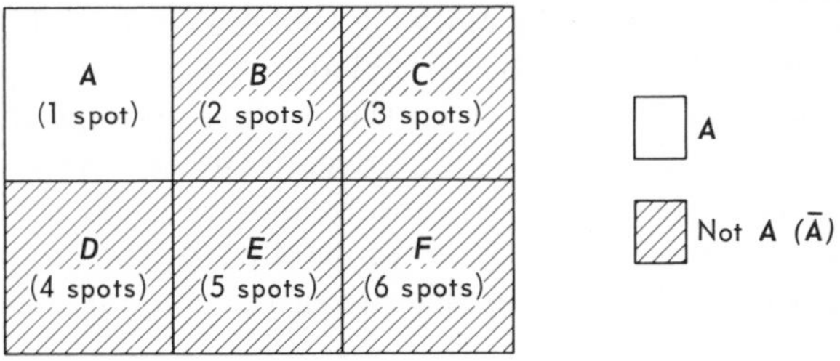

FIG. 4.1.   Venn diagram of outcomes for the event, roll a standard die.

sample space ($\bar{A}$ is composed of the areas B, C, D, E, and F). These are the total possible outcomes for the event: roll a standard, fair, six-sided die and observe the number of spots which appear on the upper face after it comes to rest. Each of these outcomes is considered equally probable and is represented by an equal area (the die is a "standard, fair" die). In addition the outcomes are nonoverlapping (mutually exclusive) and exhaustive (account for all possible outcomes). The probability of any event (say A) would be equal to its area (A) over the total area (A, B, C, D, E, F). The probability of *some* outcome (*either* 1, 2, 3, 4, 5, *or* 6 spots) would equal the involved areas (A, B, C, D, E, F) over the total area (χ) or (χ/χ) or one.

Sometimes we wish to compute the probabilities for a combination of events where it is desired to evaluate the probability that all of the events do occur. The appropriate rule is sometimes referred to as the "and" rule.

4.20 $P(A \text{ and } B) = P(A)P(B|A)$

which is read as the probability of A times the probability of B, *given* that A has occurred. This rule says that the probability that both of two events will occur is the probability of the first multiplied by the probability that if the first has occurred the second will also occur. It is also called the *joint probability* of A and B. The probability of the second event occurring if the first has occurred is called the *conditional probability* of the second, given the first.

To clarify the notion of conditional probability refer again to the die example and Figure 4.1. Suppose we were told that the die had been rolled and the result was either a one, two, or three, what is the probability of its being a one (after the roll)? There are three equally probable possibilities (one, two, three) and the probability of a one is now 1/3 (given that one of the three has occurred).

The following example should clarify this rule. Suppose you are to select one card from a deck of common playing cards containing four suits (hearts, spades, diamonds, clubs) of thirteen cards each (Ace, 2, 3, 4, 5, 6, 7, 8, 9, 10, Jack, Queen, King). What is the probability of drawing aces on two successive draws from the deck, assuming the first card is not replaced? The probability of an ace on the first draw is obviously 4/52. If an ace is drawn as the first card, then there are 51 cards remaining of which only three are aces, so the probability of the second card also being an ace is only 3/51 and the chance of the combined event is

$$4/52(3/51) = 12/2652 = 1/221$$

What if, in making the two draws as above, the first card were to be replaced and the deck thoroughly shuffled before the second draw is made? Then the result on the second draw would be influenced in no way by the result on the first draw and the *conditional* probability of B is equal to the *simple* probability of B. That is, for *independent* events,

$$P(B/A) = P(B), \text{ and}$$

4.21 $P(A \text{ and } B) = P(A)P(B)$

Which says that if a compound event be made up of the simultaneous occurrence of a number of separate and independent subevents, the joint probability of the occurrence of the compound event is the product of the simple probabilities of each of the subevents occurring.

We sometimes desire to compute the probability that some one of several different outcomes will occur. In such cases individual probabilities can be added according to the following general rule (sometimes referred to as the "or" rule).

4.30 $P(A \text{ or } B) = P(A) + P(B) - P(A \text{ and } B)$

That is, the probability of one or more of the events occurring is the sum of their probabilities of occurring individually *minus* the probability of their occurring together.

Let us turn once again to the deck of common playing cards for an example to illustrate this rule. What is the probability of drawing an ace? Since there are only four aces (one in each suit) and 52 cards in total, the chances are 4/52 or 1/13. What is the probability of drawing a heart? There are 13 heart in the deck of 52 so there are 13 chances in 52 or a probability of 1/4. But what is the chance of drawing an ace *or* a heart? There are 4 aces and 13 hearts, but one of the aces is also a heart so we can see that there are only 16 different cards which will satisfy the requirements of the draw, giving a probability of 16/52. Applying 4.20 and recognizing that the probability of selecting an ace *and* a heart is only 1/52, we would compute

$$P \text{ (Ace or Heart)} = P \text{ (Ace)} + P \text{ (Heart)} - P \text{ (Ace and Heart)}$$

or

$$P \text{ (Ace or Heart)} = 4/52 + 13/52 - 1/52 = 16/52$$

which is the result obtained by direct calculation.

Many of you have noted that if the results being evaluated are mutually exclusive 4.30 becomes simply:

4.31 $P(A \text{ or } B) = P(A) + P(B)$

because $P(A \text{ and } B) = 0$ if A and B are mutually exclusive events.

Three situations are diagrammed in Figure 4.2 which further illustrate 4.30 and 4.31. Situation 1 involves the evaluation of the occurrence of either or both of two overlapping events. Situation 2 illustrates the case for two mutually exclusive events. Situation 3 diagrams the situation for three overlapping events.

Note that in Situation 1 the area of overlap (A and B) is part of A and part of B. Therefore the sum of A plus B counts this area twice. Similarly, in Situation 3 the areas (A and B), (A and C), and (B and C)

Situation 1: Two Overlapping Events

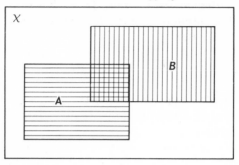

Situation 2: Two Mutually Exclusive Events

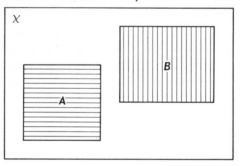

Situation 3: Three Overlapping Events

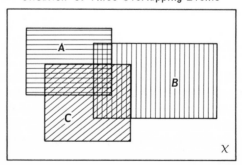

FIG. 4.2.   Venn diagrams of outcomes for mutually exclusive and nonmutually exclusive (overlapping) events.

would each be counted twice in a simple sum. The area $(A$ and B and $C)$ would be counted *three* times. Thus the probability of A or B or C would be:

$$P(A \text{ or } B \text{ or } C) = P(A) + P(B) + P(C) - P(A \text{ and } B) - P(A \text{ and } C)$$
$$- P(B \text{ and } C) + P(A \text{ and } B \text{ and } C)$$

The area $(A$ and B and $C)$ must be added back because it was subtracted three times and it was originally counted only three times.

Revision of Probabilities with Later Information

Businessmen often find themselves in a situation where they have some information about the true state of nature before they take a sample. In such cases it does not seem reasonable to rely only on the new *(sample)* information, but rather to use this new information to revise what is already known (the *prior* information). A hypothetical example will be used to illustrate how prior probabilities are revised in such situations.

The Dry-Cell Company produces small batteries. These batteries are packaged 20 to a carton, and 30 cartons are stacked on a wooden pallet as the last step in the production process. Normally, two percent of these batteries are later found to be improperly sealed. It is discovered that a lot of 60 cartons (two pallets) were run off while a sealing machine was operating improperly. It is validly estimated that ten percent of the batteries produced during this period are improperly sealed. Unfortunately, the defective sealing machine was not reported until the morning after this lot was produced, and the two pallets containing the high proportion of defective batteries cannot be definitely identified. It has been ascertained, however, that these pallets were placed in a particular storage bay which holds ten pallets altogether.

What is the probability that a pallet selected from the storage bay in which the "bad" pallets are located will be one of the "bad" pallets? It seems safe to assume that our lack of knowledge concerning the location of the bad pallets means that each of the ten pallets has an equal probability of selection, then the probability is $2/10$.

Suppose a box of batteries is chosen at random from the selected pallet. Upon examination it is found that two of the 20 batteries contained in the box are improperly sealed. Reference to a proper table (Appendix Table B-4, as will be explained in Chapter 5) indicates that the probability of such a result if the box were drawn from a bad pallet is 0.285. The probability of this result if the box were from an ordinary pallet is only 0.053. These probabilities are the *conditional probabilities* that two defectives would, by chance, be present in a sample of 20 items (a box) if the sample were drawn from the population (kind of pallet) specified.

The probability of choosing a bad pallet P (bad) and then finding two defectively sealed batteries in a box (sample of 20) from that pallet (population) is the *joint* probability of the two events, P (bad *and* 2 def.). By 2.20

$$P \text{ (bad } and \text{ 2 def.)} = P \text{ (bad)} \cdot P \text{ (2 def.|bad)}$$

We know that

$$P \text{ (bad)} = 0.20 \text{ and } P \text{ (2 def.|bad)} = 0.285$$

Therefore,

$$P(\text{bad } and \text{ 2 def.}) = (0.20)(0.285)$$
$$= \mathbf{0.0570}$$

Similarly the probability of the given result (two defectives in a sample of 20) following the selection of an ordinary pallet is computed as:

$$P \text{ (ord. } and \text{ 2 def.)} = P \text{ (ord.)} \cdot P \text{ (2 def.|ord.)}$$
$$= (0.80)(0.053)$$
$$= \mathbf{0.0424}$$

But our interest centers in determining the probability of having selected *either* a bad or an ordinary pallet *given* that two defectives were found in a sample of twenty from the pallet selected, that is, $P(A_i|B)$, where A_i refers to either an ordinary pallet or a bad pallet.

We know from 4.20 that

$$P(A_i \text{ and } B) = P(A_i)P(B|A_i)$$

and, since if we work in reverse

$$P(B \text{ and } A_i) = P(B)P(A_i|B)$$

But, it must be true that

$$P(B \text{ and } A_i) = P(A_i \text{ and } B)$$

since they are the same compound of events. Therefore,

$$P(B)P(A_i|B) = P(A_i)P(B|A_i)$$

and, finally,

4.40 $P(A_i|B) = \dfrac{P(A_i)P(B|A_i)}{P(B)}$

For our problem, there are only two possible prior states of nature, A_1 and A_2, and

$$P(B) = P(A_1 \text{ and } B) + P(A_2 \text{ and } B)$$

Therefore, 4.40 would be rewritten.

$$P(A_i|B) = \frac{P(A_i)P(B|A_i)}{P(A_1)P(B|A_1) + P(A_2)P(B|A_2)}$$

or, more generally, for k prior conditions,

4.41 $P(A_i|B) = \dfrac{P(A_i)P(B|A_i)}{\displaystyle\sum_{i=1}^{k} P(A_i)P(B|A_i)}$

The above rule is called "Bayes' rule" (Thomas Bayes was an English mathematician and clergyman of the eighteenth century) and can be understood by reference to 4.00 and 4.20 and the example we are considering. The denominator is the number of ways in which exactly two defective items could have been obtained in the sample box. We recognize only two mutually exclusive ways in which such an outcome could occur, either when we drew from a bad pallet or when we drew from an ordinary pallet. Thus, we find the probability of obtaining two defectively sealed batteries in the sample of twenty is:

$$
\begin{aligned}
P \text{ (2 def.)} &= P \text{ (bad } and \text{ 2 def.)} + P \text{ (ord. } and \text{ 2 def.)} \\
&= 0.0570 + 0.0424 \\
&= \mathbf{0.0994}
\end{aligned}
$$

The numerator of 4.40 and 4.41 is the joint probability of the outcome and the prior condition being evaluated if both are true; in short, it is the number of ways in which the prior condition would be true. What is being evaluated is the probability that A_i is the true prior condition. We can now compute the desired probabilities. First, let A_i stand for "a bad pallet":

$$P \text{ (bad|2 def.)} = \frac{0.0570}{0.0994} = \mathbf{0.573}$$

Second, let A_i stand for "an ordinary pallet":

$$P \text{ (ord.|2 def.)} = \frac{0.0424}{0.0994} = \mathbf{0.427}$$

These computations are summarized in Table 4.1.

It is, of course, nice that the results we have obtained in this case agree with our intuitive judgment. Most of us would expect the average number of defectively sealed batteries per box when the process is operating in the ordinary manner to be about two percent of the batteries

TABLE 4.1

COMPUTATION OF REVISED (POSTERIORI) PROBABILITIES OF BAD OR ORDINARY PALLET AFTER FINDING TWO DEFECTIVES IN BOX FROM PALLET

Kind of Pallet A_i	Simple Prob. $P(A_i)$	Conditional Prob. of 2 Def. in Box $P(B\|A_i)$	Joint Prob. Kind of Pallet and 2 Def. in Box $P(A_i \text{ and } B)$	Revised (Posteriori) Prob. of Kind of Pallet $P(A_i\|B)$
A_1 = bad	0.20	0.285	0.0570	0.57
A_2 = ord.	0.80	0.053	0.0424	0.43
Totals	1.00	—	0.0994	1.00

in the box. That is, if we use d to stand for the number of defective batteries in a box, the average value of d would be 20(0.02) or 0.40 batteries. However, the expected number of defectives in a box from a bad pallet would be 2, since the probability of defectives in a bad pallet is 10 percent and 0.10(20) = 2. The intuitive answer, then, is that this is a *bad* pallet.

What if there had been only one defective in the box? Referral to the proper table, as previously, reveals that the conditional probability of one defective in a sample of 20 is 0.2725 if the pallet is ordinary, that is, if P(def.) = 0.02, and is 0.2701 if the pallet is bad, that is, if P(def.) = 0.10. Carrying through the calculations as before, it is found that the *posteriori* probabilities are:

$$P \text{ (bad|1 def.)} = \mathbf{0.20}$$
$$P \text{ (ord.|1 def.)} = \mathbf{0.80}$$

(The details of the calculations are left as an exercise for the reader.)

Do the above results agree with your intuitive judgment? Would you have given such a large probability to the possibility that the box came from an ordinary pallet? Similarly, in the first example where two defectives were found in the box, would you have assigned so nearly even probabilities to the two possibilities?

Joint Probability Tables

In working with probability problems, particularly those where observed relative frequencies are used as probabilities, the device of a joint probability table is often useful. For example, suppose the following information had been developed during a study of a management trainee program instituted at Big Corporation almost ten years ago. The records of the 400 persons from the various divisions of the company who completed the training program at least five years ago have been assembled and a table developed (Table 4.2, Part A). These data have been expressed as relative frequencies with the total (400) as 1.00 in Part B of Table 4.2.

Part B of Table 4.2 can be considered a *joint probability table* if the original data can be considered an adequate representation of the population studied. It seems reasonable to make that assumption in this case. Such joint probability tables are a useful tool in understanding the interpretation and use of probabilities.

The relative frequencies found in the margins of the table (the Totals column and Totals row) represent the probabilities of each of the elementary events. Thus, the simple (sometimes called Marginal) probability of a randomly selected member of this group being a manager at level 3 or above is 0.18. The simple (marginal) probability of randomly selecting a trainee who performed above average in the training program is 0.28.

Each relative frequency in the body of the table represents the joint probability of the (two) corresponding characteristics (events) shown in the headings of that row and column both being characteristics of a person randomly chosen from the group (of both events occurring).

TABLE 4.2

PRESENT STATUS OF PERSONNEL WHO COMPLETED THE MANAGEMENT
TRAINEE PROGRAM AT LEAST FIVE YEARS AGO

Part A. ORIGINAL DATA

Training Course Performance

Present Status	A_1 Above Average	A_2 Average	A_3 Below Average	Totals
B_1 Not a manager or left company	40	40	8	88
B_2 Manager, below level 3	60	112	68	240
B_3 Manager, level 3 or above	12	40	20	72
Totals	112	192	96	400

Part B. ORIGINAL DATA EXPRESSED AS RELATIVE FREQUENCIES

Training Course Performance

Present Status	A_1 Above Average	A_2 Average	A_3 Below Average	$P(B_i)$
B_1 Not a manager or left company	0.10	0.10	0.02	0.22
B_2 Manager, below level 3	0.15	0.28	0.17	0.60
B_3 Manager, level 3 or above	0.03	0.10	0.05	0.18
$P(A_i)$	0.28	0.48	0.24	1.00

Thus, the probability of randomly choosing a person who performed above average in the training program *and* is a manager at level 3 or above is 0.03.

The purpose of a study such as the one generating the data in Table 4.2 would be to determine if the training program does affect a trainee's managerial development. For example, does doing well in the training program increase a trainee's chances of becoming a top level manager? We note that the probability of being a manager at Level 3 or above at least five years after completing the course is 0.18. For those trainees receiving an above-average rating the probability of reaching the upper levels of management after at least five years is 0.03/0.28 or about 0.107, indicating that these two events are not *independent* events ($P(B_3|A_1)$ $\neq P(B_3)$). For persons doing average work in the training course, the probability of becoming a top level manager is 0.10/0.48 or about 0.208. Again, since $0.208 \neq 0.18$ ($P(B_3|A_2) \neq P(B_3)$), the two events are not statistically independent. What we have computed here are *conditional* probabilities, the probability of one event given another. Using the symbols shown in Table 4.2 to represent the events, the table shows:

$$P(A_1 \text{ and } B_3) = 0.03$$
$$P(A_1) = 0.28$$

and, we know that

$$P(A_1 \text{ and } B_3) = P(A_1)P(B_3|A_1) \qquad (4.20)$$

so

$$P(B_3|A_1) = \frac{P(A_1 \text{ and } B_3)}{P(A_1)} \qquad (4.40)$$
$$= \frac{0.03}{0.28} = \mathbf{0.107}$$

Note that all the conditional probabilities with a particular *given* event sum to 1.0. Thus,

$$P(A_1|B_1) = \frac{0.10}{0.22}$$
$$P(A_2|B_1) = \frac{0.10}{0.22}$$
$$P(A_3|B_1) = \frac{0.02}{0.22}$$

and the sum of these values is 1.00.

Note also that the sum of the joint probabilities involving a particular elementary event sum to the marginal (simple) probability of that event. Thus,

$$P(A_2 \text{ and } B_1) = 0.10$$
$$P(A_2 \text{ and } B_2) = 0.28$$
$$P(A_2 \text{ and } B_3) = 0.10$$
$$\text{Sum} = \mathbf{0.48} = P(A_2)$$

These relationships can be useful when constructing a joint probability table from partial information.

It is left as an exercise for the reader to work out the meaning of the relationships shown in Table 4.2 (see Exercise 12).

COUNTING CHANCES

The determination of the number of possible outcomes or the number of possible favorable outcomes of a particular trial or event is not always a simple task. The rules of permutations and combinations have been developed for that specific purpose. *Permutations* are recognizably different *orderings* of available items, such as a deck of cards or boxes of goods on a shelf. *Combinations* are recognizably different *groupings* (*combinations*) of available items. Different ordering of the same grouping does not indicate another combination but would be counted as an additional permutation.

Counting Permutations

In how many different ways can you arrange three different objects, say the letters a, b, and c?

We have six orders, ways, or permutations: *abc, acb, bac, bca, cab, cba.*

This results from the fact that we have three ways in which to make the first choice, then two ways to make the second choice, and only one way to make the third choice. Thus, $3 \cdot 2 \cdot 1 = 6$.

The method of counting permutations of n things, taken r at a time $(r \leq n)$ has been formalized.

4.50 $P(n, r) = n!/(n - r)!$

where $P(n, r)$ is the number of possible permutations of n things taken r at a time, and the symbols on the right have the following meanings:

n is the number of different objects
r is the number of objects taken at a time
$n!$ is the product $n \cdot (n - 1) \cdot (n - 2) \cdots [n - (n - 2)]$
$$\cdot [n - (n - 1)]$$

By definition, $0! = 1! = 1$

thus, for the letter example, taking all three letters at a time,

$$P(3,3) = 3!/(3 - 3)!$$
$$= (3 \cdot 2 \cdot 1)/1$$
$$= \mathbf{6}$$

But suppose we consider the possible arrangements if we take only two of the three letters at a time. We have ab, ba, ac, ca, bc, and cb for six permutations. By 2.50,

$$P(3, 2) = 3!/(3 - 2)!$$
$$= 6/1 = \mathbf{6}$$

What is the number of permutations of four objects taken two at a time?

$$P(4, 2) = 4!/(4 - 2)!$$
$$= (4 \cdot 3 \cdot 2 \cdot 1)/(2 \cdot 1)$$
$$= \mathbf{12}$$

Set down a, b, c, and d in pairs of letters in all possible orderings and check this result.

Permutations with Repetitions Permitted

4.51 $P(n, r$, repetitions permitted) is equal to n^r.

In how many different ways can you arrange three different objects, say a, b, and c, if the same letter may be repeated up to three times.

Obviously, if there are three ways of making the first choice, three ways of making the second choice, and three ways of making the third choice, we have

$$3^3 = \mathbf{27} \text{ ways}$$

Try this out by setting down a, b, c with repetitions of each letter permitted.

Number of Permutations of n Objects of Two Types

4.52 $P(n_1 \text{ alike}, n_2 \text{ alike}) = n!/(n_1)!(n_2)!$
where $n = n_1 + n_2$

In how many recognizable ways can you arrange five objects consisting of three a's and two b's?

By 4.52

$$5!/3! \cdot 2! = (5 \cdot 4 \cdot 3 \cdot 2 \cdot 1)/(3 \cdot 2 \cdot 1)(2 \cdot 1)$$
$$= 120/12$$
$$= \mathbf{10}$$

Try arranging the five letters A, A, A, b, b to check the above result.

Counting Combinations

A combination consists of a grouping of objects regardless of their order.

Three objects a, b, c may be set down in six different orders or permutations but three objects taken three at a time form only one combination.

Three objects a, b, c taken two at a time may be ordered in six ways or permutations but three objects taken two at a time form three combinations.

We obtain the number of combinations by dividing the number of permutations by factorial r, that is, $r!$, because we do not recognize the r factorial orderings of each set of r items as a different combination.

4.60 $C(n, r) = P(n, r)/r! = \dfrac{n!}{r!(n - r)!}$

For the combinations of three objects two at a time:

$$C(3, 2) = \frac{3!}{2!1!}$$
$$= \frac{6}{2} = 3$$

Similarly,

$$C(10, 4) = \frac{10!}{4!(10 - 4)!}$$
$$= \frac{10 \cdot 9 \cdot 8 \cdot 7 \cdot 6 \cdot 5 \cdot 4 \cdot 3 \cdot 2 \cdot 1}{(4 \cdot 3 \cdot 2 \cdot 1)(6 \cdot 5 \cdot 4 \cdot 3 \cdot 2 \cdot 1)}$$
$$= \mathbf{210}$$

Note that this value can be read directly from Part a of Table 3 in Appendix B. The value in the eleventh row (for $n = 10$) of the fifth column (for things taken four at a time) of Table B-3 is 210, the value computed above.

Combinations with Repetitions Permitted. Sometimes we are interested in allowing objects to appear more than once in a combination. In such a case we would use the following rule.

4.61 $C(n, r, \text{repetitions permitted}) = C(n + r - 1, r)$
$$= \frac{(n + r - 1)!}{r!(n - 1)!}$$

The reader should use the three letters a, b, c taken two at a time (with repetition permitted) to test 4.61. The answer is 6.

Some Simple Illustrations of the Laws of Probability and the Counting Rules

In tossing a two-faced coin, we know that the probability of a head appearing is $1/2$ and the probability of a tail is $1/2$. It is a certainty that one or the other will appear. Thus the probability of either one or the other is the sum of the probabilities of these mutually exclusive events, or 1. (According to 4.31).

Since the probability of tossing a head is $1/2$ and the probability of a tail appearing is also $1/2$, then, if we toss a coin twice, we can get either head and head, tail and tail, head and then tail, or tail and then head. Each event is a compound event made up of two separate and independent subevents, and we find the probability of the compound event by multiplying the probabilities of the subevents:

$$1/2 \cdot 1/2 = 1/4$$

This can be demonstrated by calculating that there are four compound events each of which is equally likely. (According to 4.21.)

Toss three coins simultaneously, or one coin three times and you have eight possibilities:

H-H-H   T-T-T   H-H-T   H-T-T   H-T-H   T-T-H   T-H-T   T-H-H

The compound probability of any particular outcome is $1/2 \cdot 1/2 \cdot 1/2$ $= 1/8$ and we say the odds are 7 to 1 against doing it. (According to 4.21.)

If you have three ways to go to Chicago, say by plane, train, or bus, and, having chosen your means of going, you must choose one of the other two ways to return, you can vary your round-trip in six ways:

plane-train, train-plane, plane-bus, bus-plane, train-bus, bus-train

This is the permutation of three things taken two at a time. (By 4.50.)

On the other hand, if we could repeat the mode of transportation, it would add three more ways to make the round trip. We would be using the rule of permutations with repetitions permitted:

$$n^r = 3^2 = 9 \text{ (by 4.51).}$$

Suppose you have a box containing one dozen eggs, four white and eight brown. If one egg is chosen at random, what is the probability that it is white? Obviously it is 1/3 (by the definition of probability). What is the probability that the next egg drawn (the first egg is not replaced) will also be white? Obviously it is 3/11. What then is the probability of the combined event, two draws both obtaining white eggs?

$$1/3 \cdot 3/11 = 1/11 \text{ (by 4.20).}$$

Suppose that each of the eggs were numbered so that they could be identified. How many identifiably different ways could two eggs be drawn from the twelve?

$$P(12, 2) = 12!/(12 - 2)!$$
$$= 12 \cdot 11 \cdot 10!/10!$$
$$= 132 \text{ (by 4.50).}$$

Suppose the eggs had not been numbered. How many recognizably different ways might they be ordered into the box? By 4.52,

$$P(n_1 = 4, n_2 = 8) = n!/(n_1)!(n_2)!$$
$$= 12!/(4! \cdot 8!)$$
$$= 495$$

SUMMARY

The probability of a particular outcome for a chance event is the relative frequency of occurrence of that outcome among all possible outcomes (4.00). These probabilities may be determined by deductive logic (*a priori*) or through experience (*empirically*). Subjectively determined "degrees of belief" (4.01) may also be considered as probabilities. Three general rules are useful in the manipulation of probabilities:

(1) The *complement* rule:

$$P(A) = 1 - P(\bar{A}) \qquad (4.14)$$

(2) The *and* rule:

$$P(A \text{ and } B) = P(A)P(B|A) \qquad (4.20)$$

(3) The *or* rule:

$$P(A \text{ or } B) = P(A) + P(B) - P(A \text{ and } B) \qquad (4.30)$$

The *and* rule can be simplified in the case of *independent* events ($P(B|A) = P(B)$)) and the *or* rule can be simplified in the case of *mutually exclusive* events ($P(A \text{ and } B) = 0$).

We sometimes desire to revise the probabilities which apply to a situation as additional information becomes available. In such a case we apply Bayes' rule

$$P(A_i|B) = \frac{P(A_i)P(B|A_i)}{\sum_{i=1}^{k} P(A_i)P(B|A_i)} \qquad (4.41)$$

Knowing how to manipulate probabilities is necessary, but we first must know how to obtain the counts of outcomes from which they are derived. Rules for permutations and combinations have been briefly reviewed (4.50–4.61).

DISCUSSION QUESTIONS

1. Define the following concepts in *your own words* (do not use symbols):

   (a) probability   (e) joint probability
   (b) conditional probability   (f) marginal probability
   (c) mutually exclusive events (g) subjective probability
   (d) independent events   (h) a priori probability

2. Early in this chapter, probability was defined as "relative frequency of occurrence." Later the concept was equated to "degree of belief." Can these two definitions be reconciled, or are they truly different concepts?

Hint: In your discussion, consider carefully how "relative frequency of occurrence" is interpreted in actual use. Also consider the possibility of placing restrictions on the concept of "degree of belief." Is such a restriction necessary?

3. What does it mean to say that the probability of an event is .20? Hint: Probability is a "long-run" concept.

4. Are mutually exclusive events also independent events? Explain carefully.

Hint: In your discussion it would be well to distinguish between events which occur concurrently (together) as the result of a single trial and events that occur in some sequence or as the result of two or more trials.

5. For each of the following decision problems:
   (1) Identify the critical state of nature upon which the decision depends.
   (2) State whether it would be desirable and appropriate to assign a "probability" to the occurrence of a favorable state of nature.
   (3) Indicate how such "probabilities" might be obtained where they are desirable.
   (a) A defense industry firm has bid on a major contract with the armed forces which will be let next year. The company is considering hiring a number of available scientists who can be used in only a limited way if the contract is not obtained.
   (b) A mining firm is considering an intensive survey including test drilling and the development of "prospect" holes in an area where they hope to find commercially valuable mineral deposits.
   (c) A construction firm is considering preparing a bid on a major contract. The preparation is expected to cost a minimum of $50,000 and could go as high as $125,000.
   (d) A professional football team is considering hiring a college star. They know that it will require a "bonus" of at least $150,000 to get the player.
   (e) A dealer in surplus goods and industry "seconds" has an opportunity to purchase a lot (all or none) of 2000 typewriters at $15 each. He would have to sell them for $30 each to make a normal profit.

DISCUSSION PROBLEMS

Show your method on all solutions.

1. Suppose you have 25 friends, each of whom will invite you to his (her) birthday party this year. What is the probability that you will be

asked to at least two parties on the same day? (Assume you know none of the birth dates and there are no twins in the group.)

Hint: To compute this probability directly requires the use of the *or* rule (4.30) and would be very difficult. Compute the probability of no two persons having the same birthday using the *and* rule (4.21) and then apply the complement rule (4.14).

2. Joe Filer is productively working only 70 percent of the time he is on the job. What is the probability that at a randomly selected moment he will be not working?

Hint: Does it make any difference whether Joe's pattern of work and not work is regular or irregular (for example, Joe gossips with fellow workers for about ten minutes at the beginning of each half day, spends five minutes at the water cooler at about 11:00 A.M. and again at about 2:00 P.M.)? Remember that the moment is selected randomly which means that all moments during the day are equally likely to be selected.

3. Supervisor Tom Boss decides to check on Joe Filer's activities by work sampling. On Monday, Tom uses random selection techniques to choose four times when he will observe Joe's activities on Tuesday.

(a) What is the probability that Tom will find Joe loafing just one of the four times?

Hint: Apply the *and* rule since the events (visits by Tom) are independent. Note that to satisfy this condition, Joe could be found loafing on any visit (first, second, third, or fourth). Is it necessary to work out each of these possibilities independently?

(b) What is the probability that Joe will not be found idle on any visits?

(c) What is the probability that Joe will be found idle at least one time?

Hint: This may be worked with either the *or* rule (4.30) or the *and* rule (4.20). Which is easier? Can 4.21 be used instead of 4.20?

4. The Personnel Department is studying a new aptitude test for salesmen. A test group of 100 salesmen has been selected and the following information developed. A salesman is to be chosen at random from the hundred.

TEST SCORE

	Above 500 (B_1)	Below 500 (B_2)	Totals
Successful salesmen (A_1)	48	22	70
Unsuccessful salesmen (A_2)	12	18	30
Totals	60	40	100

(a) What is the verbal meaning of the following:
  (1) $P(A_1|B_1)$?
  (2) $P(B_2|A_1)$?
  (3) $P(A_1 \text{ and } B_2)$?
  (4) $P(A_2 \text{ or } B_2)$?
Hint: If B_1 is true, that means that the individual is in the first column.
(b) What are the values of the items listed in (a)?
Hint: If an individual is known to be in a particular column, the probability of his then being in a particular row is the probability ratio of the cell value over the column total.
(c) What is the conditional probability of the selected salesman being a successful salesman, given that he has a test score above 500:
  (1) in symbols?
  (2) as a value?
(d) The simple probability of the event, test score above 500, is obviously 0.70. This is sometimes called the *marginal* probability of that event. What is the *marginal* probability of:
  (1) B_2?
  (2) A_2?
(e) Is there a statistical relationship between test score and sales performance? How do you know?
5. You are a member of a committee of seven from whom a subcommittee of three will be chosen. If the selection is random, what is the probability you will be chosen?
  Hints: 1. How many different committees of three can be chosen? How many selections include you, that is, in how many ways can the two additional members be selected if you are chosen?
  2. Alternatively, you may calculate directly from basic probabilities the compound probability of your selection by application of 4.20. Do you know why?

EXERCISES

Show your method on all solutions.

1. In a box containing twelve individually packaged toy guns there are three broken guns. Three customers have each ordered one gun. If the clerk randomly selects three guns to fill these orders, what is the probability that
  (a) at least one of the customers gets a broken gun?
  (b) all three customers get broken guns?

   (c) none of the customers gets a broken gun?

   (d) exactly one customer gets a broken gun?

   (e) exactly two customers get broken guns?

2. The probability of failure during a three-hour test for any individual part of an electronic machine containing 200 parts is 0.001 for each part. For this situation, *set up the solutions* for the following. *Do not work out the arithmetic.*

   (a) What is the probability that the machine will function properly during the test? (Assume that the failure of any individual part is independent of failure of any other part, but all parts must work for the full period for the test to be successfully completed.)

   (b) If it were desired to produce a machine with a 0.95 probability of successfully completing the test and the reliability of the individual parts could not be changed, but the number of parts was variable, show how you would set up the problem to compute the maximum allowable number of parts.

   (c) Alternatively to b, what improvement in the reliability of each part (ability to complete the test) would be needed to give the machine with 200 parts a 0.95 probability of successfully completing the test? (Set up only.)

3. The Board of Directors of Big Corporation is considering a price increase for one of their products. A randomly selected committee of five directors is to study the question and provide a recommendation on the basis of a majority vote. If the ten directors are divided six for the price increase and four against, what is the probability that the committee will recommend a price increase?

4. The Office Manager of Bookkeepers, Inc., decides to check to see if his employees are working all the time. If he checks four times, what is the probability that he will catch Joe Slumber who loafs 50 percent of the time?

5. If we are drawing from a lot of 100 items of which five are defective, what is the probability of:

   (a) selecting one good and one defective item (in that order) on the first two draws?

   (b) selecting one defective and one good item (in that order) on the first two draws?

   (c) why do the results in (a) and (b) have the particular relationship they do?

6. The Hyvolt Manufacturing Company has three production lines assembling electric heaters. A lot of 4000 heaters produced by the

three lines was examined and graded as to whether the heaters were acceptable or must be reassembled. The results are:

	Assembly Line			
	1 (A_1)	2 (A_2)	3 (A_3)	All lines
Acceptable (B_1)	1220	1160	1380	3760
Unacceptable (B_2)	80	40	120	240
Totals	1300	1200	1500	4000

(a) If one part is selected at random from the lot, what is the probability that it:
   (1) came from assembly line 1 and is satisfactory?
   (2) is unacceptable and must be reassembled?
   (3) came from line 2 and is unacceptable?
(b) Use the symbols in parentheses in the column headings and stubs of the table to present the probability of selecting a heater that:
   (1) was produced on assembly line 3.
   (2) is acceptable.
   (3) was produced on line 2 and is unacceptable.
   (4) is known to have come from assembly line 2 and will be found unacceptable.
   (5) has been found to be acceptable and will then be found to come from line 3.
(c) Suppose a part has been randomly selected and determined unsatisfactory. What is the probability that it was assembled on:
   (1) line 1?
   (2) line 2?
   (3) line 3?
(d) Is the occurrence of an incorrect assembly independent of the line on which it was made? How do you know?
(e) A sublot of 50 heaters has been isolated and we are attempting to determine which line assembled it.
   (1) What is the prior probability that it came from:
      (a) line 1?
      (b) line 2?
      (c) line 3?
   The sublot of 50 is examined and found to contain three unacceptably assembled heaters. The conditional probabilities of obtain-

ing the random sample of 50 from each line are:

Line	P	Conditional Probability of 3 Def. in 50 Heaters
1	0.06	0.2311
2	0.03	0.1264
3	0.08	0.1993

(2) What are the revised (*posteriori*) probabilities of this sublot coming from each of the three assembly lines?

7. In a lot of 400 study lamps, ten have defective finishes and eight are assembled incorrectly. For this lot of lamps,
   (a) What else must be known to determine the total number of lamps with defects?
   (b) What is the probability that a randomly selected lamp will be only incorrectly assembled if six lamps have only defective finishes?
   (c) What is the probability of a randomly selected lamp being defective if (b) is true?

8. Mr. Seer claims to be able to distinguish among four popular brands of coffee by taste. After being blindfolded, he is given a sample of each of the four brands to identify. Mr. Seer is told that each brand is represented once. What is the probability that, purely by chance alone, he will correctly identify:
   (a) exactly one brand?
   (b) exactly two brands?
   (c) exactly three brands?
   (d) all four brands?
   (e) at least one brand?
   Caution: Be careful about the use of permutations and combinations on this problem. Be sure that the probabilities have the proper interrelations.

9. Assume that the following information was developed from responses to a survey of television viewers.

   A_1 family has no TV set.
   A_2 family has one TV set.
   A_3 family has two or more TV sets.
   B_1 family income is under $4000.
   B_2 family income is at least $4000 but less than $10,000.
   B_3 family income is $10,000 or more.

In the population studied:

$$P(A_1) = 0.100 \qquad P(A_1|B_3) = 0.500$$
$$P(A_2) = 0.750 \qquad P(A_1|B_1) = 0.086$$
$$P(B_1) = 0.350 \qquad P(A_3 \text{ and } B_3) = 0.020$$
$$P(B_3) = 0.100 \qquad P(A_2|B_2) = 0.782$$

(a) Compute $P(A_2 \text{ or } B_1)$. What is the verbal meaning of this value?
(b) Compute $P(A_1 \text{ and } B_1)$. What is the verbal meaning of this value?
(c) Compute $P(B_2|A_1)$. What is the verbal meaning of this value?
(d) Is there a statistical relationship between family income and TV ownership? If so, explain its general nature and why you have concluded that it exists. If not, explain why it is not true.

10. If A stands for the fact that a person has graduated from a college of business administration and B stands for a person attaining success as a business manager, write the following probabilities in symbolic form:
(a) The probability that a person is a B.A. graduate *and* a successful business manager.
(b) The probability that a B.A. graduate is a successful business manager.
(c) The probability that a successful business manager graduated from a college of business administration.
Define in words the meaning of the following:
(d) $P(B|A)$
(e) $P(A|B)$
(f) $P(\bar{A}|B)$
(g) $P(\bar{B}|A)$

11. Burpop Corporation has developed a surplus cash reserve and is interested in finding a use for these funds. Even if the firm expands in the Bigtown area, it will have excess cash, and must find another way to use the money within the business or find some outside investment. One internal use is to provide self insurance. Currently, the firm has an annual business interruption insurance policy which reimburses all losses of profits which are due to damage of a plant, its physical facilities, or its stock by fire, flood, or wind. By placing its excess cash in high quality, short-term securities, the reserve can earn interest and perform the self-insurance function.

Before undertaking the venture Burpop wishes to determine the risks involved in self-insurance. Consultation with trade associations and considerable additional research uncover the following information:

Business interruptions for approximately 10,000 plants comparable in construction, location, and general type of material handled (as these would be reflected in risk of damage by wind, fire, or flood) were found to be:

Primary Cause of Interruption	Number of Interruptions per 1000 Plants
Fire	20
Flood	50
Wind	30

In addition, it was determined that in 20 percent of the cases where flooding was the primary cause of interruption and in 30 percent of the cases where wind was the primary cause of interruption, a major fire resulted. In these cases insurance covering fire hazards alone would have covered the full loss in profits.

(a) Assuming that the information obtained is accurate, what is the probability that a specific one of the plants in the chain will sustain an uninsured loss of profits from one of the three causes mentioned if:

    (1) fire and flood protection only are continued?

    (2) fire and wind protection only are maintained?

    (3) fire protection alone is continued?

(b) Burpop has ten plants. What would you have to assume in order to be able to compute the probability of a loss for any of the plants if only fire and flood insurance were continued and only the information given in the table were available.

(c) Even if you did not recognize the assumption required under (b), compute the probability specified.

12. Refer to the Big Corporation training program problem in this chapter and interpret the meaning of the results shown in Table 4.2.

5
values,
distributions,
and chance

INTRODUCTION

This text deals with the use of quantifiable information in decision making. Quantifiable information means numbers. These numbers are values attached to observations, events, or outcomes. For example, in Chapter 1 we spoke of using data concerning the incomes of families living in a particular geographic market area and data describing attitudes of businessmen concerning economic conditions. In addition, the outcomes of "random experiments" (the tossing of a coin and the results of a sample survey) were indicated to have possible uses in decision making. In all these cases, however, we would ordinarily have to consider a distribution of values, even when our final calculations involved only a single number. This chapter is concerned with the description and summarization of such distributions. In addition, it describes and illustrates the usefulness of some "readymade" probability distributions with wide application to business decision making.

RANDOM VARIABLES

In examples considered up to now, outcomes of our "games" have been varied: heads and tails, defective and not defective, will or will not buy, amount of expected sales, and so forth. Many of these outcomes are not necessarily numbers. Analysis is simpler when outcomes are numbers. For this reason, whenever possible we represent outcomes with numbers. Thus, we look at the outcome, say head, and assign a number (1); the alternative outcome (tail) is assigned a different number (0). The rule (mathematicians say *"function"*) which assigns numerical values to each possible outcome of a "game" (mathematicians say "chance experiment") is called a *random variable*. The number assigned to the outcome is called the *value of the random variable*. The observed value of the random variable is unknown until the event occurs.

Probability Distribution of a Random Variable

Each value of the random variable has a unique probability of occurrence defined as the sum of the probabilities of the outcomes to which that value is assigned. A simple example will help to make this point clear.

Consider tossing two coins (or the same coin twice). The possible results are

$$HH, HT, TH, TT$$

Let X be the random variable whose value is the number of heads. Then,

$$X(HH) = 2, X(HT) = X(TH) = 1, X(TT) = 0$$

and the probability of each of these values is

$$P(2) = 1/4, P(1) = 1/4 + 1/4 = 1/2, P(0) = 1/4$$

All of these probabilities together form the *probability distribution* given in Table 5.1.

TABLE 5.1

PROBABILITY DISTRIBUTION OF RANDOM VARIABLE,
X = NUMBER OF HEADS WHEN TOSSING TWO COINS

Value of Random Variable (X_i)	Probability of Occurrence of X_i $P(X_i)$
2	1/4
1	1/2
0	1/4
	1.0

Expected Value of a Random Variable

While information on *all* values of a random variable is interesting, it is often difficult (or impossible) to make rational decisions strictly from this multiplicity of information. Thus, in Chapter 1 we were interested in the *average* number of children between eight and eighteen in each family. In playing the coin game in Chapter 1, we were interested in the *average* result (the *expected value* of the game).

5.00   The *expected value* of a random variable is the sum of the values of the random variable each weighted by its probability of occurrence. In symbols,

$$E(X) = \sum_{i=1}^{N} X_i P(X_i)$$

where

$E(X)$ is read "expected value of X"
X_i is the ith value of the random variable X
$\displaystyle\sum_{i=1}^{N}$ is read "sum from $i = 1$ to $i = N$ and N is the total number of X_i values"
$P(X_i)$ is the probability (relative frequency of occurrence) of X_i

Note that the summation takes place *after* all of the individual multiplications are completed. Some readers may recognize the expected value as an arithmetic mean. The term "mean" and the symbol $\bar{X}$ refer only to the arithmetic average of the X_i values. Only when $\bar{X}$ (the mean) is a weighted arithmetic average computed with probabilities of occurrence as weights do we refer to $\bar{X}$ as an expected value.

TABLE 5.2

ILLUSTRATION OF THE COMPUTATION OF THE EXPECTED VALUE OF THE
RANDOM VARIABLE, X = NUMBER OF HEADS IN TWO TOSSES OF A COIN

Values of the Random Variable X_i	Probability of X_i $P(X_i)$	Weighted Values of X_i $X_i P(X_i)$
2	0.25	0.50
1	0.50	0.50
0	0.25	0.00
	1.00	$E(X_i) = 1.00$

The computation of the expected value of the random variable, X = number of heads in two tosses of a coin, is illustrated in Table 5.2.

Variance of a Random Variable

Seldom are all values of a random variable equal to the expected value. Rather they tend to be dispersed about this measure of central tendency. The standard measures of dispersion about a mean or expected value are the *variance* and the *standard deviation*. These are descriptive constants in the same way that the mean itself is a descriptive constant. They are merely summary values used to describe an important characteristic of the distribution, its scatter.

5.01 The *variance* of a random variable is computed as the sum of the squared deviations of the values of the random variable from their expected value weighted by the probability of the deviation.

$$\text{Var}(X_i) = \sum_{i=1}^{N} [X_i - E(X)]^2 P(X_i) = \sigma^2$$

The symbol σ is the small Greek letter "sigma." Using this formula, the variance of the random variable, X = number of heads in two tosses of a coin is computed in Table 5.3.

TABLE 5.3

VARIANCE OF THE RANDOM VARIABLE, X = NUMBER OF HEADS IN
TWO TOSSES OF A COIN

Value of the Random Variable X_i	Deviation of X_i from $E(X)$ $(X_i - E(X))$	Square of Deviation $(X_i - E(X))^2$	Probability of Deviation $P(X_i)$	Weighted Squared Dev. $(X_i - E(X))^2 P(X_i)$
2	1	1	0.25	0.25
1	0	0	0.50	0.00
0	−1	1	0.25	0.25
			var(X) =	0.50 = σ^2

A computationally simpler form of the formula in 5.01 could be used to obtain the same result.

5.02 $\sigma^2 = E(X_i^2) - [E(X)]^2$

The necessary value $E(X_i^2)$ is computed in Table 5.4. By substituting this value and the expected value (see Table 5.2) into formula 5.02 the variance is computed.

$$\sigma^2 = 1.50 - (1.00)^2$$
$$= 0.50$$

This result agrees with the result computed in Table 5.3 by the use of formula 5.01.

TABLE 5.4

COMPUTATION OF $E(X_i^2)$ FOR THE RANDOM VARIABLE, X = NUMBER OF HEADS IN TWO TOSSES OF A COIN

Value of Random Variable X_i	Squared Values of Random Variable X_i^2	Probability of Value $P(X_i)$	Weighted Squares $X_i^2 P(X_i)$
2	4	0.25	1.00
1	1	0.50	0.50
0	0	0.25	0.00
			$E(X_i^2) = \overline{1.50}$

The reader may find it comforting to note that the variance is the expected value of the squared deviations from the expected value $[X_i - E(X)]^2$. It is a type of average just as is the expected value.

Standard Deviation of a Random Variable

The variance may seem inappropriate as a measure of dispersion about the expected value since it is developed from squared deviations and is therefore not stated in the same units as the expected value. This problem is solved by use of the standard deviation.

5.03   The *standard deviation* is the square root of the variance. It is usually designated by σ (small sigma).

In the example we have been using, the standard deviation would be $\sqrt{0.50}$ or **0.71**. The standard deviation is widely used in describing the scatter of distributions. Several examples are given in later sections of this chapter.

**Effects of Changes of Location and Scale
on the Expected Value and Variance of a Random Variable**

We sometimes have occasion to study the distribution of a random variable formed by taking each of the values of some other random variable and adding (or subtracting) a constant amount. Such change of location obviously increases (decreases) each individual value of the variable by the constant amount. Consider the random variable, number of heads on two tosses of a fair coin plus one. The possible values of this random variable are 3, 2, and 1, which the reader will recognize as the distribution given in Table 5.1 with 1 added to each value of the random variable given there. Applying 5.00, the expected value of this new random variable is found to be:

$$3(0.25) + 2(0.50) + 1(0.25) = \mathbf{2.00}$$

Since the expected value is changed by the same amount and in the same direction as is every individual value when the variable is changed by a constant amount, it follows that the differences between the expected value and the individual values, $[X_i - E(X)]$'s, are unchanged:

$$(X_i + c) - [E(X) + c] = X_i - E(X)$$

Since the variance is computed from these deviations, it follows that it is unaffected. Therefore, the standard deviation is also unaffected.

The above reasoning leads to the following rule:

5.04   Adding a constant amount to (or subtracting a constant amount from) every value of a random variable increases (decreases) the expected value by the constant amount but does not change the variance or standard deviation.

Often we are interested in the distribution of a random variable formed by multiplying (or dividing) each value of some other random variable by some constant factor. Thus consider the random variable, number of heads on two tosses of a fair coin multiplied by three. The values of this new variable are 6, 3, and 0. Note that the new distribution has the same characteristics as the original distribution except that it is "stretched out" over a longer scale. It is three times as far from 0 to 3 and 3 to 6 as it was from 0 to 1 and 1 to 2. The expected value of this new distribution is effected by this rescaling and is three times as large as previously (3 instead of 1). (The reader should verify this by application of 5.00.) The differences between the individual values and the expected value are also three times as large:

$$[3X_i - 3E(X)] = 3[X_i - E(X)]$$

The squares of these differences are *nine* times as large:

$$[X_i - E(X)]^2 = X_i^2 - 2X_iE(X) + E(X)^2$$

but

$$[3X_i - 3E(X)]^2 = 9X_i^2 - 18X_iE(X) + 9E(X)^2$$
$$= 9[X_i^2 - 2X_iE(X) + E(X)^2]$$

In general if c were substituted for 3, we would conclude that the new expected value equals $cE(X)$ and the new variance equals $c^2\sigma^2$. Since the standard deviation is the square root of the variance, it will be equal to $c\sigma$. Therefore, it can be stated:

5.05 Multiplying (dividing) every value in a distribution by the same *positive* factor, the expected value and standard deviation are multiplied (divided) by that same factor and the variance is multiplied (divided) by the square of that factor.

The reader should consider why it is necessary to specify that the factor be positive. It would also be instructive to demonstrate that the above rule holds true for division as well as multiplication.

SOME USEFUL PROBABILITY DISTRIBUTIONS

There are four principal distributions which are widely used in quantitative decision making in business. These are: (1) combinatorial (hypergeometric), (2) binomial, (3) normal, and (4) Poisson. These distributions underlie the statistics on which control charts and acceptance sampling are based. In addition, they are widely used as normative approximations to the distributions of many populations in the business world. They are developed and discussed here as a part of the background on which the development of quantitative decision processes in later chapters will be based. Before discussing these four distributions, however, the concepts of *continuous* and *discrete* are necessary.

Continuous and Discrete Distributions

In Chapter 4 and in earlier sections of this chapter we considered some methods of applying probabilities when the *possible outcomes* are clearly differentiable (discrete). Thus, for our coin-tossing game (number of heads when tossing 2 coins) there are only *three* possible outcomes (2, 1, 0). We would represent these possible outcomes as distinguishable *points* on a scale:

Possible Numbers of Heads
When Tossing Two Coins

.   .   .

0   1   2

Any time the possible values of a random variable can be represented as distinguishable points on a scale we say the variable is *discrete*.

It is easy to think of distributions whose values are not whole numbers, but fractions which could not be represented as points on a scale. For example, if we think of the weight of packages of sugar put up on a production line designed to put five pounds of sugar in each package, it is obvious that the weight of the packages (if measured very precisely) varies over a range of weights around five pounds. If we could make our weight measurements extremely precise, we would find so many possible weights (an infinite number) that it would be possible to represent these weights only as a line over the possible range:

Possible Weights of Packages of Sugar
Packaged on Machine Set to Put Five Pounds in Each Package

pounds

Anytime that the *possible values* of a variable can be represented only by a line, the variable is said to be *continuous*.

Note that our examples would also indicate that *counts* are generally discrete variables and *measurements* are generally continuous variables. Counts involve only whole numbers in any case, thus, *sets* of *points*. Measurements can be made more and more precise, and thus can be completely represented only by sets of *fractions*. Theoretically, measurements can be made infinitely precise so that they must be represented by infinite fractions.

Note that the *number* of possible outcomes is only indirectly involved in the definitions above. Truly continuous variables obviously have an *infinite* set of possible values since those values can be represented only by a line (which contains an infinite number of fractional points regardless of its length). A discrete variable, however, can have an infinite or a finite number of possible values. For example, think of a variable whose values are the set of positive integers (positive whole numbers, 1, 2, 3, . . . , ∞). By definition there is an infinite number of positive integers.

To approximate a discrete variable on a continuous scale is common. Theoretically, the discrete values are represented by ranges along the line. For example, if we talk of the number of United States voters in random samples of 100 voters who favor a particular political candidate, we are speaking of a discrete random variable. The number of favorable voters can, theoretically, vary from 0 to 100. (We are assuming that at least 100 voters *do* prefer this candidate and that at least 100 voters *do not* prefer this candidate.) This is a counting situation and the variable is discrete. To represent the possible outcomes as a line, we must let intervals stand for points:

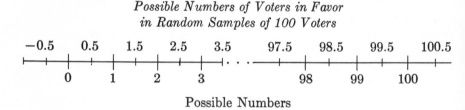

Possible Numbers of Voters in Favor
in Random Samples of 100 Voters

Possible Numbers

Probability Distributions for Discrete and Continuous Random Variables

Probability distributions defined on discrete random variables are called *mass* functions and exist (take on positive values) only at the discrete values assumed by the random variable. The *mass* function depicting the probability distribution for the random variable, number of heads when tossing two "fair" coins, is shown in Figure 5.1. The heights of the lines at the points 0, 1, and 2 indicate the probability of occurrence of each value. Note that these heights sum to one (1.0).

Probability distributions defined on continuous random variables are called *density* functions and exist (take on positive values) at all points over the range of the random variable. The probability density function for the random variable, weights of packages of sugar packaged on a machine set to put five pounds in each package, would look much like that shown in Figure 5.2. The relative height of the curve at any point indicates the probability of the random variable assuming the value shown on the horizontal axis at that point. The total area under the curve sums to one. Since there are an infinite number of points within the range of the values of the random variable, the probability of any

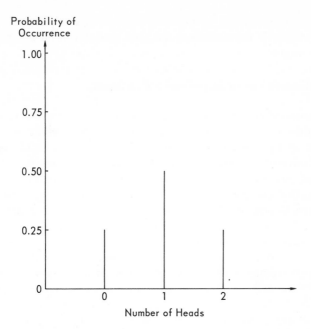

FIG. 5.1.   Probability mass function for the random variable, number of heads when tossing two fair coins.

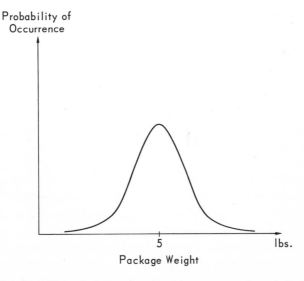

FIG. 5.2.   Hypothetical probability density function for the random variable, weights of packages of sugar packaged on a machine set to put five pounds in each package.

single value occurring is zero. However, the probability of some finite range of values is measured as the area under the curve (the density) over that range.

The Combinatorial or Hypergeometric Distribution

In practical business problems, populations of attributes often occur in *finite* populations. The acceptability or unacceptability of items in a particular *lot* of manufactured product and the favorable or unfavorable attitudes of employees in a particular *department* are examples of such situations. In such cases, the probability of selecting any one item into the sample is conditional upon the items selected before that item rather than independent of the prior selection of other items. We are assuming of course, that items selected into the sample are *not replaced* before the next selection is made.

The distribution which describes the exact probability distribution for attributes from a finite dichotomous population is known as the *hypergeometric* or *combinatorial* distribution. It involves the repeated application of the conditional probability rule 4.20. If we consider the presence of the attribute sought a "success," then the probabilities for obtaining a specified number of "successes" in samples drawn without replacement from *finite* populations can be computed from the following formula:

5.10 $$P(X = x | N, M, n) = \frac{C(M, x)C(N - M, n - x)}{C(N, n)}$$

where the symbols have the following meanings:

N = size of the *finite* population from which the sample is drawn
M = actual number of "successes" in the population
n = sample size
X = number of "successes" in a sample (a particular number of draws)
x = the arbitrary value of X whose probability is being evaluated

$P(X = x | N, M, n)$ is read "the probability that X will equal x given a population of size N containing M successes and n selections are to be made from the population". This is further translated as "the probability that there will be exactly x 'successes' in a sample of size n, given that there are exactly M 'successes' in the population of finite size N."

The right-hand side of 5.10 can be verbalized also. In the numerator we have first the number of ways (combinations) in which x "successes" in the sample can be drawn from the M "successes" in the population. This value is multiplied by the number of ways (combinations) in which $n - x$ "nonsuccesses" in the sample can be drawn from the $N - M$ "nonsuccesses" in the population. Obviously x cannot be larger than M ($x \leq M$) nor n ($x \leq n$) and n cannot be larger than N ($n \leq N$). In the denominator of 5.10 we have the number of different samples of n items which can be drawn from a finite population of N items.

An example will help to clarify the use of the above formula. Suppose we have a box containing 20 batteries and it is known that there are four defective batteries in the box. What is the probability distribution for the number of defective batteries in a sample of five selected at random from the box? Note that a "success" here is the occurrence of a defective battery. The possible number of defectives varies from zero to four. Let us evaluate the possibility of zero defectives without directly applying 5.10.

In order to draw zero defectives, we must select five nondefectives in five draws. Applying 4.20, this would be

$$16/20 \cdot 15/19 \cdot 14/18 \cdot 13/17 \cdot 12/16 = 91/323$$
$$= \mathbf{0.282}$$

Now, let us check our result by applying 5.10.

$$P(X = 0|N = 20, M = 4, n = 5) = \frac{C(4, 0)C(16, 5)}{C(20, 5)}$$

$$= \frac{\dfrac{4!}{0!4!} \cdot \dfrac{16!}{5!11!}}{\dfrac{20!}{5!15!}}$$

Invert and multiply

$$= \frac{16!}{5!11!} \cdot \frac{5!15!}{20!}$$

restate

$$= \frac{(16 \cdot 15 \cdot 14 \cdot 13 \cdot 12 \cdot 11!) \cdot 5! \cdot 15!}{5! \cdot 11! \cdot (20 \cdot 19 \cdot 18 \cdot 17 \cdot 16 \cdot 15!)}$$

cancel like terms

$$= \frac{16 \cdot 15 \cdot 14 \cdot 13 \cdot 12}{20 \cdot 19 \cdot 18 \cdot 17 \cdot 16} = \frac{91}{323}$$
$$= .282$$

This answer agrees perfectly with our previous result.

The probability of one defective in the sample is similarly computed. By 4.20,

$$P(X = 1 | N = 20, M = 4, n = 5) = \frac{16}{20} \cdot \frac{15}{19} \cdot \frac{14}{18} \cdot \frac{13}{17} \cdot \frac{4}{16} \cdot 5$$

Here, it is assumed first that the defective item is found on the last draw. It does not change the arithmetic result if it occurs on any other draw (the numbers in the numerator are merely reordered). There are five possibilities, each equally likely (the one defective could occur on any one of the five trials), so we multiply by five to take care of this. Working out the arithmetic, we obtain

$$P(X = 1 | N = 20, M = 4, n = 5) = \frac{455}{969}$$
$$= 0.470$$

Applying 5.10,

$$P(X = 1) = \frac{C(4, 1)C(16, 4)}{C(20, 5)}$$
$$= \frac{\dfrac{4!}{1!3!} \cdot \dfrac{16!}{4!12!}}{\dfrac{20!}{5!15!}}$$

Only now let us cancel only those factorials which are equal (4!) and refer to appendix Table B-1. Then, we must solve

$$P(X = 1) = \frac{16!5!15!}{3!12!20!}$$

$\log_{10} 16! = 13.32062$	$\log_{10} 3! = 0.77815$
$\log_{10} 5! = 2.07918$	$\log_{10} 12! = 8.68034$
$\log_{10} 15! = 12.11650$	$\log_{10} 20! = 18.38612$
$\log_{10} (16!5!15!) = 27.51630$	$\log_{10} (3!12!20!) = 27.84461$

and

$$\log_{10} P(X = 1) = 27.51630 – 27.84461$$

or

$$
\begin{array}{r}
37.51630{-}10 \\
27.84461 \\
\hline
9.67169{-}10
\end{array}
$$

The antilog of 9.67169–10 = **0.4695** or **0.470**.

The actual computation of the remaining probabilities in this distribution is left as an exercise for the reader. The results are summarized in Table 5.5.

TABLE 5.5

PROBABILITY DISTRIBUTION OF THE RANDOM VARIABLE, X = NUMBER OF
DEFECTIVES IN A SAMPLE OF 5 DRAWN FROM A LOT OF 20
CONTAINING EXACTLY 4 DEFECTIVES

Number of Defectives X	Probability of No. of Defectives P(X)
0	0.282
1	0.470
2	0.217
3	0.031
4	0.001
Total	1.001†

† 0.001 difference from 1.000 due to rounding.

5.11 The expected value of a hypergeometric distribution is

$$E(X) = \frac{nM}{N}$$

5.12 The variance of a hypergeometric distribution is

$$\text{Var }(X) = \frac{nM}{N}\left(1 - \frac{M}{N}\right)\left(\frac{N - n}{N - 1}\right) = \sigma^2$$

Thus, for the distribution given in Table 5.5, we can compute these values:

$$E(X) = \frac{(5)(4)}{20}$$

$$= 1$$

$$\sigma^2 = \frac{(5)(4)}{20}\left(1 - \frac{4}{20}\right)\left(\frac{20-5}{20-1}\right)$$

$$= 0.632$$

As a check on these computations, the necessary calculations to compute the expected value and variance of this distribution by application of 5.00 and 5.01 are given in Table 5.6. The results are consistent with the values derived above.

TABLE 5.6

EXPECTED VALUE AND VARIANCE OF THE RANDOM VARIABLE, X = NUMBER OF DEFECTIVES IN A SAMPLE OF 5 DRAWN FROM A LOT OF 20 CONTAINING EXACTLY 4 DEFECTIVES

No. of Defectives X_i	Probability of No. of Defectives $P(X_i)$	Weighted Values of X_i $X_i P(X_i)$	Deviations of X_i from $E(X)$ $(X_i - E(X))$	Squared Deviations $(X_i - E(X))^2$	Weighted Squared Deviations $(X_i - E(X))^2 P(X_i)$
0	0.282	0.000	-1	1	0.282
1	0.470	0.470	0	0	0.000
2	0.217	0.434	1	1	0.217
3	0.031	0.093	2	4	0.124
4	0.001	0.004	3	9	0.009
	1.001†	1.001†			0.632

† .001 differences of $P(X_i)$ and $E(X)$ from 1.000 are due to rounding.

The Bernoulli Process and the Binomial Distribution

Businessmen often have occasion to work with trials or chance experiments where the outcomes are discrete, two-valued "attributes" or "counts" as contrasted to a measurement. Examples of such possible outcomes are numerous: success or failure of a program, heads or tails when tossing a coin, customers prefer or do not prefer a new package or a new design, and many more.

5.20 When there are only *two possible outcomes* whose *probabilities* of occurrence are *constant* for all trials, the *outcome* of any trial is *independent* of the outcome of any previous trial, and the *number of trials is finite*, a *Bernoulli process* is operating.

Examples of Bernoulli processes are numerous. One of the simplest is tossing a fair coin. Others of greater interest to businessmen include quality of output on a production line which produces a proportion defective constant at least during each run (the proportion defective may vary with different control settings for different runs) and answers to surveys of random samples of customers to determine their preferences for two styles of packaging or two kinds of product (for example, toothpaste or tooth powder) or even two competing brands of the same product. Note that for these "business" situations to be Bernoulli processes the occurrence of good and defective items on the production line would have to be essentially random (have no identifiable order of occurrence and tend toward a constant ratio of good and defective), and the samples of consumers would also have to exhibit no pattern of favorable and unfavorable preferences other than a limiting constant for the ratio of favorable and unfavorable. These conditions are necessary to meet the condition of independence of outcomes in a Bernoulli process.

5.21 The probability distribution which describes the relative frequency of occurrence of each of the possible outcomes of a Bernoulli process is the *binomial probability distribution*.

5.22 In a binomial probability distribution the probability that the number of outcomes of the type being evaluated (X) will equal a particular value (x) in a given finite number of trials (n) is

$$P(X = x|P, n) = C(n, x)P^x(1 - P)^{n-x}$$

where $P =$ the probability of occurrence of the outcome being evaluated (a "success"). Since there are only two possible outcomes, $1 - P$ is the probability of occurrence for the *other* outcome.

Note that 5.22 defines only one term in the binomial expansion of $(P + Q)^n$ which is generalized as:

$$P^n + C(n, n - 1)P^{n-1}Q + C(n, n - 2)P^{n-2}Q^2 + \cdots + C(n, x)P^xQ^{n-x} + \cdots + Q^n$$

where $Q = 1 - P$. Note also that the binomial is a discrete distribution.

5.23 The expected value of a binomial distribution, the expected value of X for n trials, is nP.

5.24 The variance of a binomial distribution is

$$\text{Var } (X) = nP(1 - P)$$

5.25 The standard deviation of a binomial distribution is

$$\sigma_X = \sqrt{nP(1 - P)}$$

Definitions 5.22–5.25 make it clear that to obtain a full description of a binomial distribution, all that one needs to know is the proportion of "successes," P, and the number of trials, n.

As an example, let us consider a process of throwing four dice and determine:

1. The relative frequency of 0, 1, 2, 3, 4, "successes" in a sample of 4.
2. The expected number of successes of this Bernoulli process.
3. The standard deviation of the random variable generated.

Our Bernoulli process consists of rolling four standard dice (we assume they are "fair" dice); the face with six pips will represent a "success" (call this X).

We can compute the probability of zero "successes," $P(X = 0)$, the hard way. Zero number of sixes can be thrown in only one way, that is, having four "nonsuccesses." The probability of a "nonsuccess" is 5/6 and of a "success" (a 6) is 1/6. Thus, four nonsuccesses will have the probability of $(5/6)^4$ or

$$P(X = 0 | P = 1/6, n = 4) = 625/1296$$
$$= \mathbf{0.4823}$$

By application of 5.22,

$$P(X = 0 | P = 1/6, n = 4) = C(4, 0)(1/6)^0(5/6)^4$$
$$= \mathbf{0.4823}$$

The probability of one 6, $P(X = 1)$, is also computed both ways. One number of sixes can be thrown in four ways because the 6 could be any one of the four dice. The probability of a nonsuccess is 5/6 as before, and that of a success is 1/6. Thus, three nonsuccesses and one success, times the ways these events can happen is:

$$4(5/6)^3(1/6)$$

which amounts to

$$P(X = 1) = 4(125)/1296$$
$$= \mathbf{0.3858}$$

Alternately,

$$P(X = 1) = C(4,\ 1)(1/6)^1(5/6)^3$$
$$= 4(1/6)(5/6)^3$$
$$= \mathbf{0.3858}$$

The calculation of the remaining probabilities is left as an exercise for the reader. The results are presented in the second column of Table 5.7

TABLE 5.7

CALCULATION OF THE EXPECTED VALUE AND VARIANCE OF THE RANDOM VARIABLE, X = NUMBER OF 6'S ON THE ROLL OF 4 FAIR DICE

Number of 6's X_i	Relative Frequency $P(X_i)$	Number of 6's Times Relative Frequency $X_i P(X_i)$	Square of Number of 6's X_i^2	Square of Number of 6's Times Relative Frequency $X_i^2 P(X_i)$
0	0.4823	0.0000	0	0.0000
1	0.3858	0.3858	1	0.3858
2	0.1157	0.2314	4	0.4628
3	0.0154	0.0462	9	0.1386
4	0.0008	0.0032	16	0.0128
	1.0000	$E(X) = 0.6666$		1.0000

where the calculations necessary to the computation of the expected value, variance, and standard deviation are found.

Completing the calculations, the expected value (by 5.23) is:

$$nP = 4(1/6)$$
$$= \mathbf{0.6666}$$

from the table (by 5.00),

$$E(X) = \sum_{i=1}^{4} X_i P(X_i)$$
$$= \mathbf{0.6666}$$

The variance (by 5.24) is:

$$\sigma_X{}^2 = nP(1 - P)$$
$$= 4(1/6)(5/6)$$
$$= \mathbf{0.5555}$$

from the table (by 5.02),

$$\mathrm{Var}(X) = E(X^2) - [E(X)]^2$$
$$= 1.0000 - (0.6666)^2$$
$$= \mathbf{0.5555}$$

The standard deviation (by 5.25) is:

$$\sigma_{np} = \sqrt{nP(1 - P)}$$
$$= \sqrt{4(1/6)(5/6)}$$
$$= \sqrt{\mathbf{0.5555}}$$
$$= \mathbf{0.745}$$

Obviously, 5.03 would give the same result as 5.25 since it identifies the standard deviation of a random variable as the square root of the variance ($\sqrt{0.5555}$).

Suppose we were dealing with a production process whose output is one sixth or $16\frac{2}{3}$ percent defective. The "six-spots" represent bad items or defectives, and the other spots represent good pieces. The probability of getting no defectives in random samples of size 4 would be 48.2 percent or almost even odds. The chances of having not over one bad item in four would be the heavy odds of 87 to 13 (the combined probabilities of zero bad and one bad). This illustrates the optimism of small samples. If a sampling plan were based on a small sample of four with the direction to accept the lot if no bad item appeared, and reject if even one bad item appeared, then with a process producing $16\frac{2}{3}$ percent defective, we would be inclined to accept almost half of the lots submitted, 48.2 percent.

As indicated in the discussion of the Dry-Cell Company problem in an earlier section, the lengthy computation of binomial probabilities has been carried out for a large number of possibilities, and the results published in tables. Appendix Table B-4 is useful here. To illustrate the use of this table, let us return to the Dry-Cell Company problem. It now is clear that we assumed the quality of production to be generated by a Bernoulli process.

First, let us apply the binomial formula directly. The probability of two defectives ($x = 2$) from a sample (box) of 20 batteries ($n = 20$) from an ordinary pallet $(P = 0.02)$ is given by

$$P(X = 2|n = 20, P = 0.02) = C(20, 2)(0.02)^2(0.98)^{18}$$

The value of $C(20, 2)$ is found from the last row, third column of Part a of Appendix Table B-3 to be **190**. (The reader may find it instructive to use 4.60 and the appropriate values from Table B-1 to check this.) The value of the term $(0.02)^2(0.98)^{18}$ found by the use of logarithms is **0.000278**. (The reader should check this.)

Therefore,

$$P(X = 2|n = 20, P = 0.02) = (190)(0.000278)$$
$$= 0.0528$$

If the lot is bad, $P = 0.10$ and the term to be evaluated is

$$C(20, 2)(0.10)^2(0.90)^{18}$$

We know that $C(20, 2) = 190$. The value of $(0.10)^2(0.90)^{18}$ is computed as **0.001501** and

$$P(X = 2|n = 20, P = 0.10) = 0.2852$$

These same values can be obtained more easily from Table B-4 which gives the *cumulative* probability of at least x successes in n tries. That is,

$$P(X \geq x|n, P) = \sum_{x}^{x=n} C(n, x)P^x(1 - P)^{n-x}$$

The probability of two defectives in a sample of 20 is found by looking first in the row of the table for $n = 20$, $x = 2$. In the column headed $P = 0.02$ we find the value 0.0599. This represents the probability of two *or more* defectives. The probability of *exactly* two defectives is found by subtracting the probability of three *or more* defectives from this. The probability of three or more defectives is the value in the next row below (0.0071). The result of the subtraction is **0.0528**, which agrees with our previous result. To recapitulate,

$$P(X = 2) = P(X \geq 2) - P(X \geq 3)$$
$$= 0.0599 - 0.0071$$
$$= 0.0528$$

The probability of two defectives when $P = 0.10$ (we are choosing from a bad lot) is found the same way from Table B-4. From the row for

$n = 20$, $x = 2$ and the column $P = 0.10$ we obtain **0.6083**. From the row for $n = 20$, $x = 3$ in the same column ($P = 0.10$) we obtain 0.3231. The difference $= $ **0.2852**.

The results obtained from the two methods are completely consistent. Either may be used but the table is faster and easier if it covers the desired values of n, x, and P.

The Normal Probability Distribution

Under certain conditions, the binomial probability distribution becomes indistinguishable from a widely used (and misused) and perhaps better known probability distribution. This latter distribution is the *normal probability distribution*. The normal is a continuous and symmetrical distribution with wide application to physical and theoretical statistical distributions. The binomial is a discrete distribution and is asymmetrical if P and $1 - P$ are not equal. However, if P and $1 - P$ are equal and n becomes infinitely large, the binomial becomes indistinguishable from the normal (approaches the normal as a limit). Even when P and $1 - P$ are only approximately equal and n is still finite, but large, the normal probability distribution is an excellent approximation for the binomial probability distribution.

The normal distribution is an extremely important distribution in its own right. Many numerical populations are essentially normally distributed. This is particularly true of the characteristics of items produced by physical processes (for example, lengths and diameters of bolts and rods produced by milling; hardness of tablets, chalk sticks, and so forth, produced by compacting; exterior dimensions of flatwork, such as tin or paper, cut on a machine; useful life of batteries, bulbs, and tubes; weight or bulk of materials loaded into boxes, cans, or bottles by filling machines; and many more). It also provides an adequate description of measures of human performance when large numbers of persons are involved. All of us are familiar with the "normal curve" applied to grade distributions. Average typing speeds in error-free words per minute and average numbers of units handled (processed) in some unit of time (say one hour) in manual production, assembly, or data processing, are further examples of quantitative measures of human ability which usually are normally distributed. Finally, the normal distribution is often encountered when making decisions on the basis of many probability approaches including manipulation of scientific samples. Examples of these latter situations will appear repeatedly in later chapters.

Normal probability distributions are *continuous*. Thus any one of an infinite number of values within the total range of the random variable generating the distribution is a possible value in the distribution. Normal

probability distributions (density functions) are bell-shaped and symmetrical around a single peak (see Figure 5.1). They differ, however, as to
the location of the peak (central point, expected value, modal value) and
the range (variability) of the distribution about the peak. One normal
distribution may have an expected value or mean (arithmetic average)
of $100 and a standard deviation of $10; another may have an expected
value of $100 and a standard deviation of only $4; a third may have an
expected value of 8 pounds and a standard deviation of 3 pounds; a
fourth may have an expected value of 20 pounds and a standard deviation
of 3 pounds. Figure 5.3 illustrates these possibilities.

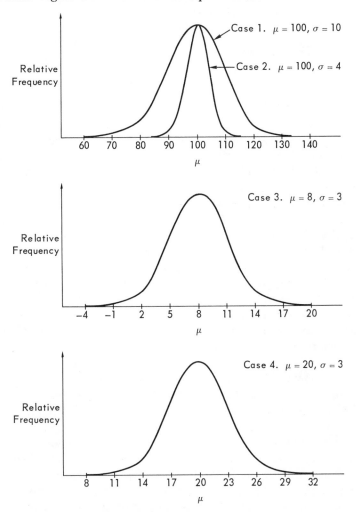

FIG. 5.3. Several normal distributions.

The equation for the normal curve which gives the height of the curve at any value, X, is:

5.30 $\quad h(X|\mu, \sigma) = \dfrac{1}{\sigma \sqrt{2\pi}} e^{-\frac{1}{2}\left(\frac{X-\mu}{\sigma}\right)^2}$

where

$\pi \doteq 3.141593$, a mathematical constant
$e \doteq 2.71828$, the base of the natural logarithms
$\mu = E(X)$, the mean of the distribution
$\sigma = $ standard deviation of the distribution

or, with the constants written out, approximate values are:

5.31 $\quad h(X|\mu, \sigma) = \dfrac{1}{2.5066\sigma} 2.71828^{\frac{-(X-\mu)^2}{2\sigma^2}}$

The probability of occurrence of any single value in a normal distribution is indicated by the relative height (or the density) of the distribution at that point. These relative heights would, of course, total to one. Unfortunately, the relative height at a point is impossible to determine. There are an infinite number of points and if any finite value (such as one) is divided into an infinite number of lesser values, these values are individually equal to zero. It is true that the total area under the curve sums to one since this is a probability distribution. Also, the probability of occurrence of values over any range falling within the limits of the distribution is equal to the area under the curve directly over that range of values. The area involved can be determined by "integrating," adding up the area of, the distribution function over the interval. The probability of a single value remains at zero since the area over a *point* has height, but zero width and the area is thus zero.

To calculate the integral for a desired range is not necessary. Any normal probability distribution can be fully reproduced if the values of its expected value and standard deviation are known. The proportion of the total area between the expected value (μ) of the distribution and a point a given number (say z) standard deviation (σ) units away is the same for all normal probability distributions. What is happening in these cases is that the normal distributions are being standardized, that is, converted to the *standard normal probability distribution*. Any normal probability distribution can be transformed by converting the values (X's) in the original distribution into *standard normal deviates*

(z's) as follows:

5.32 $z = \dfrac{X - \mu}{\sigma}$

It is easier to understand the effects of this transformation if we consider it as two steps.

Step 1. Subtract the value of μ from each value in the distribution (each X). We know from 5.04 that this transformation will reduce the mean by the same amount, μ. Thus, at this point:

$$\begin{aligned} \mu_z{}' &= \mu_x - \mu_x \\ &= 0 \end{aligned}$$

The standard deviation is not affected by this first transformation.

$$\sigma_z{}' = \sigma_x$$

Step 2. The transformed values, $(X - \mu)$'s are multiplied by $1/\sigma$. According to 5.05, the expected value and standard deviation are both multiplied by the factor $1/\sigma$. But our expected value from Step 1 is zero

$$\mu_z{}' = 0$$

and

$$\begin{aligned} 0 \cdot 1/\sigma &= 0/\sigma \\ &= 0 \end{aligned}$$

Thus, we demonstrate that

5.33 $\mu_z = 0$

but σ is changed

$$\begin{aligned} \sigma_z &= \sigma_z{}' \cdot 1/\sigma_x \\ &= \frac{\sigma_z{}'}{\sigma_x} \end{aligned}$$

But, $\sigma_z{}' = \sigma_x$ and it is obvious that

5.34 $\sigma_z = 1$

The above argument is completely general since it does not specify particular values of μ and σ for the original distribution. Therefore, any relationships that hold between μ_z and σ_z also hold between μ and σ of any normal distribution. Thus, relationships such as the following hold true for all normal distributions:

$$P \ (X \text{ in the interval } \mu \pm \sigma) \ = \ \mathbf{0.6827}$$
$$P[(\mu - 2\sigma) \leq X \leq (\mu + 2\sigma)] \ = \ \mathbf{0.9545}$$
$$P[(\mu - 3\sigma) \leq X \leq (\mu + 3\sigma)] \ = \ \mathbf{0.9973}$$

Table 5 in Appendix B can be used to compute these and other probabilities. Since all normal distributions are symmetrical, the area under the curve between μ and a (the point at $\mu - z\sigma$) is equal to the area under the curve between μ and a' (the point at $\mu + z\sigma$). For this reason Table B-5 shows areas under the curve between μ and a point $z\sigma$ *away in either* direction. To determine the probability of a value falling in the range between $\mu - \sigma$ and $\mu + \sigma$, we look down the row and column headings for $z = 1.00$. This is found to be in the eleventh row and the first column of the body of the table. The value given there is 0.34134. That is the proportion of area over either the range $\mu - \sigma$ *or* the range $\mu + \sigma$. To get the area over the total range from $\mu - \sigma$ to $\mu + \sigma$, we must double this value.

$$P[(\mu - \sigma) \leq X \leq (\mu + \sigma)] \ = \ 2(0.34134)$$
$$= \ \mathbf{0.6827}$$

Similarly, when $z = 2.00$, we obtain from the twenty-first row and first column 0.47725, which must be doubled to obtain the probability of a value in the distribution falling in that interval.

$$P[(\mu - 2\sigma) \leq X \leq (\mu + 2\sigma)] \ = \ 2(0.47725)$$
$$= \ \mathbf{0.9545}$$

For the 3σ interval we obtain 0.49865 from the table and find that

$$P[(\mu - 3\sigma) \leq X \leq (\mu + 3\sigma)] \ = \ 2(0.49865)$$
$$= \ \mathbf{0.9973}$$

Sometimes we are interested in asymmetrical areas, that is, areas such as "above X." For example, suppose that Office, Inc., is faced with the problem of reducing clerical staff. It is decided that the less efficient workers will be the first to go. The distribution of average typing speeds is judged to be normal. All clerk-typists whose average typing speed is below 45 words per minute will be laid off. If the company employs 200 typists whose overall average speed (μ) is 52 w.p.m. with a standard deviation (σ) of 8 w.p.m., how many workers will be laid off?

The question resolves to: What proportion of a normal distribution with $\mu = 52$ and $\sigma = 8$ will fall below 45? This will be found by determining how far below μ 45 is found to be in standard deviation units. We define this distance as

$$z = \frac{X - \mu}{\sigma} \tag{5.32}$$

In this instance,

$$z = \frac{45 - 52}{8} = -7/8$$
$$= -0.875$$

This relationship is shown in Figure 5.4. The shaded area is calculated from Table B-5.

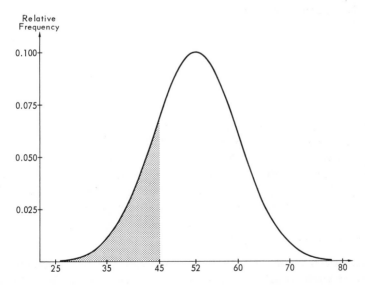

FIG. 5.4. Proportion of a normal distribution with $\mu = 52$ and $\sigma = 8$ falling below 45.

(1) Area between 52 and 45, that is, area between μ and $\mu - 0.8750\sigma$, (row nine, columns 8 and 9) is interpolated as $\frac{1}{2}(0.30785 + 0.31057)$ = **0.30921**

(2) Area below 45 (shaded area) = 0.50000 − 0.30921
$$= \textbf{0.1908}$$

(3) If 0.1908 of the 200 workers are to be laid off, then

$$0.1908(200) = \textbf{38.16}$$

or 39 workers will be laid off.

Suppose that the management at Office, Inc., decided to reduce the typing staff by 20 persons, that is, 10 percent. What would be the minimum speed (in words per minute) of the typists retained?

The question resolves to: What is the value (words per minute) below which 10 percent of the distribution is found? Symbolically, we want to know the value of k such that:

$$P(X < k) = 0.10$$

Table B-5 indicates that 0.4000 of the area under a normal curve falls between μ and a point 1.28σ away (in either direction). Then 10 percent of the distribution must be found below the value 1.28σ below μ. That is,

$$
\begin{aligned}
k &= \mu - 1.28\sigma \\
&= 52 - 1.28(8) \\
&= 52 - 10.24 \\
&= \textbf{41.76}
\end{aligned}
$$

We, therefore, conclude that the minimum average typing speed of typists retained will be 42 words per minute.

As an exercise for the reader, how many clerk-typists would be retained if those typing less than 50 w.p.m. were laid off? Note that this could be found easily by reference to Table B-6, Part C, first row. Table B-6 is useful in other situations which are illustrated in later chapters.

The Poisson Distribution

Under certain conditions, the binomial probability distribution becomes indistinguishable from the Poisson probability distribution. When an event has *many* opportunities to occur but is extremely unlikely to occur at any given opportunity, the Poisson exponential binomial limit, or

Poisson distribution is used. The event may be the breakdown of a particular part (for example, a vacuum tube) in a piece of equipment such as a radio; a defect occurring in a small segment along a continuous wire, tape, chain, or cable; a production flaw in a section of a large sheet of glass or in a single glass bottle, the time pattern of arrival of calls at a telephone exchange, the number of sales of a particular product during a given time period, and many more.

The Poisson is an approximation to the binomial in which the approximation becomes closer and closer as the value of n becomes larger and larger and the value of P becomes smaller and smaller. Under the circumstances of n approaching infinity and P getting smaller, the limit of $(1 - P)$ is 1.

5.40   The expected value of the binomial is nP and so is the *expected value* of the Poisson only the expected value of the Poisson is called c to distinguish it.

5.41   The variance of the binomial is $nP(1 - P)$ but for the Poisson it becomes nP or c because $(1 - P)$ becomes 1 and is dropped.

5.42   The standard deviation of the Poisson is the square root of its expected value, $\sqrt{c}$.

Note that neither n nor P need to be known, but only their product (c) in order to work with a Poisson situation.

To determine the probability of the exact number of occurrences under the Poisson law requires the use either of a table giving the summation of terms of Poisson's exponential binomial limit, a chart of cumulative probability curves for this distribution, or the following formula:

5.43 $P(X = x) = \dfrac{e^{-c}c^x}{x!}$

The value of e is (approximately) 2.718. The value e is a mathematical constant, the base of the natural logarithms. A small table of exponential values (e^{-x}) is given in Table 7, Appendix B.

Suppose that in an operation for enameling template, the average number (c) of defects per standard surface is 0.5, that is, on the average, one flaw is found on each two standard surfaces. Then the probability of no defects on an inspected surface is

$$P(O) = \frac{(2.718)^{-0.5}(0.5)^0}{0!}$$
$$= 0.6065$$

The probability of one defect is

$$P(1) = \frac{(2.718)^{-0.5}(0.5)^1}{1!}$$
$$= 0.3033$$

The probability of two defects is

$$P(2) = \frac{(2.718)^{-0.5}(0.5)^2}{2!}$$
$$= 0.0758$$

The above values can be determined more easily from Table 8, Appendix B, the cumulative Poisson distribution which shows

$$P(X \geq x|c) = \sum_{X=x}^{X=\infty} (e^{-c}c^x/x!)$$

Note that regardless of the value of c, the probability that X is equal to 0 or greater is always 1.000.

Using the same reasoning as when discussing the cumulative binomial (Table B-4),

$$P(X = 0) = P(X \geq 0) - P(X \geq 1)$$

therefore,

$$P(X = 0|c = 0.5) = 1.0000 - 0.3935$$
$$= 0.6065$$

and

$$P(X = 1|c = .5) = P(X \geq 1|c = 0.5) - P(X \geq 2|c = 0.5)$$
$$= 0.3935 - 0.0902$$
$$= 0.3033$$

The calculation of $P(X = 2|c = 0.5)$ from Table B-8 is left as an exercise for the reader.

Relation of $\bar{X}$ and σ in Any Distribution

A theorem developed by Chebyshev (P. L. Chebyshev was a Russian mathematician, 1821–1894) tells us how close one can expect any value of any discrete random variable to be to the mean (expected value) of the distribution.

5.50 If X is a random variable whose distribution has the mean (expected value) $\bar{X}$ and the finite standard deviation σ, then for any positive constant k the probability that X assumes a value less than $\bar{X} - k\sigma$ or greater than $\bar{X} + k\sigma$ is less than $1/k^2$. That is:

$$P(|X - \bar{X}| > k\sigma) < 1/k^2$$

Chebyshev's inequality can be restated in a more interesting form:

5.51 $P[(\bar{X} - k\sigma) \leq X \leq (\bar{X} + k\sigma)] \geq 1 - 1/k^2$

This means that the probability that X assumes a value within two standard deviations of the mean is at least 3/4, and the probability that it assumes a value within three standard deviations is at least 8/9. Thus we are provided with a general means of observing how σ relates to the dispersion of any variable about its mean. Note that the exact distribution of the variable is unknown and thus this rule is not very "powerful." We are given only a minimal probability, not an exact probability.

Relation of the "Ready-Made" Probability Distributions to One Another

It has been indicated in the discussions above that the normal and Poisson distributions can be used to approximate the probabilities of the binomial distribution under certain conditions. It is also true that the binomial can be used to approximate some hypergeometric probabilities. Table 5.8 summarizes the characteristics of the four distributions and indicates where each applies. The reader is urged to study it carefully. Understanding of this table will make much of the later material much easier to master. The discussion below is also helpful in this regard.

More exact rules of substitution between the normal, binomial and Poisson distributions are given in Table 5.9.

The binomial distribution differs from the hypergeometric only in that it applies to a Bernoulli process, that is, a process where the proportion of "successes," P, is a constant. If P is not constant, the hypergeometric

TABLE 5.8

APPLICATION OF THE MAJOR PROBABILITY DISTRIBUTIONS

POPULATION STUDIED

Distribution	DICHOTOMOUS (*Attributes or Counts*)		CONTINUOUS (*Measurements*)	
	Finite	Infinite	Infinite	Finite‡
Hypergeometric	Yes	No	No	No
Binomial	If $\frac{n}{N} \to 0$†	Yes	No	No
Poisson	If $\frac{n}{N} \to 0$ and $P \to 0$	If $P \to 0$ and n large (see Table 5.9)	No	No
Normal	If $\frac{n}{N} \to 0$ and n is sufficiently large given P (see Table 5.9)	If n is sufficiently large given P (see Table 5.9)	If the random variable is normally distributed	With correction of formulas $\frac{N - n}{N - 1}$ = finite population correction (f.p.c.)§

† $\frac{n}{N} \to 0$ is read, as the ratio $\frac{n}{N}$ approaches zero.

‡ Technically, this is impossible since a continuous population is infinite by definition, but measurements taken from a large finite population can reasonably be assumed to have come from an infinite, continuous population.

§ The finite population correction is explained in Chapter 8.

distribution applies. This would indicate that in any case where the total population (lot) was finite in size and not produced by a continuous (Bernoulli) process, the probabilities would have to be calculated by the combinatorial technique. Actually, however, the binomial can be used successfully as an approximation for the hypergeometric whenever P is *approximately* constant. Thus, when the population is large though finite and also large in relation to the sample drawn from it the binomial can be substituted for the hypergeometric.

For example, let us consider the probability of getting exactly five heads on ten tosses of an honest coin. First, let us apply the binomial (5.22).

$$P(x = 5 | P = 0.5, n = 10) = C(10, 5)(0.5)^5(0.5)^5$$
$$= \frac{10!}{5!5!}(0.5)^{10}$$
$$= \frac{252}{1024}$$
$$= \mathbf{0.246}$$

This value can also be found from Table B-4.

TABLE 5.9

APPROXIMATING THE BINOMIAL WITH THE NORMAL AND THE POISSON

Use Normal Approximation to the Binomial if $n \geq n'$ (n')	If P Approximates	Use Poisson Approximation to the Binomial If $n \geq n'$ (n')
30	0.50	—†
50	0.40 or 0.60	—†
80	0.30 or 0.70	—†
200	0.20 or 0.80	—†
600	0.10 or 0.90	100
1400	0.05 or 0.95	50
—†	0.01 or 0.99	10

† No appropriate size known.

Now let us try the normal approximation. Remember that we must use a continuity correction. On the continuous scale we are interested in the probability of being in the interval between 4.5 and 5.5. We must also compute the mean and standard deviation. By 5.23 and using $\hat{\mu}$ as "estimated μ,"

$$\hat{\mu} = nP$$
$$= 10(0.5)$$
$$= 5$$

By 5.24 and using $\hat{\sigma}$ as "estimated σ,"

$$\hat{\sigma} = \sqrt{nP(1 - P)}$$
$$= \sqrt{10(0.5)(0.5)}$$
$$= \sqrt{2.5}$$
$$= \mathbf{1.58}$$

Applying the continuity correction and using 5.32,

$$z' = \frac{4.50 - 5.0}{1.58}$$
$$= -0.317$$
$$z'' = \frac{5.50 - 5.0}{1.58}$$
$$= +0.317$$

For the probability of z between -0.317 and $+0.317$, we use Table B-5. Looking down the stub and across the column headings for values of z, we interpolate between $z = 0.31$ (0.12172) and $z = 0.32$ (0.12552) and obtain 0.12362 as the proportion of area under the curve between μ and a point 0.317σ away in either direction. Therefore, the probability of five heads in ten tosses of an honest coin is approximately 2(0.12362) = 0.24724 or about 0.247.

The normal approximatiom compares reasonably well with the value obtained from the binomial, being only 0.001 larger:

normal approximation = 0.247
binomial probability = 0.246
difference   **+0.001**

Note that according to Table 5.9, the approximation is not recommended in this case.

SUMMARY

The idea on which this chapter is based is the idea of a random variable, a rule which assigns values to the outcomes of a chance process. Each random variable has an expected value, variance, and standard deviation:

$$E(X) = \sum_{i=1}^{N} X_i P(X_i) \qquad (5.00)$$

$$\text{Var}(X) = \sigma^2 = \sum_{i=1}^{N} [X_i - E(X)]^2 P(X_i) \qquad (5.01)$$

$$= E(X_i^2) - [E(X)]^2 \qquad (5.02)$$

$$\sigma = \sqrt{\sigma^2} \qquad (5.03)$$

Each random variable also has a probability distribution. Four "ready-made" distributions are widely used as normative approximations to population distributions and as theoretical distributions of statistics drawn from samples. The four distributions fall into two classes:

I. Probability distributions for discrete variables from dichotomous (two-valued) populations.[1]

A. Hypergeometric or combinatorial probability distribution:

$$P(X = r | N, M, N) = \frac{C(M, r)C(N - M, n - r)}{C(N, n)}$$

$$r \leq M, r \leq n \leq N \qquad (5.10)$$

$$E(X) = \frac{nM}{N} \qquad (5.11)$$

$$\text{Var}(X) = \sigma^2 = \frac{nM}{N}\left(1 - \frac{M}{N}\right)\left(\frac{N - n}{N - 1}\right) \qquad (5.12)$$

B. Binomial probability distribution:

$$P(X = x | n, P) = C(n, x)P^x(1 - P)^{n-x}$$

$$x \leq n \qquad (5.22)$$

$$E(X) = nP \qquad (5.23)$$

$$\text{Var}(X) = \sigma_X^2 = nP(1 - P) \qquad (5.24)$$

C. Poisson probability distribution:

$$P(X = x | c) = \frac{c^x e^{-c}}{x!} \qquad (5.43)$$

$$E(X) = c = nP \qquad (5.40)$$

$$\text{Var}(X) = \sigma^2 = c \qquad (5.41)$$

$$\sigma = \sqrt{c} \qquad (5.42)$$

II. The normal probability distributions for continuous variables.

A. Normal probability distribution:

$$h(X | \mu, \sigma) = \frac{1}{\sigma\sqrt{2\pi}} e^{-\frac{1}{2}\left(\frac{X-\mu}{\sigma}\right)^2} \qquad (5.30)$$

$$= \frac{1}{2.5066\sigma} 2.71828^{-\frac{(X-\mu)^2}{2\sigma^2}} \qquad (5.31)$$

[1] All symbols are defined in the glossary at the end of this section.

B. Standard or unit normal probability distribution:

$$z = \frac{X - \mu}{\sigma} \tag{5.32}$$

$$E(z) = 0 \tag{5.33}$$

$$\text{Var}(z) = \sigma_z = 1 \tag{5.34}$$

The situations to which these distributions apply and the relationships between the distributions are summarized in Tables 5.8 and 5.9.

For both continuous and discrete random variables, the expected value, $E(X)$, and standard deviation, σ, can be used to describe the variability of the items in the distribution according to Chebyshev's inequality:

$$P[[E(X) - k\sigma] \leq X \leq [E(X) + k\sigma]] \geq 1 - 1/k^2 \tag{5.51}$$

GLOSSARY OF SYMBOLS

x = a particular value of the random variable, X (the value whose probability of occurrence is being evaluated)

N = size of a population; $N = \infty$ for infinite populations

M = number of "successes" in a finite population

n = number of trials ("plays," "tosses") or sample size

$C(n, r)$ = combination of n things taken r at a time = $\dfrac{n!}{r!(n - r)!}$

$P(A|B)$ = probability that A is true given that B is true

$E(X)$ = the "expected value" of the random variable X

$\sigma_X{}^2$ or σ^2 = variance of the random variable X

P = proportion of "successes" in the population (assumed constant over all trials)

c = expected number of "successes" in n trials for a Poisson distribution = nP

$e \doteq 2.71828$ (a mathematical constant); ($\doteq$ is read "approximately equal")

"$P \to 0$" is read "P approaches zero"; "$(1 - P) \to 1$" is read "$(1 - P)$ approaches 1"

$h(X)$ = height of the normal curve at the value X

μ = mean of a continuous population distribution

σ = standard deviation of the random variable X

$\pi \doteq 3.141593$ (a mathematical constant)

z = standard normal deviate (see 5.32)

DISCUSSION QUESTIONS

1. Define the following concepts in your own words (do *not* use symbols or verbal formulas).

   (a) random variable
   (b) probability distribution
   (c) arithmetic average
   (d) expected value
   (e) standard deviation

   (f) discrete variable
   (g) continuous variable
   (h) infinite population
   (i) finite population
   (j) Bernoulli process

2. A random sample of 200 persons is selected and the height of each person measured.

   (a) Is a random variable created? If so, what is it? (See page 135.)
   (b) Is the variable of interest continuous or discrete? Explain. (See page 141.)
   (c) Is the population from which the sample is drawn finite or infinite? (See page 164.)
   (d) If the color of the hair of each of these persons were also determined, could this be considered a random variable? Explain fully.

   Hint: Consider carefully the definition of a random variable.

3. For each of the situations described below:

   (a) Indicate which of the ready-made probability distribution presented in this chapter is *theoretically* most appropriate.
   (b) Indicate which of the ready-made distributions you would suggest for each of the situations considering practical considerations such as ease of computation and practical approximations.

   Situations:

   (1) Describe the pattern of variation in the number of defective tiles per case of tiles (100 tiles) when the production process averages 0.4 defective tiles per case.
   (2) Describe the pattern of variation in measurements of a given level of pressure made by pressure gauges produced by a standardized production process.
   (3) Describe the pattern of variation in the number of persons, in randomly selected samples of 100 persons from Bigtown, who are (or are not) watching a particular television program on a national network.
   (4) Describe the pattern of variation in the number of defective bolts in random samples of 25 bolts taken from the output of a mechanical production process.
   (5) Describe the pattern of variation in number of defectives in samples of 10 items each randomly selected from a lot of 50 items.

(6) Describe the pattern of variation in responses to a yes-no question on a sample survey of voters in Midtown (population 36,000; registered voters 15,000).

(7) Describe the pattern of variation in heights of male students registered at State U. during the current quarter (approximately 19,000 male students).

(8) Describe the pattern of variation in favorable-unfavorable opinions on a public issue by the 6 members of a randomly selected committee of the Smalltown Chamber of Commerce (54 members).

(9) Describe the pattern of variation in heights of male human beings.

(10) Describe the pattern of variation in arithmetic average heights of random samples of 100 male citizens of the United States.

Hints:

(1) Ask yourself the following questions about each situation:

   (a) Is the population dichotomous?

   (b) Is the variable discrete or continuous?

   (c) Is the population finite or infinite? Alternatively, is this a sample of a process or of a limited group?

(2) Given the theoretical distribution, is there a satisfactory approximation which is easier to use?

4. (a) If a coin has been tossed five times and has come up heads all five times, what is the probability that it will come up heads on the sixth toss? (Assume a "fair" coin.)

   Hint: Does the coin have a memory?

   (b) Suppose the coin had come up heads ten times in succession and is a "fair" coin, what is the probability that it will come up heads on the eleventh toss?

   (c) What would be your answer if we asked for the probability of five heads in a row when tossing a "fair" coin?

   (d) If the only information on the coin were that it had come up heads five times in succession, what would you expect on the sixth toss? Why?

5. Answer the following:

   (a) What is the probability of rolling a 2 on one roll of a single die?

   (b) What is the probability that a red ace will be drawn from an ordinary deck of 52 playing cards on one random draw?

   (c) What is the probability that you will pass this course?

   (d) What is the probability that you will receive at least a "B" grade in this course?

(e) Explain how you arrived at each of the probabilities given in answers a–d above.

(f) For each of the answers given above (a–d) explain the exact meaning of the probability given. Does each probability represent a relative frequency of occurrence in the long run? Is any one in any sense subjectively determined? Explain fully.

DISCUSSION PROBLEMS

Show your method on all solutions.

1. What is the maximum amount one should pay *per roll* to play a game in which one won 15 cents each time an odd number (1, 3, 5) came up as the number of spots on the upper face of a standard die after the roll?

   Hint: Follow the method of Table 5.2.

2. Suppose you were offered a chance to play the following games:

   Game 1: The player pays 25 cents per toss and an honest coin is tossed. If the coin lands heads up, the player receives $1. If the coin lands tails up, the player pays an additional 50 cents.

   Game 2: The player pays 25 cents per roll and an honest die is rolled. If the number of spots on the upper face of the die after the die comes to rest is either 1 or 2, the player receives $2.25. If the number of spots comes up 3, 4, 5, or 6, the player pays an additional 75 cents.

   (a) Which game has the higher expected value? number 1? number 2? neither? (See Table 5.2.)

   (b) Which game has the larger variance in returns? number 1? number 2? neither? (Apply 5.02.)

   (c) If you could play only one of these games, which would you choose? Why?

3. A production line produces 10 percent defectives. A sample of 20 items is randomly selected from the output of the line. What is the probability that the sample will contain:

   (a) no defectives?

   (b) 5 defectives?

   (c) at least 5 defectives?

   (d) 10 defectives?

   Hint: Is the variable continuous? discrete? Is this a Bernoulli process, that is, is the proportion of defectives constant? Now, which of the probability distributions applies?

4. Refer to the production line and sample of problem 3 and answer the following:
   (a) What will be the average number of defectives in samples of 20 items?
   (b) If we select a sample with five defectives, how likely is it that the line still is producing 10 percent defectives? Explain.
   (c) If the sample contains no defectives, would you feel it is reasonable to accept that the process still is producing 10 percent defectives? Explain.

   Hints: For (a), see 5.23. For (b) and (c) use Table B-4. For (c), it would be helpful to sketch a rough graph of the probability distribution involved and show which portion (or portions) you wish to consider. Reasonableness is not specific and must be decided by each individual. Could you be wrong in your decision? How much chance of error are you willing to accept?

5. The probability that a person contacted in a sample survey conducted by Quest, Inc., will complete and return the questionnaire is 0.20.
   (a) What is the probability that:
      (1) at least three of ten persons contacted in Littleville, population 86, will complete and return the questionnaire?
      (2) at least 30 of 100 persons contacted in Midburg, population 2640, will complete and return the questionnaire?
      (3) at least 300 of 1000 persons contacted in Bigtown, population 100,000 will complete and return the questionnaire?
      (4) at least 3000 of 10,000 persons contacted in New York City will complete and return the questionnaire?
   (b) Why do the probabilities in (a) differ in each of the situations?
   Hint: What do all these situations have in common? Is the population finite or infinite?
   (c) What is the one single thing that changes with each situation?
   Hint: Consider 5.32 and 5.24 (to be substituted in 5.32) and note the variables appearing in both. Which variable changes with each situation? Why can either of these be the theoretically correct equation?

6. The Board of Directors of Burpop Corporation is considering an advertising campaign to improve the company image with the public. A randomly selected committee of 6 directors is to study the question and provide a recommendation. If the 12 directors are divided, 7 for the campaign and 5 against, what is the probability that the majority report of the committee will favor conducting the campaign?
   (a) Work this problem using 5.10 (hypergeometric).

(b) Work this problem using 5.20 (*and* rule). The results should be the same.

EXERCISES

Show your method on all solutions.

1. Jim Sewer and Bill Seamer operate stitching machines for the Den Products Company. The company pays them on a piecework basis. If they produce 200 or more acceptable pieces in one day, they receive a bonus of 2 cents per piece. In the past, Jim and Bill have compiled the following records of performance on daily number of acceptable pieces:

	Jim Sewer	*Bill Seamer*
Mean number of pieces	180	170
Standard deviation	30	20

If the daily number of pieces for both workers are normally distributed, compute:
 (a) On what percent of the days Sewer will receive the bonus.
 (b) On what percent of the days Seamer will receive the bonus.
 (c) Which of these workers would you consider to be the superior employee? Explain fully, considering such elements as the desirability of uniform production rates, probable proportion of unacceptable pieces produced, and so forth.
2. What is the probability of drawing at least 2 defective items in a sample of 20 from a lot of 10,000 items containing 1000 defectives?
3. In manufacturing bottles it is found that 5 percent are defective. What is the probability that in a sample of 10 bottles there are:
 (a) 0 defectives?
 (b) 2 defectives?
 (c) no more than 1 defective?
 (d) at least 1 defective?
4. Suppose you adopt the following decision rule for determining the answer to a true-false examination: Toss a coin; heads equals true, tails equals false.
 (a) What is your expected relative score if you get one point for each correct answer?
 (b) What is your expected relative score if you get one point for each correct answer and are docked two points for each wrong answer?

5. Suppose you roll a six-sided fair die and let 1 or 2 equal true, 3, 4 or 5 equal false and 6 equal leave blank. What is your expected relative score if you receive 2 points for each correct answer, lose 1 point for each blank, and lose 2 points for each wrong answer?

6. Suppose that you are offered a game whereby you will receive $3.80 each time a 6 comes up on the roll of a single die.
   (a) How much should you pay per roll to make this game equitable?
   (b) How would the amount change if you paid only when a result other than 6 (1, 2, 3, 4, 5) came up?

7. A shipment of 20 television picture tubes contains 4 defective tubes. Using random selection, what is the probability:
   (a) of drawing two tubes which are both defective on the first two draws?
   (b) of drawing two defective tubes on the first five draws?
   (c) of drawing all four of the defective tubes within five draws?
   (d) of drawing at least one of the defective tubes in five draws?
   (e) of drawing at least two of the defective tubes in five draws?
   (f) of drawing none of the defective tubes in five draws?
   (g) of drawing no more than two of the defective tubes in five draws?

8. What is the maximum amount one should pay per roll to play a game in which one wins each time an odd number of spots comes up on the upper face of a standard die?
   (a) If one wins 15 cents when an odd number comes up?
   (b) If one wins 25 cents when an odd number comes up?

9. What is the probability that the number of defective parts in samples of ten parts randomly selected from the output of a production process producing ten percent defectives will be:
   (a) exactly one?
   (b) at least one?
   (c) less than two?
   (d) exactly two?
   (e) no more than two?

10. Mr. Sepay is supervisor of the accounting department of Lessloss Department Stores. He has established the standard that the number of posting errors in his department will be no more than 0.1 percent of the total number of items posted. As statistician for Lessloss you are convinced that the number of posting errors per day is Poisson distributed. If 2000 postings are made on a given day and Mr. Sepay's standard is being realized:
    (a) how many posting errors would you expect that day?
    (b) how likely is it that there would be as many as 3 errors?

(c) how likely is it that there would be no more than 2 posting errors?

(d) How likely is it that there would be *no* posting errors?

11. The Mercury Taxi Company has fitted its fleet of 25 cabs with Hardy Tires (4 tires per cab). The Hardy Tires are asserted to travel an average of 22,000 miles with a standard deviation of 900 miles before being worn smooth. Each of the Mercury taxis travels approximately 4500 miles per month. Mercury wishes to set up a logical purchase policy. Assuming the tire life is normally distributed:

(a) How soon should they expect to start replacing tires? (Give answer in months from date of purchase.)

(b) How many tires will be replaced within (from date of purchase):

(1) five months?

(2) six months?

(3) nine months?

12. A student received a grade of 89 on an examination where the class average was 73 and the standard deviation of the examination was 6. The class average of a second examination was 66 and the standard deviation increased to 8. What grade should the student have on the second examination in order to equal his performance on the first test? (Assume the grades to be Normally distributed.)

13. Mr. Newboss is shifting Sam Loafer from Department B to Department D in the factory. Permission has been obtained from Sam's union. In Department B the average production per man is 1750 parts per week; the standard deviation is 150 parts per week. In Department D the average production is 4250 parts per week with a standard deviation of 350 parts per week.

(a) If Sam is producing an average of 1450 parts per week in Department B, how many parts can Mr. Newboss fairly expect him to produce per week (on the average) in Department D to equal his output level in Department B? (Assume that Sam L. will be given time to become oriented to the new job.)

(b) What have you assumed about the distribution of production rates in the two departments in order to answer (a)? Why?

14. Suppose you are asking a well-designed question which will yield a yes-no answer and that the population of about 10 million persons is divided into 30 percent yes and 70 percent no on the question. Sample size is 5.

(a) What is the mean number of yes answers per sample one would expect if many random samples of this size were taken?

(b) In what proportion of the samples which might be taken under these conditions would one expect 5 yes answers?

6
estimation
and sampling

The discussion of decision making in Chapter 1 implied that a decision problem exists only if action is possible and will be taken. Quantitative analysis can be used to provide a basis for action in such decision situations if the action depends upon facts or relationships which can be stated in numerical form. For example, the decision on whether or not to produce the new product of our inventive businessman depends, at least in part, on how many units can be sold at a price sufficient to give a satisfactory return to all factors used in its production. If this number were known, the decision problem would be greatly simplified (one level of uncertainty would be removed). This number will be known with certainty only if the product is produced and sold. Obviously, we are ignoring the fact that the amount sold will be a function of *how* it is marketed, as well as *how* it is made, and, perhaps, even *what* it is called.

Although the unit sales of the new product cannot be known, they *must* be estimated. The question is how. The examples below together with comments already made in Chapter 1 may suggest a solution.

Expected Values and Variances

One method of estimation has already been discussed. The concept of the *expected value* was introduced in Chapter 1 and applied to random

176

variables in Chapter 5. Any time we have an uncertain future outcome, but one for which all possible values and their probabilities of occurrence are specified, we can use this concept.

For example, let us consider the problem of Neet-Lawn Service Company which provides lawn and shrub care, spraying for control of insects and plant diseases, development of new lawns, tree pruning, and other general yard work for individual homeowners in Richburg. A base of regular customers with annual contracts requires the services of four full-time crews of three men each. However, from five to twelve such crews are used each working day. The additional crews are used on special jobs for which orders are received daily. A tentative schedule of work is available before each day but potential customers are called early on the scheduled day (between 7 and 9 A.M.) to confirm the order before all crews are actually dispatched. In addition, customers often call in and request crews for the day on which they call. The manager of Neet-Lawn supplements his regular workers with students on vacation and other day workers when demand is brisk. The problem is to estimate the number of crews required each day.

A study of company records provides the information on the relative frequency with which the various numbers of crews have been required as shown in Table 6.1.

TABLE 6.1

RELATIVE FREQUENCY OF OCCURRENCE OF VARIOUS DAILY DEMANDS FOR SERVICE CREWS OF NEET-LAWN SERVICE COMPANY AND RELATED COMPUTATIONS

Crews Demanded per Day X_i	Relative Frequency of Demands $P(X_i)$	Weighted Demand $X_i P(X_i)$	Demands Squared X_i^2	Weighted Squares $X_i^2 P(X_i)$
5	0.02	0.10	25	0.50
6	0.05	0.30	36	1.80
7	0.12	0.84	49	5.88
8	0.17	1.36	64	10.88
9	0.26	2.34	81	21.06
10	0.18	1.80	100	18.00
11	0.15	1.65	121	18.15
12	0.05	0.60	144	7.20
Totals	1.00	8.99		83.47

Completing the computations started in Table 6.1 (applying 5.00, 5.02, and 5.03) summary measures for the distribution would be:

$$E(X) = \textbf{8.99 or 9.0}$$
$$\sigma^2 = 83.47 - (8.99)^2$$
$$= \textbf{2.6}$$
$$\sigma = \sqrt{2.6}$$
$$= \textbf{1.6}$$

(Note that it was necessary to use $E(X)$ in unrounded form in 5.02.)

Thus Neet-Lawn should expect to need an average of nine crews per day. But the actual number needed will vary from day to day. Applying Chebyshev's inequality in the form given in 5.51 (and assuming the number of crews demanded is a discrete random variable) we find that:

$$P(9.0 - 2(1.6)) \le X \le (9.0 + 2(1.6))] \ge 1 - \tfrac{1}{4}$$
$$P(5.8 \le X \le 12.2) \ge 0.75$$

In other words, the manager can expect a need for from about five to twelve crews at least three fourths of the time! It would, therefore, appear that the inequality in this case is not very useful. We have found only that we will need some number of crews within the usual (experienced) range of demand!

Point Estimates and Interval Estimates

We have seen in the previous section a *point estimate* (expected value) and an *interval estimate* (Chebyshev inequality). It is instructive to consider which gives more imformation. The probability that X will be equal to the expected value is often not large. A point estimate (such as the expected value) usually tells us nothing about the dispersion of the X values about that point. Unless we have some measure of dispersion (σ or σ^2), we do not have a very good idea of how reliable the estimate really is.

The mere specification of variability as well as central tendency does not give much information to the reader who is untrained in statistics. The preferable manner in which to give such a person information is to tell directly just how reliable the point estimate actually is. Thus, we can say, as above, that the number of crews demanded each day will be within the range five to twelve *at least* 75 percent of the time. It is easy to grasp the worth of such an estimate. It is easy to compare such an estimate with another which might specify, for instance, that the number of crews demanded each day will be within the range seven to ten almost three-fourths of the time. The latter estimate appears more precise, doesn't it? This estimate is based on *all* information given in the distribution of Table 6.1. Such an estimate requires the assumption that the probability distribution for number of crews demanded is sufficiently accurate as given and that the given historical distribution is an adequate representation of the distribution of future demand. Whether or not these assumptions are appropriate depends upon how the distribution was obtained. If it was developed from the maximum information (the complete history of demand for crews) and if that history covers a sufficiently long period, then it could be considered valid. If developed from only part of the information available (a sample of the available information), it must have less reliability. That possibility is discussed below. Note also that the use of Table 6.1 assumes that there are no seasonal or trend factors influencing the relative frequencies of demand.

ESTIMATES FROM SAMPLES

Suppose that the distribution given in Table 6.1 were developed from a sample of Neet-Lawn history. How would this affect our interpretation of the data? Obviously, this will depend upon how reliable we consider the sample to be. We measure a sample's reliability by its *accuracy* and by its *precision*.

Accuracy in a sample means that it is free from bias. A biased sample is one which does not measure what it is intended to measure. For example, suppose our inventive businessman of Chapter 1 is interested in measuring the proportion of families who would be willing to buy his product. In an attempt to "sample opinion" he polls the businessmen at the next luncheon meeting of his local Chamber of Commerce. These men obviously do not represent a cross-section of all families. His results are therefore unrepresentative of the population of interest, the so-called *target population;* he has a "biased" sample.

Precision, on the other hand, is related primarily to sample size. It refers to how close the sample value is likely to be to the true population value. It is intuitively obvious that larger samples *tend* to be more representative *of the population from which they are drawn* than smaller samples. An estimate derived from a large sample should be closer to the true population value than an estimate derived from a smaller sample (if the sample is unbiased). It is demonstrated in a later section that this intuitive notion is supported by statistical theory if the samples are properly selected. At this point we will consider some of the elements involved in estimation from sample data.

Nature of the Sampling Process

A *sample* is a part of a *population*. A population is the totality of the elements under study. A physical population is composed of *elementary units* (for example, families) each of which possesses a certain *characteristic of interest* (for example, willingness to buy the new product) which is under study. The *physical population* is composed of these elementary units. The totality of the individual characteristics of interest comprises the *statistical population*. It is primarily the nature and form of the statistical population and how it may be adequately represented that concern us.

Our interest centers on being able to make sufficiently precise inferences about the true values of the statistical population on the basis of values computed from the sample. We wish to select a part of the population (a sample) in such a way that the sample is a small replica of the population. Obviously, the sample values will accurately and precisely describe the population characteristics only if the sample is a small replica of the population. There are two basic problems. We must select units from the population in such a manner that the sample can be expected to be a replica of the population. The second problem is to make our selections from the proper population. Probability selection of the sample is used to insure the representativeness of the sample. The second problem is at the same time easier and more difficult to handle; it is discussed immediately after the section on probability selection.

Probability Selection

Suppose that we wished to sample a very large group of people for some characteristic. Perhaps we would like to study hair colorings of all people in the United States. How would we get a small replica of the population of hair colorings? Let us assume that we have a reliable method of assigning each head of hair to a particular color class and that we recognize fifteen such classes. With only fifteen classes, the number of heads of hair assigned to any one class would not be small. If we had all the heads divided into these fifteen classes, it would be a simple matter to take some constant proportion (for example, one half of one percent) of each class and thus obtain a small replica of the population.

It is only too obvious that if we knew enough about the population of hair colorings to divide it into fifteen mutually exclusive classes, we would not need the study. However, thinking of the population as consisting of some number of such classes is useful. It conveys the fact that we need a method for selecting elementary units (people) from the physical population that could be expected to select from every class in the statistical population in the same proportion. Think now of a deck of ordinary playing cards (52 cards divided into four suits, spades, hearts, diamonds, and clubs, and each suit containing thirteen cards marked 1 through 10 and Jack, Queen, King). How do we insure a representative selection from a deck of playing cards? We shuffle the cards carefully before drawing; we do not divide them into suits or values (Aces, Kings, Queens, and so forth), and then draw. If we could mix our population of heads of hair in a similar manner, we could easily get an uncontrolled, representative selection.

It is obvious that it would be impossible to physically mix our population of heads of hair. However, if we could assign each of the heads an identifying number and place each number on a card, we could then mix the cards, draw out the required number of cards, and choose as our sample the heads whose identifying numbers appeared on the selected cards. Even this latter technique would be difficult as described, but it can be easily approximated. First, we would assign each head a number. Second, we would use a table of random digits (see Appendix B, Table 9) to select a sample of numbers. A table of random digits is constructed by giving every digit an equal probability of being selected each time a digit is selected for the table. Since the numbers from the random digit table, if selected in some logical sequence, would be a set of random numbers with no bias in their selection, the sample of heads so defined would be a randomly selected sample. Each head would have been given an equal opportunity of being selected into the sample.

Let us illustrate the above procedure. Suppose our population consisted of 10,000 accounts receivable numbered consecutively from 0000 through 9999. We desire a sample of 100 accounts. We need 100 four-digit numbers between 0000 and 9999. We turn to Table B-9 and arbitrarily choose one five-digit group of random digits which we will use to determine an essentially random starting point for selecting the 100 numbers (we choose 08569). We use the first digit (0) of that group to indicate which of the ten columns of five-digit groups to enter (Column 10). The second digit (8) to indicate which of the ten groups of five in the column to enter (the eighth group from the top). The third digit (5) is used to determine which of the five 5-digit groups to use (1 or 6 = first group, 2 or 7 = second group, and so forth), so we use the fifth group. The fourth digit (6) is used to determine if we read the first four or the last four digits of each group (odd number = first 4, even number = last 4), so we will use the last four. Finally, the last digit (9) is used to determine whether to go up or down the column from the starting point (odd means up, even means down); we go up. A serpentine pattern is used to continue through the table as indicated in Figure 6.1.

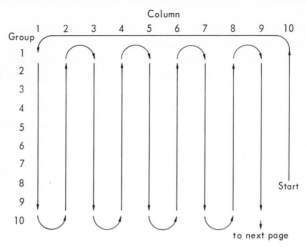

FIG. 6.1.   Example of a pattern for reading table of random digits.

This elaborate system is described to indicate that care must be taken to *insure* that the selection process is *truly random*.

One problem which arises in using the random digit table in selecting a sample occurs with very large or infinite populations. The problem is to assign a number to each element in the population. It is obviously impossible to number an infinite number of elements. We get around this problem by using a cluster or area sample. That is, the elements in the population are grouped in some way (by age, location, income, size, and so forth). Selection is then made among these groups. If these initial groups are too large, they can again be subdivided into smaller groups and selection made from these smaller groups. This process can be continued until, at the final selection, individual items are being selected. Thus, it is theoretically possible to number each individual elementary unit in the population.

Target Population and Sampling Frame

To insure a known probability of selection from a particular listing (or population) does not necessarily insure an *accurate* sample. We must be certain that the sample is drawn from the *target population*, the population whose characteristics are of interest to us. For example, even if the businessmen attending the luncheon meeting of the local Chamber of Commerce are truly a random sample of the membership of the Chamber of Commerce, they do not constitute an appropriate sample for our inventive businessman. The *target population* for our inventive businessman is all families with one or more children between the ages of six and eighteen years of age. The families represented by the members of the local Chamber of Commerce are not an adequate representation of that target population. The membership list of the Chamber of Commerce is not an adequate *sampling frame*. It does not adequately reflect the true extent and nature of the target population.

Consider again the problem of selecting a random sample from the population of 10,000 accounts receivable. In the real world it is extremely doubtful that we would find the accounts consecutively numbered from 0000 through 9999. Rather, the largest number would be likely to be well over 9999 (say 13,249, for example) and some numbers between 00000 and 13,249 would refer to accounts which had been closed. Thus our *sampling frame*, the list of account numbers, should have gaps in it.

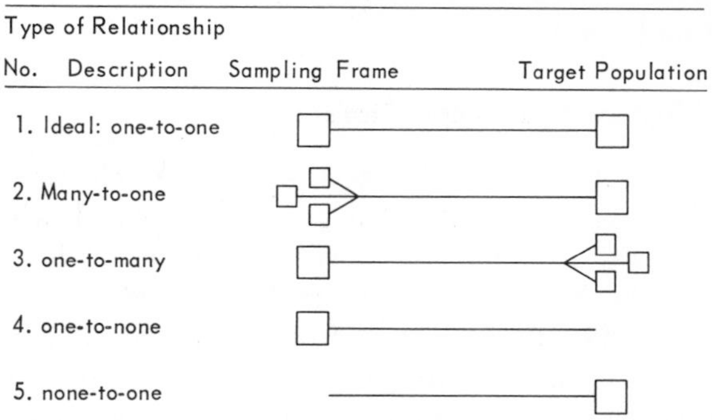

Type of Relationship

| No. | Description | Sampling Frame | Target Population |

1. Ideal: one-to-one
2. Many-to-one
3. one-to-many
4. one-to-none
5. none-to-one

FIG. 6.2.   Possible relationships between elementary units in sampling frame and target population (each represents an elementary unit).

Figure 6.2 illustrates some of the common problems we encounter in sample selection from common frames such as telephone books, membership lists, city directories, lists of students as representatives of families, voluntarily contributed opinions (such as letters to a Congressman), and so forth. It is easy to recognize such problems, but often difficult to deal with them adequately. For conditions 2 to 4, it is necessary to adopt rules of selection which modify the probabilities of selection from the sampling frame so that the probabilities of selection from the population remain equal for each elementary unit. For condition 5, it is often necessary to supplement the major sampling frame with a secondary frame.

Sample Statistic and Population Parameter

In most sampling situations our interest centers on obtaining accurate and precise estimates of one or more population values (*parameters*) on the basis of the values derived from the sample (*sample statistics*). We want to know the *population parameter* (the true population value) appropriately describing the characteristic we are interested in. But all we do know is the *statistic* (the estimated value) computed from the sample. Obviously the *sample statistic* will be an accurate and precise estimate of the *population parameter* only if the sample is a small replica of the population and the estimate is properly computed from the sample data. For instance, we would not usually use the sample median (central value in an ordered array of sample values) as an estimator of the arithmetic mean of the population. Rather, we would be more likely to use the arithmetic mean of the sample to estimate the arithmetic mean of the population. But we still are faced with the problem of evaluating the worth of a particular sample statistic as an estimator of a particular population parameter.

Sampling Distribution of a Sample Statistic

If probability selection is used as the basis of selecting values (x_i's) for the sample, it is obvious that the exact value which will be obtained on any particular draw is uncertain. We are dealing with a random variable. If the sample observations, x_i's, are determined by a chance process, then any sample statistic computed from those values is also the result of the operation of a random variable. Thus, suppose we randomly select a sample of students from the population of students currently attending State U. and compute an arithmetic average (mean) age from that sample. Assume we then select a second sample by the same random selection process. The samples are of the same size and they are both randomly selected. Will they contain the same x_i's (the same set of individual ages)? Probably not. If we do not get exactly the same sample, we shall probably get a different sample mean (average age). Thus, if we repeat a probability sampling operation many times and compute the same *statistic* from each sample, we should obtain a distribution of values for that sample statistic. The relative frequency with which the possible alternative values of the statistic appear is determined by the probabilities of selection for each of the individual values, X_i's, in the population.

6.00 The probability distribution which describes the probability of the occurrence of each of the possible alternative values of a sample statistic in repeated samplings from a given population is called the *sampling distribution* of that sample statistic.

For example, it should now be obvious that the binomial probability distribution of "successes" in samples of n items drawn from a Bernoulli process where the probability of a "success" is equal to P is a *sampling distribution* for x_i in samples of size n. Specifically, consider the sampling distribution of the number of "successes" in random drawings of ten items each taken from a population with 0.5 "successes." This is given in Table 6.2. [(x_i = number of successes in the sample = np.) (Note that P denotes the population proportion of successes, the population parameter; p denotes the proportion of successes in the sample = x/n, where x = the number of successes in the sample and n is sample size.)]

It is easy to see that the sampling distribution for x will change if n or P changes. Note also that we have assumed random selection. It is true that the sampling distribution would change if the method of sampling were changed. In the case of a Bernoulli process, if the sampling is nonrandom, the probability of selecting a success on any draw will not be equal to P but will be a conditional probability value formed by a combination of P and the probability of selection for each type of item.

TABLE 6.2

SAMPLING DISTRIBUTION OF THE NUMBER OF SUCCESSES IN TEN RANDOM DRAWS FROM A BERNOULLI PROCESS WHERE $P = 0.5$

Number of Successes in Ten Draws X_i	Probability of Occurrence $P(x_i)$
0	0.0010
1	0.0098
2	0.0439
3	0.1172
4	0.2051
5	0.2461
6	0.2051
7	0.1172
8	0.0439
9	0.0098
10	0.0010
Total	1.0001†

† Difference from 1.0000 is due to rounding.

At this time it is not possible to list each and every sample statistic and its probability distribution and demonstrate that each of those sampling distributions will also change with any change in the sample size, the sampling method, or the population sampled. It is well known, however, that statistical sampling distributions depend upon these factors. To summarize:

6.01 Every sample statistic has a sampling distribution whose characteristics are determined by:
(1) the sample statistic considered
(2) the size of the sample
(3) the method of sampling
(4) the population sampled

The truth of the above statement will be illustrated as the specific sampling distribution for each specific sample statistic is considered in Chapter 8 (and subsequent chapters where appropriate).

Standard Error of a Sample Statistic

We have stated that every sample statistic is a random variable and thus has a probability distribution (sampling distribution). It is also true then that each sampling distribution has an *expected value*, a *variance*, and a *standard deviation*. The variance and standard deviation of the sampling distribution are recognized as measures of the *sampling error* in the statistic. They are due solely to the chance variation in the sample statistic which arises from the chance process of selecting values (x_i's) into the sample. We give the standard deviation of the sampling distribution a special name to signify this fact.

6.02 The standard deviation of the sampling distribution of a sample statistic is called the *standard error* of that sample statistic.

Interval Estimates For Sample Statistics

The standard error of a sample statistic is very important as a measure of our uncertainty in using the sample statistic as an estimate of the corresponding population parameter. We learned in Chapter 5 that the probability distribution of any random variable can be used in setting intervals around the expected value of that variable within which there are stated probabilities of finding values in that distribution. Thus suppose we know that a sample statistic computed from repeated samples of size n, drawn from the same population by the same method of sampling will follow a normal distribution. (The sampling distribution of that statistic is the normal probability distribution.) If the expected value of the sample statistic is equal to the population parameter, then it is also true that

$$P[(PP - 1\sigma_{ss}) \leq ss \leq (PP + 1\sigma_{ss})] = 0.6827$$

where

PP is "population parameter"
ss is "sample statistic"
σ_{ss} is "standard error of the sample statistic"

That is, 68 percent of the sample statistics which form this normal distribution are within the range of one standard error from the expected value of the sample statistic. If the expected value of the sample statistic is actually equal to the population parameter, then there is a 0.68 probability that if one specific value of the sample statistic is randomly selected from the sampling distribution, the population parameter will be included within the range of one standard error from that one specific, observed sample statistic. That is:

6.10   Given:
   (1) a sample statistic whose sampling distribution is the normal probability distribution
   (2) the standard error of that sample statistic (the standard deviation of the sampling distribution)
   (3) a specific value of the sample statistic randomly selected from that sampling distribution
   Then

$$P[(ss - 1\sigma_{ss}) \leq PP \leq (ss - 1\sigma_{ss})] = 0.6827$$

The reader should take a moment to review 6.00 and 6.01 (sampling distribution) and 6.02 (standard error of a sample statistic) while considering 6.10.

Obviously, if the sampling distribution is something other than a normal distribution, 6.10 will not be true. It would be possible, however, to construct a probability statement of the same type by reference to the appropriate probability distribution to obtain the probability value. For the hypergeometric distribution only Chebyshev's inequality (5.51) would be used after the standard error had been computed.

The reader should note one particular property of 6.10. Note that what we have defined is a *process* for obtaining estimates. To that process we attach a probability statement. We cannot, however, attach that same probability to a specific interval derived by that process. It is analogous to shaking a "fair" die within a closed box and, after the die has come to rest, deciding upon whether or not the die has "come up 6" (has six pips on the upper face). Until the box is opened, we do not know the answer. It is obvious, however, that either the die has come up 6 or it has not; the outcome is fixed, but unknown. If pressed, we would say we were "one sixth certain" that the result was a 6. We are talking about only *one already determined outcome* out of an infinite number of trials, however, and probability does not apply. We can only state our *confidence* in our statement based upon the single specific outcome.

The reader should also note that 6.10 holds true only if the expected value of the sample statistic is equal to the population parameter. We should turn our attention to the evaluation of estimation methods to learn more about such desirable properties of estimation techniques.

DESIRABLE PROPERTIES OF STATISTICAL ESTIMATORS

It has now been established that each sample statistic when computed from a probability sample can be considered a random variable with its own probability distribution (*sampling distribution*) which is dependent upon the size of the sample, the method of sampling, the population being sampled, and, of course, the particular sample statistic being considered. When a sample statistic is used as an estimate of some population parameter, we have found that its worth is evaluated by reference to the applicable sampling distribution. It should be clear, however, that little can be said about the specific value of the sample statistic which is developed. The worth or closeness of an *estimate* (value) can be measured only because the random variable (process) which creates that estimate has known characteristics. This random variable is called the *estimator* and it would be nice if this *estimator* were known to possess certain desirable properties. There are four such properties which have been recognized as desirable by mathematicians and statisticians. They are *efficiency, unbiasedness, consistency,* and *sufficiency.*

6.20 *Efficiency* is a relative property. One estimator is said to be more efficient than a second estimator if, for a given sample size, the variance of the sampling distribution of the statistic is smaller than the variance of the sampling distribution of the statistic developed by the application of the second estimator.

Obviously, we would prefer to estimate with a process that provides estimates which deviate from the population parameter by small amounts.

6.21 An estimator is said to be *unbiased* if the expected value of the statistic produced is equal to the value of the parameter being estimated. That is, if

$$E(ss) = PP$$

where

> ss stands for sample statistic
> PP stands for population parameter

Unbiasedness has intuitive appeal as a property of an estimator since it indicates that if the process were repeated many times, the average of the estimates obtained would be very, very close to the true population parameter.

While unbiasedness is certainly a desirable property for any estimator to possess, it is not enough simply to know that the estimates are right on the average. This tells us nothing about how close those estimates are to the true value of the parameter. It seems obviously desirable that as sample size increases the estimates should approach more closely to the true population value.

6.22 An estimator is said to be *consistent* if the probability that the estimate derived will differ from the true population parameter by more than any constant amount approaches zero as n approaches N. That is,

$$P(|ss - PP| \geq c) \to 0 \qquad \text{as} \qquad n \to N$$

where

> c is any arbitrary constant
> n is sample size
> N is population size (which may be equal to infinity)

If an estimator is consistent, we are assured that for sufficiently large sample sizes the estimates provided will be very close to the population value being estimated.

Sufficiency is a difficult mathematical concept to explain and we will be satisfied with merely stating its general meaning.

6.23   An estimator is said to be *sufficient* if it uses all the information relevant to the estimation of the parameter of interest that is contained in the sample.

Obviously this means that if we compute an estimate with a sufficient estimator, the sample values cannot provide any further information about the parameter being estimated.

It should be emphasized that the properties discussed above apply only to *estimators* and do not transfer to any specific *estimate* (value) which may be computed using these estimators. That is, they do not really tell how good (or bad) the specific value is, but only give us the assurance that if the estimate is derived from the operation of an estimator possessing these characteristics, it is likely to be better than an estimate derived with some other estimator which does not possess these properties. For example, while we do not know that the mean of a specific random sample, $\bar{x} = \Sigma x_i/n$, will be equal to the population mean, μ, it is reassuring to know that $E(\bar{x}) = \mu$, that there is no more efficient estimator of μ, that if n is sufficiently large, $\bar{x}$ is very close to μ and, finally, that $\bar{x}$ is also a sufficient estimator for μ. Much more will be said about $\bar{x}$ and μ in Chapter 8.

We can now provide a definition of an estimator.

6.24   An *estimator* is the rule by which a value is attached to the outcome of a chance experiment, that is, the *estimator* is the random variable and the estimate is only a value of the random variable. A sample statistic is such a random variable.

The properties we have identified attach only to the estimator (sample statistic) and not to each value created by its application.

It should also be emphasized that the presence of one of these properties in an estimator does not indicate the presence of any other. Thus, an estimator may be efficient but biased. It also may be consistent although biased. Conversely, it may be unbiased, but not consistent nor efficient. Happily, estimators classed as *most* efficient are also *sufficient*.

There are obviously times when one might prefer an estimation procedure which does not possess one or more of the above characteristics. As an example of a biased estimator that might be preferred to an unbiased estimator, think of the problem of estimating the average height of male college students. If funds were so limited that only small samples of students could be contacted and measured for height, a superior estimate might be gotten by interviewing the campus physician. It is probable that the doctor's estimation procedure would be biased, but it is also likely that his estimate would be closer to the true average than would the average of a single small sample. It is also true that the doctor's estimation process would not possess the property of consistency.

SUMMARY

Estimates of population values (*population parameters*) can be either *point estimates* (just one value) or *interval estimates* (a range of values). The best interval estimates have attached to them a statement indicating how confident we are that the stated interval actually includes the true value being estimated.

Estimates are necessary when only partial information (a sample) is available or if future values must be based on a historical record. The worth of future estimates derived from a historical record must be determined by use of qualitative analysis of historical-future relationships and are not considered here. The worth of estimates computed from sample data is judged by reference to the way in which the sample is selected and to the *estimator* (estimation process or sample statistic) used. Statisticians use *probability selection* in an attempt to obtain a small replica of the population (an *accurate* sample). Sample size is varied to obtain *sample statistics* (sample values) which are sufficiently close to the *population parameters* (true population values) being estimated (sufficiently *precise*). Care must be taken when sampling to be sure that the *sampling frame* (the representation of the population from which selection is made) is adequate to obtain a probability sample of the *target population*.

Estimators are to be preferred if they are more *efficient* than other estimators (6.20), *unbiased* (6.21), *consistent* (6.22), and *sufficient* (6.23).

Sample statistics computed from repeated probability samples (samples for which the probability of selecting each elementary unit of the population is known) of the same type and the same size from a given population distribute themselves in a predictable way. The probability distributions used to describe these distributions of sample statistics are called *sampling distributions*. The standard deviation of a sampling distribution is called the *standard error* of that sample statistic. The standard error is a measure of *sampling error*, the variability introduced into the estimation process by the use of probability sampling. The sample statistic, the sampling distribution, and the standard error can be used to obtain interval estimates of the population parameter in which we can have a specific degree of *confidence* that the interval actually includes the population parameter.

DISCUSSION QUESTIONS

1. Define the following in *your own* words (*no formulas* in symbols or words).

   (a) an estimate
   (b) a point estimate
   (c) an interval estimate
   (d) accuracy
   (e) precision
   (f) population (two meanings)
   (g) elementary unit
   (h) population parameter
   (i) sample statistic
   (j) probability sample
   (k) random selection

   (l) random digit
   (m) sampling frame
   (n) sampling distribution
   (o) standard error of a sample statistic
   (p) efficiency
   (q) unbiasedness
   (r) consistency
   (s) an estimator
   (t) sampling error
   (u) confidence

2. Is it possible to get a biased *estimate* from an unbiased *estimator?*
   Hint: Consider the nature of the property of unbiasedness (4.31).

3. An estimate derived by an unbiased procedure may or may not be closer to the true population value than an estimate derived by a biased procedure. Discuss fully.
   Hint: At least three points are involved.
   (1) Unbiasedness is a property of estimators, not estimates.
   (2) Efficiency must be considered.
   (3) Whether or not the estimation process creates a random variable must be considered.

4. Distinguish between the concepts of efficiency, precision, and consistency.
   Hint: Ask yourself two questions:
   (1) What is the meaning of each term?
   (2) How is each affected by changes in sample size?

5. How is accuracy related to the properties of unbiasedness and consistency?
   Hint: See hint for question 4.

6. A survey is to be made to determine why people ride trains instead of using some other form of transportation. For this survey, identify the following.
   (a) the physical population
   (b) the elementary unit
   (c) the characteristic of interest
   (d) the statistical population

7. For the survey indicated in question 6, personal interviews are to be used. Several alternative methods of selecting a sample have been suggested. For each suggested technique indicate whether the method

will provide a random sample of the appropriate population. Clearly indicate any deficiencies you recognize in each selection technique.

(a) Go to a local railway station in New York City and interview every fifth person you are able to find in the passenger waiting room until a sufficiently large sample is obtained.

(b) Station a group of interviewers at the windows where passenger tickets are sold and interview every fifth person purchasing a ticket until a sufficiently large sample is obtained.

(c) Pay the railroad company to obtain the names and home addresses of every fifth person purchasing a ticket on that railroad during the next ten days. Interview them at their homes later.

(d) Obtain the cooperation of several major and minor railway lines providing passenger service to obtain the names of every twentieth person purchasing a ticket during the period from August 1 to November 30.

(e) Randomly select several major and minor rail lines, several weeks over a year and several regularly scheduled passenger runs on each line, being sure to obtain adequate representation of the several kinds of passenger service provided by the railroads. Place interviewers on the trains and after a random start among the first twenty passengers entering the train, interview every subsequent twentieth passenger entering the train.

Hint: Consider carefully your answers to question 6 and the definition of random selection as you examine each alternative.

8. A simple random sample was taken of the city subscribers of the Bigtown News to determine how many of them read a certain advertisement. Explain for this case the terms "precision" and "accuracy" of the sampling result, utilizing the statistical terms introduced in this chapter, particularly the concepts of "frame," "estimator," "bias," and "sampling error."

DISCUSSION PROBLEMS

Show your method on all solutions.

1. Take ten pennies (or dimes), preferably new ones; toss the ten coins thirty times, recording the number of heads that result after each toss.

(a) Construct a relative frequency distribution of the results.

(b) Is this an example of random sampling? Explain carefully.

(c) Refer to Chapter 5 and apply 5.22 to obtain the theoretical frequency distribution for tosses of 10 "fair" coins.

(d) What name is given to the distribution obtained in (c) in statistical sampling theory?

(e) Compare your results for (a) and (c).

(f) What do you conclude about the "fairness" of the coins you used? Explain fully.

Hint: Note that $n = 10$, not 30.

Note: These results will be used again at the end of Chapter 9.

2. Combine the results obtained in Problem 1(a) by some other student with your own results so that you obtain a frequency distribution for 60 tosses of ten coins each.

(a) Compare this enlarged sample with the theoretical distribution computed in Problem 1(c).

(b) Compare the results you and your friend obtained with those obtained by other pairs of students. What is the general conclusion?

(c) Can you relate the conclusions reached in (b) with any of the properties of estimators discussed in this chapter?

Hint: Consider especially those properties which are influenced by sample size.

3. Suppose the new product developed by the businessman of Chapter 1 is a new type of bicycle.

(a) How would you suggest he go about obtaining an estimate of possible sales per year? Suggest two methods, one of which depends on sampling of potential final consumers (purchasers of bicycles for individual use) and one which does not. Explain each carefully but as briefly as possible.

(b) Which of the two methods you outlined in (a) would you expect to provide the *"technically better"* answer? Carefully define the sense(s) in which you interpret the phrase "technically better."

(c) Which of the two methods would you recommend that the businessman actually use? Explain fully.

(d) There are obviously several methods of obtaining this estimate that you have not included in (a). *List* at least three such methods and give for each the *primary* reason you did *not* include that method as one of the two suggested.

(e) Compare your answers for (a–d) to those of other students. Is there any general agreement on appropriate methods?

Hint: There can be no absolutely correct *answers* for this problem, only correct *applications of principles.*

4. A random sample of the residents of Bigtown is desired to obtain their reaction to: "The city government should finance a sports stadium to attract major league sports to Bigtown." It has been

decided to send a questionnaire to every twentieth name in the telephone directory for Bigtown.
(a) Is the telephone directory an adequate frame?
Hint: Refer to Figure 6.2 and related discussion.
(b) Can you suggest a superior sampling frame and sampling method?
Include in your recommendation a clear definition of the appropriate "target population."

EXERCISES

Show your method on all solutions.

1. (a) Use Table B-9 to draw a simple random sample of 10 numbers
from the following matrix containing 150 values. Explain clearly
how the selection was made.
  (b) Compute the mean ($\bar{x}$) for the values drawn.
  (c) Contact five other students in the class and obtain the value
each has computed for the mean (before coming to class). Students should be allowed to compare the results to both (b) and
(c) for all students in class.

17	22	19	20	18	11	16	23	19	15
14	17	21	16	10	24	10	16	21	20
19	11	14	17	22	16	17	14	14	18
22	15	17	10	16	12	14	19	17	12
16	23	15	20	21	22	15	11	15	16
21	14	13	19	16	18	20	20	13	17
15	9	19	18	18	9	18	16	19	13
12	13	18	20	14	19	14	15	18	20
21	16	15	23	19	18	15	16	15	19
11	15	21	12	13	17	17	17	21	14
15	21	10	14	15	13	12	18	15	18
10	20	16	17	17	16	19	14	23	13
15	23	14	16	24	14	18	17	17	24
18	16	17	18	19	12	11	15	19	12
16	13	22	23	15	16	12	16	11	17

2. Outline the method you would use to obtain a random sample of
100 students from:
  (a) the 23,000 undergraduates currently enrolled at State U.
  (b) the 4200 juniors enrolled at State U.
  (c) the approximately 50,000 high school students currently enrolled
at the eleven high schools in Bigtown.

3. Suppose you were asked to determine the preference of eligible voters in Bigtown (population 563,000) for allowing retail groceries to stay open on Sunday.
   (a) What is the physical population?
   (b) What is the statistical population?
   (c) Is the characteristic of interest a discrete variable (attribute) or a continuous variable?
   (d) Suggest an appropriate sampling frame.

4. Contrast random errors with nonrandom errors in sampling in regard to:
   (a) the identification of the error
   (b) the source of the error
   (c) the importance of the error
   (d) the control of the error
   (e) the elimination of the error

5. (a) Can sampling ever be free from bias? Explain fully.
   (b) How can bias in sampling be reduced?
   (c) Is bias measurable? If so, how, when?
   (d) Is bias influenced by changes in sample size?
   (e) Can precision be improved by a reduction in bias?

6. We often hear comments such as:
   "An overwhelming majority of informed persons I have come into contact with have indicated that they are in agreement with my candidate's views on this issue. Obviously, my candidate has the correct position."
   (a) Has the speaker drawn a reasonable conclusion from the sample data available to him?
   (b) Is the sampling frame used by this speaker appropriate to the conclusion drawn?

7. In a study of characteristics of their graduates, State U. mailed questionnaires to every tenth name (after a random start) on the membership list of the Alumni Association and to every tenth name on the list of graduates whose addresses were known, but who were not members of the Alumni Association. Almost 2000 usable replies were received. Do these returns constitute a random sample of the alumni of State U.? Explain carefully.

8. Mr. Prober, an accountant, is auditing the books of a grocery wholesaler. He wishes to confirm the balances of the accounts receivable shown on the wholesalers books. The accounts are numbered and arranged alphabetically.
   (a) If Mr. Prober examines only a sample of the accounts, can he determine what proportion of all accounts receivable are in error? Explain fully.

(b) Mr. Prober is considering several methods of selecting his sample. Indicate which of the following would provide a random sample:

(1) Select all accounts over $10,000 plus the accounts for customers whose names begin with G (the letter G was randomly selected).

(2) It is known that there are about 3500 accounts and that the account numbers run from 1098 to 7263. All accounts with numbers between 3000 and 3500 will be selected.

(3) Select all accounts for which there were entries during the week beginning May 11. (A list happens to be available).

9. The Koloredi Company assembles about 165 television sets each working day. Every set is inspected as a check on the quality of the assembly process. Are the 165 sets a sample? Explain.

10. Suppose we are interested in measuring the per family income of people living in Bigtown.

(a) What is the statistical population?

(b) What terms in the statement of the problem would have to be defined in developing a sampling frame? Be exhaustive.

11. The following estimates provide information about the life time (in hours) of TV picture tubes produced by the Big-I Tube Company.

(1) The lifetimes of Big-I tubes have been found to be normally distributed and fall between 775 and 1525 hours (except for a few extreme cases).

(2) The lifetimes of Big-I tubes have been found to be normally distributed and fall between 900 and 1400 hours approximately 95 percent of the time.

(3) The lifetimes of Big-I tubes have been found to be normally distributed with a mean of 1150 hours and a standard deviation of 125 hours.

(4) The lifetimes of Big-I tubes are normally distributed and fall between 1025 and 1275 hours 68 percent of the time.

(a) Which of the above estimates would be most meaningful to a statistician?

(b) Is any one of the above estimates superior to all the others in the amount of information provided? Explain.

(c) Is any one of the above estimates inferior to the others in the amount of information provided? Explain.

(d) Is there any difference in the informational content of estimates (2) and (3)?

12. It is commonly believed that the larger the sample the better the information supplied about the population. Is this true? Explain fully.

13. What is the difference between a standard deviation and a standard error?

14. The president of the Goodbuy chain of grocery supermarkets wishes to determine the number of stores he should establish in the Bigtown Metropolitan Area. He asks you to conduct the study; you decide upon a sample survey of food expenditure patterns in the area.

    (a) What is the population? Indicate the nature of any definitions which would be necessary in defining this population.

    (b) What is the appropriate elementary unit? Circle your choice.

        a. individuals   b. expenditures   c. dwelling units

        d. families   e. households   f. other (specify)

    (c) Suggest an appropriate frame; indicate its advantages and limitations in this study.

    (d) Define the characteristic(s) of interest for each elementary unit.

    (e) Would the characteristic(s) of interest be classed as a discrete or continuous variable(s)? Explain.

    (f) Is this population finite or infinite?

    (g) Discuss the decision problem faced by the chain store executive. What are the alternative courses of action? What are the decision parameters?

7
conditional expectation and the cost of uncertainty

CONDITIONAL OUTCOMES

States of the World

In Chapter 1 we learned that one basic step in the decision making process is to "determine and compare the possible outcomes and the probability of success in reaching the objective for the alternative courses of action." This means that for each possible alternative act (course of action or strategy), we must evaluate the effect on the objective of each possible outcome. The result of a specific act is usually uncertain. It depends upon a basic event or *state of the world*. Thus, the manager of Neet-Lawn Service may choose to plan for nine crews each day on the basis of information given in Table 6.1, but the number of crews required each day will be exactly equal to nine only about one fourth of the time. The demand which is actually realized is a *state of the world* which is beyond the direct control of the manager.

Conditional Outcomes

The *outcome* (result of) following a particular plan is usually stated in terms pertinent to the planner's objective. For Neet-Lawn Service the objective of using the crews is to realize a return over and above their total cost. Thus a pertinent way to measure outcomes is in terms of the

199

net dollar returns. It may be more profitable to plan for *more* than nine crews or *less* than nine crews, as a *general* rule.

To answer this question, we first must construct a *payoff table*. For each possible outcome (*state of the world* or *nature*) which might exist, we must determine what would be the payoff for each of the available *acts* (alternative strategies). Each row in the table will tell us the *exact* result of choosing each alternative act (strategy) if, in fact, the "state of the world" indicated for that row (in the table stub) actually were to occur. Note that this is an assumption and is not influenced by the fact that the "state of the world" which actually exists is unknown and variable and thus cannot be predicted with certainty. Thus, we know that the number of crews demanded varies between five and twelve. If we assume that five crews will be used and five are actually made available, what is the result? Similarly, what is the net return if five crews are needed, but six are provided? In each case, it is necessary to list every item of cash or equivalent which will flow into the firm and every item of cash or equivalent which will flow out of the firm.

To illustrate, let us assume that the Neet-Lawn Service Company is faced with a simplified income-cost structure of the following nature. A crew and its equipment cost $72.00 per day, put in an average of five productive hours at $18.00 per hour and return $90.00 total and $18.00 net return. In order to realize this return, crews must be notified on the previous evening. A crew called up and not used costs $20 in standby labor and related charges. A crew ordered on the day used, loses part of the day and can be expected to do no more than break even for the day (a $0 return). These values form the basis for the calculations giving the values in Table 7.1.

Let us see how the values in the first row of Table 7.1 actually were computed. It is assumed in calculating this row that the realized demand will be for five crews regardless of how many crews the manager may decide to call in. (Note that we can ignore the manager's problem of meeting demand by calling in crews the day that they are ordered since this results in a net return of $0. In order to make a profit on a crew, the manager must "order" the crew the afternoon of the day before the day it is used.) When the demand is five, if the manager orders exactly five crews, he will realize a gross return of $450, a gross cost of $360, and a *net* return of $90. If the manager orders six crews and only five are needed, he *nets* only $70, and so forth. Now consider a column, say the fifth column (call nine crews each day). It is assumed that the manager has decided to call the nine crews every day and take his chances on this average demand being realized. If demand is for only five crews, he will gross $450 from the five crews, pay out $80 to the four crews called up

TABLE 7.1

NEET-LAWN PROBLEM, CONDITIONAL NET RETURNS (CREW USED,
RETURNS $18; CREW NOT USED, COSTS $20)

Level of Demand = "State of Nature"	Conditional Return by Act (Act = No. of Crews Called)							
	5	6	7	8	9	10	11	12
5	$90	$ 70	$ 50	$ 30	$ 10	$ −10	$ −30	$ −50
6	90	108	88	68	48	28	8	−12
7	90	108	126	106	86	66	46	26
8	90	108	126	144	124	104	84	64
9	90	108	126	144	162	142	122	102
10	90	108	126	144	162	180	160	140
11	90	108	126	144	162	180	198	178
12	90	108	126	144	162	180	198	216

but not used, pay out $360 to the five crews used, and thus realize a net return of $450 − $80 − $360 = $10. If realized demand is for six crews, the net return is increased to $48 ($10 + $18 net return on the additional crew used + $20 not paid as standby wages, or $10 + $38). When the number of crews demanded exceeds nine, the return remains at $162 since, if additional crews are called to cover the larger demands as they are realized, no net return will accrue. If additional crews are *not* called, no additional revenue can possibly be created.

The values in Table 7.1 are called *conditional* returns, because they are computed on the condition that the demand shown in the stub and the act (number of crews "ordered") both take place. Thus, they are outcomes for compound events such as the return from calling ("ordering") six crews and experiencing a demand for only five crews (the $70 in row 1, column 2).

UNCONDITIONAL OUTCOMES

Expected Gain

We have already stated that the level of demand is uncertain and can be predicted only in probability terms. Each row in Table 7.1 shows what the net return for each of the available acts will be if the indicated "state of the world" is actually the one realized. But we know the relative frequency with which each level of demand has been realized in the past. Under the assumption that basic conditions will not change in the future, we can use these historical data as probabilities and compute the expected or *unconditional* net return for each of the alternative acts. This has been done in Table 7.2.

The figures in the body of Table 7.2 were derived by weighting the conditional net returns of Table 7.1 by the probabilities shown in the first column of Table 7.2. Thus, for the first row, each value in the first row of Table 7.1 (the conditional net returns from each act given that the level of demand was for five crews) is multiplied by 0.02 (the probability that exactly five crews will be demanded). The remaining rows are similarly computed.

The total at the bottom of each column is the *expected* net return (*expected gain*) of the "act" shown at the top of the column. Thus the expected gain for the act, call up five crews, is $90.00. This is obviously a correct expected value since we know that at least five crews are needed each day. Therefore, the five crews called will *always* be used and no crew will have to be paid on standby wages. The net return from calling up and using five crews is $90 (see Table 7.1), so our answer is correct.

The unconditional net return from choosing to call up more than five crews varies with the number of crews called. Since there is always at least a small chance that a called crew will not be used, the unconditional net return for each of these acts is less than the conditional return associated with calling that number of crews and using them all. Table 7.2 indicates that calling nine crews is the best strategy. This alternative can be expected to return (on the average) at least $4.32 more than any other if used as a continuing policy.

Expected Opportunity Losses

Another manner of choosing among alternative acts (strategies) is to choose that act which provides the least chance for improving the decision. For example, if the actual demand is for five crews, to use any alternative other than calling five crews returns less than the alternative of calling five crews. Similarly, the conditional return from calling six crews given a demand for six crews is greater than the conditional return from any other alternative act given the same state of the world (level of demand). To choose any alternative but the best for any given state of the world results in a loss. This loss is called *opportunity loss*. The conditional opportunity losses for the Neet-Lawn problem are shown in Table 7.3.

To be sure that we understand the concept of opportunity loss, let us look at the first row of Table 7.3. Refer to Table 7.1 and see that the

TABLE 7.2

NEET-LAWN PROBLEM, UNCONDITIONAL NET RETURNS

Level of Demand	Probability of Demand $P(D_i)$	Unconditional Net Return by Act (No. of Crews Called)							
		5	6	7	8	9	10	11	12
5	0.02	$ 1.80	$ 1.40	$ 1.00	$ 0.60	$ 0.20	$-0.20	$-0.60	$-1.00
6	0.05	4.50	5.40	4.40	3.40	2.40	1.40	0.40	-0.60
7	0.12	10.80	12.96	15.12	12.72	10.32	7.92	5.52	3.12
8	0.17	15.30	18.36	21.42	24.48	21.08	17.68	14.28	10.88
9	0.26	23.40	28.08	32.76	37.44	42.12	36.92	31.72	26.52
10	0.18	16.20	19.44	22.68	25.92	29.16	32.40	28.80	25.20
11	0.15	13.50	16.20	18.90	21.60	24.30	27.00	29.70	26.70
12	0.05	4.50	5.40	6.30	7.20	8.10	9.00	9.90	10.80
Totals†		$90.00	$107.24	$122.58	$133.36	$137.68	$132.12	$119.72	$101.62

† Unconditional expected returns for each act.

highest conditional return for this row is in the first column, call five crews. If six crews are called the net return is only $70, $20 less than the $90 net return obtained from calling five crews. Similarly, the reduction from the maximum possible net return for this state of the world when seven crews are called is $40, and so forth. In the first column of Table 7.3, the opportunity loss of $36 opposite the level of demand of seven crews is derived

TABLE 7.3

NEET-LAWN PROBLEM, CONDITIONAL OPPORTUNITY LOSS

| Level of Demand "State of Nature" | Conditional Opportunity Losses by Act (*Alternative Acts = No. of Crews Called*) | | | | | | |
	5	6	7	8	9	10	11	12
5	$ 0	$ 20	$40	$60	$80	$100	$120	$140
6	18	0	20	40	60	80	100	120
7	36	18	0	20	40	60	80	100
8	54	36	18	0	20	40	60	80
9	72	54	36	18	0	20	40	60
10	90	72	54	36	18	0	20	40
11	108	90	72	54	36	18	0	20
12	126	108	90	72	54	36	18	0

as the difference between the net return from calling only five crews when seven are demanded ($90) and the net return from calling seven crews when seven are demanded ($126).

The expected opportunity loss of each alternative act can be computed in the same way that expected net returns (*unconditional net returns*) were computed. The values are shown in Table 7.4. The conditional opportunity losses in each row of Table 7.3 have been weighted by the probabilities of that level of demand being realized from the first column of Table 7.2.

The definition of opportunity loss makes it obvious that the act with the lowest expected opportunity loss would be the act providing the largest expected net return. This is certainly true in the Neet-Lawn problem. The act, order nine crews, which provided the largest unconditional net return also incurs the lowest unconditional opportunity loss. Note also that the difference between the expected net returns of any two acts is equal in magnitude but opposite in sign to the difference between their expected opportunity losses. The expected

TABLE 7.4

NEET-LAWN PROBLEM, UNCONDITIONAL OPPORTUNITY LOSS

Level of Demand	Unconditional Opportunity Loss by Act							
	5	6	7	8	9	10	11	12
5	$ 0	$ 0.40	$ 0.80	$ 1.20	$ 1.60	$ 2.00	$ 2.40	$ 2.80
6	0.90	0	1.00	2.00	3.00	4.00	5.00	6.00
7	4.32	2.16	0	2.40	4.80	7.20	9.60	12.00
8	9.18	6.12	3.06	0	3.40	6.80	10.20	13.60
9	18.72	14.04	9.36	4.68	0	5.20	10.40	15.60
10	16.20	12.96	9.72	6.48	3.24	0	3.60	7.20
11	16.20	13.50	10.80	8.10	5.40	2.70	0	3.00
12	6.30	5.40	4.50	3.60	2.70	1.80	0.90	0
Totals†	$71.82	$54.58	$39.24	$28.46	$24.14	$29.70	$42.10	$60.20

† Expected opportunity cost for each act.

net returns and expected opportunity losses of the alternative acts are presented in Table 7.5. The reader should satisfy himself that the statements made in the preceding paragraphs are true.

Table 7.5 clearly indicates that to call for nine crews is the best single strategy for the manager of Neet Lawn to follow. However, it also indicates that even this strategy is subject to opportunity loss. If the manager were clairvoyant and thus could call for the exact number of crews

TABLE 7.5

NEET-LAWN PROBLEM, EXPECTED NET RETURNS AND OPPORTUNITY COSTS

Number of Crews Called	Expected Net Return	Expected Opportunity Loss
5	$ 90.00	$71.82
6	107.24	54.58
7	122.58	39.24
8	133.36	28.46
9	137.68	24.14
10	132.12	29.70
11	119.72	42.10
12	101.62	60.20

needed each day and the relative frequencies of occurrence of each level of demand remain as given in Table 7.2, he could realize, on the average, an additional $24.14 per day. This is clearly shown in Table 7.6. This

TABLE 7.6

NEET-LAWN PROBLEM, ALTERNATIVE COMPUTATION OF COST OF UNCERTAINTY

Number of Crews Demanded D_i	Probability of Demand $P(D_i)$	Conditional Return of Perfect Act Call D_i Crews	Unconditional Expected Return of Perfect Act Call D_i Crews
5	0.02	$ 90	$ 1.80
6	0.05	108	5.40
7	0.12	126	15.12
8	0.17	144	24.48
9	0.26	162	42.12
10	0.18	180	32.40
11	0.15	198	29.70
12	0.05	216	10.80
			$161.82

cost of uncertainty = expected net return (perfect acts) less expected
net return (best act under certainty)
= $161.82 − $137.68 = **$24.14**

$24.14 represents what the uncertainty in his knowledge costs him, it is the *cost of uncertainty*. It is the difference between the expected net return from the *best* decision he can make and the net return he could expect to realize with perfect information (certainty as to what the state of nature will be each day). If he could reduce his uncertainty to zero for less than $24.14 per day, it would pay him to do so. In that case (no uncertainty), his net return would be $24.14 more than it is with the act, "order nine crews every day." As a general rule, if there is uncertainty involved in a decision process, it will always pay the decision maker to invest in additional information so long as the return from the resulting reduction in uncertainty exceeds the cost of obtaining the additional information.

DIAGRAMMING EXPECTATIONS

Mr. Lesser is considering purchasing $5000 worth of either of two common stocks. He is having trouble making up his mind. If he buys

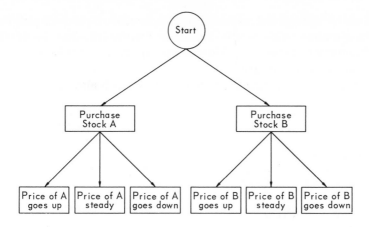

FIG. 7.1.   Tree diagram for purchase of two stocks.

Stock A, its price may go up, stay unchanged, or go down; similarly, the price of Stock B also may go up, stay unchanged, or go down. Figure 7.1 presents a *tree diagram* for this decisions situation.

Suppose Lesser decides to toss an "honest" coin to make the decision. Suppose further that a panel of expert stock market analysts provide the information given in Table 7.7. If Mr. Lesser accepts the opinion

TABLE 7.7

EXPECTED PERFORMANCE OF STOCK A AND STOCK B OVER NEXT SIX
MONTHS (CONSENSUS OF PANEL OF EXPERTS)

Possible Change in Stock Price		Probability of Change in Stock Price	
Percent	Dollar Amount†	Stock A	Stock B
+20	+1000	0.05	0.05
+15	+ 750	0.10	0.15
+10	+ 500	0.30	0.15
+ 5	+ 250	0.20	0.05
0	0	0	0
− 5	− 250	0.05	0.10
−10	− 500	0.10	0.20
−15	− 750	0.15	0.20
−20	−1000	0.05	0.10
		1.00	1.00

† Assumes an investment of exactly $5000.00.

consensus of the market experts, he has expanded (and simplified) his decision problem. This is illustrated in Figure 7.2. The probabilities provided by Mr. Lesser's decision to toss a coin and those provided by the market experts are also entered on the tree diagram. Mr. Lesser is now in a position to evaluate the likelihood of each alternative outcome.

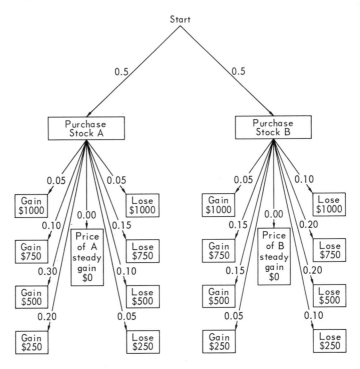

FIG. 7.2. Detailed tree diagram for purchase of two stocks.

For example, what is the probability that Mr. Lesser will buy Stock A and gain $1000? The probability that Mr. Lesser buys Stock A is 0.5 and the probability of a $1000 gain on Stock A is 0.05. It seems safe to assume that these are independent events so that we can use 4.21 and compute:

$$P(A \text{ and } +\$1000) = (0.5)(0.05)$$
$$= \mathbf{0.025}$$

Mr. Lesser is probably more interested in whether he will gain $1000 from the application of his decision-making rule. He may gain $1000 if he buys Stock A *and* its price increases 20 percent *or* he may gain $1000 if he buys Stock B *and* its price increases 20 percent. We have already computed the first of the two mutually exclusive events, buy A *and* gain $1000. The probability of buying B *and* gaining $1000 is (by 4.21)

$$P(B \text{ and } +\$1000) = (0.5)(0.05)$$
$$= \mathbf{0.025}$$

Therefore, the probability of gaining $1000 is

$$P[(A \text{ and } +\$1000) \text{ or } (B \text{ and } +\$1000)] = 0.025 + .025$$
$$= \mathbf{0.05}$$

Alternatively, what is the probability of losing $1000 with this decision process?

$$P(-\$1000) = P[(A \text{ and } -\$1000) \text{ or } (B \text{ and } -\$1000)]$$
$$= (0.5)(0.05) + (0.5)(0.10)$$
$$= \mathbf{0.075}$$

The probabilities of each of the possible outcomes are presented in Table 7.8. (The reader should check the computation of a few of these

TABLE 7.8

PROBABILITY OF EACH OF THE POSSIBLE OUTCOMES FOR MR. LESSER

Possible Outcome	Probability of Outcome
$+1000	0.050
+ 750	0.125
+ 500	0.225
+ 250	0.125
0	0
− 250	0.075
− 500	0.150
− 750	0.175
−1000	0.075
Total	1.000

values to be certain the method is understood.) Note also that the probabilities of the final outcomes sum to 1.000. Should they? (Refer to 4.11.)

EXPECTED VALUE AND VARIANCE OF RETURNS

Examination of the tree diagram presented in Figure 7.2 and Table 7.8 and some reflection should convince the reader that expected value is not always the appropriate single criterion for decision making. Mr. Lesser may feel that he cannot afford to risk a loss greater than $250. Perhaps the $5000 is needed in six months to complete a business deal he is undertaking now. Table 7.8 indicates that with this situation and this decision rule, he has a 0.40 probability of losing more than $250 and a 0.40 chance of making more than $250. But it is also obvious that the two stocks are not equally desirable investments. Referring to Table 7.7, we compute the expected net return from investing in Stock A as a gain of $100, from investing in Stock B as a loss of $125. It would appear that Mr. Lesser should invest in Stock A if he wishes to maximize his expected gain. Table 7.7 also indicates that with Stock A he still has a 0.40 chance of losing at least $250. Further, Stock A apparently provides at least a 0.45 chance of gaining at least $500 against a 0.30 chance of losing at least $500. Obviously, Mr. Lesser must consider these things in his final decision. If he must have the money at the end of six months, perhaps he should put it in a bank to draw interest. What would *you* do? It depends upon that nebulous quality we define as "utility." It is influenced by the variance of the possible returns as well as their expected value. This variance must be matched against the "risk preference" or "risk aversion" of the decision maker.

Suppose that the consensus of the market experts was that given in Table 7.9. The expected returns would be equal at a gain of $100. The variance of returns from the two stocks, however, are different. With Stock A, the chance of a gain of $250 or more is 0.60, the chance of as large a loss is only 0.30. For Stock B, on the other hand, the chance of a gain of $250 or more is 0.55 and the chance of a loss of $250 or more is 0.45. Also, with Stock A, the chance of a gain or a loss of $1000 is zero; with Stock B, there is a 0.10 chance of such a gain and a 0.05 chance of that amount of loss. Which stock is to be preferred? That question can be answered only by the person who must make the decision, since it depends upon his readiness to assume risk of loss versus chance for gain.

Only if the decision maker has a utility function which is "linear in money terms" will expected monetary value serve as an adequate criterion for choosing among alternatives. A utility function is "linear in money terms" if its possessor considers $2 twice as desirable as $1, $3 three times as desirable as $1, $10 twice as desirable as $5, a $1 loss as exactly offset by a $1 gain, and so forth. Most persons in their individual actions reflect utility functions which are not linear in money terms because of

TABLE 7.9

EXPECTED PERFORMANCE OF STOCK A AND STOCK B OVER NEXT SIX
MONTHS (REVISED CONSENSUS OF PANEL OF EXPERTS)

Possible Change in Stock Price		Probability of Change in Stock Price	
Percent	Dollar Amount	Stock A	Stock B
+20	+1000	0.00	0.10
+15	+ 750	0.10	0.15
+10	+ 500	0.30	0.20
+ 5	+ 250	0.20	0.10
0	0	0.10	0
− 5	− 250	0.05	0.15
−10	− 500	0.10	0.15
−15	− 750	0.15	0.10
−20	−1000	0.00	0.05
		1.00	1.00

their limited financial resources. Business decisions the success or failure of which do not seriously threaten the financial position of the firm are made appropriately on the basis of expected monetary value. A utility measure is more useful than dollars as a guide to decision making, but its determination is difficult and would distract from the central discussion. In the remainder of this book, we will operate on the assumption that dollar value is the appropriate measure of value and expected monetary value an acceptable criterion for decision making. The reader should keep in mind the nature of the assumption which has been made and recognize the need to examine the variance in returns for a particular act as well as the expected value.

SUMMARY

The specific *outcome* of a specific *act* is often *uncertain*. The outcome depends upon what *state of the world* exists. The *state of the world* is often beyond the direct control of the decision maker.

Outcomes are usually stated in terms pertinent to the decision maker's objective. Often they are stated in equivalent money returns. A *payoff table* is a matrix of conditional returns, each entry represents the return which would accrue if a specific act were chosen and a specific state of the world actually were true. *Unconditional returns* are found by weighting each conditional return for each act by the probability that the corresponding state of the world is true. The *expected net return* for a specific act is the sum of the conditional returns of that act each weighted by the probability of the corresponding conditional *state of the world* being true.

Outcomes can be stated in terms of gains (net returns) or in terms of losses. Of particular importance are *opportunity losses,* the possible greater return which could be obtained by choosing a different act. The *best* act for a given state of the world (the act with the highest conditional net return for that state of the world) has an opportunity loss of zero. The difference between the conditional net return of the best act and any other act is the conditional opportunity loss of that act for that state of the world. The *expected opportunity loss* of a specific act is the sum of the conditional opportunity losses of that act each weighted by the probability of the corresponding conditional state of the world being true. The expected opportunity loss of the best act (the act with the highest expected net return and the lowest expected opportunity loss) is the *cost of uncertainty.*

Decision processes can be diagrammed with *tree diagrams* which are often useful in indicating the exact nature of the alternatives facing the decision maker. Tree diagrams are particularly useful when probabilities can be attached to each of the branches on the tree. In such situations, we can compute expected values to guide decisions. In addition, the tree diagram can make it obvious that expected value is not always the appropriate single criterion for making a decision. This idea is reinforced when alternative acts have similar expected returns but different variances.

DISCUSSION QUESTIONS

1. Define the following in your *own* words (no formulas):

    (a) a state of the world   (f) opportunity loss
    (b) a strategy   (g) cost of uncertainty
    (c) an act   (h) tree diagram
    (d) conditional outcome   (i) payoff table
    (e) expected gain

2. "The desirability of a course of action depends upon which state of the world is true." Discuss, illustrating your discussion with an original example.

    Hint: Review the definitions in Question 1.

3. Under what conditions is expected net return an appropriate criterion for making decisions?
   Hint: What does expected net return tell you? What does it fail to tell you?
4. What is the importance of the value, "cost of uncertainty?"
   Hint: What use can be made of this value?
5. What is the significance of the variance of possible returns in basing decisions on expected values?
   Hint: Risk of loss must be considered.

DISCUSSION PROBLEMS

Show your method on all solutions.

1. You wish to buy a gallon of paint for a fencing job. The closest hardware store has 10 one-gallon cans of such paint. The store proprietor tells you that three of the ten cans contain defective paint, but he cannot determine which three. He offers the following alternatives:
    (1) Make a single payment of $8.00 (the regular price at which the paint can be purchased all over town) and, if the paint is bad, return it and get another can, continuing to return bad cans until a good one is obtained.
    (2) Pay $6.00 and randomly select a can of paint which you must keep whether it is good or bad. In this case, if you get a bad can on any selection, you must pay another $6.00 to make the next selection.
    (a) Draw the tree diagram for this situation. Remember that if you accept alternative (2) you may need to draw four times to get a good can of paint.
    (b) Compute the probabilities for the final outcomes shown in the tree diagram prepared for (a).
    (c) Which alternative provides the higher expected return?
    (d) Suppose you have only $12, must pay cash, and feel that you must complete the fence painting job today. Which alternative would you select? Why?
2. For the situation of Problem 1, assume you talk the store proprietor into changing the price on alternative (2) to $5.00.
    (a) Which alternative has the higher expected value now?
    (b) Reconsider your answer to problem 1(d). Explain your decision.
3. The Koloredi Company manufactures colored television sets. Three new model designs, the Supra, Prima, and Eclipse, are being con-

sidered for next year. The company can produce at most only two of the models. Thus, the company has the possible acts and the conditional returns shown in the following table:

ALTERNATIVE ACTS AND CONDITIONAL RETURNS (LOSSES)
(*All figures in thousands*)

| Acts (Produce the set(s) shown) | Conditional Set-up Costs | Conditional Net Returns (Losses) above All but Setup Costs | | |
		Both Models Successful	One Model Successful	Neither Model Successful
Supra	$50	—	600	0
Prima	40	—	800	0
Eclipse	40	—	800	0
Supra & Prima	60	900	400	0
Supra & Eclipse	60	900	400	0
Prima & Eclipse	60	1000	600	0

(a) Draw the tree diagram for this decision problem.

(b) If all states of the world are considered equally probable, what is the best course of action for Koloredi?

Hint: Remember that a model, if produced, can be successful or not successful. Some acts can therefore succeed fully, partially, or not at all.

4. Refer to Exercise 1, Chapter 5. What is the average amount of bonus Jim Sewer can expect to receive in those months in which he works 20 days?

Hint: He is paid 2 cents per piece for each piece over 200. The probability that he produces 201 pieces is the probability that he produces between 200.5 and 201.5 pieces. What is the probability that he produces 202 pieces? 203?

EXERCISES

Show your method on all solutions.

1. Gregory Fundless, a student, lives in the men's dormitory at State U. In order to earn money necessary to remain in school, Gregory operates a hamburger concession. Each evening, except Saturday, he drives to a local restaurant and buys hamburgers which he brings back to the dormitory and resells. He pays 20 cents each for the

hamburgers and sells them for 40 cents. Any unsold hamburgers are thrown away. Gregory has kept a careful record of the demand for his hamburgers over the last 200 days. This record is shown in the following table.

HISTORY OF DEMAND FOR HAMBURGERS OVER LAST 200 DAYS
(Note: These are amounts which *could* have been sold, *not* actual sales.)

No. of Hamburgers Demanded X_i	No. of Days Demanded $k(X_i)$	Proportion of Days Demanded $P(X_i)$
10	1	0.005
11	2	0.010
12	4	0.020
13	6	0.030
14	8	0.040
15	11	0.055
16	13	0.065
17	15	0.075
18	17	0.085
19	18	0.090
20	18	0.090
21	17	0.085
22	16	0.080
23	13	0.065
24	12	0.060
25	9	0.045
26	7	0.035
27	5	0.025
28	4	0.020
29	3	0.015
30	1	0.005
Totals	200	1.000

(a) What is the expected return for Gregory if he always buys 24 hamburgers? 20 hamburgers? 16 hamburgers?

(b) What is the optimum number of hamburgers for Gregory to order every evening? Show enough calculations to illustrate clearly your method of reaching your conclusion.

(c) What is the cost of uncertainty of always ordering the optimum number of hamburgers?

(d) What theoretical probability distribution would you recommend as the closest approximation to the distribution of demands given above?

Hint: It is *not* a normal distribution.

(e) Use the theoretical distribution chosen in (d) to find the probability of a demand for:
(1) 10 hamburgers
(2) 20 hamburgers
(3) 25 hamburgers
(4) 30 hamburgers

(f) Compare the probabilities found in (e) with the relative frequencies given in the table of demands.

2. Lessloss Department Stores intends to open a new branch. Three locations are being considered. A thorough market analysis indicates that the conditional net returns at the three locations are:

Net Returns

Location	Branch Successful	Branch Unsuccessful	Probability of Success
A	$80,000	$ −20,000	0.50
B	70,000	−30,000	0.60
C	90,000	−10,000	0.40

Where should Lessloss establish the new branch in order to maximize expected net returns? Explain your choice.

3. Suppose that the data for Exercise 2 were:

Net Returns

Location	Branch Successful	Branch Unsuccessful	Probability of Success
A	$60,000	$ −15,000	0.5
B	50,000	−10,000	0.5
C	70,000	−20,000	0.5

Where should Lessloss establish its branch in order to maximize expected net returns?

4. Two grocery chains in Bigtown return inducements to their customers. The Lossless chain gives a merchandise stamp for each 10 cents of purchases. A book of stamps (1000 stamps) is redeemable for $2.25 in merchandise. The Moreloss chain issues each customer a card which is punched each time a purchase of $1 is made. The card is fully punched after $1000 in purchases. A number on the

card is matched against a master list and the customer is paid the dollar amount shown opposite the number on the card. Out of every 1000 numbers, 850 have $1 printed beside them, 100 have $2, 25 have $5, 15 have $10, 5 have $25, 4 have $50, and 1 has $100. Which chain offers the larger dividend to its customers?

5. Mr. Lesser lives in the Mountain Heights District of Bigtown. He wishes to insure his home for $30,000. The insurance company figures its overhead and processing expenses average ten percent of the premiums collected. If the following table (based on experience) truly reflects risks of fire and other casualty losses (per year) in the area, what annual premium should Lesser pay?

Extent of Loss (Proportion of Total)	Frequency of Occurrence
1.00	0.001
0.86–0.99	0.001
0.71–0.85	0.002
0.56–0.70	0.010
0.41–0.55	0.015
0.26–0.40	0.015
0.11–0.25	0.020
0.01–0.10	0.030
0	0.906
	1.000

6. Mr. Seller, Sales Manager for Hardsell Corporation, has calculated from past records that 26 out of each 100 sales contacts result in a sale. His records also show sales amounts to be Poisson distributed with a mean amount of $80.00. If Hardsell receives 45 cents on each dollar of sales, how much is a salesman worth to the company (per week) if he averages 50 contacts per week?

7. The lifetimes of Bright-Eye TV picture tubes are normally distributed with an average of 2200 hours and a standard deviation of 200 hours. The tubes return $40 per tube when installed, but cost $40 to replace. If they are sold with an 1800 hour replacement guarantee, what is the expected return per 1000 tubes?

8. The Little Grocery stocks fresh strawberries during the local production season. Mr. Little, proprietor, is trying to determine how many flats of berries he should order per day from his supplier to cover daily demands. He pays $2.00 per flat and sells them for $3.00 each. Any flats unsold at the end of each day are sold to a local processor for $1.75 per flat. Records for the last two seasons reveal the following pattern of demand.

Demand Level (Flats)	Number of Occurrences (Days)
19	1
20	2
21	3
22	5
23	6
24	8
25	7
26	6
27	5
28	3
29	2
30	1
31	1

(a) What is the expected number of flats which will be sold per day?

(b) At what level of sales is the maximum net return per day? What is the return?

(c) How many flats should Mr. Little plan to order each day to maximize his unconditional net dollar return?

(d) What is the cost of uncertainty associated with the optimum inventory level?

9. Mr. Moneyman has $50,000 to invest. He can invest it in the stock market, the bond market, or real estate. The results of a careful study of these alternatives are summarized as follows:

Possible Net Returns per Year	Estimated Probabilities of Realizing Net Return		
	Invest in Stock Market	Invest in Bond Market	Invest in Real Estate
+15,000	0.03	0.00	0.06
+10,000	0.06	0.01	0.09
+ 5,000	0.09	0.08	0.10
+ 3,000	0.10	0.10	0.16
+ 2,000	0.12	0.25	0.12
+ 1,000	0.14	0.35	0.04
0	0.16	0.15	0.00
− 1,000	0.12	0.04	0.00
− 2,000	0.08	0.02	0.15
− 3,000	0.06	0.00	0.10
− 5,000	0.03	0.00	0.09
−10,000	0.01	0.00	0.06
−15,000	0.00	0.00	0.03

(a) Which alternative offers the greatest chance for gain?
(b) Which alternative offers the greatest chance for loss?
(c) Which alternative offers the greatest expected return?
(d) Which alternative would you suggest Mr. Moneyman choose? Explain your choice.
(e) Would your recommendation change if Mr. Moneyman informed you that this $50,000 is his total wealth? Explain carefully.

10. This question refers to Discussion Problem 3. The Market Research Department estimates the probabilities of success for the three new Koloredi models to be Supra 0.6, Prima 0.7, Eclipse 0.8 on the basis of past experience and expected market conditions. These are the probabilities of selling *at least* enough sets to break even in each case. The results for the three models are considered independent of one another.

(a) What is the unconditional expected return of the six alternative acts?
(b) What is the unconditional expected opportunity loss of each of the six alternative acts?
(c) Which act should be selected if net returns are to be maximized?
(d) What is the cost of uncertainty associated with choice of the act which maximizes expected net returns?

8
statistics, parameters, and confidence statements

INTRODUCTION

Most of the time, decisions are not involved with choice among certain alternatives. Rather, the state of the world is unknown, the outcome of a particular trial is *uncertain*. It is then impossible to *know* the outcome which will be realized. In such situations we are forced to make *inferences* about unknown events on the basis of present levels of knowledge which rest on a systematic analysis of past experience. An inference is a guess based upon prior experience or logical analysis of available data.

Obviously, inferences are made concerning the unknown. For example, the level of sales in a future period is unknown. Similarly, the current rate of defective production may also be unknown. Even a historical fact is unknown to someone who has not observed the fact at the time of its occurrence or received information of it from an impartial observer.

The scientific method of problem solving has been stated in many ways. One view of this method was presented in Chapter 1. At that point we indicated that quantification enters the decision process at the point where alternatives are specified and the probability of success in attaining some quantifiable objective is evaluated for each alternative. The actual result (success or failure) depends upon what is the actual situation in the real world (the "state of the world"). In the parlance of Chapter 5, the value of the random variable (outcome of the decision) is unknown until the trial is completed. We are very much interested, however, in what "state of the world" actually exists, for example, how many units of product will be sold if the product is produced and marketed. The state of the world often can be satisfactorily described by the value of a particular population parameter, the *decision parameter*, knowledge of which exerts a critical influence on our decision. Estimates of decision parameters can be derived from sample information. The purpose of this chapter is to define some techniques used for the accomplishment of this task.

In Chapter 6, we considered in a general way the problem of estimating population parameters from sample statistics. There we learned that each sample statistic has a sampling distribution and a standard error. We also learned that interval estimates of the population parameter can be developed from the corresponding sample statistic and its standard error. A confidence coefficient is attached to these intervals indicating how strongly it is believed that the given interval actually includes the population parameter. The remaining sections of this chapter present specific techniques for deriving confidence interval estimates from random samples.

ESTIMATION OF THE POPULATION VARIANCE AND STANDARD DEVIATION

We pointed out in Chapter 6 that it is preferable when reporting an estimate to give its standard deviation or, even better, to make the estimate in the form of a *confidence interval* (an interval for which we have a stated *degree of confidence* that it contains the population parameter being estimated). We also learned that each sample statistic from a sample of a given size by a given method of sampling has a *sampling distribution* and a *standard error* (standard deviation of the sampling distribution). Finally, we learned that the standard errors are used in setting up the confidence intervals.

The size of the standard errors are determined by the variance of the population and the size of the sample. That is, the variability in results from repeated samples is a result of the random selection of variable items from populations whose individual elementary units possess differing values. It seems appropriate, therefore, to learn first how to obtain reliable estimates of the population variance and standard deviation before learning to estimate other parameters.

The Sample Variance as an Estimate of Population Variance

In Chapter 5, we defined the variance of a random variable as:

$$\sigma^2 = \sum_{i=1}^{N} (X_i - \bar{X})^2 P(X_i) \qquad (5.01)$$

For a simple random sample, 5.01 would be restated as

8.00 $\quad s^2 = \dfrac{1}{n} \sum_{i=1}^{n} (x_i - \bar{x})^2$

Where $\bar{x}$ is the average value of the values drawn into the sample (the x_i's). Note that $x_1, x_2, \cdots, x_n$ are values drawn in the sample. Also, $\bar{x}$ and s^2 are each sample statistics. The reader should recognize that s^2 is *not* the variance of a random variable, but is itself a random variable.

Unfortunately, s^2 is a biased estimator of σ^2, tending to underestimate the population variance. It can be shown that the expected value of the variances of all possible random samples of size n is related to the population variance as follows:

$$E(s^2) = \frac{n-1}{n} \sigma^2$$

Therefore, to obtain an unbiased estimate of σ^2 we must correct s^2.

8.02 $\quad \hat{\sigma}^2 = \dfrac{n}{n-1} s^2$

(The "caret" or "circumflex accent" over the symbol for a population parameter indicates a "best" unbiased estimate of that parameter.)

When μ (the population mean) is known, an unbiased estimate of σ^2 is given by $\dfrac{1}{n} \sum_{i=1}^{n} (x_i - \mu)^2$. This explains why the sample variance tends to underestimate the true population variance. The sum of the squares of the deviations for *any* distribution is at a minimum when the deviations are taken around the mean of *that* distribution. Therefore, unless the sample mean ($\bar{x}$) just happens to be equal to the population mean (μ), the sum of the squared deviations taken around the sample mean, $\Sigma(x_i - \bar{x})^2$, will be less than if the deviations were taken around the population mean, $\Sigma(x_i - \mu)^2$. That is

$$\Sigma(x_i - \bar{x})^2 \leq \Sigma(x_i - \mu)^2$$

The reader should note that where n is large, the bias correction has little effect. In fact, when $n \geq 30$, it is very often ignored. Theoretically, however, s^2 is always a biased estimator and the bias correction is necessary.

The Sampling Distribution of the Sample Variance

We demonstrated in the previous section that

$$E(\hat{\sigma}^2) = \frac{n}{n - 1} s^2 = \sigma^2$$

That is, we have demonstrated that $\hat{\sigma}^2$ has a sampling distribution centered at σ^2. We are also interested in the variance of the sampling distribution of $\hat{\sigma}^2$ and in the shape of the distribution.

The sampling distribution of the sample variance ($\hat{\sigma}^2$) is different from any distribution we have yet encountered unless we are taking very large samples from normally distributed populations. In the particular case of a "normal" population, the sampling distribution of $\hat{\sigma}^2$ is "asymptotically normal," that is, as n increases, the sampling distribution of $\hat{\sigma}^2$ approaches the normal distribution. Basically, however, the distribution of variances of random samples from even normal populations follows a positively skewed curve (tapered toward the high values), the exact shape of which depends upon the values of σ^2 and n. Fortunately, it can be proven mathematically that the statistic

8.03 $\chi^2 = \dfrac{(n - 1)\hat{\sigma}^2}{\sigma^2}$

has a chi-square (χ^2) distribution with $n - 1$ "degrees of freedom."

A *degree of freedom* indicates the ability of a value to enter a distribution without restriction. For example, if the total of a distribution of five values is specified as 50, any four values can be specified freely, but the fifth must then be chosen so as to satisfy the restriction that the total be 50. Specifying the total has removed one degree of freedom for values to enter the distribution. A second example would be for a sportscaster to choose the winning and losing teams for ten games and claim that he is making 20 prognostications. Ignoring tie games, the sportscaster is making only ten prognostications; if one team wins, the other must lose. The sportscaster has only ten degrees of freedom in making his choices, not 20.

There is a different chi-square probability distribution for each number of degrees of freedom. Its mean is equal to the number of degrees of freedom and its variance is equal to twice the degrees of freedom. It is a continuous probability distribution whose height (probability density) at a point X is given by:

8.04 $h(X) = \dfrac{X^{m-1}e^{-X/2}}{2^m(m-1)!}$

where

X = the value of χ^2 whose probability density (height) is being computed

m = d.f./2 (degrees of freedom/2)

e = 2.71828 (a mathematical constant)

Obviously, the computation of probabilities for particular values of χ^2 is impossible. As with the normal distribution, we can use the calculus to compute the probability of χ^2 falling within a particular range of values. Tables have been developed which make this labor unnecessary. In reality, there is a complete table for each degree of freedom, but these tables have been condensed into a single table which presents selected values for each of several numbers of degrees of freedom. Table 10 in Appendix B is such a table. The χ^2 table is set up to show the probability that the particular value of χ^2 given in the body of the table will be exceeded purely by chance. The probabilities are shown at the top of each column.

Because the χ^2 distribution is asymptotically normal, values for d.f. above 30 are not tabled. For larger numbers of degrees of freedom the expression $\sqrt{2\chi^2} - \sqrt{2\,d.f. - 1}$ may be used as a normal deviate with $\sigma = 1$ and $\mu = 0$ (that is, a standard normal deviate).

A simple example will illustrate the use of the table of chi-square values presented in Table 10 of Appendix B. Suppose we had a normally distributed population with a known variance, σ^2, of 100. Suppose we draw from that population a simple random sample of ten items and compute $\sigma^2 = 90$ from that sample. How likely is it that a sample of ten items with a variance of 90 could be randomly selected from a normally distributed population with a variance of 100? Referring to Table B-10, we see in the body of the table in the row for nine degrees of freedom (9 $d.f.$) that the χ^2 value computed from 8.03,

$$\chi^2 = \frac{9(90)}{100}$$
$$= 8.10$$

falls between the columns for $\chi^2_{0.90}$ and $\chi^2_{0.10}$. This means that somewhere between ten percent and 90 percent of all possible simple random samples of ten items each from such a population would have computed $\hat{\sigma}^2$ values of at least 90. That is, 90 percent of the time the χ^2 value for 9 $d.f.$ would equal or exceed 4.17; ten percent of the time χ^2 for 9 $d.f.$ would equal or exceed 14.68.

Confidence Interval Estimates of σ^2

Suppose we wished to use the value of $\hat{\sigma}^2$ computed above to estimate σ^2. By application of 8.03 and Table B-10, we can say that there is a probability of 0.05 (1 minus the 0.95 probability shown in Table B-10) that $9\hat{\sigma}^2/\sigma^2 \leq 3.3$ and there is a 0.05 probability that $9\hat{\sigma}^2/\sigma^2 \geq 16.9$. That is, there is a 0.90 probability that the value of χ^2 computed from 6.03 with nine degrees of freedom will fall between 3.3 and 16.9. In symbols,

$$P\left[\chi^2_{(C+1)/2} < \frac{(n-1)\hat{\sigma}^2}{\sigma^2} < \chi^2_{(1-C)/2}\right] = C$$

where C is the level of confidence.

Solving for σ^2 gives

8.05 $P\left[\dfrac{(n-1)\hat{\sigma}^2}{\chi^2_{(C+1)/2}} < \sigma^2 < \dfrac{(n-1)\hat{\sigma}^2}{\chi^2_{(1-C)/2}}\right] = C$

Applying 8.05 to the example above, the 90 percent confidence interval estimate of σ^2 based on $\hat{\sigma}^2$ is

$$\frac{9(90)}{16.9} < \sigma^2 < \frac{9(90)}{3.3}$$

or

$$48 < \sigma^2 < 245$$

The above estimation procedure assumed that we were sampling from a normally distributed population. Unfortunately, there is no general theorem regarding the form of the distribution of sample variances (and sample standard deviations) from other populations. However, the standard deviations of sample variances computed from large samples (at an absolute minimum, $n \geq 30$; preferably, $n \geq 50$) can be approximated.

8.06 $\sigma_{s^2} = \sqrt{\dfrac{m_4' - (m_2')^2}{n}}$

where m_k' is the estimated kth moment about the mean, defined as,

8.07 $m_k' = \dfrac{\Sigma(x_i - \bar{x})^k}{n}$

Thus,

$$m_4' = \frac{\Sigma(x_i - \bar{x})^4}{n}$$

If the moments m_2' and m_4' can be estimated, this standard error can be used with the Chebyshev inequality to set up confidence interval estimates of σ^2.

More precise estimates may be possible even if the shape of the distribution is unknown. If it can be assumed safely that the population distribution is uni-modal (has only one most frequently occurring value), the Camp-Meidel extension of Chebyshev's inequality can be utilized.

8.08 $P(|X - \bar{X}| \geq k\sigma) \leq \dfrac{1}{2.25k^2}$

s^2 would be substituted for X, σ for $\bar{X}$, and σ_s^2 for σ and the interval derived from

8.09 $P[(s^2 - k\sigma_s^2) \leq \sigma^2 \leq (s^2 + k\sigma_s^2)] \geq 1 - \dfrac{1}{2.25k^2}$

Note that we are working from s^2, not $\hat{\sigma}^2$.

One possible point estimate of the population standard deviation is:

8.10 $\hat{\sigma} = \sqrt{\hat{\sigma}^2}$

Confidence limits for that estimate are obtained directly from 8.05 by taking the square roots of the three terms.

8.11 $P\left[\sqrt{\dfrac{(n-1)\hat{\sigma}^2}{\chi^2_{(C+1)/2}}} < \sigma < \sqrt{\dfrac{(n-1)\hat{\sigma}^2}{\chi^2_{(1-C)/2}}}\right] = C$

Note that σ can be estimated by 8.10 and 8.11 only when the population being sampled is normally distributed. Even then, $\hat{\sigma}$ is *not* an unbiased estimate of σ. However, if samples are large (at an absolute minimum, $n \geq 30$; preferably, $n \geq 50$), the expected value of $\hat{\sigma}$ is approximately equal to the population standard deviation. This is because, for large samples, $\hat{\sigma}$ will not differ much from σ. Therefore, the average value of $\hat{\sigma}$ will approximate σ. Again, if n is large, the standard deviation of the distribution of sample standard deviations (the standard error of the standard deviation) from any universe can be approximated.

8.12 $\sigma_s = \dfrac{\sigma}{\sqrt{2n}}$

A more exact formula for the σ_s is

8.13 $\sigma_s = \dfrac{\sigma}{\sqrt{2n}} \sqrt{1 + \dfrac{\dfrac{m_4'}{\sigma^4} - 3}{2}}$

where m_4' is the fourth moment about the mean, that is,

$$m_4' = \dfrac{\Sigma(x_i - \bar{x})^4}{n}$$

For a normal distribution the term m_4'/σ^4 is equal to 3 and the short version given above (8.12) is obtained. Note that 8.12 provides σ_s, not $\sigma_{\hat{\sigma}}$. Obviously $\hat{\sigma}$ usually must be substituted for σ in 8.12 since estimates of σ_s seldom would be required where σ was known. The operable form of 8.12 becomes

8.14 $\sigma_s = \dfrac{\hat{\sigma}}{\sqrt{2n}}$

The Range as a Variance Estimator

In small samples, the range and standard deviation can be expected to fluctuate together. The inclusion of an extreme value from the population will have a significant effect on both measures. In large samples this will not be as true; the range will be influenced more than the standard deviation. This is because the value of the range is dependent only upon the two extreme values, but the standard deviation is influenced by every value. The range may often be used as a substitute for the standard deviation when analysis is based on small samples. The range is almost as efficient an estimator of σ as is s and it is much easier to calculate.

Tables of the distribution of the ratio of the average range to the population standard deviation $\dfrac{\bar{R}}{\sigma} = d_2$ have been worked out for several sample sizes where samples are drawn from a normally distributed parent population. Table 11 of Appendix B gives the average value of d_2 for each of several sample sizes. Quality control statisticians commonly compute R from each of a series of small samples, obtain the average, $\bar{R}$, of these values and compute an estimate of σ.

8.15 $\quad \hat{\sigma} = \dfrac{\bar{R}}{d_2}$

For example, suppose ten samples of four items each were drawn from the bolts produced by a standard process and the ranges of the bolt diameters in each sample determined (in inches) as 0.015, 0.016, 0.024, 0.025, 0.018, 0.022, 0.021, 0.016, 0.019, 0.020. $\bar{R}$ is 0.0196 and d_2 for $n = 4$ is 2.059 (from Table B-11). Therefore, the population standard deviation is estimated as

$$\hat{\sigma} = \frac{0.0196}{2.059}$$
$$= \mathbf{0.0095}$$

THE SAMPLE MEAN AS AN ESTIMATOR
OF THE POPULATION MEAN

In Chapter 5 we defined the expected value of a random variable as

$$E(X) = \sum_{i=1}^{N} X_i P(X_i) \qquad (5.00)$$

For a simple random sample, 5.00 is restated as

8.20 $\bar{x} = \dfrac{1}{n} \displaystyle\sum_{i=1}^{n} x_i$

The sample mean, $\bar{x}$, is an unbiased, consistent, sufficient, and most efficient estimator of μ.

The Sampling Distribution of the Sample Mean

The distribution of individual members randomly selected from a population (samples of one element each) will reproduce the parent population. But what about the distribution of means from larger samples? The individual members of each sample are randomly selected, and, therefore, statistically independent. A well-known theorem in mathematics tells us that

8.21 The expected sum of independent random variables is the sum of the expectations and the variance of the sum is the sum of the variances.

Therefore, the expected sum of all possible samples would be

$$E \text{ (sum)} = \sum_{i=1}^{n} [E(x_i)]$$
$$= n[E(x_i)]$$

but, the expected value of the individual sample elements would be the expected value of the population elements, μ. Therefore,

$$E \text{ (sum of samples of size } n) = n\mu$$

Since the sample mean is defined as $\dfrac{1}{n} \displaystyle\sum (x_i)$, we conclude:

$$E(\bar{x}) = \frac{1}{n} \left[E \left(\sum_{i=1}^{n} x_i \right) \right]$$
$$= \frac{1}{n} (n\mu)$$

8.22 $E(\bar{x}) = \mu$

If the variance of the sum is the sum of the variances (8.21) then

$$\text{Var (Sum)} = \sum_{i=1}^{n} [\text{Var } (x_i)]$$

but, the variance of the x_i is σ^2, the variance of the individual elements in the population. Therefore, the variance of the sample means from all possible samples of size n would be (by application of 5.05)

$$\text{Var } (\bar{x}) = \frac{1}{n^2} \left[\sum_{i=1}^{n} \sigma_{x_i}^{2} \right]$$

$$= \frac{1}{n^2} (n\sigma^2)$$

8.23 $\sigma_{\bar{x}}^{2} = \dfrac{\sigma^2}{n}$

To summarize, we have demonstrated that for the sampling distribution of the sample mean two things are true. First, its expected value is equal to the mean of the population. That is,

$$E(\bar{x}) = \mu \tag{8.22}$$

Second, the variance of the sampling distribution of the mean is equal to the population variance divided by the sample size. That is,

$$\sigma_{\bar{x}}^{2} = \frac{\sigma^2}{n} \tag{8.23}$$

The standard deviation of the sampling distribution of the mean is the *standard error of the mean* (by 6.02). It can be obtained by taking the square root of both sides of 8.23.

8.24 $\sigma_{\bar{x}} = \dfrac{\sigma}{\sqrt{n}}$

Equations 8.23 and 8.24 make it clear that the sampling error involved in the determination of the mean is dependent upon sample size and the population sampled. When sampling from a given population, σ^2 is fixed and the sampling variance and the standard error of the mean vary inversely with changes in sample size; the variance varies in inverse proportion to changes in sample size, the standard error in inverse proportion to the changes in the square root of sample size. With a given size sample, n fixed, from different populations, the sampling variance and standard error of the mean will vary in direct proportion to changes in the population variance and the population standard deviation, respectively.

Knowing the mean and standard deviation of the sampling distribution for the mean does not give us sufficient information to provide inference statements about the population mean. We also must know the "shape" of the sampling distribution. One of the most important theorems in mathematical statistics, the *central limit theorem*, concerns the distribution of the sample mean.

8.25   If x_i, x_2, $\cdot\ \cdot\ \cdot$, x_n are independent random variables having the same distribution with mean μ and finite variance σ^2, then when n is large, the distribution of the sample mean is approximately the normal distribution with mean μ and standard deviation $\sigma/\sqrt{n}$.

The central limit theorem says, in effect, that for reasonably large random samples, *regardless of the "shape" of the parent population*, the sampling distribution of the sample mean can be approximated with the normal distribution. Thus, we can state that

8.26 $z = \dfrac{\bar{x} - \mu}{\sigma/\sqrt{n}}$

is a standard normal deviate with zero mean ($\mu_z = 0$) and unit standard deviation ($\sigma_z = 1$) when n is large.

We find, then, that the distribution of the sample mean, like the distributions of the sample variance and the sample standard deviation, is asymptotically normal. There is, however, an important difference with regard to the mean. The sampling distribution of the sample mean can be successfully approximated with the normal distribution at much smaller sample sizes. The simple example which follows illustrates this point.

Let us consider the population of positive integers from 0 through 9. Suppose we were to draw all possible samples (an infinite number) of size $n = 2$ with replacement between draws and compute a mean from each. How would the infinite number of sample means be distributed about the population μ of 4.5? According to the central limit theorem (8.25), the distribution would be approximately normal with an expected value equal to μ (4.5) and a standard deviation equal to the standard deviation of the population over the square root of sample size. For this population, $\sigma = 2.872$ (the reader should check this) and the standard error of the mean should be:

$$\sigma_{\bar{x}} = \frac{2.872}{\sqrt{2}}$$

$$= \frac{2.872}{1.4142} = \mathbf{2.03}$$

As an empirical representation of this unobtainable distribution, 500 samples of two items each were drawn from the population of integers (with replacement) by drawing pairs of numbers from a table of random digits. The results are shown in Table 8.1 and graphed in Figure 8.1.

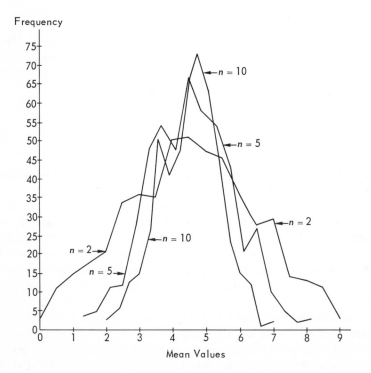

FIG. 8.1.   Illustration of sampling distribution of sample mean, infinite rectangular population, $\mu = 4.5$, $\sigma = 2.872$.

TABLE 8.1

ILLUSTRATION OF SAMPLING DISTRIBUTION OF THE SAMPLE MEAN WHEN
DRAWING FROM RECTANGULAR INFINITE POPULATION: RANDOM
DIGITS 0 THROUGH 9; SAMPLE SIZES: $n = 2$, $n = 5$, $n = 10$

Distributions of Sample Means						
$n = 2$		$n = 5$		$n = 10$		Normal Distribution
Mean Values	Freq.	Mean Values	Freq.	Mean Values	Freq.	Freq.
0	3					
0.5	11	1.2–1.4	4	Under 2.3	3	3.4
1.0	15	1.6–1.8	5	2.3–2.5	6	4.5
1.5	18	2.0–2.2	11	2.6–2.8	13	9.3
2.0	21	2.4–2.6	12	2.9–3.1	15	16.9
2.5	34	2.8–3.0	28	3.2–3.4	26	27.5
3.0	36	3.2–3.4	48	3.5–3.7	50	40.3
3.5	35	3.6–3.8	54	3.8–4.0	41	52.9
4.0	50	4.0–4.2	48	4.1–4.3	47	62.3
4.5	51	4.4–4.6	67	4.4–4.6	66	65.8
5.0	47	4.8–5.0	58	4.7–4.9	73	62.3
5.5	46	5.2–5.4	54	5.0–5.2	63	52.9
6.0	35	5.6–5.8	43	5.3–5.5	44	40.3
6.5	28	6.0–6.2	21	5.6–5.8	23	27.5
7.0	29	6.4–6.6	27	5.9–6.1	15	16.9
7.5	14	6.8–7.0	10	6.2–6.4	12	9.3
8.0	13	7.2–7.4	5	6.5–6.7	1	4.5
8.5	11	7.6–7.8	2	Over 6.7	2	3.4
9.0	3	8.0–8.2	3			
	500		500		500	500.0
$\bar{\bar{x}} = 4.49$		$\bar{\bar{x}} = 4.54$		$\bar{\bar{x}} = 4.49$		$\mu = 4.5$
$\hat{\sigma}_{\bar{x}} = 1.96$		$\hat{\sigma}_{\bar{x}} = 1.26$		$\hat{\sigma}_{\bar{x}} = 0.85$		$\sigma = 0.91$
$\sigma_{\bar{x}} = 2.03$		$\sigma_{\bar{x}} = 1.22$		$\sigma_{\bar{x}} = 0.91$		$N = 500$

Also shown in Table 8.1 and Figure 8.1 are the results of drawing 500 samples of five and of ten items each. The increase in sample size from two to five to ten appears to give a more symmetrical, more bell-shaped (more normal) distribution. To indicate the closeness of the fit for the 500 samples of size $n = 10$, a normal distribution of $N = 500$, $\mu = 4.5$, and $\sigma = 0.91$ is shown in the final column of Table 8.1. In Chapter 11 we present a method for testing whether the observed and expected distributions are essentially the same. At present, a visual comparison is sufficient.

Sampling Error Estimates from Finite Populations

In Chapter 5, we dealt with the binomial and hypergeometric distributions. At that point we presented two formulas:

For the hypergeometric distribution,

$$\sigma^2 = \frac{nM}{N}\left(1 - \frac{M}{N}\right)\left(\frac{N - n}{N - 1}\right) \tag{5.12}$$

For the binomial distribution,

$$\sigma^2 = nP(1 - P) \tag{5.24}$$

If we examine these formulas closely, we see that, at the first draw, $\frac{M}{N}$ and P (the proportion of successes in the population) are indistinguishable and $1 - \frac{M}{N}$ is indistinguishable from $1 - P$. Thus, the only difference in the two equations is the term $\left(\frac{N - n}{N - 1}\right)$.

8.30   The term $\left(\frac{N - n}{N - 1}\right)$ is called the *finite population correction* or *f.p.c.*

If we replaced items between draws from a finite two-valued population, we would be dealing with a Bernoulli process and would use 3.24 (the binomial). Not replacing the objects between draws introduces the *f.p.c.* Obviously if N were very large in relation to n, the *f.p.c.* would make little difference. When N is large, the difference between N and the $N - 1$ in the denominator is insignificant. Then the correction factor can be considered as $\frac{N - n}{N}$ or $1 - \frac{n}{N}$. This immediately makes it clear that the important consideration is the ratio n/N. When n/N is small (not more than 0.05), the correction usually is ignored.

The *f.p.c.* should be used also with many-valued variables (measurements) when the population is finite and the sample relatively large. When elementary units are drawn from *any finite population without replacement*, whether the population is two-valued or many-valued, the probability of selection for elementary units possessing a particular characteristic changes with each draw. Consider, for example, the selection of a sample of 20 accounts payable from the 50 accounts payable of the Little Grocery. Suppose 20 of these accounts have balances greater than \$150. On the first draw we have a $20/50 = 0.40$ chance of drawing an account with a balance greater than \$150. On the second draw, the chance of selecting such an account is either $19/49 = 0.3878$ or $20/49 = 0.4081$, depending on the kind of account selected on the first draw. The results of the two draws are not independent; if we select an account with a large balance on the first draw, we change the odds for the next draw *against* selecting such an account on that draw. Conversely, failure to draw a large account on the first draw changes the odds *in favor* of selecting a large account.

After 19 draws, it is remotely possible to have drawn either 19 large accounts or no large accounts. If 19 large accounts had been drawn, the chance of selecting a large account would be only $1/31 = 0.0323$. At the other extreme, if no large accounts had been drawn, the chance of selecting a large account on the last draw would be $20/31 = 0.6452$. It seems imperative to recognize this disparity in probabilities in calculating the sampling variance.

Suppose, on the other hand, we were drawing a sample of 50 accounts payable from the 1500 accounts payable of the Lossless Grocery Stores. Assume that the same proportion, 0.40, or 600, of the 1500 accounts are classified as large. The chance of selecting a large account on the first draw is 0.40; on the second draw, it is either $600/1499 = 0.4027$ or $599/1499 = 0.3995$. It would seem safe to assume the probability of selection had not changed after the first draw. Even after 49 draws, the chance of selecting a large account is, *at worst*, either $600/1451 = 0.4135$ or $551/1451 = 0.3797$. It is highly unlikely that either of these extreme conditions would be realized. It therefore seems reasonable to assume that the probability of selection remains constant at 0.40 since neither of these values deviates a great deal from 0.40.

The above examples indicate that when the sample is a significant portion of a finite population, the probability of selection on each draw (without replacement) changes appreciably. When the ratio of sample size to population size is sufficiently small, however, the change in probability of selection is minor and can be ignored with safety. A few calculations with the *f.p.c.* itself will reinforce this view. These have been carried out in Table 8.2. The last column, $\sqrt{(N - n)/(N - 1)}$, shows the effect of the *f.p.c.* on the standard error. Note that the significant factor in these calculations is neither the absolute size of the population nor the absolute size of the sample, but the ratio of sample size to population size.

The question remains: where is the *f.p.c.* to be used? Note that both the hypergeometric and binomial distributions are sampling distributions for sampling from two-valued populations. The standard deviations we compute using 3.12 and 3.24 are standard errors. Note that 3.12 is the

TABLE 8.2

Sample of Finite Population
Correction Factors

N	n	$\dfrac{n}{N}$	$\dfrac{N-n}{N-1}$	$\sqrt{\dfrac{N-n}{N-1}}$
		A. N Fixed, n Variable		
100	50	0.5	0.5051	0.7107
100	25	0.25	0.7576	0.8704
100	115	0.15	0.8586	0.9266
100	10	0.10	0.9091	0.9534
100	5	0.05	0.9595	0.9795
		B. N Variable, n Fixed		
100	50	0.5	0.5051	0.7107
200	50	0.25	0.7538	0.8682
333	50	0.15	0.8524	0.9233
500	50	0.10	0.9018	0.9496
1000	50	0.05	0.9510	0.9752

formula for the standard error of the sample statistic "number of successes in n draws, *without replacement*, from a *finite* two-valued population." Similarly defined, 3.24 is the formula for the standard error of the sample statistic "number of successes in *either n* draws *with replacement* from a *finite* two-valued population *or n* draws from an *infinite* two-valued population." It is thus demonstrated that *the f.p.c. is applied to computations of standard errors computed for samples drawn without replacement from finite populations.* (Drawing from a finite population with replacement transforms the population into an infinite population.)

The formula for computing the standard error of the mean when sampling from a finite population would be:

8.31 $\sigma_{\bar{x}} = \dfrac{\sigma}{\sqrt{n}} \sqrt{\dfrac{N-n}{N-1}}$ and $\acute{\sigma}_{\bar{x}} = \dfrac{\acute{\sigma}}{\sqrt{n}} \sqrt{\dfrac{N-n}{N-1}}$

Suppose we draw all possible samples of $n = 2$ *without replacement* from the population of positive integers 1 through 10. This will give us $C(10, 2) = 45$ samples. The distribution of the 45 possible means is shown in the third and fourth columns of Table 8.3 and graphed in Figure 8.2. The distribution is unimodal (one peak) and symmetrical about that peak. It is obviously more nearly a normal distribution than is the parent rectangular population.

TABLE 8.3

ILLUSTRATION OF SAMPLING DISTRIBUTION OF THE SAMPLE MEAN WHEN
DRAWING FROM FINITE POPULATION WITHOUT REPLACEMENT
POPULATION: POSITIVE INTEGERS FROM 1 THROUGH 10
SAMPLE SIZES: $n = 2$, $n = 3$, $n = 5$

| Finite Population | | Distributions of Sample Means | | | | | | Normal Distribution |
| | | $n = 2$ | | $n = 3$ | | $n = 5$ | | |
Values	Freq.	Values	Freq.	Values	Freq.	Values	Freq.	Freq.†
1	1	1.5	1	2.00	1	3.0	1	0.7
2	1	2.0	1	2.33	1	3.2	1	1.2
3	1	2.5	2	2.67	2	3.4	2	1.9
4	1	3.0	2	3.00	3	3.6	3	3.0
5	1	3.5	3	3.33	4	3.8	5	5.2
6	1	4.0	3	3.67	5	4.0	7	6 2
7	1	4.5	4	4.00	7	4.2	9	8.4
8	1	5.0	4	4.33	8	4.4	11	10.9
9	1	5.5	5	4.67	9	4.6	14	13.4
10	1	6.0	4	5.00	10	4.8	16	16.0
	10	6.5	4	5.33	10	5.0	18	18.3
		7.0	3	5.67	10	5.2	19	20.0
		7.5	3	6.00	10	5.4	20	20.9
		8.0	2	6.33	9	5.6	20	20.9
		8.5	2	6.67	8	5.8	19	20.0
		9.0	1	7.00	7	6.0	18	18.3
		9.5	1	7.33	5	6.2	16	16.0
			45	7.67	4	6.4	14	13.4
				8.00	3	6.6	11	10.9
				8.33	2	6.8	9	8.4
				8.67	1	7.0	7	6.2
				9.00	1	7.2	5	5 2
					120	7.4	3	3.0
						7.6	2	1.9
						7.8	1	1.2
						8.0	1	0.7
							252	252.0

† $\mu = 5.5$, $\sigma = 0.96$, $N = 252$

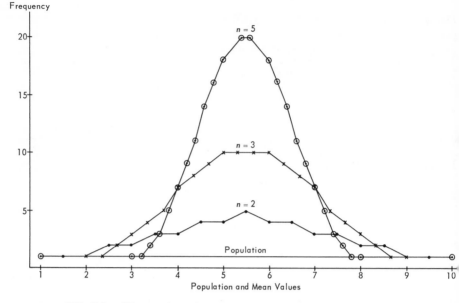

FIG. 8.2. Illustration of sampling distribution of sample mean.

Table 8.3 and Figure 8.2 also illustrate what happens as sample size is increased. The distribution of means becomes more normal. The last column of Table 8.3 gives the frequencies for a normally distributed population of the same size ($N = 500$) and with same μ and σ. These frequencies were derived from a slightly modified form of 5.31 as will be explained in Chapter 11 when we will learn to judge just how close the two distributions are. For now, visual examination indicates that the two distributions are quite close.

Let us check the computed values of $\sigma_{\bar{x}}$ for the three sample sizes against the theoretical result using 8.31. Substituting $\sigma = 2.872$ and $N = 10$ into 8.31, we obtain:

$$\text{for } n = 2, \; \sigma_{\bar{x}} = \frac{2.872}{\sqrt{2}} \sqrt{\frac{8}{9}}$$

$$= \mathbf{1.91}$$

$$\text{for } n = 3, \; \sigma_{\bar{x}} = \frac{2.872}{\sqrt{3}} \sqrt{\frac{7}{9}}$$

$$= \mathbf{1.46}$$

$$\text{for } n = 5, \; \sigma_{\bar{x}} = \frac{2.872}{\sqrt{5}} \sqrt{\frac{5}{9}}$$

$$= \mathbf{0.96}$$

Direct computation of these standard errors from the distribution of the means of all possible samples of each size given in Table 8.3 using the computing form of the standard deviation formula (5.02) gives the following values:

$$\text{for } n = 2, \sigma_{\bar{x}} = 1.92$$
$$\text{for } n = 3, \sigma_{\bar{x}} = 1.46$$
$$\text{for } n = 5, \sigma_{\bar{x}} = 0.96$$

Rounding errors account for the slight difference for samples of $n = 2$.

Confidence Interval Estimates of μ, σ Known

We have demonstrated that the sampling distribution of the mean can be considered essentially normal, particularly for large samples, regardless of the shape of the underlying population. If the sampling distribution is normal, then we can make statements such as the following about the sample mean, $\bar{x}$, from samples of a given size.

$$P(\mu - \sigma_{\bar{x}} < \bar{x} < \mu + \sigma_{\bar{x}}) = 0.6827$$
$$P(\mu - 2\sigma_{\bar{x}} < \bar{x} < \mu + 2\sigma_{\bar{x}}) = 0.9545$$

This is because it is true that 68.27 percent of the sample means from samples of the same size are within the range of one standard error around μ. Similarly, 95.45 percent of the means from samples of the same size will fall within the range of two standard errors of the mean from μ.

If 68.27 percent of the sample means fall within one $\sigma_{\bar{x}}$ from μ, then if we have one sample mean from this distribution of sample means, the probability is 0.6827 that it is no more than one $\sigma_{\bar{x}}$ away from μ. But remember that μ is fixed, it does not float around; $\bar{x}$ is the random variable. Therefore, when we infer a range for including μ from our knowledge of a specific value of $\bar{x}$, we are no longer dealing in probabilities directly. If we set up the range $\bar{x}' \pm \sigma_{\bar{x}}$, μ either *is* in that specific range or it *is not* in that specific range. We can only be 68.27 percent *confident* that it *is* in that range.

Generally, when σ is known, symmetric confidence interval estimates for μ are constructed as follows:

8.40   Confidence limits $= \bar{x} \pm z_C(\sigma/\sqrt{n})$

where $z_C =$ the standard normal deviate corresponding to the level of confidence C.

To illustrate, suppose we randomly select (without replacement) a sample of $n = 5$ from our population of the first ten positive integers and get 5, 7, 3, 9, 2. The mean of this sample is 5.2. The standard error of the mean $(\sigma_{\bar{x}})$ for samples of $n = 5$ from a population of $N = 10$ and $\sigma = 2.87$ has been computed as 0.96. Suppose we wish to obtain a 90 percent confidence interval estimate for μ.

$$\bar{x} = 5.2,\ \sigma_{\bar{x}} = 0.96,\ z_C = 1.65$$

So, the 90 percent confidence interval for μ is (applying 8.40)

$$5.2 \pm 1.65(0.96)$$
$$\text{or } \mathbf{3.62} \text{ to } \mathbf{6.78}$$

That is, we can be 90 percent *confident* that μ is found in the interval between 3.62 and 6.78.

Confidence Interval Estimates of μ, σ Unknown

There are many situations, particularly in the statistical control of the quality of production, where σ is known. There are many more situations where σ is unknown. Most of the time when we set out to determine the mean for a given population, we do not know much about that population. In most such cases we must rely on the sample itself for *all* our knowledge concerning the population. In setting up confidence intervals, we must use s or $\hat{\sigma}$ as estimates of σ. But the central limit theorem does not say anything about the distribution of the sample mean when $\hat{\sigma}$ is substituted for σ. The denominator of the ratio

8.41 $\quad t = \dfrac{\bar{x} - \mu}{\hat{\sigma}/\sqrt{n}}$

is a sample statistic (and therefore a random variable). This ratio cannot be considered a standard normal deviate and thus is given a definitional symbol, t, which is also the name of its probability distribution. Student's t distribution, like the chi-square distribution, has as a parameter the degrees of freedom involved in its computation. There is a complete t distribution for each different number of degrees of freedom. As the degrees of freedom increase, the t distribution approaches the normal distribution and is usually approximated by the normal if $d.f. \geq 30$.

The student t distribution is a continuous distribution, unimodal, and symmetrical with zero mean, but there is greater probability of getting values falling into the two tails of the distribution than for the normal. As with the normal and chi-square distributions (or any continuous distribution), we can only calculate probabilities for t falling within a particular range of values. Table 12 in Appendix B gives selected values of t. The probability at the top of each column is the probability of occurrence of an absolute value of t as large as or larger than the t value shown in the body of the table for the number of degrees of freedom $(d.f.)$ in the left column. Note that Table B-12 indicates the probability of being in *either or both* of the two tails. The probability of being in one particular tail is one half of that shown for the given t and $d.f.$

Duplicating the argument used in developing 8.40, symmetrical confidence interval estimates for μ when σ is unknown are developed as follows:

$$P\left[\bar{x} - t_C \frac{\hat{\sigma}}{\sqrt{n}} < \mu < \bar{x} + t_C \frac{\hat{\sigma}}{\sqrt{n}}\right] = C$$

where t_C is the t value given in Table B-12 for the probability $(1 - C)$ and $n - 1$ $d.f.$ Symmetrical confidence intervals are therefore developed by

8.42   Confidence limits $= \bar{x} \pm t_C \dfrac{\hat{\sigma}}{\sqrt{n}}$

To illustrate the application of 8.42, let us turn once again to our population of the first ten positive integers and our sample of $n = 5$ which contains the integers 5, 7, 3, 9, 2. The mean, $\bar{x}$, is equal to 5.2. The estimate, $\hat{\sigma}$, is derived from the sample as follows:

$$\sum_{i=1}^{n} x_i^2 = 168, \ \sum_{i=1}^{n} x_i = 26, \ \bar{x} = 5.2, \text{ and}$$

$$s^2 = \frac{168}{5} - \left(\frac{26}{5}\right)^2 \qquad \text{(by 5.02)}$$

$$= \mathbf{6.56}$$

$$\hat{\sigma}^2 = 6.56(\tfrac{5}{4}) \qquad \text{(by 8.02)}$$

$$= \mathbf{8.20}$$

$$\hat{\sigma} = \sqrt{8.20} \qquad \text{(by 8.11)}$$

$$= \mathbf{2.86}$$

The standard error of the mean is estimated as

$$\hat{\sigma}_{\bar{x}} = \frac{\hat{\sigma}}{\sqrt{n}} \sqrt{\frac{N-n}{N-1}} \qquad \text{(by 8.31)}$$

$$= \frac{2.86}{\sqrt{5}} \sqrt{\frac{5}{9}}$$

$$= \frac{2.86}{3}$$

$$= \mathbf{0.95}$$

Note that we could derive our estimate, $\hat{\sigma}_{\bar{x}}$, by combining some of the above steps

$$\hat{\sigma}_{\bar{x}}^2 = \frac{s^2 \left(\dfrac{n}{n-1}\right)}{n} \left(\frac{N-n}{N-1}\right) \qquad \text{(by 8.02 and 8.31)}$$

or

8.43 $\quad \hat{\sigma}_{\bar{x}}^2 = \dfrac{s^2}{n-1}\left(\dfrac{N-n}{N-1}\right)$

Here, we would obtain

$$\hat{\sigma}_{\bar{x}}^2 = \frac{6.56}{4}\left(\frac{5}{9}\right)$$

$$= \mathbf{0.91}, \text{ and}$$

$$\hat{\sigma}_{\bar{x}} = \mathbf{0.95}$$

Suppose we would like a symmetrical 90 percent confidence interval for μ. To apply 8.42 we must have the value of t for $C = 0.90$ from Table B-12 for 4 $d.f.$ We look in the column for the $(1 - C) = 0.10$ tail probability and in the row for 4 $d.f.$ and find $t = 2.13$. The confidence interval is

$$5.2 \pm 2.13(0.95)$$
$$5.2 \pm 2.02, \text{ or}$$
$$\mathbf{3.18 \text{ to } 7.22}$$

So, we can be 90 percent *confident* that this interval, derived entirely from sample data, does include the population mean μ.

THE SAMPLE PROPORTION AS AN ESTIMATOR
OF THE POPULATION PROPORTION

We saw in Chapter 5 that in order to apply statistical analysis to qualitative data (attributes of population elements) each observation is considered a count (tally) within a particular classification. In this way, the observations are quantified as the number of observations within each category. We often wish to know the proportion of the population falling within a particular category, such as the preference of housewives for soaps over detergents, the proportion of the members of the labor force that is employed (or unemployed), what proportion of persons over 25 years of age have (or have not) attended college at least two years, the proportion of the items produced on a production line which are defective in some specific (or nonspecific) way, and many more. We generally use the proportion of occurrences in a sample (p) to estimate the proportion of occurrences in the population (P).

If we label the number of occurrences of the desired characteristic in a sample of n observations as x, then

8.50 $p = \dfrac{x}{n}$

As defined, x is a sum. "Successes" are coded as ones (1's) and "non-successes" are coded as zeroes (0's). The number of "successes" in the sample is the sum of the sample observations. Defined thus, p can be considered a mean, that is, p is equal to the sum of the observations over the number of observations. If p is a sample mean, the P must be a population mean, a μ. Looked at this way, it can be accepted that p is an unbiased, consistent, sufficient, and most efficient estimator of P.

The Sampling Distribution of the Sample Proportion

In our discussion of the binomial probability distribution in Chapter 5, we confined ourselves to discussing X, the number of successes in n trials, where P was the probability of a success on any trial. As pointed out when discussing the finite population correction factor earlier in this chapter, what we were really discussing was x, the number of "successes" in samples of n trials. We defined the expected number of successes in n trials as nP (5.23). Since we divide x by n in obtaining p, the expected value of p is P (by 5.05). That is,

8.51 $E(p) = \dfrac{nP}{n} = P$

Applying the same rule (5.05) the *standard error of p* (the standard deviation of the sampling distribution of p) is derived.

$$\sigma_p = \frac{\sqrt{nP(1 - P)}}{n}$$

or

8.52 $\sigma_p = \sqrt{\dfrac{P(1 - P)}{n}}$

Since p and P are means, the central limit theorem applies and we conclude that the sampling distribution of p is normal for reasonably large samples. But this asymptotic property of the sample mean, unfortunately, is not so strong in the case of two-valued populations as in the case of many-valued populations. As we learned in Chapter 3, unless P is approximately equal to 0.5, the normal approximation does not hold for small sample sizes. The student is referred once again to Tables 5.8 and 5.9 and related discussion for more exact rules for approximation of the binomial with the normal.

For reasonably large samples from finite populations the *f.p.c.* must be added to the formula for the standard error of the proportion.

8.53 $\sigma_p = \sqrt{\dfrac{P(1 - P)}{n}} \sqrt{\dfrac{N - n}{N - 1}}$

Note that 8.53 is merely a more general form of 8.52. If the population is infinite in size, the *f.p.c.* reduces to 1 and disappears.

Confidence Interval Estimates for the Population Proportion

We have noted that the standard error of a proportion is

$$\sigma_p = \sqrt{\frac{P(1 - P)}{n}} \tag{8.51}$$

For large samples the usual procedure for the computation of a confidence interval would be

$$\text{Confidence limits} = p \pm z_C \sigma_P$$

But the standard error of p depends upon the value of P. If we know P, no estimate is necessary. We must substitute p for P. But there is a further problem, the above formula will provide the usual symmetrical confidence interval about the sample statistic (p) with which we are now familiar. But the confidence interval estimate actually should be symmetrical about p *only when* $p = 0.50$. Reference to 8.51 indicates why this is true; σ_p varies with the value of the population proportion P. It reaches its maximum value for a given sample size when $P = 0.50$. To illustrate, suppose $n = 100$ and

(a) $P = 0.50$

$$\sigma_p = \sqrt{\frac{(0.50)(0.50)}{100}} = \mathbf{0.05}$$

(b) $P = 0.30$ (or 0.70)

$$\sigma_p = \sqrt{\frac{(0.30)(0.70)}{100}} = \mathbf{0.046}$$

(c) $P = 0.10$ (or 0.90)

$$\sigma_p = \sqrt{\frac{(0.10)(0.90)}{100}} = \mathbf{0.030}$$

To be correct, the confidence interval estimate for P should be asymmetrical about p with the side toward 0.50 wider. An accurate method of obtaining an interval estimate of P makes use of the fact that for large n, the binomial distribution can be approximated with the normal distribution. In such a case,

8.54 $z = \dfrac{x - nP}{\sqrt{nP(1 - P)}}$

can be considered a standard normal deviate. An interval for P with confidence coefficient C may be obtained from

$$-z_C < \frac{x - nP}{\sqrt{nP(1 - P)}} < z_C$$

Solving this double inequality for P, we obtain the limits of the C confidence interval for P.

8.55 Confidence limits $= \dfrac{x + (\frac{1}{2})z_c^2 \pm z_c \sqrt{\dfrac{x(n-x)}{n} + (\frac{1}{4})z_c^2}}{n + z_c^2}$

where x = the number of successes observed in the sample of size n.

A somewhat simpler large sample approximation can be obtained by substituting p for P in 8.54. When this substitution is made, we lose a degree of freedom in estimating σ_p. Technically this should be reflected in the computation of $\hat{\sigma}_p$.

8.56 $\hat{\sigma}_p = \sqrt{\dfrac{p(1-p)}{n-1}}$ or $\hat{\sigma}_p = \sqrt{\dfrac{p(1-p)}{n-1}} \sqrt{\dfrac{N-n}{N-1}}$

When n is large, however, the difference between $\sqrt{\dfrac{p(1-p)}{n-1}}$ and $\sqrt{\dfrac{p(1-p)}{n}}$ is small and the simpler form provides a satisfactory approximation. Using either large sample approximation, confidence interval estimates of P are obtained from

8.57 Confidence limits $= p \pm z_c\hat{\sigma}_P$

For smaller samples, the confidence intervals should be obtained either from 8.55 or, for very small samples, by direct reference to the Binomial.

To illustrate the estimation of P, suppose we have a random sample of 900 TV sets in operation in Bigtown during the broadcast of a certain show on Station KUKU; 330 of the operating sets were tuned to station KUKU. Assume we want a 95 percent confidence interval estimate for the proportion of operating TV sets which actually were tuned to Station KUKU.

$$n = 900$$

$$p = \frac{x}{n} = \frac{330}{900} \qquad \text{(by 8.50)}$$

$$= 0.367$$

$$\hat{\sigma}_p = \sqrt{\frac{p(1-p)}{n}} \qquad \text{(by 8.54)}$$

$$= \sqrt{\frac{(0.367)(0.633)}{900}}$$

$$= 0.016$$

Substituting into 8.57 using 1.96 as the value of z_C for a symmetrical 95 percent confidence interval,

$$\text{Confidence limits} = p \pm 1.96\hat{\sigma}_p$$
$$= 0.367 \pm 1.96(0.016)$$
$$= \mathbf{0.336} \text{ and } \mathbf{0.398}$$

The limits for the more accurate asymmetrical interval can be calculated by substituting into 8.55

$$x = 330, z_C = 1.96, n = 900, n - x = 570$$

$$\text{Confidence limits} = \frac{330 + \frac{1}{2}(1.96)^2 \pm 1.96\sqrt{\frac{(330)(570)}{900} + \frac{1}{4}(1.96)^2}}{900 + (1.96)^2}$$

$$= \frac{331.92 \pm 1.96(14.49)}{903.84}$$

$$= \frac{303.62}{903.84} \text{ and } \frac{360.22}{903.84}$$

$$= \mathbf{0.336} \text{ and } \mathbf{0.399}$$

The small difference in only the upper limit is because n is so large. Suppose n were only 90 and x were only 33. Using 8.57,

$$\text{Confidence limits} = 0.367 \pm (1.96)\sqrt{\frac{(0.367)(0.633)}{90 - 1}}$$

$$= 0.367 \pm (1.96)(0.510)$$
$$= \mathbf{0.267} \text{ and } \mathbf{0.467}$$

Using 8.55,

$$\text{Confidence limits} = \frac{33 + \frac{1}{2}(1.96)^2 \pm 1.96\sqrt{\frac{(33)(57)}{90} + \frac{1}{4}(1.96)^2}}{90 + (1.96)^2}$$

$$= \frac{25.75}{93.84} \text{ and } \frac{44.09}{93.84}$$

$$= \mathbf{0.274} \text{ and } \mathbf{0.470}$$

The difference in limits is more noticeable.

As n and x become smaller, the asymmetrical nature of the more accurate interval makes for larger differences in the limits. Suppose $n = 30$ and $x = 11$. Using 8.57,

$$\text{Confidence limits} = 0.367 \pm 1.96 \sqrt{\frac{(0.367)(0.633)}{30 - 1}}$$

$$= \mathbf{0.193} \text{ and } \mathbf{0.541}$$

Using 8.55,

$$\text{Confidence limits} = \frac{11 + \frac{1}{2}(1.96)^2 \pm 1.96 \sqrt{\frac{(11)(19)}{30} + \frac{1}{4}(1.96)^2}}{30 + (1.96)^2}$$

$$= \frac{7.39}{33.84} \text{ and } \frac{18.45}{33.84}$$

$$= \mathbf{0.218} \text{ and } \mathbf{0.545}$$

The calculations performed to illustrate confidence interval estimation of P also illustrate the effects of size of sample on the precision of sampling estimates. As the size of the sample decreased, the width of the 95 percent confidence interval increased. This relationship is put to use in the final section of this chapter.

Suppose that Mr. Dunner, the Credit Manager of Lossless Grocery Stores, wishes to know the proportion of the accounts receivable at each branch store which are more than 30 days past due. There are 2000 accounts receivable at the Uptown branch. The accountant at Uptown randomly selects 225 accounts and determines that 50, or 22 percent, of them are at least 30 days past due. What would be the symmetrical 90 percent confidence interval estimate of the true proportion of accounts receivable at the Uptown branch which are at least 30 days overdue?

In this case, we note that n/N exceeds 0.05 (actually the ratio is $225/2000 = \mathbf{0.1125}$) and the finite population correction, $f.p.c.$, must be used in computing the sampling error. Substituting into 8.57,

$$\text{Confidence limits} = 0.22 \pm 1.65 \sqrt{\frac{(0.22)(0.78)}{225}} \sqrt{\frac{2000 - 225}{2000 - 1}}$$

$$= 0.22 \pm 1.65(0.087)(0.888)$$

$$= 0.22 \pm 0.13$$

$$= \mathbf{0.09} \text{ and } \mathbf{0.35}$$

Note that the *f.p.c. reduced* the width of the confidence interval. If the *f.p.c.* had not been used, the limits would have been 0.08 and 0.36.

RELATION OF ESTIMATOR EFFICIENCY AND SAMPLE SIZE

Generally speaking, an important objective in using sample statistics to estimate population parameters is to obtain the best estimate for a given cost or an estimate of a given precision at a minimum cost. Two decisions are necessary to the attainment of this objective. One involves the choice of a method of sampling. We have restricted our discussion to simple random sampling. Some of the things we have learned about this method are transferable to other sampling methods. Most important, it should now be recognized that any method of probability sampling contains elements of uncertainty. The value of a given sample statistic varies from one sample to another. A useful measure of that variability is the standard error of the sample statistic, particularly when the sampling distribution of the statistic can be considered normal. A useful technique for choosing the method of sample selection is to compare the standard errors associated with the methods being considered and choose that method with the smallest standard error for a given sample size.

Once the sampling method is selected, a second decision is necessary, namely, what is to be the size of the sample? Space does not allow us a full discussion of the several different methods of sample selection, but we can take time to show how an adequate size for a simple random sample is determined in a given situation. We will restrict ourselves to problems involving estimation of the sample mean and the sample proportion. The method explained can be used (after appropriate modification of the standard error formulas) with any method of probability selection.

The basic determinant of the appropriate size of simple random sample is the answer to the question: "How much uncertainty in the estimate can be tolerated?" This question has two parts: (1) "How large an error in the estimate can be tolerated?" and (2) "How large a risk of exceeding that tolerance should be assumed?" Once these two questions have been answered, the minimum size of the sample necessary to insure that these limits will not be exceeded can be set.

Obviously, the size of the error that can be tolerated and the risk of exceeding that error that can be assumed depend upon the nature of the problem and the consequences of reaching an incorrect decision on the basis of the sample evidence. This decision is based on relative costs and their significance. Once again, we would find it necessary to include utility weights in the calculations to obtain precise estimates. We must be satisfied to conclude that this is an analysis that must be carried out by the decision maker. For purposes of this exposition we will take the results of such analysis as our starting point.

Size of Sample Required to Estimate μ With Given Precision

Looking back at the population of the first ten integers and our one example of $n = 5$ (5, 7, 3, 9, 2) we found the 90 percent confidence limits based on the sample to be 3.62 and 6.78. What if we had required an estimate within 1.60 (for our sample, $z\sigma_{\bar{x}} = 1.58$) of the population μ with a confidence of 90 percent? How large a simple random sample would be required? We knew the following things: $\sigma = 2.87$, $z_{0.90} = 1.65$, and total allowable sampling error (e) = 1.6. But, total allowable sampling error (e) is

8.60 $e = z_C \sigma_{\bar{x}}$

In this case $e = 1.65\sigma_{\bar{x}}$. We also know that, for a finite population

$$\sigma_{\bar{x}} = \frac{\sigma}{\sqrt{n}} \sqrt{\frac{N - n}{N - 1}} \qquad (8.31)$$

Substituting into 8.60,

$$e = z_C \frac{\sigma}{\sqrt{n}} \sqrt{\frac{N - n}{N - 1}}$$

Squaring both sides and solving for n,

8.61 $n = \dfrac{N z_C{}^2 \sigma^2}{e^2(N - 1) + z_C{}^2 \sigma^2}$

In this instance,

$$
\begin{aligned}
n &= \frac{10(1.65)^2(2.87)^2}{(1.60)^2(9) + (1.65)^2(2.87)^2} \\
&= \frac{222.42}{45.46} \\
&= 4.89 \text{ or } 5
\end{aligned}
$$

If the population being sampled were not finite or at least very large, the computation of n would be simplified. Substituting 8.24 into 8.60

$$e = z_C \frac{\sigma}{\sqrt{n}}$$

Squaring both sides and solving for n.

8.62 $n = \dfrac{z_C^2 \sigma^2}{e^2}$

Suppose that Mr. Dunner, Credit Manager of Lossless Grocery Stores, wanted to know the average amount owed on accounts receivable of the stores. How large a sample of accounts would need to be drawn from the 10,000 accounts receivable of Lossless? Information available from past studies indicates that the *variance* of the amounts receivable on each account is no greater than $1900. Mr. Dunner indicates that he would like 19 chances in 20 (95 percent confidence) of obtaining an estimate within $5.00 of the true average amount. To summarize:

$$\sigma^2 = 1900, \ z_{0.95} = 1.96, \ e = 5$$

Substituting into 8.62,

$$n = \frac{(1.96)^2(1900)}{(5)^2}$$
$$= \textbf{291.8 or 292}$$

Mr. Dunner should ask for a simple random sample of approximately 300 accounts.

Size of Sample Required to Estimate P with Given Precision

The general method of determining the minimum sample size required to obtain a given precision has been illustrated for the sample mean. The only difference in this determination when estimating P is that we are working with the sampling distribution of p rather than the sampling distribution of $\bar{x}$. The formulas must be modified by substituting σ_p in place of $\sigma_{\bar{x}}$. Note that we are assuming a large sample so that the binomial sampling distribution of p can be approximated with the normal distribution. Restating 8.60,

8.63 $e = z_C \sigma_p$

For a finite population

$$\sigma_p = \sqrt{\frac{P(1-P)}{n}}\sqrt{\frac{N-n}{N-1}} \qquad (8.53)$$

Substituting into 8.63 and solving for n,

8.64 $\quad n = \dfrac{Nz_c{}^2P(1-P)}{e^2(N-1) + z_c{}^2P(1-P)}$

Suppose Mr. Dunner had instructed the accountant at the Uptown branch of Lossless Grocery Stores to obtain an estimate of the proportion of the 2000 accounts receivable at the Uptown branch over 30 days past due with no more than a 0.10 error and no more than a ten percent chance of exceeding that allowable error. Then,

$$N = 2000,\ z_{0.90} = 1.65,\ e = 0.10$$

But what is the value of P? The accountant must estimate this value to substitute into 8.64. The value of P which would require the largest sample size to attain the required precision would be $P = 0.50$. Suppose the accountant asserts that it is impossible for P to be so high; he believes that P could not possibly exceed 0.35 for the Uptown branch. Substituting this maximum estimate of P into 8.64 will protect us from taking too small a sample. On the other hand, it does not protect us from taking a sample that is larger than is needed. Once again, we see that statistical science does not remove the need for making arbitrary decisions. Note, however, that it does make clear just what risks we are taking in making those decisions. As we will learn in Chapter 10, in some situations (where cost functions are known) statistical science can reduce the need for arbitrary decisions even further.

At the moment, let us substitute $P = 0.35$ into 8.64. Then, the minimum size of simple random sample required to estimate P with the required precision can be *estimated*.

$$n = \frac{2000(1.65)^2(0.35)(0.65)}{(0.1)^2(1999) - (1.65)^2(0.35)(0.65)}$$
$$= \frac{1237.6}{19.37}$$
$$= 63.89 \text{ or } \mathbf{64}$$

Suppose Mr. Dunner wished to estimate the proportion of the total 10,000 accounts receivable of Lossless which were at least 30 days overdue. He specifies an allowable error of ten points (0.10) with a confidence level of 95 percent (C = 95 percent). It seems safe to assume that the sample will be less than five percent of the population, so we can use a formula for estimating the minimum n which does not involve the $f.p.c.$

Substituting 8.51 into 8.63,

$$e = z_C \sqrt{\frac{P(1 - P)}{n}}$$

Squaring and solving for n,

8.65 $n = \dfrac{z_C{}^2 P(1 - P)}{e^2}$

For Mr. Dunner's problem, suppose he asserts that the maximum possible value of P is 0.40. Then,

$$z_{.95} = 1.96,\ P = 0.40,\ e = 0.10$$

Substituting into 8.65,

$$n = \frac{(1.96)^2(0.40)(0.60)}{(0.10)^2}$$
$$= \frac{0.9216}{0.01}$$
$$= 92.16\ \text{or}\ \mathbf{93}$$

Mr. Dunner should be able to get the precision he requires from a sample of about 95.

What if Mr. Dunner had required only 90 percent confidence in his estimate of the proportion of total accounts in error? Then, $z_C = 1.65$ (from Table B-5) and

$$n = \frac{(1.65)^2(0.40)(0.60)}{(0.10)^2}$$
$$= \frac{0.6528}{0.01}$$
$$= 65.28\ \text{or}\ \mathbf{66}$$

Note that this is only slightly larger than the size of sample estimated to be required for an estimate of the proportion of overdue accounts at the Uptown branch. The *only* reasons that it differs are that the estimated maximum value of P differs by 0.05 and the $f.p.c.$ was used in estimating sample size for the branch. These two factors tend to be offsetting. The difference in population size has no effect other than in the $f.p.c.$

SUMMARY

Statistical estimation involves selecting, on the basis of knowledge gained from sample information, an estimate of the population parameter whose value is to serve as a basis for making a decision (*decision parameter*). A point estimate provides only a single value; an interval estimate provides a range of values. A confidence interval specifies a range of values which has a specified *confidence* of including the true parameter value. This confidence is based on the probability distribution (sampling distribution of the sample statistic) showing the distribution of the sample statistic (the random variable) around the parameter (a fixed value). The *process* (rule) by which the confidence limits are obtained is also a random variable with a probability distribution. It is true, however, that a specific interval set up around a specific sample value either does or does not include the parameter. We cannot specify a probability for that inclusion, only a confidence derived from the probabilities associated with the process from which the limits are obtained.

The sampling distributions of the sample variance and sample standard deviation for samples drawn from normal populations have been discussed. In the process, the chi-square (χ^2) distribution (8.04) was introduced and its use in providing confidence interval estimates of the sample variance and sample standard deviation (8.03, 8.05, 8.12) indicated. More general methods of estimation of σ and σ^2 were also covered (8.06–8.11 and 8.13–8.15). It was shown also that it is possible to estimate σ from the sample range (8.16).

The central limit theorem tells us that the distribution of $\bar{x}$'s from simple random samples of size n drawn from a population with mean μ and finite variance σ^2 is approximately normal with mean μ and standard deviation $\sigma/\sqrt{n}$ (8.21–8.25). Confidence limits for μ are estimated as follows for infinite populations:
  (a) With σ known:

$$\text{Confidence limits} = \bar{x} \pm z_C(\sigma/\sqrt{n}) \qquad (8.40)$$

  (b) With σ unknown:

$$\text{Confidence limits} = \bar{x} \pm t_C(\hat{\sigma}/\sqrt{n}) \qquad (8.43)$$

where z_C is the confidence interval coefficient taken from the normal distribution and t_c is the confidence interval coefficient taken from the Student t distribution for $n - 1$ *degrees of freedom.*

For finite populations, the *finite population correction (f.p.c.)* must be added to the standard error formulas for the mean (8.31)

$$\sigma_{\bar{x}} = \frac{\sigma}{\sqrt{n}} \sqrt{\frac{N - n}{N - 1}} \quad \text{and} \quad \acute{\sigma}_{\bar{x}} = \frac{\acute{\sigma}}{\sqrt{n}} \sqrt{\frac{N - n}{N - 1}}$$

The theoretical sampling distribution of the sample proportion is the binomial, but for large enough samples from infinite populations the normal approximation is used where the standard deviation is

$$\sigma_p = \sqrt{\frac{P(1 - P)}{n}} \tag{8.52}$$

But P is the parameter being estimated. Estimates based on p and $\acute{\sigma}_p$ must be used.

$$\acute{\sigma}_p = \sqrt{\frac{p(1 - p)}{n - 1}} \quad \text{or} \quad \acute{\sigma}_p = \sqrt{\frac{p(1 - p)}{n - 1}} \sqrt{\frac{N - n}{N - 1}} \tag{8.56}$$

If an allowable error and an acceptable risk of exceeding that error can be specified, the minimum size of sample required to provide an estimate of the required precision can be estimated. The formulas for estimating sample sizes needed to provide means and proportions of given precision have been developed (8.60–8.64).

DISCUSSION QUESTIONS

1. Define the following *in your own* words (*no formulas* in symbols *or* words).

   (a) confidence interval
   (b) confidence coefficient
   (c) standard error of a sample mean
   (d) standard error of a sample proportion
   (e) the central limit theorem
   (f) the finite population correction
   (g) the allowable error
   (h) decision parameter
   (i) sampling distribution
   (j) confidence

2. "The objective of statistics is to provide a basis for action in the face of uncertainty." Discuss.

3. How does one determine the confidence coefficient (0.95, 0.99, and so forth)?

4. Why is it that estimation processes involving the normal distribution are often used even when the population from which the sample is drawn is not normally distributed?

    Hint: Refer to your answers to Question 1 as well as Table 5.8 and 5.9. Does one of the concepts defined in Question 1 help to explain Tables 5.8 and 5.9?

5. The general public often accepts the laws of the natural sciences as absolute truth.

    (a) What are the merits of such a philosophy, that is, one which (1) always believes strongly whatever is currently believed, thus leading to decisive actions, and (2) revises beliefs in steps rather than in gradual modifications?

    (b) What are the limitations of such a philosophy:
        (1) if held by a scientist?
        (2) if held by a business executive?

    Hint: Remember that scientific knowledge is frequently revised. This could create a problem of a lack of confidence in the new pronouncements when the previous belief is rejected. Must this risk be assumed by each of the above persons? Finally, is *any* knowledge absolute?

6. Suppose that you have an "honest," well-balanced coin with two faces, a head and a tail.

    (a) What would you say are the *chances* that if the coin is "honestly" tossed it will come to rest with the head face up?

    (b) Suppose you place the coin in a box and shake the box, then set it down on the table. Without looking in the box what would you say are the *chances* that the coin is resting with the head face up?

    (c) Given the conditions described in (b), what is the *probability* that the coin is resting with the head face up?

    (d) Would you define the "chances" of (a) and (b) differently if asked to give a verbal description of each? Explain fully.

    Hint: Refer to your definition of confidence in Question 1(j) and to your previous definition of probability.

DISCUSSION PROBLEMS

Show your method on all solutions.

1. A machine produces steel washers whose inside diameter is approximately normally distributed with a mean of 0.375 inches and a stand-

ard deviation of 0.0025 inches. What is the probability that a *single washer* chosen at random from those produced on the machine will have a diameter:
(a) greater than 0.380 of an inch?
(b) between 0.370 and 0.380 of an inch?
(c) between 0.370 and 0.375 of an inch?
(d) less than 0.325 of an inch?
Hint: Use Table B-5 and 5.32.

2. Referring to the washers of Problem 1, if the mean diameters of 25 randomly selected washers are taken, what is the probability that the average will be:
(a) less than 0.3765 of an inch?
(b) between 0.3750 and 0.3760 of an inch?
(c) between 0.3745 and 0.3760 of an inch?
(d) greater than 0.3745 of an inch?
Hint: Use Table B-5 and 8.26.

3. Suppose that for the situation described in Problem 2, σ were unknown, but for the sample of $n = 25$, $\acute{s} = 0.0025$ inches.
(a) Recompute the probabilities for 2(a) and 2(b).
(b) Compare your answers in (a) with your answers to 2(a) and 2(b). Do they differ? If so, should they? Explain.
Hint: Use t (8.41) and Table B-12. Remember that B-12 shows *both* tail areas beyond $t\sigma$.

4. Tests show that the lifetimes of Big-I TV picture tubes are approximately normally distributed with an average life of 2200 hours with a standard deviation of 240 hours.
(a) Out of 400 new tubes put into service by the Hi-Value Repair Service, what are the replacement needs likely to be after all tubes have served 1800 hours? 2500 hours?
(b) What is the probability that any one tube will last for 3000 hours?
(c) How likely is it that the average lifetimes of the 400 tubes will be as high as 2255 hours? As low as 2175 hours?
Hint: Part (c) requires the use of 8.26 and Table B-5. Can parts (a) and (b) be solved in exactly the same way?

5. Calculate a 90 percent confidence interval for the means of each of the populations from which the given sample and other information were taken.
(a) $n = 400$, $\bar{x} = 46.50$, $s = 5.16$
(b) $n = 10$, $\bar{x} = 46.50$, $s = 5.16$
(c) $n = 400$, $\bar{x} = 25.10$, $s = 2.41$
(d) $n = 10$, $\bar{x} = 25.10$, $\acute{s} = 2.41$
(e) $n = 10$, $\bar{x} = 25.10$, $\sigma = 2.41$

Hint: Does it make any difference in your calculations that n changes, and that $\hat{\sigma}$ instead of s is given in part (d)? and that σ is given in part (e)?

(f) Why did your answer to (a) differ from your answer to (b), and your answer to (d) differ from your answer to (e)?

6. What is the 95 percent confidence interval for an estimate of the true proportion of women in the Bigtown metropolitan area preferring a new version of a popular cosmetic (assume random sampling):

    (a) if 8 out of 10 housewives interviewed preferred the new version?
    (b) if 160 out of 200 housewives interviewed preferred the new version?
    (c) What do the differences in method used in working the problems of parts (a) and (b) indicate?
    (d) What do the differences in the sizes of the confidence intervals for parts (a) and (b) illustrate?

    Hints: (1) Does sample size ever influence choice of method? (see Tables 5.8 and 5.9)
    (2) Does sample size effect size of sampling error?

7. List the 45 possible samples of $n = 2$ from the population of the first ten positive integers the distribution of whose means are shown in Table 8.1. Compute the 45 values of $\hat{\sigma}^2$ and $\hat{\sigma}$. Show their distribution in a table. Compute the mean of each distribution. Also compute the population values of σ^2 and σ. Do both means equal their related population value? Should they? Explain.

8. Compute the ranges of the 45 samples of $n = 2$ from the population of the first ten positive integers. Compute their average. What is the ratio of this average to the value of σ for the population? Refer to Table B-11 and check your ratio against the value of d_2 for $n = 2$. Are they equal? Should they be?

EXERCISES

Show your method on all calculations.

1. As a ginger-ale producer entering a new territory, you need an estimate of the proportion of consumers that prefer to buy ginger-ale in cans. A consulting firm agrees to make a survey of the ginger-ale buyers for $2000 plus $4.00 per interview. Assuming they will use a simple random sample and that the population proportion is equal to 0.50, answer the following:

    (a) How much will the survey cost if the error in estimating the proportion is to be no greater than 5 percentage points at the 90 percent confidence level?

(b) How much will the survey cost if the error is not to exceed 5 percentage points at the 98 percent confidence level?

2. Test runs with 5 stock machines of the latest model of the NoKut 18 inch lawn mower on a "standard-lawn" test plot indicate that, on the average, this model consumes 64 ounces of gas to cut 5000 square feet of grass (from a height of approximately 2.25 inches to a height of 1.50 inches) with a standard deviation of 4 ounces. As statistician for NoKut you are provided with the above sample information and asked to specify the following: With 95 percent confidence that the value will not be exceeded, what is the *minimum value* the company can advertize:

(a) as the *maximum gas consumption* for this model per 5000 square feet of "standard" lawn? (Note that the estimate required is a point estimate derived as the single limit for an open-ended asymmetrical confidence interval.)

(b) as the *average gas consumption* for this model per 5000 square feet of "standard" lawn?

3. As sales manager for Burpop you must determine the proportion of the potential customers in the Bigtown area who prefer to buy pop in cans. This information is important because Burpop is expanding its operations in the Bigtown area and is attempting to determine what type of plant and equipment should be installed. You are willing to pay up to $4000 to get an estimate that has 19 chances in 20 of being within five percentage points of the correct value. Your chief statistician estimates that the true proportion is almost certainly between 0.30 and 0.40. You know that the MagnaStat Research Company normally charges $2500 plus $2.50 per interview for such jobs in the Bigtown area. If they charge their normal rates, will you be able to get the company to do this job for $4000 or less? What is the minimum amount you should have to pay them for the job?

4. A random sample of 625 families in Big Town, U.S.A., reported an annual average income of $8200, with a standard deviation of $850. With a risk of only *ten* chances in one hundred of being wrong, estimate the *total income* of Big Town's 900,000 *families*.

5. What is the distinguishing characteristic which differentiates the concepts of *probability* and *confidence?* Can you find more than one? Explain fully.

6. In a sample of 480 listeners polled in Richburg, 160 had their radios tuned to station KRUD between 7:00 and 8:00 P.M. on September 4. What is the 95 percent confidence interval estimate of the true proportion of listeners who were tuned to KRUD?

7. The City of Bigtown is being urged to float a bond issue to finance a

new city center as a place to hold sports and cultural events and to give Bigtown a chance to bid for large conventions. The backers of the proposal feel that *at least* 60 percent of the voters in Bigtown are in favor. Opponents contend the true proportion is *no greater than* 0.40. A public opinion poll is being planned. How large a simple random sample would you suggest should be taken? Clearly state any assumptions you feel it is necessary to make. Explain your choice of assumptions.

8. The Magna-Pollex Company produces balance scales. A new production line has just been built. Fifty scales have been produced in a test run. A standard 10-ounce weight has been weighed by each of the scales and the following information developed:

$$\text{sum of 50 weights} = 498 \text{ ounces}$$
$$\text{sum of 50 squared weights} = 4980.27$$

(a) What is the minimum value (to the nearest one thousandth of an ounce) Magna-Pollex can assert is the maximum variance of balance scales built on this line (when weighing items weighing 10 ounces) with no more than five chances in 100 of that value being exceeded?

(b) What is the minimum average error (to the nearest thousandth of an ounce) of scales built on this line when used to measure items weighing 10 ounces if we accept no more than five chances in 100 of that average being exceeded?

9. In setting up a new line to produce steel pins where length of the pin is a critical factor, an estimate of the variability in length is desired. Ten small samples of pins (5 pins each) have been produced. The average range of these ten samples is 0.009 millimeters. What is the standard deviation in millimeters of pins produced by this line?

10. The MagnaStat Research Company is developing a bid on a sampling project for the Lossless Grocery Stores. In determining sample design, the variance of family expenditures for food is an important control variable. A pilot sample of 25 randomly selected families has given an estimate of $\hat{\sigma}^2 = 2116$.

(a) What is the maximum estimate of the population variance such that there would be no more than five chances in 100 that it would fall below the true population value?

(b) What is the minimum size of simple random sample that the company should suggest if there is to be no more than a 10 percent chance that their estimate of the average food expenditure per family misses the true value by more than $25?

(c) Since the distribution of family food expenditures could be expected to be nonnormal in that it would taper (be skewed) toward the larger expenditures, how do you justify the methods used to obtain the answers to (a) and (b)?

11. Refer to Exercise 9, and estimate how likely it is that one of the samples of 5 pins reported there could have a mean length of 16.030 millimeters if the true average length of the process is 16.025 millimeters.

12. Estimate the population mean and variance for a very large and normally distributed population from which the samples with the following characteristics were drawn. Allow yourself no more than five chances in 100 of being wrong.

(a) $n = 100$, $\bar{x} = 16$, $s = 14$

(b) $n = 17$, $\bar{x} = 16$, $\hat{\sigma} = 14$

(c) $n = 36$, $\bar{x} = 16$, $s = 14$

(d) $n = 225$, $\bar{x} = 16$, $\hat{\sigma} = 14$

(e) $n = 225$, $\bar{x} = 16$, $s = 14$

(f) Justify the differences in the estimates you have given, since all the samples report essentially the same values.

9
hypotheses
and statistics

INTRODUCTION

In Chapter 1, a decision was identified as the selection of one action or sequence of actions from a number of possible alternative actions or sequences of actions. *Statistical decision making* obviously implies basing those selections on statistics (sample data) and/or statistical analysis. That is, the outcomes for each of the alternatives must be known only in the "statistical" ("probability") sense. We saw in Chapter 7 that outcomes may not be known with certainty even where the data on which selection is based are *not* sample statistics. This situation arises where the state of the world varies in such a way that the outcome can be predicted only in a "probability" sense. That is, our *knowledge* concerning the possible states of the world only reveals (perhaps imperfectly) the probability of the occurrence of each possible state of the world.

We learned in Chapter 8 that sample statistics arising from the selection of random (probability) samples are values resulting from the operation of a random variable and thus predictable only in the "probability" sense. Because this is true, we are faced with the question: "What state of the world should I assume is true on the basis of the available sample statistic(s)?" More explicitly, we ask: "Is the state of the world favorable or unfavorable to each alternative action or sequence of actions?" We cannot say definitely what the true value of the critical population parameter (*decision parameter*) may be, so it is obvious that we cannot say without doubt which alternative will prove to be "best." We can only specify that the available sample is more (or less) likely to have been drawn from a population with a specified parameter value (or value within some range) than from a population with a different parameter value (or value within a range).

In Chapter 7, we saw how decision making based on uncertain (probabilistic) knowledge of the possible states of the world was subject to risk. The best alternative suggested in that chapter was to base a decision on the average result in the long run (expected value) for each alternative action. This, however, did not completely solve the problem because alternatives with similar *expected* outcomes may be widely variable in the absolute risk of loss to which they expose the decision maker.

This chapter, together with Chapter 10, will demonstrate that decisions based on sample statistics are also risky and that the chance for loss (error in decision making) also is present in such situations. All we can do is to examine the chance for error in applying statistical rules for making decisions and decide, on the basis of the possible losses and gains involved, taking into consideration all costs, including the cost of the analysis leading to the decision, which alternative yields the highest expected return. Once again, the problem of risk remains.

STATISTICAL DECISION RULES

A statistical decision rule specifies the exact way in which a statistic will be obtained and evaluated. It must specify how the sample is to be drawn, how many items are to be selected, how the required statistic is to be computed from the sample observations obtained, and, finally, how the statistic is to be evaluated.

Consider a variation of the Dry-Cell battery problem of Chapter 4. It was asserted that under ordinary operating conditions, two percent of the batteries produced are defectively sealed. If more than two percent are defectively sealed, then excessive costs are incurred because the defectively sealed batteries must be identified and scrapped. This requires 100 percent inspection of the production lot and results in a loss for each battery scrapped. If lots containing more than two percent defectively sealed batteries are shipped, additional costs are incurred. Shipped lots may be refused by customers and/or customers may shift to some other supplier. Therefore, Dry-Cell is interested in maintaining a proportion of defectives produced which does not exceed two percent.[1]

[1] The logic justifying this level of defectives will be presented in Chapter 10.

To clean and adjust a sealing machine when it begins to perform incorrectly is also costly. The line must be shut down, idling several workers, and a maintenance crew must be called in to perform the cleaning and adjustment. Management is continuously faced with a decision: Should the line be closed down and the machine cleaned and adjusted or should the line be continued in operation? The correct decision depends on the proportion of defectively sealed batteries which the line is producing. This proportion is a population parameter for a Bernoulli process (see 5.20). For this decision problem the *decision parameter* is the true proportion of defectives being produced.

The test for a defective seal requires that the battery be given a destructive test, that is, a test which destroys the battery. It is therefore impossible to test every battery. A sample is required. We must depend upon the sample statistic p to tell us whether or not we should believe that the true proportion P is not greater than two percent. The questions arise: How large a sample? How frequently? How many defectively sealed batteries in the sample will clearly indicate that the machine is performing improperly?

The answers to the preceding questions constitute a statistical decision rule. Those answers depend upon how likely it is that the sample of (indefinite) size n will contain at least some (critical) number of defective batteries, x^*. Note that the probability distribution of x, the number of defectives in the sample, is (theoretically) a binomial distribution.

Let us consider the problem in the context of a decision problem. The alternative acts are: (A_1) close down the line and clean and adjust the sealing machine; (A_2) allow the line to operate as is. The possible states of the world are: (W_1) the line is producing no more than two percent defectives; (W_2) the line is producing more than two percent defectives. A *decision matrix* for this problem is presented in Table 9.1. It can

TABLE 9.1

DECISION MATRIX FOR DRY-CELL BATTERY PROBLEM

	States of the World	
Alternative Acts	$P \leq 0.02$ (W_1)	$P > 0.02$ (W_2)
Stop process, clean and adjust machine (A_1)	Wrong	Right
Allow process to run (A_2)	Right	Wrong

be seen that there are only two possible acts and only two possible states of the world. If the state of the world is W_1 ($P \leq 0.02$), then act A_2 (allow process to run) is proper. Act A_1 is the proper alternative if W_2 is the state of world ($P > 0.02$).

The decision matrix presented in Table 9.1 makes it clear that we would like a rule which would choose Act A_2 if the state of the world were W_1 and choose Act A_1 if W_2 were the true state of the world.

In other words, we would like a decision rule which would differentiate between two possible states of the world and make it possible for us to choose the proper one of two alternative acts.

Null **and Alternate Hypotheses**

One logical approach to the problem of deciding whether or not the state of the world favors Act 1 or Act 2 is to assume one of the two possible states of the world is true and determine how likely it is that the observed sample would have occurred. Which state of the world should be assumed to be true? Suppose we stated the assumption (hypothesis) $P \leq 0.02$ as the hypothesis to be tested. It is possible to commit two errors: (1) reject the hypothesis when it is true and (2) accept the hypothesis when it is false. Which would be the *worst* error? Obviously, the answer to this question depends upon what each of these errors will cost. Is it more expensive to stop and adjust the process needlessly or is it more expensive to fail to stop and adjust the process when $P > 0.02$? Unless we have these costs specified it is difficult to tell which is the worst error.

Let us *assume* that the more expensive error (the worst error) has been defined to be stopping and adjusting the process needlessly, that is, when $P \leq 0.02$. We now can state that we would like to minimize the chance of making this error. If we take as our hypothesis that $P \leq 0.02$, the worst error would be to reject the hypothesis when it is true. Alternatively, if we chose the hypothesis $P > 0.02$, the worst error we could make would be to accept the hypothesis when it was not true. In both instances, if we committed the worst error, we would stop and adjust the process when $P \leq 0.02$.

Statisticians have generally agreed to accept as their *major* hypothesis that hypothesis for which the worst kind of error is that error involved in rejecting the major hypothesis when it is true. They label their major hypothesis the *null hypothesis*.[2] The other hypothesis is called the *alternate hypothesis*.

[2] An alternative definition of the *null* hypothesis may help to clarify the definition given. That is, in problems where one of two acts can result in much larger losses

Note that a hypothesis merely tells which state of the world is true. In general, to accept the null hypothesis is to reject the alternate hypothesis, and vice versa. It is also possible, however, to reserve judgment and ask for more information. In any situation where the cost of each error is known, it should be possible to determine which hypothesis should be accepted. When costs cannot be fully specified, it may be wiser to either accept the *null* hypothesis or reserve judgment and ask for more evidence.

As in the footnote example, most statistical hypotheses are statements about the parameters of assumed or known distributions. The hypotheses may imply knowledge of the functional form of the distributions. Statistical hypotheses which specify the *functional form* of the underlying distribution as well as *all* its parameters are called *simple* hypotheses; those that do not specify functional form and parameters are called *composite* hypotheses. To illustrate, consider the hypotheses $H_0:P \leq 0.02$, $H_a:P > 0.02$. These are *composite* hypotheses since many distributions could be specified within these restrictions. A *simple null* hypothesis would be of the form, $H_0:P = 0.02$. The concept of *simple* and *composite* hypotheses applies also to alternative hypotheses. Thus, the hypothesis labeled H_a in the first example of this paragraph is *composite*. A *simple* alternate hypothesis would be $H_a:P = 0.10$ (the alternate hypothesis in the original problem of Chapter 4).

Let us summarize and organize what has been said about hypotheses.

9.00 The *null* hypothesis is the hypothesis which it is desired to test, the hypothesis whose rejection when true would lead to the worst kind of (most costly) error.

9.01 The *alternate* hypothesis is a competing hypothesis formulated to provide a criterion for testing the *null* hypothesis.

9.02 A *simple* hypothesis completely specifies the underlying distribution, its functional form and all parameters.

9.03 A *composite* hypothesis does not completely specify the underlying distribution.

We are interested in both simple and composite hypotheses It is somewhat easier to demonstrate the theoretical basis of simple hypotheses. Composite hypotheses are more often useful, however, and will be most frequently used here.

---

than the other, the hypothesis whose acceptance leads to the less risky act is called the *null* hypothesis. An obvious example arises in the production and sale of possibly poisonous drugs. The safest course would be to assume the drugs were poisonous and that assumption is adopted as the *null* hypothesis in testing batches of the drugs prior to sale.

Type I and Type II Errors

Statisticians have also agreed on the labeling of the two basic errors involved in testing a statistical hypothesis.

9.04   To reject a statistical *null* hypothesis when it is true is to make a *Type I error* (often called an α *error*).

9.05   To accept a statistical *null* hypothesis when it is false is to make a *Type II error* (often called a β *error*).

Note that the definition of *null* hypothesis given in the previous section indicates that we attempt to state the *null* hypothesis in such a way that the associated Type I error (to reject the hypothesis when it is true) is the worst possible kind of error we can make.

Statistical Decision Rules

Turning again to the Dry-Cell battery problem, suppose we decide to randomly select 20 batteries and test them for defective sealing. Let us take as our *null* hypothesis $H_0:P \leq 0.02$. Suppose we decide that if the sample of 20 batteries contains one or more defectively sealed batteries we will reject the *null* hypothesis and accept the *alternate* hypothesis. That is, if $x \geq 1$ (x is the number of defectives in the sample), we will decide that $P > 0.02$. Alternatively, if $x = 0$, we will decide that $P \leq 0.02$. To summarize, our statistical decision rule contains the following elements:

1. A *simple random* sample
2. Of *size n* = 20
3. A *null* hypothesis, $H_0:P \leq 0.02$, and
4. An *alternative* hypothesis, $H_a:P > 0.02$
5. A *sample statistic*, x = number of defectives in the sample
6. An *acceptance level (interval)*: if $x = 0$, accept H_0 and reject H_a
7. A *rejection level (interval)*: if $x \geq 1$, reject H_0 and accept H_a (or reserve judgment)

Generalizing, we state,

9.06   A statistical decision rule consists of seven elements:
1. A *sampling method*
2. A *sample size*
3. A *null hypothesis*
4. An *alternative hypothesis*
5. A *sample statistic*
6. An *acceptance interval*
7. A *rejection interval*.

This definition of a statistical decision rule illustrates why statistics is said to be the science of making decisions on the basis of partial (sample) information. Note, however, that to reject the *null* hypothesis does not *always* mean that the *alternative* hypothesis must be accepted since the acceptance and rejection interval are stated for the *null* hypothesis. Also, the acceptance and rejection intervals, when specified, define a specific *significance level* (probability of Type I error, alpha (α)).

Error Characteristics of Statistical Decision Rules

We have now chosen a decision rule and we are interested in determining how well it works. How likely is it that we will make an error if we use this rule? Since we are using a simple random sample, we know that the sampling distribution for our sample statistic, x, is the binomial. We have only to consult Table B-4 to determine how likely it is that (a) we will reject the hypothesis when it is true, or that (b) we will accept the hypothesis when it is false. The probability of making a Type I error (α) is given by

$$\alpha = P(x \geq 1 | P \leq 0.02)$$

but this cannot exceed

$$P(x \geq 1 | P = 0.02)$$

By Table B-4, we see that the probability of $x \geq 1$ given that $P = 0.02$ and $n = 20$ is 0.3324. If $P = 0.01$, the probability of at least one defective in the sample of 20 is only 0.1821. If $P = 0$, the probability obviously is zero. These probabilities constitute the probabilities of a Type I error for our composite *null* hypothesis.

The probability (β) of a Type II error (accepting that $P \leq 0.02$ when in fact $P > 0.02$) is more difficult to compute. From Table B-4, we see that if $P = 0.03$, then $P(x = 0) = 0.5438$; if $P = 0.04$, the probability is 0.4420, and so forth. The probabilities once again depend upon the actual value of P, but there are more values within the range of the composite alternative hypothesis than there were within the range of the composite *null* hypothesis (the range $P > 0.02$ extends to $P = 1.00$).

The above error characteristics are summarized in Table 9.2 and Figure 9.1. Note that the error probabilities shown are *conditional* probabilities, they state the probability of an error *given* that P assumes

TABLE 9.2

ERROR CHARACTERISTICS OF THE DECISION RULE, $n = 20$ AND $x^* = 1$
(n = SAMPLE SIZE, x^* = SMALLEST NUMBER OF DEFECTIVES AT
WHICH *null* HYPOTHESIS WILL BE REJECTED)

Possible Values of P (States of the World)	Conditional Probabilities of Error	
	Type I (α) $P(x \geq 1 \mid P \leq 0.02)$	Type II (β) $P(x = 0 \mid P > 0.02)$
0.00	0.0000	
0.01	0.1821	
0.02	0.3324	0.6676
0.03		0.5438
0.04		0.4420
0.05		0.3585
0.06		0.2901
0.08		0.1887
0.10		0.1216
0.12		0.0776
0.14		0.0490
0.17		0.0241
0.20		0.0115

a particular value. In Figure 9.1, the possible values of P are listed on the horizontal axis and the probability of error is measured along the vertical axis. Note that when $P = 0.02$, the two curves are complimentary (the sum of their values adds to 1.0).

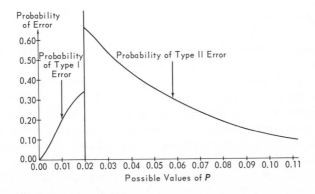

FIG. 9.1.   Error characteristics of decision rule $n = 20$, $x^* = 1$.

Effects of Changing n and/or the Critical Value of x

We have stated only one decision rule, that is, that $n = 20$ and x^* (the critical value of x) = 1. The error characteristics of this decision rule and four others are shown in Figure 9.2. The second rule is $n = 20$ and $x^* = 2$, third is $n = 50$ and $x^* = 2$, the fourth is $n = 50$, $x^* = 4$, and the fifth is $n = 100$, $x^* = 5$.

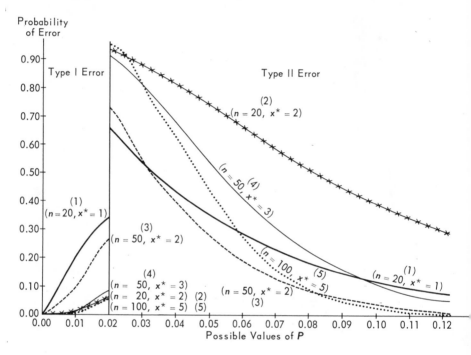

FIG. 9.2.   Error characteristics of several decision rules.

Figure 9.2 illustrates the effects of changing sample size and/or the acceptance interval (critical value of x). It can be seen that increasing the value of x^* (widening the acceptance interval) while holding n constant tends to decrease the probability of Type I error and increase the probability of Type II error. Increasing n and holding x^* constant has the opposite effect, increasing the probability of making a Type I error while decreasing the probability of a Type II error. Increasing both n and x^* in the same proportion, for example, $n = 100$, $x^* = 5$ corresponds to $n = 20$, $x^* = 1$, gives a more discriminating decision rule. The probability of a Type I error is decreased while the probability of a Type II error is increased near the break-even value of P (that value of P where we are indifferent as to which decision is made) but decreased for extreme values of P.

Figure 9.2 illustrates one other important relationship. Note that as long as sample size is fixed, the probability of a Type I error can be decreased only at the expense of an increase in the probability of a Type II error. However, if n is increased, the probability of both errors can be reduced.

Hypothesis Testing and Interval Estimation

Careful readers have no doubt realized that hypothesis testing (by applying statistical decision rules) is related to statistical interval estimation of population parameters. Both rely on the basic fact that a sample statistic computed from a probability sample is generally distributed in a known way in accordance with some standard probability distribution, that is, each statistic has a known sampling distribution. It would therefore seem possible to test a hypothesis by setting up a confidence interval about the sample statistic. If this interval does not include the value of the decision parameter specified by the *null* hypothesis, the hypothesis is rejected. This process "works" but is technically inappropriate. The graphs in Figure 9.3 should help to explain why this is so.

Note that all the (sampling) distributions shown in Figure 9.3 are centered on population values, either assumed (hypothesized) or possible (estimated). In the case of hypothesis testing, there is only one sampling distribution to be considered, the one which would occur if H_0 were true (the population parameter were equal to PP_0). In the case of interval estimation, on the other hand, there are many possible sampling distributions which might contain the sample statistic (ss). The two extreme sampling distributions which enter into consideration are those centered on the possible population parameters (PP^* and PP_*) indicated by the extremes of the interval estimate.

The reader must recognize also that the estimation interval could be nonsymmetric and the hypothesis test could be a one-tail test. One might wish to estimate only the minimum (maximum) value that the decision parameter might attain. Similarly, one might wish to test only whether the population parameter exceeded some minimum (or fell below some maximum). In more complicated situations, one might wish to make two-sided estimates with the confidence interval nonsymmetric (for example, one might want no more than one chance in one hundred of the parameter falling below the interval but be willing to take four chances in 100 that it fall above the interval). The interval would still

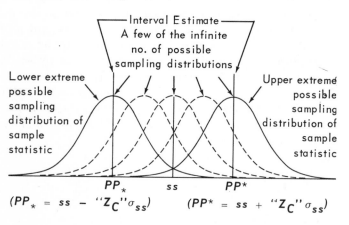

a. Hypothesis Testing $H_0: PP = PP_0$

Sampling Distribution of Sample Statistic

Lower Rejection Interval   Upper Rejection Interval
$P = \alpha/2$ $P = \alpha/2$

ss_* PP_0 ss^*

Acceptance Interval
$P = 1 - \alpha$, if $PP = PP_0$

b. Interval Estimating

Interval Estimate
A few of the infinite
no. of possible
sampling distributions

Lower extreme   Upper extreme
possible   possible
sampling   sampling
distribution of   distribution of
sample   sample
statistic   statistic

PP_* ss PP^*

$(PP_* = ss - \text{``}Z_C\text{''}\sigma_{ss})$    $(PP^* = ss + \text{``}Z_C\text{''}\sigma_{ss})$

FIG. 9.3.   Relationship between statistical hypothesis testing and statistical interval estimating.

be a 95 percent confidence interval. Similarly, in testing some hypothesis, one might be willing to accept a larger chance of making a Type I error in one direction, say on the lower side of PP_0, than in the other direction, the upper side of PP_0. The total chance of a Type I error (α, the *significance level* of the test) would be the sum of the two tail probabilities even though the rejection areas in the two tails were unequal.

TESTING COMMON HYPOTHESES

Testing Hypotheses about the Mean

The hypothesis that $\mu = \mu_0$ is generally a composite hypothesis, even if the population variance (and standard deviation) can be assumed to be known. It is a simple hypothesis only in those cases where the population distribution is completely specified by the values of μ and σ^2. The central limit theorem tells us that the sampling distribution of the sample mean $\bar{x}$ is asymptotically normal regardless of the shape of the population distribution. It is true, then, that if μ and σ are (assumed to be) known, the assumption that the distribution of sample means follows the normal probability distribution can be used as a basis for obtaining probability answers to questions about μ. If σ is not (assumed to be) known, the t ratio can be utilized.

One-sided Tests, σ Known. In choosing between $\mu = \mu_0$ and $\mu = \mu_a$, where $\mu_a > \mu_0$, we would prefer μ_0 for small values of $\bar{x}$ and μ_a for large values of $\bar{x}$. A decision rule based on finding a critical value of $\bar{x}$ which reflects these considerations would be of the form "reject H_0 if $\bar{x} > \bar{x}^*$." In fact, such a rejection interval would be reasonable for any hypothesis where the (possible) value or values of μ_0 are smaller than the (possible) value or values of μ_a. That is, any of the following hypotheses are of this type:

1. $H_0:\mu = 20$ and $H_a:\mu = 30$
2. $H_0:\mu = 20$ and $H_a:\mu > 20$
3. $H_0:\mu \leq 20$ and $H_a:\mu > 20$

Suppose the Den Products Company is investigating a new method for training men as stitching machine operators. Under the old training methods, trainees were able to average 150 pieces per day after five days of training with a standard deviation of twelve pieces per day. A class of sixteen men has just completed five days under the new method. They produce an average of 166 pieces in a one-day test. Is the new training method superior? It would appear that it is. Suppose we adopt the following decision rule:

$$H_0:\mu = 150$$

$$H_a:\mu > 150$$

$$\alpha = 0.05 \text{ (one tail)}$$

$$z_\alpha = +1.65$$

Where z_α is the critical value of the ratio $\dfrac{\bar{x} - \mu}{\sigma/\sqrt{n}}$ corresponding to the number of sigma units between μ_0 and the limit of the acceptance interval. We will reject H_0 if z is equal to or larger than $+1.65$. (This is analogous to rejecting H_0 if $\bar{x}$ is equal to or larger than $\bar{x}^*$, where $\bar{x}^* = \mu + z_\alpha \sigma_{\bar{x}}$.) The population standard deviation is known to be 12, so that 8.26 may be used.

$$
\begin{aligned}
z &= \frac{\bar{x} - \mu}{\sigma/\sqrt{n}} \\
&= \frac{166 - 150}{12/\sqrt{16}} \\
&= \frac{16}{3} \\
&= 5.33
\end{aligned}
$$

Since z exceeds z_α, we reject H and accept H_a.

Management objects to this decision rule because it does not take account of the costs involved. They insist that $H_0:\mu = 150$ is inappropriate; the assumed value of μ_0 must be higher so that the additional cost of the new program can be recovered. The new program requires an expenditure of \$2000 for new training films and equipment. Management is willing to adopt the new method only if there is no more than five chances in 100 that this \$2000 will *not* be recovered within the first year. Past experience indicates that 200 operators are trained each year. After the end of the five-day training period, they have improved steadily so that by the time they go on the piece rate one month later they are producing 175 pieces per day. This means they have an average production rate of $(150 + 175)/2$ or 162.5 pieces per day for an average cost to the company of \$0.09846 per piece. In order to pay its way, the new system must reduce the average cost per unit enough to pay for the system over 200 trainees. The average cost per unit is equal to the amount of daily pay (\$16) divided by the average number of units produced over the one-month period (under the old program, $\mu_m = 162.5$ units). Therefore, we must find the average production rate (μ_m') over 22 working days (one month) for 200 trainees which will reduce the average cost enough to provide \$2000 in savings. That is

$$
200(22)(\mu_m')\left(0.09846 - \frac{16}{\mu_m'}\right) = 2000
$$
$$
0.0946\mu_m' - 16 = 2000/4400
$$
$$
0.09846\mu_m' = 16.454545
$$
$$
\mu_m' = 167.1
$$

But, for the sample, we know only the average production rate at the end of five days' training ($\bar{x}_t$). It is reasonable to assume that the new training program does not change the final average level of performance, so that, if μ_t' is the breakeven average production rate at the end of training,

$$\mu_m' = (\mu_t' + 175)/2$$

Therefore,

$$\mu_t' = 2\mu_m' - 175$$
$$= 2(167.1) - 175$$
$$= \mathbf{159.2}$$

Management, then, wants the following decision rule

$$H_0{:}\mu < 159.2 \qquad H_a{:}\mu \geq 159.2$$
$$\alpha = 0.05 \text{ (one tail)} \qquad z_\alpha = +1.65$$

The result would be:

$$z = \frac{166 - 159.2}{3} \qquad \text{(by 8.26)}$$
$$= \mathbf{+2.27}$$

Since z exceeds z_α, H_0 is rejected and H_a is accepted. Thus, we conclude that there are not as many five chances in 100 that the new system of training will fail to pay for itself within one year. The new system should be adopted under this criterion.

Two-Sided Tests, σ Known.   As a packager of frozen foods the Duravit Corporation carefully controls the net weight of frozen food packages. If the weight drops too much below the labeled level, Duravit is liable for prosecution and will lose customers. At the same time, the weight must not be allowed to go too high because that will reduce the amount of salable product derived from a given amount of raw material. One such frozen food is whole strawberries which are put up in one pound (net weight) cartons. The quality control supervisor intends to select a random sample of sixteen packages of strawberries from the output of the process at regular intervals and use their average weight to indicate the average weight of all packages being produced. Controlled runs of the process indicate the package weights to be normally distributed with a standard deviation of 0.40 ounces. Suppose the inspector decides to select samples of sixteen packages each from production runs and one such sample averages only 15.8 ounces. Should he conclude the process is out of control?

An analysis of the costs of rejected runs, lost revenues, and so forth, has convinced the quality control inspector that he can accept as many as five chances in 100 of stopping the process needlessly in attempting to prevent underweight packages. This means that his decision rule would be:

$$n = 16 \qquad H_0:\mu = 16.00 \qquad H_a:\mu < 16.00$$
$$z_\alpha = -1.64 \; (\alpha = 0.05, \text{ lower tail only})$$

and by 8.26

$$z = \frac{\bar{x} - \mu}{\sigma/\sqrt{n}}$$
$$= \frac{15.8 - 16.0}{0.40/\sqrt{16}}$$
$$= -2.0$$

Since the value of z is less than the critical value of z_α ($-2.00 < -1.64$) the inspector should order that the process be stopped and the filling machine readjusted. We could also say that the *absolute* value of z is *greater* than the *absolute* value of z_α. The use of z_α is analagous to setting a rejection limit for $\bar{x}$ as

$$\bar{x}_* = \mu - z_\alpha \sigma_{\bar{x}}$$
$$= 16.00 - 1.64(0.40/\sqrt{16})$$
$$= 15.836$$

At the next inspection, the inspector's sample ($n = 16$) has a mean weight of 16.20 ounces. Previous analysis of the costs of stopping to adjust the machine, putting an excess of product in each carton, and so forth, has convinced the quality control supervisor that he can accept a 0.02 probability of stopping the packing needlessly when preventing the production of cartons containing more than one pound of straw-berries. This gives him a decision rule which contains the following elements:

$$n = 16 \qquad H_0:\mu \leq 16.00 \qquad H_a:\mu > 16.00$$
$$z_\alpha = +2.05 \; (\alpha = 0.02, \text{ one tail})$$

and

$$z = \frac{\bar{x} - \mu}{\sigma_{\bar{x}}}$$
$$= \frac{16.2 - 16.0}{0.10}$$
$$= \frac{+0.2}{0.10}$$
$$= +2.00$$

Since the value of z is less than z_α ($+2.00 < +2.05$), the inspector should allow the process to continue to operate as it is.

Let us summarize this example. What is involved is a simple null hypothesis ($\mu = 16.00$ ounces) and a composite alternative hypothesis ($\mu \neq 16.00$ ounces). The situation is slightly complicated because it is more important to detect deviations of μ below μ_0 than to detect deviations of μ above μ_0. The complete decision rule is:

Draw a simple random sample of $n = 16$ cartons. Compute $\bar{x}$, the average weight of the contents of the 16 cartons. Use $\bar{x}$ to compute z. If $-z_\alpha \geq z \geq +z_\alpha$, reject $H_0: \mu = 16.00$ and accept $H_a: \mu \neq 16.00$.

An alternative but equivalent statement of the decision rule would be:

Draw a simple random sample of $n = 16$ cartons. Compute $\bar{x}$, the average weight of the contents of the 16 cartons. If $15.836 < \bar{x} < 16.205$ ounces, accept the *null* hypothesis that $\mu = 16.00$ ounces. If $\bar{x} \leq 15.836$ ounces or $\bar{x} \geq 16.205$ ounces, reject the *null* hypothesis and accept the alternative hypothesis that $\mu \neq 16.00$ ounces.

The error characteristics of the decision rule are sketched in Figure 9.4. The error curve is seen to have a break at the point $\mu = 16.00$. Actually, the curve should not have such a noticeable gap. It is shown here in order to emphasize an important point. A Type I error (α error) can be committed only when H_0 is true, that is, when $\mu = 16.00$. The probability of this error occurring is the significance level at which H_0 is rejected

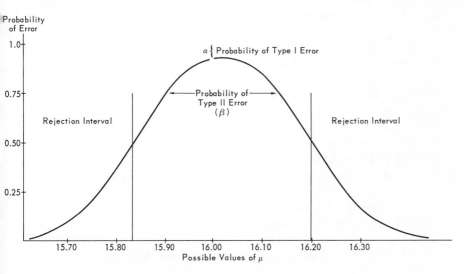

FIG. 9.4. Error characteristics of the decision rule: $n = 16$, $-z_\alpha = -1.64$, $+z_\alpha = 2.05$ ($H_0: \mu = 16.00$; $H_a: \mu \neq 16.00$).

when true. In the example being considered, this significance level differs according to the direction that $\bar{x}$ deviates from μ_0 (16.00). Type II error (β error), on the other hand, can be committed any time μ differs from 16.00 by even an infinitely small amount. The curve depicting the probability of β error has an infinitely small gap at the point where $\mu = 16.00$. The curve is shown with the observable gap to illustrate these points. To summarize, Type I error is possible only if H_0 is true, that is, only if $\mu = 16.00$, but Type II is possible at *all other values* of μ.

A second feature of this type of decision rule (simple *null* hypothesis, composite alternative hypothesis) is the unimodal nature of the associated error curve. If the acceptance interval is symmetrical about μ_0, the error curve will also be symmetrical.

Tests of a Single Mean, σ Unknown. A more common type of business problem is that encountered where the standard deviation of the population is unknown. Only in areas where significance tests are repeatedly applied do we often encounter situations where σ is known. Even in repeated testing areas, however, we often find it necessary to estimate σ when designing the statistical decision rule.

In testing hypothesis about the mean with σ unknown, we must substitute s or $\hat{\sigma}$ for σ in the error formulas. As we learned in Chapter 8 (pages 240–241) whenever a sample statistic is substituted for the population standard deviation in computing the standard error of the mean, significance levels are determined by reference to student's "t" distribution (Table B-12) rather than the normal. Only when $n > 30$ is it possible to use the normal z as an approximation for t.

Suppose that the Trupig Company has announced a new house paint. They advertise that a gallon of this new brand (Bigspred) will cover an average of 550 square feet. Mr. Ny Brush, painting contractor, decides to try the new paint since it appears to be cheaper than the brand he is now using. He buys ten gallons of the paint for the test. The ten gallons cover an average of 535.8 square feet with a sample standard deviation (s) of 35.4 square feet. Mr. Brush asks for assistance in determining the meaning of these data.

Because of the possible savings involved, Mr. Brush feels that it would be most undesirable to fail to shift to Bigspred if it actually covers an average of 550 square feet per gallon. However, because of good relations with his former paint supplier, he is desirous of protection against an unwarranted change. After further discussion of the relative costs of error, he agrees to the following decision rule:

$$n = 10 \qquad H_0{:}\mu \geq 550 \qquad H_a{:}\mu < 550$$
$$\alpha = 0.05 \text{ (one tail)} \qquad t_\alpha = -1.833$$

The critical value of t (t_α) is obtained from Table B-12 for 9 $d.f.$ Substituting into 8.41,

$$t = \frac{535.8 - 550}{35.4/\sqrt{10-1}}$$
$$= -1.20$$

Since t (-1.20) is *greater* than t_α (-1.833), Mr. Brush would be advised that it is reasonable to believe that Bigspred covers an average of 550 square feet per gallon.

Mr. Brush points out that it may also be reasonable to believe that $\mu \leq 500$. After some discussion of relative costs of error, it is decided to perform a second test using the following decision rule.

$$n = 10 \qquad H_0:\mu \leq 500 \qquad H_a:\mu > 500$$
$$\alpha = 0.10 \text{ (one tail)} \qquad t_\alpha = +1.383$$

Substituting into 8.41,

$$t = \frac{535.8 - 500}{35.4/3}$$
$$= \frac{+35.8}{11.8}$$
$$= +3.03$$

It therefore seems reasonable to believe that $\mu > 500$.

Mr. Brush has tested two *null* hypotheses, each at a different level of significance:

$$\text{I. } H_1:\mu \geq 550 \qquad \alpha = 0.05$$
$$\text{II. } H_2:\mu < 500 \qquad \alpha = 0.10$$

Suppose we try to develop a decision rule for the problem in this complete form. It appears that Mr. Brush is looking for a critical value for the sample mean ($\bar{x}^*$) such that if the observed sample mean ($\bar{x}$) falls at or above $\bar{x}^*$, he could satisfy his conditions for accepting hat $\mu \geq 550$, and if $\bar{x} < \bar{x}^*$, he could satisfy his conditions for accepting that $\mu_2 \leq 500$. Thus, he has specified two equations:

$$\text{III. } \bar{x}_1^* = \mu_1 - t_\alpha\sigma_{\bar{x}}$$
$$\text{IV. } \bar{x}_2^* = \mu_2 + t_\alpha\sigma_{\bar{x}}$$

and specified that $\bar{x}_1^* = \bar{x}_2^*$. Unfortunately, t_α would vary with sample size and sample size is the only variable which can be set at the appropriate value to get the result $\bar{x}_1^* = \bar{x}_2^*$. ($\sigma_{\bar{x}} = \sigma/\sqrt{n}$, and n is the variable.) Mr. Brush partially solves this dilemma by insisting that $n \leq 10$. We will use t_α for 9 $d.f.$ as a first approximation.

A second problem is that the value of σ must be known. We will use the sample given to get an estimate of σ, recognizing that ordinarily the value would have to come from some other source. (For example, by assuming that the ratio σ/μ is the same for both paints and using a value ten percent greater than σ for the old paint.)

$$\hat{\sigma} = s\sqrt{\frac{n}{n-1}} \qquad \text{(from 8.02)}$$

$$= 35.4\sqrt{\frac{10}{9}}$$

$$= \mathbf{37.3}$$

Then, making the appropriate substitutions,

$$\bar{x}_1^* = 550 - 1.833(37.3/\sqrt{n})$$
$$\bar{x}_2^* = 500 + 1.383(37.3/\sqrt{n})$$

and, since $\bar{x}_1^* = \bar{x}_2^*$,

$$500 + 1.383(37.3/\sqrt{n}) = 550 - 1.833(37.3/\sqrt{n})$$

and n can be determined.

$$\frac{51.59 + 68.37}{\sqrt{n}} = 50$$

$$\sqrt{n} = \frac{120.0}{50}$$

$$n = (2.4)^2$$
$$= 5.76 = \mathbf{6}$$

Substituting into equation (III) for $\bar{x}_1^*$, but using t_α (5 $d.f.$) instead of t_α (9 $d.f.$), we obtain

$$\bar{x}_1^* = 550 - 2.015(37.3/\sqrt{6})$$
$$= 550 - 2.015(15.22)$$
$$= \mathbf{519.3}$$

but, using (IV)

$$\bar{x}_2^* = 500 + 1.476(15.22)$$
$$= \mathbf{522.5}$$

Because t_α varies with n, $\bar{x}_1^*$ can be made equal to $\bar{x}_2^*$ only approximately. It is now obvious that $6 > n < 10$ and that $519.3 > \bar{x}^* < 522.5$. Trial and error iteration indicates the best decision rule to be:

$$n = 7; \bar{x}^* = 521.2 \ (\bar{x}_1^* = 521.9; \bar{x}_2^* = 520.4)$$

Tests of Hypotheses about P and nP

Tests for Infinite Populations. Mr. Sepay of Lessloss Department Stores has hired a new clerk and assigned him to the preparation of invoices. The work of the billing clerk is checked for accuracy by drawing a sample from his second week's work and checking the sample for the proportion of defective invoices. If errors are found in an invoice, it is considered defective; if no errors are found, the invoice is classed as nondefective. New billing clerks have been retained only if no more than 25 percent of the invoices prepared by them during the second week are in error. Checking has been on a 100 percent basis, but Mr. Sepay decides to cut costs through the use of a sample. He draws a sample of 20 invoices from the approximately 450 prepared by the new clerk during his second week and finds that eight are in error. Should he retain the new clerk?

Mr. Sepay is convinced (rightly or wrongly) that costs of excessive errors on invoices are greater than the costs of recruitment, training, and separation. He has decided to use the following decision rule.

$$n = 20 \qquad H_0{:}P > 0.25 \qquad H_a{:}P \leq 0.25$$
$$\alpha = 0.05 \qquad x^* = 9$$

In this instance (we are dealing with a Bernoulli process), we have merely observed a sample from a continuous process. The critical value of x (x^*) has been taken from Table B-4 for the cumulative binomial.

Mr. Sepay is dissatisfied with this result. He feels that, even though eight or more defective invoices will occur approximately ten percent of the time by chance alone, there may be too much chance of accepting a false hypothesis. He has heard how we helped Mr. Brush and asks if we can help him in the same way.

Mr. Sepay agrees that he would like to test simultaneously the following hypotheses, each at the indicated significance level.

I'. $H_1{:}P_1 \geq 0.35 \qquad \alpha = 0.10$ (one tail)
II'. $H_2{:}P_2 \leq 0.20 \qquad \alpha = 0.02$ (one tail)

Then the significant value of p (p^*) is to satisfy both of the equations:

$$\text{III}'. \quad p_1^* = P_1 - z_{0.10} \sqrt{\frac{P_1(1 - P_2)}{n}}$$

$$\text{IV}'. \quad p_2^* = P_2 + z_{0.02} \sqrt{\frac{P_2(1 - P_2)}{n}}$$

Substituting the given values, setting $p_2^* = p_1^*$ and solving for n,

$$0.20 + 2.05 \sqrt{\frac{(0.2)(0.8)}{n}} = 0.35 - 1.28 \sqrt{\frac{(0.35)(0.65)}{n}}$$

$$\frac{2.05(0.4) + 1.28(.477)}{\sqrt{n}} = 0.15$$

$$\sqrt{n} = \frac{0.820 + 0.611}{0.15}$$

$$= 9.54$$

$$n = 91$$

Solving for p^* (using III'):

$$p_1^* = 0.35 - \frac{0.611}{9.54}$$

$$= 0.286$$

Using IV' as a check:

$$p_2^* = 0.20 + \frac{0.82}{9.54}$$

$$= 0.286$$

Mr. Sepay insists that it is impossible to examine such a large sample, pointing out that such a sample would constitute almost 20 percent of the invoices handled by the clerk in one week. He asks if it might be possible to use a smaller sample if we directed our attention to the *number* of defective invoices rather than the *proportion* of defective invoices.

Using the same hypotheses as when working with the sample proportion, but restating them in terms of number of defectives:

$$\text{I}''. \quad H_1{:}nP \geq 0.35n \qquad \alpha = 0.10 \text{ (one tail)}$$
$$\text{II}''. \quad H_2{:}nP \leq 0.20n \qquad \alpha = 0.02 \text{ (one tail)}$$

The significant values of x (np) to be set equal are:

$$\text{III}''. \quad x_1^* = P_1 n - z_{0.10} \sqrt{nP_1(1 - P_1)}$$
$$\text{IV}''. \quad x_2^* = P_2 n + z_{0.02} \sqrt{nP_2 \, 1 - P_2)}$$

Substituting the given values of P_1, P_2, $z_{0.10}$, and $z_{0.02}$ and solving for n and x^*, we obtain

$$n = 91 \qquad x^* = 26$$

These results are exactly comparable to the results obtained when using proportions (P and p). In fact, $n(p^*) = 91(0.286) = \mathbf{26.0}$.

It may be possible that the normal approximation is not adequate. To check this, we refer to Table B-4 for $n = 100$ (the closest approximation to the computed n of 91) and an x^* of 26 or greater (the exact computed value of x^* for $n = 91$ was *possibly* a fraction over 26).

P	$P(x \geq 26\|P)$	$P(x \geq 27\|P)$	$P(x \geq 28\|P)$	$P(x \geq 29\|P)$
0.20	0.0875	0.0558	0.0342	0.0200
0.25	0.4465	0.3583	0.2776	0.2075
0.35	0.9789	0.9649	0.9442	0.9152

It appears that the rule $n = 100$, $x^* = 29$ would approximate the conditions specified by Mr. Sepay. This rule gives a probability of dismissal of 0.02 when P is equal to 0.20 and, at the same time, the rule gives greater than the required level of protection against keeping a clerk producing 35 percent defective invoices (0.0848 instead of 0.10).

Searching further in Table B-4 for an appropriate decision rule involving an $n \leq 50$ and capable of satisfying Mr. Sepay's prior conditions, we start at $n = 50$ and obtain the following candidates and their associated probabilities:

	$n = 50, x^* = 17$	$n = 50, x^* = 19$	$n = 50, x^* = 21$	$n = 50, x^* = 23$
P	$P(x \geq 17\|P)$	$P(x \geq 19\|P)$	$P(x \geq 21\|P)$	$P(x \geq 23\|P)$
0.20	0.0144	0.0025	0.0003	0.0000
0.25	0.0983	0.0287	0.0063	0.0010
0.35	0.6111	0.3784	0.1861	0.0710

Further search in this fashion for a decision rule to satisfy Mr. Sepay seems a waste of time. We suggest that he obtain a clearer picture of costs so that the expected losses of eligible decision rules may be compared to obtain the rule whose expected loss is a minimum. This process is explained in Chapter 10.

Tests for Finite Populations. In acceptance sampling and other areas, businessmen are often faced with the need for making decisions about the proportion or number of elements possessing a particular attribute in a finite population. In many such situations, it is practically possible for economic or other reasons to examine only a sample from the population. In such instances, the techniques of the previous sections are not theoretically correct.

Suppose the personnel manager at Lessloss Department Stores is interested in examining the attitudes of the 600 clerks and cashiers employed by the firm toward a proposed change in work rules. It has been decided that the new rules are to be adopted only if at least 75 percent of the workers involved actually favor the change. The personnel manager decides to use a sample because of the geographic distribution of the population of interest and the cost of contacting them. He wants to be 95 percent certain that the sample estimate will be within five percentage points of the true value. Using 8.64 and a hypothetical P of 0.75,

$$
\begin{aligned}
n &= \frac{600(1.96)^2(0.75)(0.25)}{(0.05)^2(599) + (1.96)^2(0.75)(0.25)} \\
&= \frac{600(0.72)}{1.4975 + 0.72} \\
&= \mathbf{195} \text{ or about } \mathbf{200}
\end{aligned}
$$

Two hundred randomly selected clerks and cashiers are contacted and 143 are found to favor the new work rules. Meanwhile, the personnel manager has been developing the remainder of his decision rule. Because the new work rules will result in significant cost reductions for Lessloss, the personnel manager wants the greatest protection against failure to adopt when he should. The rule he has developed is:

$$
\begin{aligned}
&H_0{:}P \geq 0.75 \qquad H_a{:}P < 0.75 \\
&\alpha = 0.05 \qquad\quad z_\alpha = -1.64 \text{ (one tail)}
\end{aligned}
$$

Combining this with the sample information:

$$
n = 200 \qquad P = \frac{143}{200} = 0.715
$$

by 8.53,

$$
\begin{aligned}
\hat{\sigma}_p &= \sqrt{\frac{(0.75)(0.25)}{200}} \sqrt{\frac{600 - 200}{599}} \\
&= \sqrt{0.0009375} \sqrt{\frac{400}{599}} \\
&= \mathbf{0.025}
\end{aligned}
$$

Restating 5.32, for use of the normal approximation rather than the exact hypergeometric solution,

9.10 $\quad z = \dfrac{P - P \pm 1/2n}{\hat{\sigma}_p}$

The last term $(\pm 1/2n)$ is a continuity correction applied because we are using a truly continuous distribution (the normal) to approximate what is really a discrete distribution (because x can take on only integer values in the range $0 \leq x \leq n$). The plus sign is used when $p - P$ is negative; the minus sign when $p - P$ is positive. Substituting into 9.10,

$$z = \frac{0.715 - 0.75 + (\tfrac{1}{400})}{0.025}$$
$$= \frac{-0.0325}{0.025}$$
$$= -1.30$$

Since $z > z_\alpha$, the personnel manager should conclude that it is reasonable to believe that P is at least 0.75 and install the new work rules.

The personnel manager asks why we bothered with testing for the proportion of favorable responses, why we did not look merely at the *number* of favorable responses. Suppose we use this approach. The symbol X stands for nP $[(0.75)(200)]$.

$$H_0{:}X \geq 150 \qquad H_a{:}X < 150$$
$$\alpha = 0.05 \qquad z_\alpha = -1.64 \text{ (one tail)}$$

Combining this with the sample information:

$$n = 200 \qquad \sigma_x = \sqrt{nP(1 - P)} \sqrt{\frac{N - n}{N - 1}}$$
$$x = 143 \qquad = \sqrt{200(0.75)(0.25)} \sqrt{0.6678}$$
$$= 5.00$$

To test the hypothesis, we use 8.54 with a "continuity" correction added to adjust for the use of a continuous distribution (the normal) in estimating probabilities in a discrete distribution (the hypergeometric).

9.11 $\quad z = \dfrac{x - X \pm \tfrac{1}{2}}{\sigma_x}$

As in 9.10, the plus sign applies to the continuity correction if $x - X$ is negative; the minus sign is used if $x - X$ is positive. Making the appropriate substitutions,

$$z = \frac{143 - 150 + \frac{1}{2}}{5.00}$$

$$= \frac{-6.5}{5.00}$$

$$= -1.30$$

Since $z > z_\alpha$, H_0 is accepted.

Note that the value of z is the same whether we test the difference between p and P or between x and X.

Tests of Hypotheses about the Population Variance

Many business decision problems require a knowledge of the population variance. For example, a manufacturer of a product which must meet rigid specifications needs to know something about the variability of his product, which will be determined in part by the variability of the components from which it is constructed. Personnel managers, training program directors, and supervisors often need to know what variability can be expected from human beings as workers and students. Sales managers and management planners need to know about variances in demands for products. The test described below provides a method for testing the *null* hypothesis that the variance of a normal population equals a particular constant. Methods for making more involved tests concerning equality of variances for two or more normal populations are reserved for Chapter 11.

For example, suppose we refer once again to the training method problem of the Den Products Company. In testing whether the average pieces sewed per day had increased with the new method, we assumed that the standard deviation remained the same under the new method as under the old (twelve pieces per day). Is this a reasonable assumption? A class of sixteen trainees had just completed the new training program. Suppose that the estimated standard deviation ($\hat{\sigma}$) from this (assumed randon) sample were sixteen. Might it not be true that the standard deviation had also changed? On the assumption that the hypothesis was formulated before the sample results were known, we might state our hypothesis as follows:

$$H_0{:}\sigma^2 = \sigma_0^2 = 144 \qquad H_a{:}\sigma^2 \neq \sigma_0^2 \neq 144 \qquad \alpha = 0.05$$

By 8.03 we know

$$\chi^2 = \frac{(n-1)\hat{\sigma}^2}{\sigma^2}$$

We also know that we can state the rejection intervals for our *null* hypothesis as,

Upper rejection interval: $\chi^2 \geq \chi^2_{\alpha/2}(15 \; d.f.)$
Lower rejection interval: $\chi^2 \leq \chi^2_{1-\alpha/2}(15 \; d.f.)$

Where $\chi^2_{\alpha/2}(n-1 \; d.f.)$ is that value of χ^2 which at $n-1$ degrees of freedom will be equalled or exceeded (by chance) only $\alpha/2$ proportion of the time. $\chi^2_{1-\alpha/2}(n-1 \; d.f.)$ is defined similarly but at the opposite limit. These χ^2 values are taken from Table B-10. The *null* hypothesis will be rejected if $\chi^2 \leq 6.26$ or $\chi^2 \geq 27.49$. Computing χ^2 using 8.05,

$$\chi^2 = \frac{(16-1)(16)^2}{(12)^2}$$
$$= 20$$

We conclude that σ has not changed.

Developing Statistical Decision Rules

In the tests of hypothesis for Mr. Brush and Mr. Sepay in the previous examples, we incidentally illustrated a general method for developing statistical decision rules. While the method appears to have some deficiencies since it considers costs of errors only indirectly, the reader should become familiar with this general approach.

Rules for One-Sided Tests. The developing of rules for one-sided tests (composite *null* and alternative hypotheses) was illustrated above for tests of means and proportions. In general, the method consisted of the decision maker choosing two critical values of the population parameter, PP. PP^* is a critical upper limit for PP such that failure to recognize that $PP \geq PP^*$ would lead to a disastrous result. The commission of this error is to be allowed only with some maximum probability (α_1). PP_* is a critical lower limit such that failure to recognize that $PP \leq PP_*$ would lead to a different disastrous result. The commission of this latter error is to be allowed only with some maximum probability (α_2). The resulting two hypotheses were used to set up two equations to compute a critical value of the sample statistic (ss) such that if the observed value of ss (equals or) exceeds ss^*, the hypothesis that $PP \geq PP^*$ (or that $PP > PP^*$) will be accepted. If ss (equals or) is less than ss_*, the hypothesis that $PP \leq PP_*$ (or that $PP < PP_*$) will be accepted.

Since ss^* is the same value as ss_*, the two equations are set equal to one another and solved to obtain a value for n. The computed value of n is then substituted into the equation for ss^* to obtain the value of ss^*. As a check the value of ss_* is computed and checked against ss^*.

In summary,

9.20 To obtain a complete decision rule for a one-sided test of a hypothesis,
(a) State two *null* hypotheses:

$$\text{I. } H_1 : PP \geq PP^* \quad \text{or} \quad PP > PP^*$$
$$\text{II. } H_2 : PP < PP_* \quad \text{or} \quad PP \leq PP_*$$

(b) Choose a level of α for each hypothesis, α_1 and α_2, respectively.
(c) Refer to the proper sampling distribution for Z_α values and set up equations for ss^* and ss_*

$$\text{III. } ss^* = PP^* - (Z_{\alpha_1})\sigma_{ss}$$
$$\text{IV. } ss_* = PP_* + (Z_{\alpha_2})\sigma_{ss}$$

(d) Set $ss^* = ss_*$ and solve for n.

$$PP^* - (Z_{\alpha_1})\sigma_{ss} = PP_* + (Z_{\alpha_2})\sigma_{ss}$$

(e) Use the computed value of n in III to solve for ss^*.
(f) Use the computed value of n in IV to solve for ss_*. (ss_* should equal ss^*.)

This process has been illustrated in testing means and proportions.

Rules for Two-Sided Tests. To illustrate this process, we will refer once more to the packaging problem of the Duravit Corporation. The quality control inspector had the problem of determining a decision rule for use in controlling the net weight of frozen strawberries packed in one pound boxes. The inspector had only specified his willingness to stop the process when there was no need. He had specified a willingness to stop the process needlessly five times in 100 tests (when the mean weight is equal to the production standard of 16.00 ounces) while trying to prevent underfilling. He was willing to stop the process needlessly only two times in 100 while trying to prevent overfilling. Actually, these specifications are only the first step in specifying a complete decision rule. The inspector must also specify a lower critical weight (μ_*) and an associated probability of failing to recognize that μ has fallen so low and an upper critical weight (μ^*) and an associated probability of failure to recognize that μ is so high. Suppose we develop the three sets of equations.

(1) For stopping the process needlessly:

$$H_0 : \mu = 16.00 \text{ ounces } (\alpha_a = 0.02; \; \alpha_b = 0.05)$$

then,

$$\bar{x}_1{}^* = 16.00 + 2.03 \frac{0.40}{\sqrt{n}} \qquad (\alpha_a = 0.02, \text{ one tail})$$

$$\bar{x}_* = 16.00 - 1.645 \frac{0.40}{\sqrt{n}} \qquad (\alpha_b = 0.05, \text{ one tail})$$

(2) For protecting against overfilling, the inspector settles on the following:

$$\mu^* = 16.40 \qquad \alpha = 0.05 \text{ (one tail)}$$

then,

$$\bar{x}_2{}^* = 16.40 - 1.645 \frac{0.40}{\sqrt{n}}$$

(3) For protecting against underfilling, the inspector settles on the following:

$$\mu_* = 15.60 \qquad \alpha = 0.02 \text{ (one tail)}$$

then,

$$\bar{x}_*{}' = 15.60 + 2.05 \frac{0.40}{\sqrt{n}}$$

We then have available two equations involving $\bar{x}^*$ and n as unknowns and another two equations involving $\bar{x}_*$ and n.

(4) Solving for n using the x^* equations:

$$\bar{x}_1{}^* = 16.00 + \frac{0.812}{\sqrt{n}}$$

$$\bar{x}_2{}^* = 16.40 - \frac{0.658}{\sqrt{n}}$$

and, since $\bar{x}_1^* = \bar{x}_2^*$,

$$16.00 + \frac{0.812}{\sqrt{n}} = 16.40 - \frac{0.658}{\sqrt{n}}$$

$$\sqrt{n} = \frac{1.470}{0.40}$$

$$= 3.675$$

$$n = 13.5 \text{ or } 14$$

(5) Solving for n using the $\bar{x}_*$ equations.

$$\bar{x}_* = 16.00 - \frac{0.658}{\sqrt{n}}$$

$$\bar{x}_*' = 15.60 + \frac{0.820}{\sqrt{n}}$$

and, since $\bar{x}_* = \bar{x}_*'$,

$$16.00 - \frac{0.658}{\sqrt{n}} = 15.60 + \frac{0.820}{\sqrt{n}}$$

$$\sqrt{n} = \frac{1.478}{0.40}$$

$$= 3.695$$

$$n = 13.65 \text{ or } 14$$

We, therefore, conclude that if the quality control inspector has been consistent and correct in his specifications to us, he can safely decrease his sample size to 14. However, since 16 is a natural square which leads to ease in calculation of error and since the calculated n values are minimums, it may be reasonable to retain the sample size of 16.

Substituting $n = 16$ back into either equation for $\bar{x}^*$ and either equation for $\bar{x}_*$, we can then compute these values. In this case $\bar{x}^* = 16.214$ and $\bar{x}_* = 15.820$. The actual calculations are left as an exercise for the reader. (Note: $n = 16$ is not the solution value, so that the stated critical values are averages of values obtained from the two equations in each set.)

The process described here for determining a two-tail decision rule for a mean can be converted easily to the development of a two-tail rule for a proportion. All that is required is to substitute P for μ, p^* for $\bar{x}^*$, p_* for $\bar{x}_*$, and σ_p for $\sigma_{\bar{x}}$. (Discussion Problem 8 is intended to give the reader an opportunity to test his understanding of this transferral.) The process is generalized in 9.21 below.

In summary,

9.21 To obtain a complete decision rule for a two-sided test of a hypothesis (simple *null*, composite alternative).

(a) For the *null* hypothesis, state the probabilities of rejection above (α_a) and below (α_b) PP when $PP = PP_0$.

$$H_0 : PP = PP_0 \qquad \alpha_a = \alpha_1 \qquad \alpha_b = \alpha_2$$

(Note: α_1 *may* equal α_2.)

(b) Equations for ss^* amd ss_* result.

$$\text{I. } ss_1{}^* = PP_0 + (Z_{\alpha_1})\sigma_{ss}$$
$$\text{II. } ss_* = PP_0 - (Z_{\alpha_2})\sigma_{ss}$$

(c) Develop a second equation for ss^*

$$\text{I'. } ss_2{}^* = PP^* - (Z_{\alpha_3})\sigma_{ss}$$

PP^* is an upper critical value which you wish to recognize is true with probability $1 - \alpha_3$ when it is true. (α_3 need not equal α_1 nor α_2).

(d) Develop a second equation for ss_*

$$\text{II'. } ss_*{}' = PP_* + (Z_{\alpha_4})\sigma_{ss}$$

PP_* is a lower critical value which you wish to recognize with probability $1 - \alpha_4$ when it is true. (α_4 need not equal α_3, α_1 nor α_2).

(e) Set $ss_1{}^* = ss_2{}^*$ and solve for n.

$$PP_0 + (Z_{\alpha_1})\sigma_{ss} = PP^* - (Z_{\alpha_3})\sigma_{ss}$$

(f) Set $ss_* = ss_*{}'$ and solve for n.

(g) Resolve any differences in the values of n obtained in steps (e) and (f). (If $|PP^* - PP_0| = |PP_* - PP_0|$ and $\alpha_1 = \alpha_2$ and $\alpha_3 = \alpha_4$, there should be no difference.)

(h) Substitute the computed value of n back into the equations for $\bar{x}^*$ and $\bar{x}_*$ and solve for these two values.

Unfortunately, if any difference in the values of n obtained in steps (e) and (f) does occur, there is no theoretically correct way to accomplish step (g), which is to resolve the difference. Once again, one must rely on outside considerations to resolve this uncertainty. Certainly, however, the uncertainty to be arbitrarily resolved has been much reduced by the use of statistical science.

USING PRIOR INFORMATION IN HYPOTHESIS TESTING

Most decision problems faced by businessmen are not completely new and unique, at least, if looked at as a "decision problem of businessmen." Sample evidence does not exist independently of any and all prior evidence. Like all other evidence (experience) the sample result is incorporated into our total fund of knowledge as an addition to or modification of what is already known. In the remainder of this chapter we consider techniques for combining prior evidence with sample evidence to obtain a logically consistent posterior belief about the possible states of nature as a guide to decision making.

To demonstrate the techniques for combining prior and sample information, we will return once again to the Dry-Cell battery example, which was discussed at the beginning of this chapter.

Prior Probability Distribution for a Parameter

The quality control supervisor for Dry-Cell has maintained records on the performance of the battery sealing machine. Data from those records for the past year have been used to develop the relative frequencies with which the various proportions of defectives have shown up in lots of 1000 batteries. Those relative frequencies are given in Table 9.3.

TABLE 9.3

RELATIVE FREQUENCY OF OCCURRENCE OF VARIOUS PROPORTIONS OF
DEFECTIVELY SEALED BATTERIES IN RUNS OF 1000 BATTERIES

Proportion of Defectively Sealed Batteries P_i	Relative Frequency of Occurrence $P(P_i)$
0.00	0.132
0.01	0.351
0.02	0.246
0.03	0.120
0.04	0.067
0.05	0.039
0.06	0.018
0.07	0.010
0.08	0.009
0.09	0.004
0.10	0.002
0.11	0.000
0.12	0.001
0.13	0.000
0.14	0.001
	1.000

The distribution shown in Table 9.3, like the probability distributions used in studying uncertainty in Chapter 7, implies that the population parameter (state of nature) is a random variable. It seems reasonable to act upon the belief that quantities demanded on different individual days or the proportion of defectives observed in different individual lots are not single-valued constants. Such values do vary in an individually unpredictable way, but the variability undoubtedly is limited in range and some values obviously occur more frequently than other values. Also, some information on these values is likely to be available. To ignore the existence of such information when making any decision does not seem like a reasonable action. Let us see how it can be incorporated into the total picture.

Posterior Probability Distribution for a Parameter

The first decision rule evaluated in the beginning of this chapter was the rule $n = 20$, $x^* = 1$. Suppose we assume that the quality control supervisor at Dry-Cell had arbitrarily decided to draw a sample of 20 batteries and had found one defective. According to his rule, he would call the maintenance crew and have the machine cleaned and adjusted. What is the probability that he is making the wrong decision, that is, that P is actually not as large as 0.02? Table 9.2 and Figure 9.1 indicate only the *conditional* probabilities of such an error. They do not, however, take account of all available information.

The prior probability distribution of P of Table 9.3 indicates that P is actually greater than 0.02 for only about 27 percent of the runs. Our sample estimate says $P = 0.05$. Why not combine these two pieces of information? By weighting each of the conditional probabilities of the sample result (see Table 9.1) by the probability that the corresponding value of P is actually true, we can develop a *posterior probability distribution for P* which reflects both these sets of information. This posterior probability distribution can then be used as a basis for making decisions whose outcomes depend upon the states of nature signified by the alternative values of P.

The posterior probability distribution for P is developed in Table 9.4 by the use of Bayes' rule (4.41). The joint probability of each P and the observed sample result are computed. These values are then converted into the posterior probability distribution shown in the final column by dividing each joint probability by the total of all the joint probabilities (0.2198). Thus, the posterior probability that $P = 0.01$ is $0.0579/0.2198$ = **0.263**. To see this in terms of 4.41 (Bayes' rule), let A_1 stand for the event $P = 0.01$, and call $P(A_1)$ the prior probability that $P = 0.01$. Let

TABLE 9.4

REVISION OF PRIOR PROBABILITY DISTRIBUTION FOR PROPORTION
DEFECTIVE GIVEN THE SAMPLE RESULT: $n = 20$; $x = 1$

Possible States of World P_i	Prior Probabilities of States $P(P_i)$	Conditional Probability of Sample Result $P(n, x\|P_i)$	Joint Prob. of State of World and Sample Result $P(P_i \text{ and } x)$	Revised (Posterior) Probability of States $P'(P_i)$
0.00	0.132	0.000	—	—
0.01	0.351	0.165	0.0579	0.263
0.02	0.246	0.272	0.0669	0.305
0.03	0.120	0.336	0.0403	0.183
0.04	0.067	0.368	0.0247	0.112
0.05	0.039	0.377	0.0147	0.067
0.06	0.018	0.370	0.0067	0.031
0.07	0.010	0.353	0.0035	0.016
0.08	0.009	0.328	0.0030	0.014
0.09	0.004	0.300	0.0012	0.005
0.10	0.002	0.270	0.0005	0.002
0.11	0.000	0.240	—	—
0.12	0.001	0.212	0.0002	0.001
0.13	0.000	0.184	—	—
0.14	0.001	0.159	0.0002	0.001
Totals	1.000		0.2198	1.000

A_i stand for any of the possible values of P, and B stand for the sample result $n = 20$, $x = 1$. The posterior probability, given the sample result, that $P = 0.01$ is computed by applying 4.41.

$$P(A_1|B) = \frac{P(B|A_1)P(A_1)}{\sum_i P(A_i)P(B|A_i)}$$

or

$$P(P = 0.01|n = 20, x = 1) = \frac{P(n = 20, x = 1|P = 0.01)P(P = 0.01)}{\sum_i P(P = A_i)P(n = 20, x = 1|P = A_i)}$$

$$= \frac{(0.165)(0.351)}{0.2198}$$

$$= \mathbf{0.263}$$

where once again, A_i stands for the ith possible value of P.

The posterior distribution of P, when summarized, indicates the probability that $P > 0.02$ is about 0.43. The probability that P is less than 0.02 is only about 0.26. These facts seem to favor calling the maintenance crew as the rule $n = 20$, $x^* = 1$ had specified. Note that we are assuming that at $P = 0.02$ we are indifferent as to which action is taken.

Suppose that the sample had contained no defectively sealed batteries. The resulting posterior probability distribution would indicate approximately the following probabilities:

$$P(P < 0.02) = 0.60$$
$$P(P = 0.02) = 0.23$$
$$P(P > 0.02) = 0.17$$

It is left as an exercise for the reader to develop the complete posterior probability distribution in this case. Note that the probabilities given support the decision which the decision rule, $n = 20$, $x^* = 1$ would specify.

Discrete and Continuous Prior Distributions

Prior probability distributions for possible states of nature will often be taken primarily from the frequency distribution of values actually assumed by nature (the parameter) in past periods. In many of these situations, as in the Dry-Cell example in the section above, the possible values of the parameter will be limited and the distribution will be considered discrete. In other situations, however, it will not be uncommon to encounter distributions which, while discrete in their observed form, should really be considered as *continuous* probability distributions. Thus the quality control supervisor for Duravit Corporation may have recorded the distribution of net weights of packages of frozen strawberries during previous packaging runs as the values shown in the "observed frequency" columns of Table 9.5. The discrete values and their relative frequency of occurrence are also shown in Figure 9.5. The vertical lines represent the recorded historical relative frequencies. The smooth curve seen in Figure 9.5 represents a normal probability distribution fitted to these observations. The height of the curve at each of the historically "observed" weights can be found in the "expected frequency" columns of Table 9.5. It seems reasonable to believe that the filling machine in the strawberry packaging line would generate a normal distribution of net weights. In Chapter 11 we will demonstrate the "fitting" of this curve and test the assumption that the basic data are normally distributed.

Note that, in theory, a continuous prior can be combined with sample

TABLE 9.5

OBSERVED DISTRIBUTION OF NET WEIGHTS AND FITTED
NORMAL DISTRIBUTION

Observed Weights	Observed Frequencies		Expected Normal Frequencies	
	Absolute	Relative	Absolute	Relative
15.78	0	0.000	1	0.001
15.80	1	0.001	2	0.002
15.82	4	0.004	4	0.004
15.84	10	0.010	8	0.008
15.86	13	0.013	15	0.015
15.88	30	0.030	26	0.026
15.90	42	0.042	41	0.041
15.92	60	0.060	60	0.060
15.94	76	0.076	79	0.079
15.96	98	0.098	97	0.097
15.98	109	0.109	110	0.110
16.00	111	0.111	114	0.114
16.02	106	0.106	110	0.110
16.04	95	0.095	97	0.097
16.06	82	0.082	79	0.079
16.08	61	0.061	60	0.060
16.10	42	0.042	41	0.041
16.12	25	0.025	26	0.026
16.14	16	0.016	15	0.015
16.16	10	0.010	8	0.008
16.18	5	0.005	4	0.004
16.20	3	0.003	2	0.002
16.22	1	0.001	1	0.001
	1000	1.000	1000	1.000

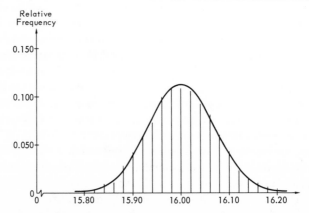

FIG. 9.5. Observed distribution of average net weights (μ_R) and fitted normal distribution.

information only by the use of the calculus. In practice, however, the probability of discrete ranges of the parameter can be assigned to the parameter value falling at the midpoint of each discrete interval. This is actually what has been done in Table 9.5. In Figure 9.5, the heights at the midpoints have been joined by a smooth curve. Discussion Problem 10 and Exercise 12 are intended to help the reader understand this application. The reader should also note that the normal is only one of several continuous probability distributions used by the statistician to describe empirical distributions. (Others are the Pascal and the exponentional.)

Objective and Subjective Prior Distributions

One reason for introducing the idea of using the normal for a prior distribution is that it is relatively "easy" to use. It has been demonstrated that if the variance of the prior distribution is large when compared with the sampling variance of the sample statistic ($\bar{x}$), the assumption that the prior distribution is a normal distribution whose mean and variance are the mean and variance specified by the prior distribution will not materially reduce the accuracy of the posterior probabilities while simplifying their calculation.[3] It seems reasonable to believe that the variance of a subjective prior would most likely be large in relation to the sampling variance of a statistic from any reasonably large sample ($n \geq 30$).

All examples we have considered to this point have used purely objective information as the basis of the prior probability distribution of the parameter. Sometimes, decisions must be made in situations where objective evidence about previous behavior of the parameter is unavailable. For example, consider once again the problem of our inventive businessman of Chapter 1. The correctness of his decision to produce (or not produce) his new product will depend upon the number of units of the product he can sell at a price which covers all necessary costs. Obviously, there can be no empirical probability distribution of levels of demand for this product. How, then, can we expect the businessman to obtain any information on the probabilities that various levels of sales may be realized (other than from a sample of prospective customers)? It is not uncommon in such situations for businessmen to consult "marketing experts" who study the situation and express their "professional opinion" as to whether the venture is most likely to succeed or fail. Seldom does the businessmen obtain the information from the expert in the form of a probability distribution, even though it seems reasonable that he should.

[3] See Schlaifer, Robert, *Probability and Statistics for Business Decisions*, New York: McGraw-Hill Book Company, Inc., 1959, Chap. 30, especially pp. 446–448.

The final recommendation of the marketing expert is obviously based on his "degree of belief" in the various levels of sale being realized. Why not ask him to express these beliefs more fully so that they may be consistently combined with any objective (sample) evidence which may be collected? Not being a statistician, the marketing expert undoubtedly would assert that he cannot express his beliefs as a complete probability distribution for the possible levels of sales (states of nature). He may even object to this interpretation on the grounds that this is a single event and cannot be considered in probability terms. This latter argument is answered by arguing that all we are asking is that he help us to assess the "process" by which he arrives at his opinion of the expected level of sales. He is undoubtedly aware (and would even insist) that his estimate of the expected level of sales is not without error. Upon questioning him we probably can get him to "bet" at even odds that total sales are within a specified range. If we can get the expert to express such a "bet" in the proper manner and we assume that his prior distribution is normal we can easily construct the entire distribution.

Suppose that such an expert consulted by our inventive businessman had specified that the "most likely" level of sales in the first year is 80,000 units. He further specifies that he is willing to bet at even odds that the level will fall somewhere between 70,000 and 90,000 units. If we assume his prior distribution is normal, then the "most likely" value is also the mean, μ, and he has asserted that 50 percent of the distribution falls in the interval 70,000 to 90,000. In a normal distribution, the symmetrical interval

$$\mu \pm 0.675\sigma$$

contains 50 percent of the area under the curve (see Table B-5). Which means that, if $X' = 70,000$,

$$
\begin{aligned}
0.675\sigma &= X' - \mu \\
&= 70,000 - 80,000 \\
&= 10,000
\end{aligned}
$$

and

$$\sigma = 14,815$$

The way in which these values can be used to develop the complete normal probability distribution is explained in Chapter 11. The relative information value of such a normal prior and a normally distributed sample statistic (such as $\bar{x}$) is explained in Chapter 10 where the use of prior probabilities for parameters and sample results in guiding decisions is considered further.

SUMMARY

Statistical hypothesis testing is the process of reaching conclusions about the values of population parameters on the basis of information derived from samples. Specifically, the process involves the statement of a supposed truth or set of truths about the population (stating a hypothesis or hypotheses), developing sample information (statistics) and deciding whether the statistics provide a reasonable basis for rejecting the hypothesis or hypotheses. The basic process involves looking at the probability of occurrence of the difference between the hypothesized population parameter and the known sample statistic given that the hypothesis is true. If the difference is so large that it is not likely to be a chance occurrence, it seems reasonable to reject the hypothesis and declare the difference *statistically significant*. It must be recognized that statistical significance has been determined with a particular probability (or probabilities) of error because statistical hypothesis testing is a decision making procedure utilizing only partial and therefore uncertain (sample) information.

Statisticians recognize two general types of error: Type I (9.04) and Type II (9.05). After the decision maker has specified acceptable probabilities for each of these errors in a decision problem, the statistician has processes (9.20 and 9.21) by which he can develop *statistical decision rules* (9.06). Each statistical decision rule has associated with it a set of *error characteristics*. In the next chapter we will see how these characteristics may be combined with existing data about states of the world and costs of the various errors to further refine the process of choosing statistical decision rules. These same processes also will enable us to fit this statistical decision procedure into the larger process of decision making.

In the final section of this chapter the use of prior information about the states of nature in combination with sample information was briefly introduced. It was found that Bayes' rule (4.41) provides a consistent method for obtaining a posterior probability distribution combining the information contained in the prior distribution and the sample results.

In discussing the prior distribution for the parameter, it was argued that it is logical to develop such information from subjective beliefs where it may be argued that those beliefs are an expression of the (subjectively) recognized uncertainty in the "process" which leads to the development of those beliefs. It was asserted also that it is often reasonable to consider that subjective prior distributions can be assumed to be normal distributions. A technique using betting odds was used to obtain reasonably reliable estimates of the parameters (μ and σ) of such normal priors.

DISCUSSION QUESTIONS

1. Define the following *in your own words*. (Do *not* use symbols or verbal formulas.)

   (a) statistical decision rule
   (b) statistical hypothesis
   (c) *null* hypothesis
   (d) alternate hypothesis
   (e) error characteristic of a decision rule
   (f) statistical hypothesis testing
   (g) prior probabilities
   (h) posterior probabilities
   (i) significance level
   (j) Type I error
   (k) Type II error
   (l) acceptance interval
   (m) statistical inference
   (n) statistical significance
   (o) prior probability distribution
   (p) posterior probability distribution

2. Contrast statistical hypothesis testing and confidence interval estimation. Are they elements of the same process?
   Hint: Note that confidence intervals center on the sample statistic, while acceptance intervals center on the (hypothetical) parameter value.

3. Why is a sample of one item inappropriate as a basis for statistical inference?
   Hint: Note that statistical inference statements involve probability statements based on the sampling distributions of sample statistics.

4. What is the effect of an increase in sample size on the probability of:
   (a) Type I error?
   (b) Type II error?
   Hint: What is the effect on *sampling* variance? How does the change in sampling variance influence the acceptance and rejection regions?

5. Can a statistical hypothesis be definitely confirmed or denied? Explain carefully and completely.
   Hint: Refer back to your definition of statistical significance.

6. Consider the following statements:
   (1) The consequences of a given decision depend only upon the course of action adopted.
   (2) The desirability of a course of action depends upon which state of nature is true.

(a) Explain the meaning of each of these statements. (See your answer to Question 1, Chapter 8.)

(b) Are the statements in conflict? Explain.

Hint: Define all terms in each statement carefully as your first step. Relate these definitions in the manner indicated by each statement.

7. It has been said that the objective of statistics is to provide a basis of action in the face of uncertainty. Explain this statement.

Hint: Think back to Chapter 7 and ask if the "uncertainty" here is the same as the "uncertainty" used there.

8. How do statisticians choose between different decision rules?

Hint: You may want to go beyond the techniques described in this chapter in formulating your answer.

9. Suppose a friend offered to allow you to invest in a scheme of his where he invests money in the commodity market each week after applying a model (formula) for picking the commodity and the operation (buy, sell, sell short, and so forth) on which a profit is most likely to be realized in that week. He asserts that his model picks a profitable commodity and operation in 60 percent of the weeks. If he is correct in his assertion, you can expect to triple any investment within 6 months.

(a) How would *you* state the *null* hypothesis in this situation?

(b) What do *you* believe is a reasonable probability of making a Type I error in this situation?

(c) How many of your fellow students generally agree with you? How many disagree? What do you conclude from these figures?

Hint: Which is worse: (1) to fail to make a possible fortune or (2) to lose one's current savings in a losing venture?

(d) Suppose your friend had suggested such schemes many times in the past. Would you consider developing a prior probability distribution for *P* (proportion of profitable picks) if:

(1) you had to rely entirely on your memory of the accuracy of his previous claims?

(2) you had retained copies of each of his previous schemes but had no objective evidence of their workability?

(3) you had retained evidence on each of his previous schemes and carefully developed *objective* evidence of the truthfulness of his evaluation of each such scheme.

Explain your answer in each of the three situations.

Hint: Should you ignore information available only in your *memory* when making a decision?

(e) Suppose your friend had never before proposed such a scheme to you but you have always felt that he was somewhat "flighty" and "apt to go off half-cocked." Would you accept his claim of a 0.60 probability of success in choosing favorable commodities for investment? Explain.

(f) Suppose your friend had always impressed you as "serious" and "trustworthy." Would you accept his claim that $P \geq 0.60$? Explain.

Note: Have you been at all inconsistent in your answers to parts (d), (e), and (f)? If you answered "no" to (d-1) should you have answered "no" to (d-2) and refused to modify P under the conditions specified in (e) and (f)?

DISCUSSION PROBLEMS

Show your method on all solutions.

1. Use the Poisson approximation to compute the error characteristics of the decision rule, $n = 20$, $x^* = 1$ for the Dry-Cell battery problem.
   (a) Plot the error characteristic curve on a graph similar to Figure 9.1.
   (b) Compare the approximation. How close is it? to the fourth decimal? the third? the second?
   (c) Refer to Tables 5.8 and 5.9. What is their recommendation in this situation? Do you agree? Explain carefully.
   Hint: Use Appendix Table B-8.

2. Refer to your results from Problem 1, Chapter 6. Assume that the 30 tosses of the ten coins constitute one sample and test the hypothesis that the true proportion of heads (P) is equal to 0.50.
   (a) At the 0.01 level of significance.
   (b) At the 0.05 level of significance.
   Hint: State H_0 and H_a and find the significant value of z using the normal approximation.

3. Using the sample of coin tosses developed for Problem 2 (and Problem 1 of Chapter 6) perform the following test:

$$H_0 : P < 0.50 \qquad H_a : P \geq 0.50 \qquad \alpha = 0.01$$

   Hint: (1) Is the *null* hypothesis simple or composite?
   (2) Does this imply: a one-tail or a two-tail rejection interval?
   (3) Be careful that z_α is chosen in accordance with the answer to the above questions.

4. Suppose Mr. Brush were making the following test:

$$H_0 : \mu \geq 550 \qquad H_a : \mu < 550 \qquad \alpha = 0.05 \text{ (one tail)}$$

(a) Mr. Brush has heard of something called Type I error and asks you to explain.

(b) Mr. Brush notes that if this error is "Type I," there must be other errors. Explain Type II error to him.

Hint: Relate the general definitions to this particular decision problem. State your answer as specific conclusions for this situation.

5. The Hyvolt Company is evaluating two competing designs for its new model, "Boreal" and "Pyro." The company plans to survey a random sample of potential customers as to which design they prefer. Variable (per unit) production costs and fixed (setup) costs for the two designs are essentially identical, so that customer preferences will provide the sole criterion for choosing between Boreal and Pyro. Specify the following:

(a) The *null* and alternate hypotheses to be tested? (Justify your choices.)

(b) The decision parameter and the critical sample statistic on which the decision would be based?

(c) The level of significance (α)? (Justify your choice.)

Hint: Remember that the relative costs of the two errors are the most important factors determining the choice of hypotheses and the significance level.

6. Suppose you are asking a question which will yield only "yes" or "no" answers and the population is divided into 40 percent "yes" and 60 percent "no" on the question. Sample size is 10.

(a) What is the mean number of "yes" answers you would expect if many random samples of this size were taken?

(b) If the sample contained nine "no" answers, would you accept the hypothesis that the proportion of "no" answers in the population were 0.60?

(1) Explain your decision.

(2) What is the probability that you are wrong?

Hint: You must consider whether or not you *can* determine this probability. What if you do use Table B-3? Can you use Bayes' rule to develop a posterior distribution for P? What prior would you use?

7. The Madave Agency oversees the televising of a weekly program featuring a vocal-instrumental group. The sponsor wants this program to appeal primarily to teenagers and young adults. He insists that the studio audience should consist of 40 percent teenagers and 60 percent adults to preserve both enthusiasm and decorum. Audience mixture is controlled by giving out tickets to groups such as social clubs. Constant checks on the efficiency of this rationing procedure are necessary. You have been assigned the responsibility of designing a

testing procedure involving a sample from the studio audience. The sponsor and the advertising team have decided that they are willing to accept two chances in 100 of rejecting the hypothesis of a 0.40 to 0.60 split in the audience if that is the split. If either proportion varies either way by as much as five percent, they desire 19 chances in 20 of recognizing that deviation. Develop the complete statistical decision rule, specifying the sample size and the intervals of acceptance and rejection.

Hint: Use 9.21; note that $\alpha_1 = \alpha_2 = 0.01$ and that $\alpha_3 = \alpha_4 = 0.05$. Remember that the hypothesized (population) value of P is always used in computing the associated value of σ_p.

8. Mr. Seller, sales manager for Hardsell Corporation, is evaluating sales penetration of the company in the Hybush area. Mr. Seller has a rule of thumb that says that, on the average, Hardsell should be selling to 30 percent of the total potential customers (1400 firms) in the Hybush area. Sales records for the previous quarter reveal that only 392 (28 percent) of the 1400 firms made purchases from Hardsell during the quarter.

(a) Mr. Seller asks you if it is reasonable to believe that sales penetration in the area is 30 percent or greater. Set up the appropriate decision rule and give him your advice based on the rule you set up. (Assume that sales last period are a sample).

(b) Can you justify the assumption that sales are a sample? Explain fully, including in your explanation a definition of the population being sampled and a consideration of the necessity for randomness.

Hints: (1) Is this a finite population or an infinite process?

(2) Must you assume a constant state process?

(3) What if Hardsell sales are subject to seasonal influences?

9. Suppose that the Hyvolt Company (Problem 5) had interviewed a sample of 256 potential customers and found that 144 favor the "Boreal" design for the new heater and the remainder (112) favor the "Pyro" design.

(a) Test the hypothesis that you developed for Problem 5.

(b) Suppose that the product development department and the marketing vice president had made a careful analysis of the models and were convinced (before the sample study was undertaken) that they would bet four to six that 60 percent of the potential customers would prefer Pyro, four to six on 50 percent favoring Pyro and only two to eight on 60 percent favoring "Boreal."

(1) Write down the prior probability distribution for P (the proportion favoring Pyro) the group has developed.

(2) Do you have any reservations about the adequacy of the prior distribution which the group developed? Explain.

(3) Combine the sample results with the prior to obtain the posterior probability distribution for P.

(4) Which model would you recommend that Hyvolt produce? Explain fully.

Hint: A four to six bet is equivalent to a subjective probability of 0.4.

EXERCISES

Show your method on all solutions.

1. The meat buyer for Lossless Grocery Stores is checking the Capon Company as a supplier of prepackaged frozen chickens. The weight of the contents of each package is required by law to be within 2 ounces of the correct weight for prepackaged chickens weighing no more than 2.5 pounds. A lot of 4 dozen (48) chickens from Capon (all indicated to weigh exactly 2.5 pounds) reveals the following characteristics (all measurements in ounces):

$$\text{Average weight per package} = 39.6$$
$$\text{Standard deviation of weights} = 0.8$$

Since there is a significant fine levied on each retail establishment found to be selling prepackaged foods which consistently weigh less than their marked weight and since such establishments also tend to suffer significant losses in trade for several months, how would you advise the buyer for Lossless?

(a) as to the decision rule he should follow?

(b) as to the decision he should make?

Justify your answers, making certain they are complete.

2. Candidate P. O. Litic claims that he will obtain at least 60 percent of the popular vote in the race for State Governor. (Approximately 2 million voted in the last gubernatorial election). Develop a decision rule to test P. O.'s claim, assuming you wish to allow no more than 10 chances in 100 of rejecting the claim if it is true and no more than 2 chances in 100 of accepting the claim if P. O.'s true proportion of votes is no greater than 0.50.

3. The *Daily News* in a by-line article carries the assertion that less than 30 percent of the families in Magnaville (population 121,000 families) either own or are buying the home in which they live. As a research assistant for the local Real Estate Association, you are asked to check this assertion. You decide to draw a simple random sample of cards from the city Tax Assessor's files.

(a) Set up a decision rule to test the above assertion. Allow only 5 chances in 100 of accepting the assertion if the true proportion is at least 0.40 and only 5 chances in 100 of rejecting the assertion if the true proportion is no greater than 0.25.

(b) Suppose you had drawn the random sample of cards from the assessors file as specified by your decision rule. What would you decide if the value of p were:
(1) 0.34?
(2) 0.32?
(3) 0.30?
Explain in each case.

4. An orchardist has his apple crop stored in a large bin in a fruit cellar. He put 1300 bushels into the storage bin in September. The apples had been sorted and washed before storage and were of the best quality at that time. Apples so stored have some tendency to get rotten as bacteria develop in bruises. In January the orchardist is considering two offers for his apples.

Offer A is from Lossless Grocery Stores and promises to buy all apples he can certify as containing no more than five percent rotten apples at $2.50 per bushel. If the percentage of rotten apples runs above five percent, the orchardist must agree to reduce the price 25 cents per bushel for each percentage point above five.

Offer B is from Apple Shippers, Inc., who offer to buy the entire 1300 bushels, as is, for $2.00 per bushel.

(a) State an appropriate *null* hypothesis for a statistical sampling test pertinent to the problem.

(b) Formally structure the problem as a decision problem.
The orchardist randomly selects 1500 apples from the bin and finds that 60 are rotten.

(c) Suppose the cost of resorting in order to remove rotten apples is $0.20 per bushel. (Note that resorting will remove *all* rotten apples, thus reducing the total amount sold).
(1) What would you advise the orchardist? Explain fully.
(2) What is the probability that you are making a wrong decision?
(3) Suppose the orchardist specifically indicates a desire for no more than two chances in 100 of selling to Lossless if at least 8 percent of the apples are rotten.

5. Did the orchardist in Exercise 4 use a reasonable statistical decision rule? Fully support your answer. If you disagree, fully develop a rule you would support as reasonable. If you agree, justify the orchardist's action in the same way.

6. Suppose the orchardist of Exercises 4 and 5 has kept careful records of spoilage rates for stored apples since he built the storage cellar 20 years ago. His records reveal the following frequency distribution of spoilage rates.

Spoilage Rate	Frequency
0.03	2
0.04	8
0.05	6
0.06	2
0.07	1
0.08	1
	20

(a) Develop the posteriori probability distribution for the spoilage rate, assuming the distribution above is a legitimate prior distribution and utilizing the sample information ($n = 1500$, $x = 60$).

(b) What decision would you advise the orchardist to make on the basis of the posteriori probabilities?

Hint: Apply Bayes' rule (4.41) to obtain the posteriori probability distribution for the spoilage rate.

7. The 1950 graduating class of Kundry U. held its fifteenth reunion in June 1965. Before the reunion, a random sample of 100 of the 800 class members was polled to obtain information about characteristics of members. The sample showed an average income of $9600 with a standard deviation (s) of $1440. At the reunion banquet, the banquet speaker stated that the average income of class members must be at least $10,000.

(a) Do you think the banquet speaker has made a reasonable statement? Explain your answer, including the significance level at which the statement would be rejected as a statistical hypothesis.

(b) What is your maximum estimate of the average income of the 1950 class members if you wish to be 90 percent certain of not being too high?

8. The Mercury Taxi Company had fitted its fleet of 25 cabs with Hardy Tires. An old tire was retained as an emergency "spare" on each cab. Hardy tires are asserted to have a life of 22,000 miles with a standard deviation of 900 miles. For Mercury, the tires averaged 21,850 miles with a standard deviation of 1000 miles.

(a) Is it reasonable to believe that the standard deviation of tire life is equal to 900? (Use the 0.05 significance level.)

Note: n is the number of tires.

(b) Should Mercury conclude that average tire life could be equal to 22,000? (Assume that they are willing to accept five chances in 100 of concluding incorrectly that tire life is not 22,000).
Note: What value did you use for σ in computing $\sigma_{\bar{x}}$? Why?

(c) Suppose Mercury were just *now considering* the purchase of Hardy Tires and called you in as statistical consultant to advise them. What statistical rule would you advise? Why?

9. Suppose Mercury Taxi Company executives supplied you with the following information about the problem discussed in Exercise 8.

(1) The value of the goodwill of their present supplier (Old West Garage), dependent upon the continuing purchase of Softy Tires, is $500 per year because of tie-in discounts on other supplies and maintenance services, and so forth.

(2) Mercury Taxis drive an average of 54,000 miles per year each.

(3) Hardy tires currently are priced at $19.00 per tire.

(4) Softy tires currently are priced at $21.50 per tire.

(5) Hardy tires are asserted to average 22,000 miles with a standard deviation of 900 miles

(6) Softy tires have averaged 20,000 miles with a standard deviation of 800 miles.

You are retained as a consulting statistician to advise Mercury on this problem *before* they buy the tires. Analyze the situation and give your advice, including answers to the following specific questions:

(a) What must be the average tire life in miles of Hardy tires to justify a switch to Hardy tires?

(b) Can the purchase and use of a set of tires on the taxis be considered a sample test of the tires? Explain fully what is being sampled.

(c) What is your advice to Mercury? Justify your answer on the basis of your answers to (a) and (b) and any other calculations assuming only that Hardy has asserted an average life of 22,000 miles with a standard deviation of 900 miles (no sample).

10. Use each set of sample data given below to test the following two sets of hypotheses. Explain the meaning of your decision to accept or reject in each instance.

$$\text{I. } H_0:\mu = 300 \qquad \text{II. } H_0:\sigma = 25$$
$$H_a:\mu \neq 300 \qquad\qquad H_a:\sigma \neq 25$$
$$\alpha = 0.10 \qquad\qquad\quad \alpha = 0.05$$

(a) $\bar{x} = 292, s = 20, n = 100$
(b) $\bar{x} = 292, s = 20, n = 10$
(c) $\bar{x} = 292, \hat{\sigma} = 20, n = 100$
(d) $\bar{x} = 292, \hat{\sigma} = 20, n = 10$

11. Use each set of sample data given to test the stated hypothesis. Explain the meaning of your decision to accept or reject in each instance.

$$H_0:\mu \geq 200 \qquad H_a:\mu < 200 \qquad \alpha = 0.30$$

(a) $\bar{x} = 195$, $s = 15$, $n = 225$
(b) $\bar{x} = 195$, $s = 15$, $n = 10$
(c) $\bar{x} = 195$, $\acute{\sigma} = 15$, $n = 10$

12. Use each set of sample data given to test the two stated hypotheses. Explain the meaning of your decision to accept or reject in each instance.

I. $H_0:P = 0.50$	II. $H_0:P \geq 0.50$
$H_a:P \neq 0.50$	$H_a:P < 0.50$
$\alpha = 0.02$	$\alpha = 0.02$

(a) $p = 0.45$, $n = 900$
(b) $p = 0.45$, $n = 225$
(c) $p = 0.45$, $n = 100$

13. Refer back to the problem of the ginger-ale producer entering a new territory given in Exercise 1 of Chapter 8. Assume that a careful study of other areas with similar population densities, and age, sex, and income distributions of the population is summarized as follows:

Proportion of Ginger-Ale Sold in Cans	Relative Frequency of Occurrence
0.30	0.15
0.35	0.20
0.40	0.25
0.45	0.20
0.50	0.15
0.55	0.05
	1.00

Suppose that the consulting firm has taken a sample of 100 persons of whom 43 prefer their pop in cans.

(a) Develop the posterior probability distribution for P.
(b) If the company requires that $P \geq 0.45$ before installing a pop "cannery," what would you advise in this case? Explain.

10
costs, returns, and sampling

In the previous chapter we dealt with statistical decision rules. One problem which arose at that time and which we did not fully resolve was the choice of the *best* decision rule. We learned only that all decision rules are subject to error and that if the decision maker can in some mysterious and unspecified fashion settle upon the amounts and probabilities of allowable error, the statistician can develop an appropriate rule. However, it was stated that the choice of error amounts and error probabilities should be made to depend upon the *costs* of each error. This chapter attempts to show how this may be done.

The use of previously available information, whether objective or subjective, develops as a natural consequence of our desire to be guided in the choice of decision rule by the expected losses associated with each rule. The admission of prior information about the states of nature into the selection process allows us to consider as one alternative a decision rule which does not involve sampling. Further, this same reasoning can be adapted to the situation after sampling to determine if the decision should be deferred and a further sample drawn.

As in the previous chapter, we will rely heavily on specific examples to illustrate the processes we wish to develop. Most of these examples will deal once again with the simplest possible case, where only two alternative actions are considered. There is no theoretical reason for this restriction, but this is an introductory text. This restriction is relaxed in the final section of the chapter.

CONDITIONAL LOSSES FOR STATISTICAL DECISION RULES

To develop the costs of error associated with a particular decision problem is not always easy and sometimes nearly impossible. In the difficult situations, very imprecise estimates must suffice.

As our first example, let us return to the Dry-Cell battery problem which was discussed in the previous chapter. At that time, the decision maker's objective was defined to be the production of batteries in such a manner as to maintain the proportion of defectively sealed batteries at no more than two percent. Let us examine the situation more closely and see why the proportion of defectives should be maintained at two percent. The cost functions we develop can then be used to obtain the conditional expected losses of operating a particular decision rule.

Conditional Costs of Error

The following data are available concerning the production and sale of batteries:

1. Batteries are produced in lots of 1000 batteries each.
2. The variable cost (direct labor and materials) of a battery is nine cents.
3. Of the defective batteries produced and shipped to retailers for sale to the final customer, 40 percent are returned for refunds.
   (a) Fifty percent of the returned defective batteries require only two new batteries (each costing $0.09 + $0.04 delivery charge or a total of $0.13 per battery) for a total cost of $0.26 for each defective battery in this category.
   (b) Fifty percent of the returned batteries have also ruined the customer's flashlight (the flashlights cost an average of $1.98 each); a total cost of $2.24 for each defective battery in this category.
   (c) The handling costs connected with the processing of each claim for refund are $2.50.
   (d) The total expected cost of each defective battery can be computed:

$$0.40[(0.5)(\$0.26) + (0.5)(\$2.24) + 2.50] = \mathbf{\$1.50}$$

(The reader should satisfy himself that he understands this computation.)

4. The cost of stopping the production line for cleaning and resetting the sealing machine totals \$15.00. After this operation the proportion of defectives is *always* equal to one percent.

The manufacturing supervisor has two actions available: he can either allow the sealing machine to operate at its old settings without special cleaning or he can call in the maintenance crew to clean and reset the sealing machine. If the maintenance crew cleans and adjusts the machine, the total cost for a run of 1000 batteries would be the cost of cleaning and adjustment, \$15.00, plus the expected cost of a defective, \$1.50, times the expected number of defectives, $(0.01)(1000)$, or

$$\text{cost (with cleaning and adjustment)} = \$15.00 + \$1.50(0.01)(1000)$$
$$= \$30.00$$

If the old adjustment is used, the cost would be only the cost of a defective times the expected number of defectives, or

$$\text{cost (with no cleaning and adjustment)} = \$1.50(1000)(P)$$
$$= \$1500P$$

where P = proportion of defectives produced by the process if left alone.

Conditional Opportunity Losses of Error

It is a simple matter to calculate the value of P (call it P_0) at which the supervisor would neither gain nor lose (he would break-even) if he were to bring in the maintenance crew and have the machine cleaned and adjusted.

$$\$1500P_0 = \$30$$
$$P_0 = \$30/\$1500$$
$$= \mathbf{0.02}$$

The reader should be certain that he understands why 0.02 is truly the break-even value of P.

Since the supervisor does not know the value of P at the time the decision to call the crew is to be made, his decision is subject to error. If he calls the crew and P turns out to be less than 0.02, he will incur an avoidable loss (he would have avoided the loss by not calling the crew). On the other hand, if he does not call the crew and P turns out to be greater than 0.02, he will also incur an avoidable loss (a loss he would not incur if the alternative action were taken). These avoidable losses are called *conditional opportunity losses*. They are *conditional* losses because their amount depends upon what the value of P really is. They are *opportunity* losses because they would have been avoided, in part at least, if an available alternative action had been taken.

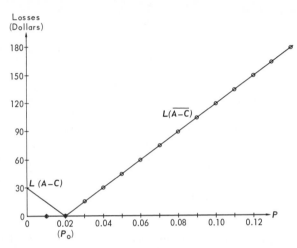

FIG. 10.1. Conditional opportunity losses of Dry-Cell quality control problem.

For the Dry-Cell problem, these opportunity losses can be summarized by simple formulas. Let $L(A\text{-}C)$ stand for "opportunity loss of adjusting and cleaning" and $L(\overline{A\text{-}C})$ stand for "opportunity loss of not adjusting and cleaning." Then,

$$L(A\text{-}C) = \begin{cases} \$1500(0.02 - P) & \text{if } P \le 0.02 \\ \$0 & \text{if } P > 0.02 \end{cases}$$

$$L(\overline{A\text{-}C}) = \begin{cases} \$0 & \text{if } P \le 0.02 \\ \$1500(P - 0.02) & \text{if } P > 0.02 \end{cases}$$

The conditional opportunity losses (COL) are shown in Table 10.1 and graphed in Figure 10.1. Note that for this simple case they are each linear (straight lines); each one point change in P is always accompanied by a change of the same constant amount in the COL.

TABLE 10.1

CONDITIONAL OPPORTUNITY LOSSES OF DRY-CELL QUALITY CONTROL
PROBLEM

Possible Values of P	Conditional Opportunity Losses $L(A\text{-}C)$	$L(\overline{A\text{-}C})$
0.00	$30	$ 0
0.01	15	0
0.02	0	0
0.03	0	15
0.04	0	30
0.05	0	45
0.06	0	60
0.07	0	75
0.08	0	90
0.09	0	105
0.10	0	120
0.12	0	150
0.14	0	180

The Third Alternative, Sampling

Obviously, rather than make an immediate choice between the two
alternative acts, the supervisor can take a sample (the first n batteries
produced on the machine without the cleaning and adjustment) and use
the sample to guide his decision. We have already seen (page 269) the
expected results if a sample of $n = 20$ is used and the hypothesis that
$P = P_0 = 0.02$ is rejected if $x \geq 1$.

Conditional Expected Opportunity Losses
of Decision Rules

By combining the information shown in Table 9.2 (and Figure 9.1)
with that shown in Table 10.1, we can more fully evaluate the statistical
decision rule

$$H_0{:}P > 0.02 \qquad H_a{:}P \leq 0.02$$
$$n = 20 \qquad\quad x^* = 1$$

The basic weakness of our approach to choosing a statistical decision rule
in Chapter 9 was that the tables and figures describing the error characteristics of a decision rule did not fully reveal the true relationship

between errors of the first and second kind. The curves in Figure 9.1 seem to indicate a larger error when P is close to 0.02. This indication is erroneous, as we see by reference to Figure 10.1. The conditional costs of error are at their lowest in the neighborhood of 0.02. Figure 9.1 shows *only* the probabilities of realizing the conditional losses shown in Figure 10.1. Each probability is conditional, however; it is applicable only if the corresponding value of P is true. Weighting of the conditional losses by their conditional probabilities of realization will give us a truer picture of what to expect from the operation of the decision rule being evaluated. The necessary calculations are shown in Table 10.2 and the resulting

TABLE 10.2

CONDITIONAL EXPECTED OPPORTUNITY LOSSES OF THE DECISION RULE,
$n = 20$, $x^* = 1$

Possible Values of P	Probabilities of Error		Conditional Opportunity Losses	Conditional Expected Opportunity Losses
	Type I $P(x^* \geq 1 \mid P \leq 0.02)$	Type II $P(x^* = 0 \mid P \geq 0.02)$		
0.00	0.000		$ 30	$ 0
0.01	0.182		15	2.73
0.02	0.332	0.668	0	0
0.03		0.544	15	8.16
0.04		0.442	30	13.26
0.05		0.359	45	16.16
0.06		0.290	60	17.40
0.07		0.235	75	17.62
0.08		0.189	90	17.01
0.09		0.153	105	16.06
0.10		0.122	120	14.64
0.12		0.078	150	11.70
0.14		0.049	180	8.22

values are graphed in Figure 10.2. Once again, it must be emphasized that the expected opportunity losses we have computed are still conditional, each will be realized only if the value of P to which it corresponds actually occurs. They are thus labeled *conditional expected opportunity losses* (CEOL). Formally,

10.00   A conditional expected opportunity loss of a statistical decision rule is the expected opportunity loss from operating the decision rule when a given state of nature is true.

Note that a decision rule has a CEOL for each and every possible state of nature. Also, if any of the CEOL are zero it is computationally more efficient and logically safe to ignore those values of the CEOL when evaluating the rule.

Examination of Tables 10.1 and 10.2 has undoubtedly raised some questions in the reader's mind. Perhaps the first question has to do with the choice of P values to include in Table 10.1 and for which losses are plotted in Figure 10.2. This choice is dictated by considerations which

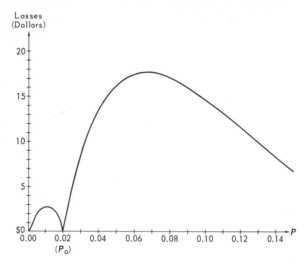

FIG. 10.2. Conditional expected opportunity losses of the decision rule, $n = 20$, $x^* = 1$.

are to be revealed in the next section of this chapter. A second question relates to the interpretation of the values in the final column in Table 10.2 which have been labeled the conditional expected opportunity losses. Each will be realized only if the corresponding value of P is realized. Each is truly an expected value; it is a weighted average where the weights are probabilities. There are two possible outcomes associated with each value of P: to make the correct decision or to make an error in decision making. A conditional value (here an opportunity loss) attaches to each of these outcomes. However, only the loss associated with the wrong decision has been included in the calculations used to arrive at the conditional expected value. The opportunity loss associated with a correct decision is zero and need not be included in the calculation.

Let us shift our attention to Table 10.3 where the conditional expected opportunity losses (CEOL) for several decision rules are found. Two

TABLE 10.3

CONDITIONAL EXPECTED OPPORTUNITY LOSSES OF SEVERAL DECISION RULES
FOR DRY-CELL QUALITY CONTROL PROBLEM

Possible Values of P_i	n 20 x^* 1	20 2	20 3	40 2	40 3	40 4	50 2	50 3	50 4	100 4	100 5	100 6
					CONDITIONAL EXPECTED OPPORTUNITY LOSSES (CEOL)							
0.00	$ 0	$ 0	$ 0	$ 0	$ 0	$ 0	$ 0	$ 0	$ 0	$0	$ 0	$ 0
0.01	2.73	0.24	0.02	0.92	0.11	0.02	1.34	0.21	0.03	0.27	0.05	0.01
0.02	0.	0	0	0	0	0	0	0	0	0	0	0
0.03	8.16	13.20	14.69	9.93	13.23	14.54	8.33	12.17	14.06	9.71	12.27	13.79
0.04	13.26	24.33	28.68	15.63	23.58	27.75	12.00	20.31	25.83	12.90	18.87	23.94
0.05	16.16	33.12	41.58	17.96	30.47	38.79	12.56	24.30	34.20	11.61	19.62	27.72
0.06	17.40	39.72	53.10	17.94	34.02	46.98	11.40	24.96	38.82	8.58	16.62	26.46
0.07	17.62	44.03	62.93	16.50	34.73	51.30	9.45	23.33	39.98	5.55	12.23	21.83
0.08	17.01	46.53	70.92	14.31	33.21	54.09	7.47	20.34	38.25	3.33	8.10	16.20
0.09	16.06	47.46	76.93	11.97	30.35	53.45	5.57	16.80	34.65	1.79	4.94	10.92
0.10	14.64	47.04	81.24	9.60	26.76	50.76	4.08	13.44	30.00	0.96	2.88	6.96
0.12	11.70	43.35	84.45	5.85	18.90	41.55	1.95	7.65	20.10	0.23	0.75	2.25
0.14	8.22	37.44	81.90	4.86	12.24	30.60	0.90	3.96	12.06	0.04	0.18	0.54

things should be noted. First, as x^* is increased for any given n, the CEOL do not all change in the same direction. The CEOL associated with Type I error decrease, but the CEOL associated with Type II error increase. Second, as n increases for any given x^* the opposite effects are noted, the CEOL associated with Type I error increase while the CEOL associated with Type II error decrease.

The reader is obviously impressed with still another fact when examining Table 10.3. Knowing the CEOL associated with decision rules provides little real assistance in choosing among those decision rules. When one attempts to compare several rules by reference to their CEOL, the comparisons are not clear cut. The only thing one is certain of is that rules specifying larger sample sizes *appear* to offer greater overall protection against incurring avoidable losses. This generalization cannot be supported without reservation, however. For one thing, larger samples necessarily involve a greater expenditure of time and effort to collect and evaluate. For another, if all values of P (states of nature) do not occur with equal frequency, it may be that some of the decision rules with higher *possible* CEOL may actually provide lower *average* losses in operation. To use the lowest maximum *possible* cost as a criterion for choosing a decision rule is an application of the general decision criterion known as *minimax*. Unfortunately, the *minimax* criterion does not always lead to a *reasonable* (nor *optimum*) choice of action.

UNCONDITIONAL EXPECTED LOSSES
OF STATISTICAL DECISION RULES

The conditional expected opportunity losses we have been discussing cannot be used in the same way as the expected opportunity losses computed in Chapter 7. At that time we assigned probabilities to the various levels of demand (the possible states of nature). Those probabilities were then used to compute an unconditional expected opportunity loss for each act as a basis for choosing an appropriate act. The act with the lowest expected opportunity loss was considered to be the superior act. In the present situation, we are dealing with probabilities and expected values each of which is applicable only when P takes on a particular value. The question naturally arises; how likely is it that P will take on each of the values shown? Available data on past activity were used in Chapter 9 to estimate the relative frequency with which P has taken on particular values. This past behavior of the sealing machine was summarized in a frequency distribution (Table 9.3). That distribution is reproduced in the first two columns of Table 10.4.

Note that the distribution (Table 10.4) is highly skewed. Smaller

TABLE 10.4

CALCULATION OF UNCONDITIONAL EXPECTED OPPORTUNITY LOSS FOR THE
DECISION RULE, $n = 20$, $x^* = 1$

Possible States of the World P_i	Probability That State of World Is True $P(P_i)$	Expected Opportunity Losses of the Decision Rule	
		Conditional CEOL	Unconditional UEOL = (CEOL)$P(P_i)$
0.00	0.132	$ 0	$0
0.01	0.351	2.73	0.958
0.02	0.246	0	0
0.03	0.120	8.16	0.979
0.04	0.067	13.26	0.888
0.05	0.039	16.16	0.630
0.06	0.018	17.40	0.313
0.07	0.010	17.62	0.176
0.08	0.009	17.01	0.153
0.09	0.004	16.06	0.064
0.10	0.002	14.64	0.029
0.12	0.001	11.70	0.012
0.14	0.001	8.22	0.008
Totals	1.000		$4.210

values of P have occurred much more frequently than larger values. It is also interesting to note that the values, $P = 0.11$ and $P = 0.13$, have never occurred, nor have values of P larger than $P = 0.14$. In an actual situation of this nature, it is doubtful that very high values of P would be recorded. Such values of P would most likely be recognized and the situation corrected before the run was completed. Since to stop, clean and adjust the machine costs only $15, it does seem reasonable that values of P which would lead to losses of more than $18 would be protected against.

Weighting each CEOL of a decision rule by the probability of occurrence of the associated possible value of the state of nature (parameter) and summing these weighted values gives the *unconditional expected opportunity loss* (UEOL) for a statistical decision rule. This is a single value and can be used directly in the comparison of alternative statistical decision rules. Let us state a formal definition.

10.01 The *unconditional expected opportunity loss* of a statistical decision rule is the *expected value* for the conditional expected opportunity losses of the rule when the *prior* probabilities of the parameter are used as probability weights.

The calculation of the unconditional expected opportunity loss (UEOL) is illustrated in Table 10.4 for the rule, $n = 20$, $x^* = 1$. The UEOL of this rule is seen to be \$4.21. Its value is compared to the UEOL's of several other decision rules in Table 10.5. The cost of sampling is also shown in Table 10.5. The values in the final column of Table 10.5, the

TABLE 10.5

UNCONDITIONAL EXPECTED OPPORTUNITY LOSSES FOR SEVERAL DECISION RULES INVOLVING SAMPLING

Decision Rule n	x^*	Unconditional Expected Opportunity Loss (UEOL)	Sampling Cost (\$1.00 + \$0.05n)	Total Expected Opportunity Loss of Sampling Rules (TEOL(S))
20	1	\$4.21	\$2.00	\$ 6.21
20	2	6.51	2.00	8.51
20	3	8.17	2.00	10.17
40	1	3.06	3.00	6.06
40	2	3.95	3.00	6.95
40	3	5.86	3.00	8.86
50	1	2.95	3.50	6.45
50	2	3.16	3.50	6.66
50	3	4.74	3.50	8.24
100	2	2.00	6.00	8.00
100	3	1.95	6.00	7.95
100	4	2.82	6.00	8.82

total expected opportunity loss of sampling rule, TEOL(S), obviously can be directly useful as guides for choosing among decision rules. In the present example, it appears that the superior rule among these evaluated is $n = 40$, $x^* = 1$. If sampling costs are ignored, the superior rule would appear to be $n = 100$, $x^* = 3$. However, the cost of sampling pushes the *total* expected cost of using this rule above five of the other alternatives shown in Table 10.5. Let us state another formal definition.

10.02 *Total expected opportunity loss of a sampling* (TEOL(S)) is equal to the unconditional expected opportunity loss of the rule plus the cost of sampling.

Examination of Table 10.5 reveals some interesting relationships. In our simplified example, we find that the minimum cost rule for each given n is that rule involving the smallest value of x^* except when $n = 100$. If we had been more realistic and complete in evaluating these rules and included proportions of defectives such as 0.0025, 0.0050, 0.0075, 0.0125, and so forth, as well as the whole percents, we would tend to get sets of costs for each of the other n which would look much more like those for $n = 100$. Also, in situations where the break-even value of P would be higher than 0.02, we would tend to find more U-shaped cost distributions traced out by varying x^* with n held constant.

If x^* is held constant while n is varied, we see that unconditional expected opportunity loss tends to decline with increasing n. Total expected loss, however, first declines and then rises as sampling costs are driven up by the increasing n. These relationships are pictured in Figure 10.3 along with an additional factor to be considered in the next section. (Note that only the lowest cost rule for each n is shown.)

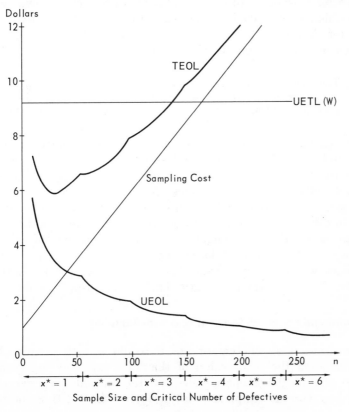

FIG. 10.3. Unconditional expected losses of several decision rules.

UNCONDITIONAL EXPECTED TERMINAL LOSS OF DECISIONS

If we have information on the value of P, why should we hesitate to use that information as the basis of our decision whether or not to call the maintenance crew to clean and adjust the machine? The prior distribution of P which we have been using (see Table 10.4) would seem to favor simply allowing the machine to run until it is definitely established that the machine is producing too high a proportion of defectives. The prior distribution indicates that over 70 percent of the time P is no greater than 0.02. But a method of reaching a decision which ignores relative costs and considers only the probability of error has proven unsatisfactory when choosing a sampling rule. Perhaps it is misleading in this situation as well.

Unconditional Expected Terminal Loss without Sampling

It seems reasonable to use expected loss as a basis for evaluating the reasonableness of relying on the prior probability distribution of P as a basis for deciding whether the sealing machine requires cleaning and adjustment before a run. This loss is defined as

10.03 The *unconditional expected terminal loss without sampling* (UETL(W)) is the *expected value* of the conditional opportunity losses using the *prior* probabilities of the possible states of nature as probability weights.

This calculation is illustrated for the Dry-Cell battery problem in Table 10.6. Note that there are *two* losses to be computed. We can wrongly decide to call the crew to clean and adjust the sealing machine when P is less than 0.02 and thus incur a loss. Alternatively, we can be wrong and incur a loss if we do not call the crew and P turns out to be larger than 0.02. In this case, it is difficult to determine what we should do by reference to the prior distribution alone. There is a difference of only \$0.03 in the two possible terminal losses. Perhaps if we draw a sample, this difference will increase enough that we can have greater faith in our decision. But, once again we must consider the costs to be incurred.

Unconditional Expected Terminal Loss with Sampling

The decision of whether or not it would pay to sample obviously depends upon the relationship of the total expected opportunity loss (TEOL(S)) of the sampling rules and the unconditional expected terminal loss without sampling (UETL(W)). If the TEOL(S) of any sam-

TABLE 10.6

UNCONDITIONAL EXPECTED TERMINAL LOSS WITHOUT SAMPLING

Possible States of Nature P_i	Probability That State of Nature Is True $P(P_i)$	Conditional Opportunity Loss COL	Unconditional Expected Terminal Loss UETL(W)	
			Do Not Call Crew	Call Crew
0.00	0.132	$ 30		$3.96
0.01	0.351	15		5.27
0.02	0.246	0	—	—
0.03	0.120	15	$1.80	
0.04	0.067	30	2.01	
0.05	0.039	45	1.76	
0.06	0.018	60	1.08	
0.07	0.010	75	0.75	
0.08	0.009	90	0.81	
0.09	0.004	105	0.42	
0.10	0.002	120	0.24	
0.12	0.001	150	0.15	
0.14	0.001	180	0.18	
	1.000	—	$9.20	$9.23

pling rule is less than the UETL(W) of the no sampling rule, then a sample should be selected. This comparison must be carried out for all possible sampling rules. Figure 10.3 presents this multiple comparison quite clearly. The UEOL curves are developed from values such as those shown in Table 10.5. Note, however, that only the *minimum cost rule* for each n is shown. The horizontal line labeled UETL(W) represents the value of $9.20, which is the expected terminal loss of not calling the crew as shown in Table 10.6. It is clear that as long as the TEOL of any sampling rule falls below the UETL(W) of the rule without sampling, it will pay to draw a sample. In the Dry-Cell problem, sampling is recommended. In fact, it can be seen in Table 10.5 that even the statistical decision rule $n = 100$, $x^* = 3$ could be expected to lead to lower costs. Remember that the TEOL(S) values for statistical decision rules graphed in Figure 10.3 are only the minimum cost rules for each n which result from combining that n and the x^* occurring at the bottom of the chart at that point. The odd shape of the curve is due to the shift in the expected loss values when it becomes more economical to shift to a larger x^*. The recommended statistical decision rule in this situation is approximately $n = 30$, $x^* = 1$, for that is the rule at which expected costs are not only below the UETL(W) but appear to be at a minimum. Therefore, the recommended action for the manufacturing supervisor is to draw and evaluate a sample of 30 batteries before deciding whether or not to call the maintenance crew to clean and adjust the machine before each run.

Unconditional Expected Terminal Loss Given a Sample

Suppose that the manufacturing supervisor had arbitrarily decided to draw a sample of 20 batteries and the sample contained one defective. Should the supervisor order the maintenance crew to clean and adjust the sealing machine? We must know, for each possible value of P, the conditional probability of obtaining such a sample. This can be combined with each prior probability of P to obtain a revised (posterior) probability distribution for P. This has already been done in the final section of Chapter 9, where the results are shown in Table 9.4. The second column of Table 9.4 shows the prior probability distribution of P. The third shows for each value of P the conditional probability of obtaining one defective in a sample of 20. By application of 4.41 (Bayes' rule), the joint probabilities obtained in the next column are converted into posterior (revised) probabilities for the possible values of P in the final column. This is a straightforward application of Bayes' rule (4.41) as discussed in Chapter 4. Finally,

10.04 *The unconditional expected terminal losses given a sample* (UETL(G)) are the *expected values* of the conditional opportunity losses using the *posterior* probabilities of the possible states of nature as probability weights. Note that there are two UETL(G)'s, one for each act.

The revised or posterior probability distribution of P from Table 9.4 is used in Table 10.7 to obtain the unconditional expected terminal losses associated with basing a decision on this revised distribution. The expected opportunity loss of the action, call the crew, is only \$3.95, making this the preferred action. The action of not calling the crew has an expected opportunity loss of \$14.26, more than \$10 higher than that of the preferred act.

Note that the addition of the sample has substantially reduced the uncertainty associated with making the decision. The unconditional expected terminal loss without sampling favored the same act, but by a margin of only three cents. The \$9.20 expected terminal loss using only

TABLE 10.7

UNCONDITIONAL EXPECTED TERMINAL LOSSES OF DECISION ON THE
BASIS OF A SAMPLE OF $n = 20$, $x = 1$

Possible States of Nature P_i	Posteriori Probabilities for States of Nature $P'(P_i)$	Conditional Opportunity Losses (COL)	Unconditional Expected Terminal Losses UETL(G)	
			Call Crew TL(G)$_1$	Do Not Call Crew TL(G)$_2$
0.00	—	$ 30	—	—
0.01	0.263	15	$3.95	—
0.02	0.305	0	—	—
0.03	0.183	15	—	$ 2.75
0.04	0.112	30	—	3.36
0.05	0.067	45	—	3.02
0.06	0.031	60	—	1.86
0.07	0.016	75	—	1.20
0.08	0.014	90	—	1.26
0.09	0.005	105	—	0.53
0.10	0.002	120	—	0.24
0.12	0.001	150	—	0.02
0.14	* 0.001	180	—	0.02
			$3.95	$14.26

the prior probabilities for P (Table 8.6) is $5.25 higher than the expected terminal loss ($3.95) given in Table 10.7.

Unconditional Expected Opportunity Loss of Further Sampling

The unconditional terminal costs after sampling are not always as clear cut as in the present example. Sometimes one is not certain which is the better decision even *after* a sample has been drawn and evaluated. The difference in expected costs of the two acts may not be sufficiently large to allow a definite decision. In such instances one must examine the possible effects of drawing a *further* sample. Suppose that we make this evaluation in the present instance despite the obviousness of our present results.

To obtain the unconditional expected opportunity loss of a decision rule involving sampling, we proceeded in the following steps:

(1) State the conditional losses of error. In the Dry-Cell example these were computed as,

$$L(A\text{-}C) = \begin{cases} \$1500(0.02 - P) & \text{if } P \leq 0.02 \\ \$0 & \text{if } P > 0.02 \end{cases}$$

$$L(\overline{A\text{-}C}) = \begin{cases} \$0 & \text{if } P \leq 0.02 \\ \$1500(P - 0.02) & \text{if } P > 0.02 \end{cases}$$

(These are shown in Table 10.1 and Figure 10.1.)

(2) The conditional expected opportunity losses are computed for each of the alternative decision rules by weighting each conditional loss associated with each value of P by the conditional probability that the rule being evaluated would lead to that loss being realized when the associated value of P is the true value of P (10.00). (Note that there are as many CEOL for each rule as there are possible values of P.)

(See Tables 10.2 and 10.3 and Figure 10.2)

(3) The unconditional expected opportunity loss of each alternative decision rule is obtained as the expected value of the CEOL using the *prior* probability for P for the probability weights (10.01). (See Tables 10.4 and 10.5 and Figure 10.3.)

In order to evaluate rules involving further sampling, we proceed along these same lines, except that step (3) is modified by the use of the *posterior* probability distribution for P instead of the *prior* as the source of the probability weights. This process is illustrated in Table 10.8 for the rule: draw an additional sample by applying the rule,

$$n = 30, \, x^* = 1.$$

Finally, we can define,

10.05 The *unconditional expected opportunity loss* of a statistical decision rule *involving additional sampling* (UEOL(A)) is the expected value of the conditional expected opportunity losses of the sampling rule using the *posterior* probability distribution for the states of nature as the probability weights.

Note that, once again, this is a single value. This value can be employed directly in comparing alternative decision rules. The first job, of course, is to determine which rule involving further sampling is best. If expected terminal loss of the *best* decision without further sampling is lower than the lowest UEOL(A), then no further sample should be taken. The

TABLE 10.8

UNCONDITIONAL EXPECTED OPPORTUNITY LOSS OF THE DECISION RULE
$n = 30$, $x^* = 1$, USING REVISED PROBABILITY DISTRIBUTION FOR P

Possible Values of P (P_i)	Revised Probabilities for P ($P'(P_i)$)	Expected Opportunity Losses of Rule	
		Conditional (CEOL)	Unconditional (UEOL(A))
0.00	0	$0	—
0.01	0.263	3.90	$1.03
0.02	0.305	0	—
0.03	0.183	6.02	1.10
0.04	0.112	8.82	0.99
0.05	0.067	9.68	0.65
0.06	0.031	9.36	0.29
0.07	0.016	8.48	0.13
0.08	0.014	7.38	0.10
0.09	0.005	6.20	0.03
0.10	0.002	5.04	0.01
0.12	0.001	3.30	0.01
0.14	0.001	1.98	—
	1.000	—	$4.34

UEOL(A) of the alternative rules involving further sampling and the UETL(G) of the decision to call the crew are shown in Figure 10.4.

Since the lowest TEOL(A) (the $6.42 for $n = 45$, $x^* = 1$) is above the UETL(G) ($3.95) of calling the maintenance crew before drawing any additional sample, the recommendation is to forget the additional sample and call the crew at once.

THE POSTERIOR DISTRIBUTION OF A MEAN
WHEN $\sigma_{\bar{x}}$ IS KNOWN

It was stated in Chapter 9 that in many situations the exact shape of the prior distribution can be approximated by a normal distribution with the same mean and standard deviation as the exact distribution without significantly affecting the posterior distribution of the basic random variable, the variable population mean. While illustrating this idea, we commented that, in theory, a continuous prior can be combined with sample information only by the use of the calculus. Because this is intended as an introductory treatment, we have chosen to assign the probabilities for a discrete range to the value falling in the center (the midpoint) of the range. This increases the calculation requirements but reduces the analytical complexity since the techniques applied to discrete distributions can be used for continuous distributions. However, one result based on the calculus will be incorporated as explained below.

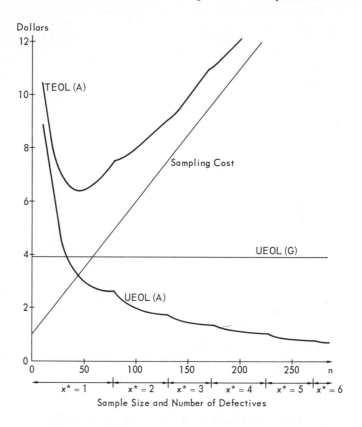

FIG. 10.4. Unconditional expected loss of several decision rules involving additional sampling.

There is a second problem associated with the use of a normal prior. This problem arises from the fact that the normal has two parameters, the mean and the standard deviation. Technically, both the mean and standard deviation of any subjective prior distribution of μ_R (we refer to such a variable population mean as μ_R) should be modified in determining the state of nature.

If we can assume that σ (standard deviation of the population) is known, then we *know* the sampling variance of the sample mean, $\sigma_{\bar{x}}^2$, since $\sigma_{\bar{x}}^2 = \dfrac{\sigma^2}{n}$. The reader should not confuse this standard deviation of the population, σ, with the standard deviation of the prior distribution for μ_R, symbolized as σ_{μ_R}.

The assumption that σ is known is not altogether unrealistic. We often know enough about the population variance to treat it as if it were known even though our knowledge of μ is insufficient to make decisions where costs (profits) depend only on the value of μ_R. Further, knowledge of the exact value of σ is of secondary importance if μ_R is the cost determining random variable. Uncertainty about σ has only a small effect on the posterior distribution for μ_R.

Consider once again the Duravit strawberry packaging problem. Suppose we have the normal prior distribution for μ_R given in Table 9.5 and Figure 9.5. The mean weights μ_R with which we are concerned may be considered as the mean weights of *runs* of packages filled on this machine. This is a *basic process* on which we define the *process* which is responsible for the population of package weights occurring within each *run* of packages on the machine. Note that μ, the average weight of all individual packages, is assumed to be exactly equal to 16.00 ounces. The mean weight for each single run, each μ_R, varies around this overall μ, but $E(\mu_R) = \mu = 16.00$ ounces. Obviously, the range of variability for μ_R is much less than the variability of the population values (weights of individual packages).

The parameters to be modified in obtaining the posterior distribution for μ_R are the mean of μ_R ($\bar{\mu}_R$) and the standard deviation of the μ_R distribution (σ_{μ_R}). The obvious question is how to obtain these revised values.

The revised value of μ_0 (μ_1) should depend upon the *prior* value of μ_0 and the sample mean $\bar{x}$. Not only should the value of μ_1 depend upon μ_0 and $\bar{x}$, but in combining these values, each value should be weighted according to the *quantity* of information it contains. Both μ_0 and $\bar{x}$ are *estimates* of the true μ. A revised estimate of μ (μ_1) combining them should be a weighted average with the weights reflecting the amount of information about μ each of the values contributes. The only measure of informational content we have is a reciprocal measure, the variance of the distribution from which the estimate is taken.

Therefore in such a problem where

(a) The prior distribution of μ_R is normal with mean μ_0 and standard deviation σ_{μ_R},

(b) The sampling distribution of $\bar{x}$ is normal with mean μ and standard deviation $\sigma_{\bar{x}}$, and

(c) The value of $\sigma_{\bar{x}}$ is known,

the posterior distribution of μ_R is normal and its mean (μ_1) is a weighted average of the prior mean and the sample mean, the weights being the reciprocals of the variances of the corresponding distributions (the prior distribution and the sampling distribution). In symbols,

10.10 $\mu_1 = \dfrac{\mu_0/\sigma_{\mu_R}{}^2 + \bar{x}/\sigma_{\bar{x}}{}^2}{1/\sigma_{\mu_R}{}^2 + 1/\sigma_{\bar{x}}{}^2}$

For these same situations, the variance of the posterior distribution ($\sigma_{\mu'_R}{}^2$) is the reciprocal of the sum of the reciprocals of the variances of the prior ($\sigma_{\mu_R}{}^2$) and the sampling distribution ($\sigma_{\bar{x}}{}^2$). In symbols,

10.11 $\sigma_{\mu'_R}{}^2 = \dfrac{1}{1/\sigma_{\mu_R}{}^2 + 1/\sigma_{\bar{x}}{}^2}$

Let us reconsider the packaging example where (see Table 9.5 and Figure 9.5)

$$\mu_0 = 16.00 \qquad \sigma_{\mu_R} = 0.07 \qquad \sigma = 0.40$$

We had a sample

$$n = 16 \qquad \bar{x} = 15.80 \qquad \sigma_{\bar{x}} = 0.10$$

Substituting into 10.10 and 10.11,

$$\mu_1 = \frac{16.00/0.0049 + 15.80/0.01}{1/0.0049 + 1/0.01}$$

$$= \frac{4845.3}{304.1}$$

$$= \mathbf{15.93}$$

$$\sigma_{\mu'_R}{}^2 = \frac{1}{1/0.0049 + 1/0.01}$$

$$= \frac{1}{304.1}$$

$$= \mathbf{0.0033}$$

$$\sigma_{\mu'_R} = \mathbf{0.058}$$

These revised values μ_1 and $\sigma_{\mu'_R}$ have been used to develop the posterior (revised) probability distribution shown in the last two columns of Table 10.9. The prior distribution for μ_R is also shown in Table 10.9 so that

TABLE 10.9

PRIOR AND POSTERIOR DISTRIBUTION FOR MEAN WEIGHTS PER RUN (μ_R)
FOR DURAVIT STRAWBERRY PACKAGE FILLING PROBLEM
(SAMPLE OF $n = 16$, $\bar{x} = 15.80$)

Average Weights (μ_R)	Prior Distribution $\mu_0 = 16.00$ $\sigma_{\mu_R} = 0.07$ Absolute	Relative	Posterior Distribution $\mu_1 = 15.93$ $\sigma_{\mu'_R} = 0.058$ Absolute	Relative
15.74	—	—	1	0.001
15.76	—	—	2	0.002
15.78	1	0.001	5	0.005
15.80	2	0.002	11	0.011
15.82	4	0.004	23	0.023
15.84	8	0.008	41	0.041
15.86	15	0.015	66	0.066
15.88	26	0.026	95	0.095
15.90	41	0.041	120	0.120
15.92	60	0.060	136	0.136
(15.93)†	—	—	(137.6)†	(0.1376)†
15.94	79	0.079	136	0.136
15.96	97	0.097	120	0.120
15.98	110	0.110	95	0.095
16.00	114	0.114	66	0.066
16.02	110	0.110	41	0.041
16.04	97	0.097	23	0.023
16.06	79	0.079	11	0.011
16.08	60	0.060	5	0.005
16.10	41	0.041	2	0.002
16.12	26	0.026	1	0.001
16.14	15	0.015	—	—
16.16	8	0.008	—	—
16.18	4	0.004	—	—
16.20	2	0.002	—	—
16.22	1	0.001	—	—
Totals	1000	1.000	1000	1.000

† 15.93 and its associated frequencies for the posterior distribution are shown only because this value is the mean of the posterior distribution. The associated frequencies are not added into the distribution, but are necessary when fitting the normal, as will be shown in Chapter 11.

the two distributions can be easily compared. These two distributions are graphically displayed in Figure 10.5.

There are two important things to note about this example. The first is the reflection in the revised value μ_1 of the relative information value of the two values from which it was computed. Logically, the reciprocals of the variances used as weights in obtaining the new estimate can be considered to reflect the confidence one can have in each of these estimates.

The second factor is an important characteristic of the revised probability distribution, its reduced variance. It should not seem surprising

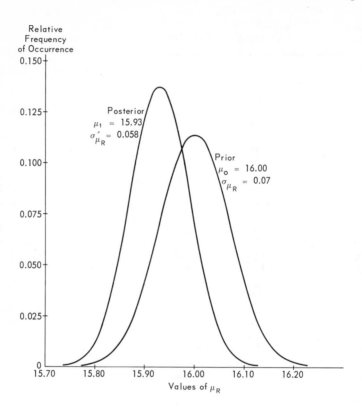

FIG. 10.5. Prior and posterior distribution for mean weights per run (μ_R) for Duravit strawberry package filling problem (sample of $n = 16$, $\bar{x} = 15.80$).

that this variance should be less than *either* the sampling variance or the variance of the prior distribution. A moment's reflection on the *amount of information* contained in this new distribution should assure that we would have greater faith in this value, μ_1, than in either μ_0 or $\bar{x}$. Therefore, it seems intuitively obvious that the variance of the distribution of μ_R' should be smaller than either the variance of the prior distribution for μ_R or the sampling distribution of $\bar{x}$.

THE GENERALIZED DECISION PROCESS
FOR TWO-ACTION PROBLEMS

Steps in the Process

We have been working with a specific example and the reader may not fully understand the nature of the decision procedure which is being applied. If we adopt decision theory terminology and call each decision rule a *strategy* and each decision an *action*, the process involves five steps as formalized below,

10.20 The steps in the decision process are:
   (1) Develop a *prior probability distribution* for the possible states of nature.
   (2) Develop the *conditional loss* associated with each action for each possible state of nature.
   (3) Develop the *conditional expected opportunity loss* for each strategy for each of the possible states of nature.
   (4) Develop the *unconditional expected opportunity loss* for each strategy as the expected value of the CEOL for all actions, using the prior probability distribution as probability weights.
   (5) If the superior strategy involves experimentation (sampling), use the experimental (sample) results to modify the prior probabilities for the possible states of nature and treat the resulting posterior probability distribution for the parameter as if it were a new prior and start the procedure over again at step 3.

This process (technically known as the Bayesian decision process) is completely general and can be applied to *any two-action* problem. In our example, the alternative actions were to call the maintenance crew and have the machine cleaned and adjusted and to *not* call the crew. The strategies were many, but can be grouped into two classifications. One class of strategies did not involve experimentation (sampling) to develop additional information. In our problem this was a single strategy, "choose between the alternative actions on the basis of the available information." The other class of strategies were those strategies which involved drawing a sample before choosing between the alternative actions. We concluded that the superior strategy was to be found in the second class, that is, to draw and evaluate a sample *before* making a choice.

The reader should also observe that this process is equally applicable to problems stated in terms of profit as to problems stated in terms of costs as ours have been. Opportunity losses can be calculated from conditional profits as well as from conditional costs. This was illustrated in Chapter 7.

The Decision Tree

One important characteristic of this process is that it is a stepwise process (has a decision tree structure). At the beginning, one chooses first whether it is better, on the basis of the information already available at that point (*the prior probability distribution*), to make the choice between the alternative actions or to delay the decision in favor of experimentation

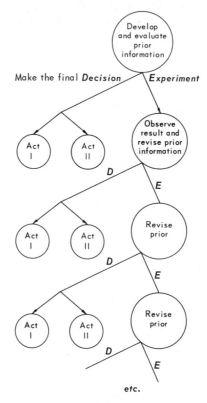

FIG. 10.6. Decision tree representation of generalized Bayesian decision process involving experimentation.

(sampling). If the choice is to delay the decision for experimentation, the experiment is then made and the experimental (sampling) results used to revise the *prior* information. On the basis of this revised (*posterior*) information, one once again considers the choice between an immediate decision or further experimentation. This process can be repeated indefinitely as required. In any situation in which costs (or profits) are available and provide a reasonable basis for choice between actions, the choice between actions at each decision point can be a rational choice between expected opportunity losses. A graphic representation of the decision process is shown in Figure 10.6.

THE DECISION PROCESS FOR MULTI-ACTION PROBLEMS

A careful review of 10.20 and Figure 10.6 reveals no restrictions that would prevent the extension of the above decision process to problems involving more than two possible actions. In the Dry-Cell problem previously discussed, the quality control supervisor had at least *three* possible actions: (1) call the maintenance crew, (2) allow the process to run as is, or (3) call for an additional sample. The examples of this section illustrate the extension to problems involving more than two acts other than the act of "delaying the decision until more information is available." It must be noted, however, that this latter alternative is *always* involved in any decision involving uncertainty concerning the true state of nature. Therefore, it remains as a central consideration in the multiple action problems.

An Example of a Multi-Action Problem

The $E = MC^2$ Nuclear Corporation owns and operates several nuclear reactors which are used primarily to produce steam for the generation of electrical power. By modification of the basic reactor, however, the corporation produces various radio-isotopes for research and other uses. One promising radio-isotope is Polonium 210. Polonium 210 has a thermal energy release of about 140 watts per gram and might prove extremely useful for propulsion and/or power systems used in space exploration and travel. Researchers on $E = MC^2$'s staff are convinced that the level of demand for P_o-210 is dependent upon whether or not a converter can be developed to harness the thermal energy of P_o-210 for space use. The research team defines three possible states of nature (levels of demand for P_o-210):

$D_1 = P_o$-210 is not adopted for space use by the controlling governmental agency; amounts required would be for experimental work only.

$D_2 = P_o$-210 is adopted for space propulsion only; quantities required reflect needs for experimental work and space propulsion.

$D_3 = P_o$-210 is adopted for both space power and space propulsion; P_o-210 will become the major isotope for space use.

A management team has evaluated the above potential states of nature and estimated the dollar volume of business $E = MC^2$ could expect to obtain if each were realized. The conditional returns on an annual basis are shown in Table 10.10.

TABLE 10.10

POSSIBLE VALUE TO $E = MC^2$ OF PRODUCING P_o-210

Level of Demand	Annual Government Expenditures in Millions of Dollars	Estimated Market Share of $E = MC^2$	Annual Direct Expenses	Annual Expected Value to $E = MC^2$ in Millions of Dollars
D_1	0.2	0	0	0
D_2	20	0.25	1	4
D_3	40	0.25	2	8

Since the pace of technological development in the space field is very rapid, the management team has decided that any new investment related to this field must pay off completely within five years. Accordingly, the possible actions of $E = MC^2$ and their possible consequences over five years must be evaluated. In Table 10.11, the conditional net

TABLE 10.11

CONDITIONAL RETURNS OVER FIVE YEARS
FOR EACH ACTION AVAILABLE

	CONDITIONAL RETURNS FOR EACH ACTION								
	a_1			a_2			a_3		
Level of Demand	Investment	Gross Return	Net Return	Investment	Gross Return	Net Return	Investment	Gross Return	Net Return
D_1	0	0	0	5	0	−5	10	0	−10
D_2	0	0	0	5	25	20	10	25	15
D_3	0	0	0	5	25	20	10	40	30

returns over this period are developed for each of the following alternative acts:

a_1 = Stay out of the space isotope business and continue to concentrate on power generation and its present by-products.

a_2 = Spend $5 million for reactor modification which would permit producing an annual volume netting E = MC^2 $4 million.

a_3 = Spend $10 million for reactor modification which would permit producing an annual volume netting E = MC^2 $8 million.

The resulting conditional returns are expressed as conditional opportunity losses in Table 10.12.

TABLE 10.12

CONDITIONAL RETURNS EXPRESSED AS OPPORTUNITY
LOSSES FOR EACH ACTION

Level of Demand	OPPORTUNITY LOSSES BY ACT		
	a_1	a_2	a_3
D_1	0	5	10
D_2	20	0	5
D_3	30	10	0

The research team was now faced with the problem of deciding how likely it is that each of the alternative demand levels (D_i's) would be realized. Interviews with space experts in government and industry have convinced the research team as indicated above that the level of demand will be determined by the government agency's action concerning P_o-210. Experts in that agency have indicated that a first condition for adoption of P_o-210 for either space propulsion or space power is the development of a successful technique for using a P_o-210 heat source in space. After further discussion with agency personnel and other space experts the research team is convinced that the decision will turn in the immediate future on the successful adoption of the hydrogen converter to use of a P_o-210 heat source.

The research team develops two sets of conditional probabilities relating the levels of demand and the modification of the hydrogen converter. These are shown in Table 10.13 where the D_i's have the same meaning as

TABLE 10.13

CONDITIONAL PROBABILITIES OF DEMAND LEVELS FOR EACH
STATE OF NATURE

Level of Demand	CONDITIONAL PROBABILITY OF OCCURRENCE	
	θ_1	θ_2
D_1	0.15	0.50
D_2	0.35	0.35
D_3	0.50	0.15
	1.00	1.00

previously and the new symbol (θ_i's) have the following meanings:

θ_1 = hydrogen converter successfully adopted to P_o-210 heat source
θ_2 = hydrogen converter modification unsuccessful

After consideration of a great deal of evidence including the opinions of many space scientists the E = MC^2 research team believes that there is a slightly better than even (0.55) chance that the converter can be successfully modified.

Combining these two pieces of information, the research team calculates the probabilities of the various levels of demand as shown in Table 10.14. The probability distribution derived in Table 10.14 can now be

TABLE 10.14

CALCULATION OF PROBABILITY DISTRIBUTION FOR ALTERNATIVE
LEVELS OF DEMAND

Success of Converter Modification	Probability of Basic States	Conditional Probability of Demand Levels $P(D_i\|\theta_i)$			Joint Probabilities of Basic States and Demand Levels $P(\theta_i \text{ and } D_i)$		
θ_i	$P(\theta_i)$	D_1	D_2	D_3	D_1	D_2	D_3
θ_1	0.55	0.15	0.35	0.50	0.0825	0.1925	0.2750
θ_2	0.45	0.50	0.35	0.15	0.2250	0.1575	0.0675
Totals	1.00				0.3075	0.3500	0.3425
					(0.31)	(0.35)	(0.34)

used in the standard way to evaluate the alternative actions. The calculations have been carried out in Table 10.15. It would appear that the

TABLE 10.15

EXPECTED OPPORTUNITY LOSS OF ALTERNATIVE ACTS FOR
$E = MC^2$ DECISION PROBLEM

Level of Demand D_i	Probability of Demand Levels $P(D_i)$	Conditional Opportunity Loss of Each Act for Each Level†			Expected Opportunity Loss of Each Act		
		a_1	a_2	a_3	a_1	a_2	a_3
D_1	0.31	0	5	10	0	1.55	3.10
D_2	0.35	20	0	5	7.00	0	1.75
D_3	0.34	30	10	0	10.20	3.40	0
Totals	1.00				17.20	4.95	4.85

† From Table 10.12.

best act would be a_3, spend \$10 million for reactor modification to obtain an annual production volume netting \$8 million. Such an act has an expected opportunity loss of only 4.85 millions of dollars.

In connection with this problem $E = MC^2$ Nuclear has received a proposal from Space Lab, Inc. Space Lab proposes to do the experimental work necessary to adapting the hydrogen converter unit under consideration for space use to use with a P_o-210 heat source. The cost of the research to $E = MC^2$ will be \$500,000. Management has asked the research team to determine if this proposal should be accepted.

The management research team knows that Space Lab has a reputation for success on such proposals. Further analysis of related experiments performed by Space Lab and other researchers and interviews with previous customers of Space Lab convince the $E = MC^2$ research team that Space Lab has at least four chances in five of designing a successful adaptation.

Obviously, if it is assumed that Space Lab performs the proposed research, the probabilities of the success or failure of the converter, (the probabilities of the Θ_i's in Table 10.14) must be changed. It appears that the probability of a successful converter being developed is now 0.80 instead of the previous value of 0.55. The research team uses the new probability set for Θ_i in Table 10.16 to recompute the probability distri-

TABLE 10.16

TABLE 10.16

REVISION OF PROBABILITY DISTRIBUTION FOR ALTERNATIVE LEVELS OF
DEMAND, SPACE LAB PROPOSAL ACCEPTED

	$P'(\theta_i)$	$P(D_i\|\theta_i)$			$P(\theta_i \text{ and } D_i)$		
		D_1	D_2	D_3	D_1	D_2	D_3
θ_1	0.80	0.15	0.35	0.50	0.12	0.28	0.40
θ_2	0.20	0.50	0.35	0.15	0.10	0.07	0.03
Totals	1.00				0.22	0.35	0.43

bution for the D_i. The revised probability distribution for the demand
levels is used to recompute the expected opportunity loss for each of the
alternative acts in Table 10.17. (Note that the conditional opportunity

TABLE 10.17

EXPECTED OPPORTUNITY LOSS OF ALTERNATIVE ACTS FOR
$E = MC^2$ IF SPACE LAB PROPOSAL IS ACCEPTED

D_i	$P'(D_i)$	Revised Conditional Opportunity Losses			Expected Opportunity Losses		
		a_1	a_2	a_3	a_1	a_2	a_3
D_1	0.22	0	5	10	0	1.10	2.20
D_2	0.35	20	0	5	7.00	0	1.75
D_3	0.43	30	10	0	12.90	4.30	0
Totals	1.00				19.90	5.40	3.95

losses for each act are not changed. The reader may find it informative
to check this by a complete recalculation of these conditional values.)

The expected opportunity loss of the preferred act (a_3) has been
decreased from $4.85 million to $3.95 million, a decrease of $900,000.
$E = MC^2$ should accept the Space Lab proposal since the cost of the
further information to be provided by the experiment ($.5 million) is less
than the value of the information to be obtained ($0.9 million).

Note that the research team has been evaluating in this last section
a decision of whether or not to buy imperfect information. The informa-

tion to be furnished by Space Lab is unknown in a specific sense and can be evaluated only in probability terms. In this sense it is similar to the information to be obtained by sampling in the Dry-Cell battery problem and the Duravit packaging problem.

Steps in the Process

The decision process illustrated by the $E = MC^2$ Nuclear example involved the following steps:

(1) We developed the *conditional return* associated with each action for each of the possible secondary states of nature (Tables 10.10 and 10.11).

(2) We developed the *conditional opportunity losses* for each action (Table 10.12).

(3) We developed *conditional probabilities* for the secondary states of nature (levels of demand) (Table 10.13), and probabilities for the primary states of nature (success and nonsuccess of the converter modification) and used Bayes' rule to obtain *unconditional probabilities* for the secondary states of nature (levels of demand) (Tables 10.14).

(4) We used the *unconditional probabilities* for the secondary states of nature to obtain the *unconditional expected opportunity loss* of each act to serve as a basis for choice of action (Table 10.15). (Note that one action alternative involved the purchase of imperfect information so that the probabilities for the basic states of nature were changed when evaluating that alternative.)

If the order of the actions listed above were modified to 2, 3, 1, 4, the list could compare more directly to the steps listed for two-action problems (10.20). In fact, for both situations the process might be summarized in three rules as follows:

10.30   The generalized decision rule says to compute the expected opportunity loss of each act by multiplying the conditional opportunity loss by the probability of the associated state of nature, summing the products for each act and selecting the act with the lowest unconditional expected opportunity loss.

10.31   In evaluating alternative strategies (specific decision rules) one should always choose that strategy for which the unconditional expected opportunity loss is least.

10.32 A decision maker should buy information if the reduction in the unconditional opportunity loss for the optimal strategy when the additional information is purchased is greater than the cost of the further information.

The illustration of techniques useful in applying this last rule has been the major purpose of this chapter.

SUMMARY

In this chapter, we have again been concerned with the mechanics of decision strategies which involve the purchase of additional information. It has been demonstrated that the same general procedure is used whether the decision maker is dealing with two-action problems or multi-action problems. Obviously, a decision maker should continue to purchase information so long as that information is worth more than it costs; in statistical decision theory terminology, so long as the information reduces expected opportunity losses by more than the cost of the information. The general rules evolved are listed in 10.20, 10.30, 10.31, and 10.32. Definitions for technical terms used in those rules are found in earlier sections of the chapter.

In the earlier sections we found that every statistical decision rule (strategy involving sampling) has associated with it not only a set of error characteristics but a set of conditional losses which can be used to determine the *conditional expected opportunity losses* (CEOL) associated with the rule (10.00). Weighting these CEOL by the probabilities for the associated states of nature gives the unconditional expected opportunity loss (UEOL) for a strategy (10.01). Adding the cost of sampling (collecting the information used) gives the total expected opportunity loss (TEOL(S)) of the strategy (10.02).

Strategies involving sampling can then be compared to strategies not involving sampling by comparing their total expected opportunity losses. This comparison can be made at any stage of the analysis (before any sample has been taken (10.03) or after a sample (or several samples) has (have) been taken (10.04 and 10.05)). In the latter connection, we encountered the problem of revising the prior probability distribution for the states of nature in light of the known sample information. Here Bayes' rule (4.41) was found useful. The modification of normal prior probability distributions was also discussed and formulas presented (10.10 and 10.11).

DISCUSSION QUESTIONS

1. Define the following in your own words (no formulas):

   (a) conditional opportunity loss
   (b) conditional expected opportunity losses
   (c) unconditional expected opportunity loss
   (d) total expected opportunity loss of a decision rule
   (e) unconditional expected terminal loss of a decision rule
   (f) prior distribution
   (g) posterior distribution
   (h) action
   (i) strategy
   (j) decision rule
   (k) decision process
   (l) information content (amount of information)

2. If possible, differentiate the following pairs of terms? If you cannot, explain fully why they are the same.

   (a) strategy and decision rule

   (b) decision rule and decision process

   (c) action (act) and strategy

   (d) state of nature and prior distribution

   (e) prior distribution and posterior distribution

   Hint: Define each term carefully and then contrast the definitions.

3. In the $E = MC^2$ Nuclear example it was emphasized that the purchase of additional information (hiring Space Lab) did not change the conditional opportunity losses for each act. Why is this true? Would it always be true that the purchase of additional information would not change the conditional opportunity losses for each act? Explain fully. Hint: Consider the Dry-Cell quality control problem.

4. In the text, sample information and experimental information are, in general, lumped together as "imperfect information." Relate this concept to the concepts of certainty and uncertainty introduced in Chapters 1 and 7.

   Hint: What is the specific source(s) from which each "uncertainty" arises?

5. Do any of the ideas introduced in this chapter have any relation to the concept of "cost of uncertainty" introduced in Chapter 7?

   Hint: This concept is also concerned when determining "value of perfect information."

6. Will the decision criterion of minimum unconditional expected opportunity cost (loss) lead to the selection of a different act than maximum

unconditional expected return? If not, why bother with opportunity cost (loss)?

Hint: Is there any value to a businessman in thinking in terms of opportunity costs in general?

Note: You may come out on either side of this issue depending on your own individual value system. But try to make a logical argument.

DISCUSSION PROBLEMS

Show your method on all solutions.

1. The quality control supervisor at Duravit Corporation had a second sample (see page 276) of 16 items for which $\bar{x} = 16.20$ ounces. Use this sample result to obtain a new estimate of the true mean (μ_1) using the posterior (revised) probability distribution of Table 10.9 and Figure 10.5 as the prior distribution for μ_R. Also compute the standard deviation for your new posterior distribution.

   Hint: Use 10.10 and 10.11. Note that the parameters of the prior distribution for this analysis are $\mu_0 = 15.93$ and $\sigma_{\mu_R} = 0.058$.

2. A manufacturer produces a gear drive assembly whose final quality is determined by one gear which he obtains from another firm in lots of 1000. If this gear is of the wrong size, too large or too small, the assembly will not operate properly. Defective assemblies are now being scrapped, although the major gear hub is salvaged by later reworking. The net loss for a defective assembly is one dollar. The manufacture recognizes three alternatives:

   (1) No inspection of the incoming gears (continue as is) but reduce the price of the outgoing product by 75 cents and send out all assemblies.

   (2) 100 percent inspection of each lot of gears as it is received. Past experience indicates that inspected lots would still contain an average of one percent defective gears. Inspection costs four cents per gear on the average.

   (3) Sample inspection of each lot as it is received (refer to Problem 3).

   Past records indicate that when the production process of the supplier is "in control," two percent of the gears are defective. When the supplier's process is "out of control," ten percent of the gears are defective. The supplier's production process has been "out of control" 20 percent of the time.

(a) Set up a table showing the conditional costs associated with the first two alternatives for a lot of 1000 gears.

(b) Compute the conditional opportunity losses associated with the first two alternatives.

(c) Compute the unconditional opportunity costs of the first two alternatives.

(d) Which of the first two alternatives is to be preferred? Explain.

3. Refer to the situation of Problem 2. The quality control statistician has recommended that one of two sampling plans be used:

$$\text{Plan A: } n = 25, x^* = 1$$
$$\text{Plan B: } n = 100, x^* = 3$$

(a) Develop the conditional loss functions associated with these two sampling plans.

(b) Develop and graph the error characteristics of each of these two sampling plans.

(c) Complete the analysis to obtain the total unconditional expected opportunity cost for each of these decision rules.

(d) Which of the three alternative actions of Problem 2 should the manufacturer adopt? Explain your choice.

4. Mr. Charles Deeds, proprietor of C-D Garden Center, is considering adding a full line of hedge clippers to his inventory. The manufacturer's representative has given him the information in the following table concerning the average monthly gross sales revenue realized from this line in stores of the same general size in similar areas throughout the country. Mr. Deeds has always found the manufacturer to be completely honest in his claims, and he is convinced that this information is reliable.

Sales Volume (per month)	Proportion of Stores
$100–$199	0.25
200– 349	0.30
350– 499	0.25
500– 999	0.15
1000 or over	0.05

Mr. Deeds has decided that the necessary investment in inventory, the profit rate, and the opportunity to use the display and storage space are such that he can profitably stock the line only if the gross sales are at least $350. (He computes his possible *net* gain as five percent of gross sales.)

(a) What is the probability that sales will be at least $350?

(b) Quest, Inc., has offered to make a survey $n = 64$ at a cost of $100 to check the market in his area. Should he buy the survey? Explain.

(c) Suppose Mr. Deeds had purchased the survey ($n = 64$) and found that the estimated gross sales revenue was $380 per month with a standard deviation of $40. What is the revised probability that sales are at least $350?

(d) Suppose the first survey (see c) has been conducted, should Mr. Deeds buy a *second* survey ($n = 64$) at $100?

5. The I-B Corporation has a contract to supply 100 drive gear assemblies to a company producing military equipment under a contract from the Defense Department. One component in this drive assembly is an unusual gear which must be produced in a special run on I-B's automatic gear cutter. It is known that not all gears cut on the machine in a run of 100 gears conform to the specifications which determine the original machine set up. Experience indicates the number of defective gears in any run of 100 gears to be Poisson distributed. The production supervisor and the quality control supervisor estimate from long experience that the proportion of defective gears for runs of gears of this complexity averages eight percent. The total cost of setup for a run is $95. The gear blanks from which the gears are cut cost $70 each. Defective gears must be scrapped and return only $5 per gear scrapped. Direct labor and machine operating costs total $15 per gear produced.

(a) What would be the expected cost if 108 gear blanks are purchased and started into production? 106? 110?

(b) Would you advise starting more or less than 108 gears into production? Explain.

Hints: (1) Consult Table B-8 to determine the probability distribution for number of defectives in each run.

(2) Compute the conditional value of the run for each result. Do not forget that failure to obtain 100 good gears from a first run will mean that a second setup will be necessary.

6. You have some prior conviction about the probability of a head as the result on the toss of a coin.

(a) Construct a prior probability distribution expressing your belief about $P(H)$.

(b) Suppose you are tossing a coin which repeatedly comes up heads. What is the maximum number of successive heads you *would* tolerate and still retain your belief that $P(H) = 0.5$? Make no calculations to obtain this answer, but explain why you chose it as best you can.

(c) Assume you had received the sample of successive heads of the maximum size you specified in (b), compute the revised probability distribution for the proportion of heads using the method of this chapter (see 10.20, note we use only part 5 and that we are really applying 4.41).

7. Suppose that you knew nothing about the operating characteristics of a bolt-cutting machine just installed in the production line of the company where you are employed as quality control supervisor. A sample of 100 bolts taken from the first hour's production is found to contain 15 defective bolts. A second sample taken from the second hour's production contains only 8 defective bolts. What would you say happened to the quality of output of the machine between the first and second hour of operation?

Hints: (1) Your initial prior probability distribution would be a uniform distribution showing equal probabilities for all possible values of P. How many possible values are there?

(2) All the data you have available is from samples. What is the conditional probabilities of each of the sample results? Can you use these probabilities?

(3) What would you conclude if asked to estimate P (proportion of defectives) on the basis of the two samples?

EXERCISES

Show your method on all solutions.

1. Compute the exact TEOL of the decision rule, $n = 30$, $x^* = 1$, for the Dry-Cell quality control problem.

2. The credit manager for Lessloss Department Stores has often expressed the belief that in the summer (June, July, and August) the accounts of regular charge customers average $35 each and that about two thirds of the balances will fall between $31 and $39. As part of a continuing analysis of regular charge accounts, a sample of 100 accounts was found to have a mean of $32 and a standard deviation of $5.50.

(a) What are the parameters of the credit manager's prior distribution for account balances?

(b) What should be the parameters of the credit manager's revised distribution if he incorporates the information contained in the sample?

3. The operator of a nut threading machine is required to stop the machine for readjustment whenever the periodic sample of ten nuts shows one or more defectives. The machine is supposed to average 7 percent defectives (assume this is the breakeven value).

(a) Compute the error characteristics of this decision rule and plot it on a graph.

(b) The quality control supervisor is considering changing the rule to $n = 20$, $x^* = 2$. Compute and plot the error characteristics of this new decision rule.

(c) Will the proposed change in decision rules result in tighter control of quality (a lower average proportion of defectives) or looser control of quality? Explain fully.

4. The quality control supervisor (Exercise 3) asks you to devise a decision rule which will have the following characteristics:

(1) No more than a 0.20 chance of stopping the machine if the process is producing no more than five percent defectives.

(2) No more than a 0.20 chance of letting the machine run if the process is producing as much as 11 percent defectives.

(a) Find the critical values of x and the size of sample necessary to obtain these results *using only* Table B-4.

(b) Compute and plot the error characteristic of this decision rule.

5. Suppose the quality control supervisor (Exercises 3 and 4) gives you the following information:

(1) Data on 1000 prior batches of 500 nuts each (the usual batch size) as follows:

Proportion of Defectives	*Frequency of Occurrence*
0.03	100
0.05	250
0.07	400
0.09	150
0.11	100
	1000

(2) Stopping the machine to readjust costs $10 and it still produces defectives at the rate of 0.03 for that batch.

(3) Each defective nut has an expected cost of fifty cents.

(4) Sampling costs 2 cents per nut tested.

(a) Which of the three rules discussed in Exercises 3 and 4 is preferable on the basis of total unconditional expected opportunity loss for each rule? Clearly develop *and* *show* your results at each step in the solution.

(b) Should *any* of these sampling rules be used? Explain fully.

6. The Allcap Company manufactures "screwdriver" type valve caps. The 40,000 caps sampled during the last year showed a mean holding pressure of 203 pounds and a standard deviation of 16 pounds. These values can be assumed to be population values. As a part of the quality control operation samples of 25 are taken each hour and tested for holding pressure.

(a) What would be the standard error of the mean for these samples?

(b) Within what limits would 95 percent of the sample means fall?

(c) The mean of the last sample was 195 pounds. What are the chances that we could take a sample of 25 and get a mean so far below the true mean purely by chance?

(d) Within what limits would 95 percent of the sample standard deviations fall?

(e) The standard deviation of the last sample ($\hat{\sigma}$) was 12.6 pounds. What are the chances that we could take a sample of 25 and get a standard deviation so far below the true value purely by chance?

(f) Given the last sample ($n = 25$, $\bar{x} = 195$, $\hat{\sigma} = 12.6$) and the population values, what should the quality control supervisor believe are the current mean and standard deviation of the population?

7. The Allcap Company has been rejecting as unsatisfactory lots of caps if the mean holding pressure for caps in the sample of 25 falls as low as 193 pounds or $\hat{\sigma}$ from the sample is over 18 pounds. What are the conditional probabilities of error for these two rules singly and in combination if previous experience indicates that variations in mean holding pressure and standard deviation of pressure for each lot are statistically independent?

8. Lessloss Department Stores requires a credit check for each new customer before opening a charge account. This requires an average of ten days and the sales department feels the delay loses sales. The credit manager supplies the following data from his records:

Average loss per account opened	$4.00
Average percent of accounts uncollectable	4 percent

The credit department employs six interviewers to take credit applications. Each has developed a habit of evaluating applicants on the basis of area of residence, speech, clothing, general attitude, occupation, and so forth, as to the kind of credit risk they will be. With their assistance the credit manager has developed the following data

	Percent of Average Loss Potential	Percent of Applicants
Good credit risk	2	65
Fair credit risk	7	20
Poor credit risk	20	15

The sales department cooperated by surveying the sales personnel and obtaining an estimate that an average of $22 in immediate sales was lost each time a customer refused to wait for a credit clearance. Ten percent of the potential charge customers refuse to wait for credit clearance. Lessloss averages 20 percent margin on sales. The credit manager has proposed that credit interviewers be allowed to evaluate each credit applicant and then the applicants be given the opportunity to make immediate credit purchases in the following amounts:

Good risks	$100
Fair risks	50
Poor risks	20

A sample of 100 customers was evaluated six months ago and the following statistics accumulated:

Risk Category	Ratings by Interviewers	Number of Accounts Overdue 3 Months or More
Good	70	3
Fair	18	2
Poor	12	3

Use the techniques learned in this and earlier chapters to evaluate the credit manager's scheme.

9. The Koloredi Company has developed a new concept in amplifier (sound) systems for its TV sets which could be marketed separately as a radio. The cost of setting up the additional production line and marketing in sufficient volume to warrant the venture is estimated at $2,000,000. The company uses a five-year planning period. The mar-

ket is such that the company feels their radio would have to be preferred by at least one third of the potential customers to provide a sufficient return. If the radio is preferred by at least one third of the market, the company can expect sales sufficient to return $600,000 per year above variable production costs. If the product is not preferred by one third of the market, it is expected that the net return will be only $300,000 per year. If they do not market it themselves, Koloredi can sell the concept to other manufacturers for $1,200,000 on the condition that it is preferred by at least one third of the market; however, the price could drop to $300,000 if it is not preferred by at least one third of the market. Experts assign a 0.70 probability to the state of nature where one third or more prefer the Koloredi radio.

(a) Should the new radio be produced and marketed by Koloredi on the basis of the above information only?

(b) A market test involving a sample of fifty yields 15 persons who prefer the Koloredi product. What should be the decision now? Hint: There are two actions, two states of nature, a prior probability distribution for the states of nature, and a sample result. Can they be combined? Should they be?

(c) Suppose the market test sample of fifty had yielded 25 persons who prefer the Koloredi amplifier. What would be your advice to Koloredi's management? Why?

10. The Compacto Company produces machine parts with pressure molding equipment. One of Compacto's machines is in the repair shop being rebuilt. It is being temporarily replaced by an older model. Compacto has just received an order for 500 of a part of a particularly difficult type. Past experience with the older model indicates that, after normal adjustment, the machine has produced defective parts on runs of 500 parts of this difficulty as follows:

Fraction Defective Parts	Historical Frequencies
0.02	200
0.05	300
0.07	500
	1000

The incremental costs of production in runs of 500 parts is $9.00 per part. It costs $5.00 to rework a defective part. A local job shop has offered to provide the required 500 good parts for $9.16 per part. Compacto requests your assistance in deciding whether to produce the parts on the old machine or subcontract the job to the job shop.

(a) What is the best act without sampling if the historical frequencies are accepted as a reliable indication of the performance characteristics of the old machine. Clearly show your method and clearly label the following:

(1) the conditional opportunity losses of each act

(2) the expected opportunity losses of each act

(3) the cost of uncertainty

(b) Inspection costs are 5 cents per part inspected and incremental costs of production increase to $9.25 per part for runs of no more than 100 parts. The quality control supervisor at Compacto has suggested running a sample of parts on the old machine as a further indication of its expected performance.

(1) What would be the optimum sampling rule involving samples of 16 parts each (one hour's production)? (*Check only $c = 1$ and $c = 2$.*) Clearly show your method. Clearly label each answer.

(2) Should Compacto use a sample rule involving a sample of 16 parts? Justify your answer on the basis of your previous calculations.

(c) Because an operator had nothing else to do, the factory foreman already had a sample of 20 parts run on the old machine late yesterday. Inspection reveals one of these parts to be defective.

(1) What is the terminal expected opportunity loss of each act at this point (after taking the sample information into account)? Clearly show your method. Label all interim results carefully. (Remember there are still two acts possible.)

(2) Which act would you advise that Compacto choose at this point? Justify your choice on the basis of your results.

(d) The shop foreman at Compacto says that the sample results lead him to believe that the machine will produce at least five percent defectives on the proposed run. The factory manager asks you to show whether or not the data do support such a belief. (Use only the cumulative binomial table in making any tests.)

11
experiments, comparisons, and associations

THE EXPERIMENTAL PROCESS

Most business decisions must consider several variables simultaneously. Some of these variables are of primary importance to the decision; others may affect the decision outcome but are not controllable or are not of interest in the problem studied. It therefore seems desirable to classify these variables in some systematic way and to look for methods of data analysis which will ferret out the effects of the important or controllable variables independent of the effects of the "confounding" variables.

In "pure" research one tries to hold all but one variable constant, to manipulate the nonconstant variable, and to observe the outcome. By repeating this process, the effects of all important variables are determined. This technique is usually difficult to apply in real business problem situations. Rather, in such situations, we must classify the variables influencing the outcome as independent (determined by outside forces) or dependent (determined by forces directly involved within the situation). The independent variables must then be further classified as variables of direct interest in the problem or as variables whose presence confuses or covers up the relationship or association of interest. Thus, if we were interested in differences in taste among various brands of a certain type of carbonated beverage, there would be several possible "confounding" variables whose effects we would like to remove. The list

353

would include: (1) the order of presentation of the brands to tasters; (2) the container in which each brand was offered (all should be the same); and (3) the brand identification (tasters might be influenced by illogical brand preferences developed through advertising, long usage, and so forth).

Basically, we attempt to look at a situation before and after the introduction of some known stimulus. If properly designed, an experiment resembles a chance process. For example, we might take a balanced (fair) die, shave one side a little, then roll the die a number of times and observe the results to determine if the shaving has changed the characteristics of the die in a discernible way. If the die were known to be balanced (fair) before the shaving, the statistical analysis would consist of comparing the outcome of the rolls performed after shaving (a sample) with the expected result for a balanced (fair) die. Suppose, however, that the rolls after shaving are performed in a manner which might change the outcomes for even a balanced (fair) die. Our analysis would be complicated by the presence of this "confounding" variable. Unless we could isolate the effect of the shaving alone, we would not know its effects.

The purpose of this chapter is to present a number of techniques which have been found useful in the analysis of experimental situations. The reader will recognize that these techniques are really statistical inference methods for the testing of hypotheses in more complicated situations than those of the immediately preceding two chapters.

Comparing Parameters from Two Populations

A very common type of problem involves choice between two populations on the basis of samples from each of the two populations. In general these processes can be generalized as tests of hypotheses concerned with differences between parameters. Thus, we might define

11.00 $D = PP_1 - PP_2$

where

D stands for true difference
PP_i stands for parameter value for population i

Unfortunately we seldom find it possible to observe the value of D directly, but must base decisions about (or estimates of) its true value on sample results. Thus,

11.01 $\quad d = ss_1 - ss_2$

where

d stands for observed difference

ss_i stands for value of the statistic (estimate of PP_i) computed from a sample drawn from population i

It seems obvious that since d is, in reality, a sample statistic, we are interested in testing to determine whether the difference between d and the hypothesized value of D is too large to be considered as resulting from the chance selection of the two samples. Also, if d is a sample statistic, it is a random variable with a probability distribution and a standard error (standard deviation of the sampling distribution for d). Thus, we are involved with the same hypothesis testing procedures as illustrated previously. We have a difference between a sample statistic (d) and a (hypothetical) population parameter (D) which we express in units of the standard error of the sample statistic (σ_d). That is, we compute the familiar ratio, call it "Z_d." If we can decide on acceptance and rejection intervals for Z_d, then we can use "Z_d" to test the hypothesis that the difference between d and D is due to chance. We define Z_d as follows:

11.02 $\quad Z_d = \dfrac{d - D}{\sigma_d}$

In later sections of this chapter we will consider differences between specific parameters (means, proportions, variances). In each case, the appropriate probability distribution for evaluating Z_d will be defined and its use illustrated.

Comparing Parameters from Many Populations

The comparison of parameters from two populations is merely a special case of a much larger problem. Often, we need to compare parameters from more than two populations. Techniques for making such comparisons (tests of differences) for specific parameters are also described in this chapter. In general, the hypotheses are of the type

11.03 $\quad H_0{:}PP_1 = PP_2 = \cdots = PP_k$
$\qquad H_a{:}$At least two parameters are not equal

Note that this is equivalent to the hypothesis that all possible differences between parameters (D's) are equal to zero.

Measuring Association

In addition to comparing parameters of two or more populations represented by statistical variables, we often are asked to answer questions about associations between variables or characteristics from a single population. For example, a personnel director might ask if he should place emphasis on the specific education of the young persons he hires from colleges and universities or look only at general "intelligence" as indicated by the applicant's grade record. Similarly, the advertising executive wants to know if the people with higher incomes are the persons who buy more of our type of product. He may also ask if advertisements featuring pretty young women create more sales than advertisements featuring attractive mature women. The production supervisor may ask if incentive pay schemes really increase worker productivity. In many of these cases, a simple measure of the degree to which these variables change together may be sufficient. Occasionally, this may be all that can be determined from the research projects that can be justified to acquire answers.

One method of testing for association between variables from the same population is to compare the observed sample *distribution* with the "expected" sample distribution. If two variables are associated, classification by the variables should reveal that the variables are not independent; that is, that the conditional probability of one characteristic prevailing given the other characteristic is not equal to the simple probability of the first characteristic. That is, if A is the first characteristic and B is the second characteristic,

$$P(A|B) \neq P(A)$$

Such dependent relationships are often described as *contingent* relationships and the analysis of them as *contingency analysis*.

In later sections of this chapter we will illustrate some elementary techniques for testing an association among variables and the presence of contingent relationships.

Useful Probability Distributions

In performing the above analyses, several new probability distributions will be used. These are discussed below in the order of their appearance.

The F Distribution. One important probability distribution with wide application in the area of interest is the distribution of the variance ratio F. The variance ratio, F, is the ratio of two independent estimates of a population variance. Suppose we were to refer to a table of random normal deviates,[1] and draw 100,000 samples of four values each. (The number 4 is arbitrary; we could use any $n > 1$.) Suppose that we number each successive pair of samples drawn as Sample (1) and Sample (2). Each pair is numbered as Pr.(1), Pr.(2), $\cdots$, Pr.(49,999), Pr.(50,000). The variance of each sample is computed and ratios of the sample variances for each of the 50,000 pairs of samples calculated. That is,

$$F_1 = \frac{\hat{\sigma}_{1,1}{}^2}{\hat{\sigma}_{2,1}{}^2}, \; F_2 = \frac{\hat{\sigma}_{1,2}{}^2}{\hat{\sigma}_{2,2}{}^2}, \; \cdots \; , F_{50,000} = \frac{\hat{\sigma}_{1,50,000}{}^2}{\hat{\sigma}_{2,50,000}{}^2}$$

or, in general,

11.10 $\quad F = \dfrac{\hat{\sigma}_1{}^2}{\hat{\sigma}_2{}^2}$

The 50,000 F ratios would be distributed as the F distribution for three and three degrees of freedom. If we define the degrees of freedom for each sample in the pair as v_1 and v_2, respectively, it could be shown that such an F distribution has the following probability distribution (probability density function):

11.11 $\quad h(F_{(v_1, \, v_2)}) = \dfrac{\left(\dfrac{v_1 + v_2}{2}\right)!}{\left(\dfrac{v_1 - 2}{2}\right)! \left(\dfrac{v_1 - 2}{2}\right)!} \left(\dfrac{v_1}{v_2}\right)^{(v_1)/2} \dfrac{F^{(v_1 - 2)/2}}{\left(\dfrac{v_1 F}{v_2}\right)^{(v_1 + v_2)/2}}$

It can be seen that the value of this expression (the probability of a given value of F) will vary if either v_1 or v_2 varies. That is, the degrees of freedom of the numerator and of the denominator of the F ratio are parameters of the F distribution. Also, 11.11 is a very complicated formula. Fortunately, the values of F have been tabulated, and we need only know the degrees of freedom of the numerator (v_1) and denominator (v_2) to make use of the F distributions. Selected values of F are shown in Table 13 of Appendix B.

Table B-13 is used as follows: Suppose a single value of F for $v_1 = 3$, $v_2 = 3$ had been calculated from just two samples of random normal deviates as described above and F calculated as 6.50. We see in Table B-13, that, for three and three degrees of freedom, no more than 10 per-

---

[1] An example would be: The Rand Corporation, *A Million Random Digits with 100,000 Normal Deviates*. New York: The Free Press, 1955.

cent of the possible F ratios would be at or above 5.39, no more than five percent would be as large or larger than 9.28, and no more than one percent would be at or above 29.5. We, therefore, conclude that the observed ratio of 6.50 has slightly more than five chances in 100 of being a member of this distribution since it is so large. That is, there are slightly more than five chances in 100 that the two samples could come from the same population and have the ratio of their variances be so large.

Notice that we did not say that the two samples have slightly more than five chances in 100 of coming from the same population. As a matter of fact that statement is untrue. Let us see why.

Since two values for degrees of freedom must be considered, the table for the F distribution is complex. Note that only the one, five, and ten percent significance points at the upper end (right tail) of the distribution are shown in Table B-13. Therefore, we must adopt the convention of putting the larger variance estimate in the numerator in order to be able to use Table B-13 as it stands. This affects our interpretation of the probability level of the observed F value. Putting the larger variance in the numerator always forces F to be greater than 1.0, and the entire region of rejection is placed in the upper tail of the distribution. This means that for single-tail tests the significance level is equal to the value of α (0.10, 0.05, 0.01). For two-tail tests, however, the significance level of the test is really 2α. To illustrate this latter statement, consider the above value, $F = 6.50$. The value 6.50 falls above the 5.39 for $F_{0.01(3,3)}$ (one tail) but below the 9.28 for $F_{0.05(3,3)}$. If we use this value to test the hypothesis that the two samples come from the same population, we must conclude that the chances of that being true are greater than ten in 100 rather than greater than five in 100.

If one needs to know the values of F for the lower tail of the distribution, they may be found by applying the following relationship:

$$11.12 \quad F_{(1-\alpha)(v_1, v_2)} = \frac{1}{F_{\alpha(v_2, v_1)}}$$

Note the reversal of the degrees of freedom for F_α (in the denominator).

One final caution about the F distribution; note that the ratio is of variances of random samples from a normally distributed population. Thus, the use of the ratio in hypothesis testing assumes that the samples utilized are from a normally distributed population(s). As is indicated below, this assumption can be violated to a degree without making the F ratio invalid for testing hypotheses. One must always keep this assumption in mind, however, so that completely erroneous conclusions are not drawn.

Nonparametric Chi Square. In Chapter 8, we were introduced to use of the chi square (χ^2) distribution in estimating σ. In this chapter we will be using the same probability distribution in a different manner. In Chapter 8 we assumed a normally distributed population as the basis for using the chi-square distribution. In using chi square in the present chapter, we do not start from that assumption; thus, the title, *nonparametric* chi square.

Nonparametric chi square is computed as

$$\text{11.13} \quad \chi^2 = \sum \left[\frac{(f_o - f_e)^2}{f_e} \right]$$

where

f_o = observed frequency in a cell
f_e = expected frequency in a cell

Only two assumptions are made in the application of nonparametric χ^2. First, it is assumed that the observations are independent of one another; that is, that the value or result on any one observation does not affect the value or result on any other observation. The second assumption is that the expected frequencies in each cell are reasonably large. A general rule of thumb is that no expected cell frequency be less than 5. The reason for this is that single unit changes in observed frequencies would exert too large an influence on the χ^2 value if the denominator of the ratio in 11.13 were a small number.

The degrees of freedom for nonparametric chi square are found by counting the total number of cells (frequencies) and subtracting the number of restrictions (estimated population parameters or totals) taken from the sample data when computing the expected frequencies. This rule will be explained further when the distribution is used in later examples.

COMPARISONS BETWEEN TWO POPULATIONS

Tests of the Difference between Two Means—Independent Samples

Mr. Newboss has been approached by the union steward from Department G, who asserts that because of discriminatory supervision the workers in his department are getting shorter coffee breaks than the workers in Department A. Mr. Newboss randomly selects nine workers from each department and checks on the time they spend on their next coffee break. He then computes the mean times and standard deviations for each department and obtains:

$$\bar{x}_A = 15.2 \qquad \hat{\sigma}_A{}^2 = 9.45$$
$$\bar{x}_G = 16.3 \qquad \hat{\sigma}_G{}^2 = 3.99$$

A Test Based on the Sampling Distribution of the Difference. It has already been established that means from random samples tend to be normally distributed (8.25). It seems reasonable to accept that the differences between means of two independent random samples would also be normally distributed. Mathematicians have established that such is actually the case.[2] For such independent random samples it is true that the mean of the differences between the sample means is expected to be equal to the difference between the population means. That is,

11.20 $\quad E(d_{\bar{x}}) = D_\mu$

where

$$d_{\bar{x}} = \bar{x}_1 - \bar{x}_2$$
$$D_\mu = \mu_1 - \mu_2$$

Further, the variance of the distribution of all possible differences (all possible d's for samples of size n_1 and n_2), in short, the error variance of the difference in the sample means, would be a weighted sum of the variances of the two sample statistics ($\bar{x}$'s):

11.21 $\quad \sigma^2{}_{\bar{x}_1-\bar{x}_2} = \sigma_{d_{\bar{x}}}{}^2 = \dfrac{\sigma_1{}^2}{n_1} + \dfrac{\sigma_2{}^2}{n_2}$

The standard error of the difference between two means is the positive square root of this error variance:

11.22 $\quad \sigma_{d_{\bar{x}}} = \sqrt{\dfrac{\sigma_1{}^2}{n_1} + \dfrac{\sigma_2{}^2}{n_2}}$

It should be obvious that in those cases where the population standard deviations are equal, that is, where

$$\sigma_1 = \sigma_2 = \sigma$$

[2] See, for example, John E. Freund, *Mathematical Statistics*, Englewood Cliffs, New Jersey: Prentice-Hall, Inc., 1962, pp. 179–182.

11.22 reduces to

11.23 $\sigma_{d_{\bar{x}}} = \sigma \sqrt{\dfrac{1}{n_1} + \dfrac{1}{n_2}}$

Since $d_{\bar{x}}$ is normally distributed, the ratio

11.24 $z = \dfrac{d_{\bar{x}} - D_\mu}{\sigma_{d_{\bar{x}}}}$

is the standard normal deviate. Remember, however, that this is true of such ratios only if the standard error used in computing the ratio is estimated from population parameters. If the standard error must be estimated from sample statistics (from the two samples), then the ratio is a t ratio, and the t distribution is the appropriate sampling distribution. That is, the ratio is

11.25 $t = \dfrac{d_{\bar{x}} - D_\mu}{\hat{\sigma}_{d_{\bar{x}}}}$

where

11.26 $\hat{\sigma}_{d_{\bar{x}}} = \sqrt{\dfrac{\hat{\sigma}_1{}^2}{n_1} + \dfrac{\hat{\sigma}_2{}^2}{n_2}}$

If two samples of different size are drawn from normally distributed populations with equal variances, a *computationally* simpler form of 11.26 can be shown to be[3]

11.27 $\hat{\sigma}_{d_{\bar{x}}} = \sqrt{\dfrac{(n_1 - 1)\hat{\sigma}_1{}^2 + (n_2 - 1)\hat{\sigma}_2{}^2}{n_1 + n_2 - 2}} \sqrt{\dfrac{1}{n_1} + \dfrac{1}{n_2}}$

If sample sizes are equal, that is, if

$$n_1 = n_2 = n$$

11.27 reduces to

11.28 $\hat{\sigma}_{d_{\bar{x}}} = \sqrt{\dfrac{\hat{\sigma}_1{}^2 + \hat{\sigma}_2{}^2}{n}}$

Note that the variance estimates provided by 11.26, 11.27, and 11.28 are the weighted sums of the variance information available from the two samples. Such estimates from sample data are often referred to as "pooled" estimates of the variance.

[3] Freund, pp. 267–268.

Returning to the problem of the difference in the time of coffee breaks in Departments A and G, we see that we have two samples. An appropriate hypothesis about the two samples is that they come from the same population or at least from two populations with equal means and variances. An appropriate form of the *null* hypothesis (H_0) and the alternate hypothesis (H_a) about the difference between means for this situation would be:

$$H_0{:}\mu_1 = \mu_2 \qquad H_a{:}\mu_1 \neq \mu_2$$

or

$$H_0{:}D_\mu = 0 \qquad H_a{:}D_\mu \neq 0$$

where μ_1 = mean time for coffee breaks in Department G and μ_2 = mean time for coffee breaks in Department A.

What would be an appropriate significance level for testing the stated *null* hypothesis? While Mr. Newboss would most certainly not wish to falsely accuse supervisors of allowing Department A workers to take longer coffee breaks than those in Department G, he would also like to avoid rejecting the allegation too easily, since it may be true. After weighing the possible consequences of Type I and Type II errors, he decides on an alpha of 0.10.

The appropriate test ratio in this situation is t (σ_d is estimated). Since the total degrees of freedom are only 16 ($n_1 - 1 + n_2 - 1$) the normal approximation to t is inappropriate. Referring to Table B-12, for sixteen degrees of freedom and an α of 0.10, the critical value of the ratio is found to be

$$t_\alpha = \mathbf{1.746}$$

Computing the t ratio (11.24)

$$t = \frac{d_{\bar{z}} - D_\mu}{\hat{\sigma}_{d_{\bar{z}}}}$$

where, $D_\mu = 0$ (*null* hypothesis)

$$d_{\bar{z}} = \bar{x}_G - \bar{x}_A$$
$$= 16.3 - 15.2$$
$$= \mathbf{1.1}$$

$$\hat{\sigma}_{d_{\bar{z}}} = \sqrt{\frac{3.99 + 9.45}{9}} \qquad \text{(by 11.28)}$$

$$= \sqrt{1.49}$$
$$= \mathbf{1.22}$$

Substituting,

$$t = \frac{1.1 - 0}{1.22}$$
$$= \mathbf{0.90}$$

Since $t < t_\alpha$, we advise Mr. Newboss to accept the *null* hypothesis and conclude that there is not a difference in the average times spent on coffee breaks by the men in Departments A and G.

Suppose that the steward from Department A is unsatisfied by the test that has been made, insisting that the samples drawn are really not representative of the two populations. Mr. Newboss agrees to draw larger samples and obtains the following results:

$$n_A = 25 \qquad \bar{x}_A = 15.4 \qquad \hat{\sigma}_A{}^2 = 7.83$$
$$n_G = 25 \qquad \bar{x}_G = 16.4 \qquad \hat{\sigma}_G{}^2 = 3.67$$

Mr. Newboss decides to test the same hypothesis with the same probability of Type I error as before. Since the test ratio involves a pooled estimate of variance taken from the two samples, it is obviously a t ratio. The degrees of freedom, $n_1 + n_2 - 2$, are now equal to 48, however, making it reasonable to use the normal approximation for t. The critical value of the z ratio for $\alpha = 0.10$ is obtained from Table B-5

$$z_\alpha = 1.64$$

The z ratio is computed by replacing $\sigma_{d_{\bar{z}}}$ with $\hat{\sigma}_{d_{\bar{z}}}$ in 11.24. That is,

$$z = \frac{d_{\bar{z}} - D_\mu}{\hat{\sigma}_{d_{\bar{z}}}}$$

where

$$D_\mu = 0$$
$$d_{\bar{z}} = \bar{x}_G - \bar{x}_A$$
$$= 16.4 - 15.4$$
$$= \mathbf{1.0}$$

$$\hat{\sigma}_{d_{\bar{z}}} = \sqrt{\frac{7.83 + 3.67}{25}} \qquad \text{(by 11.28)}$$
$$= \mathbf{0.68}$$

substituting

$$z = \frac{1.0 - 0}{0.68}$$
$$= \mathbf{1.47}$$

Since $z < z_\alpha$, Mr. Newboss still should accept the *null* hypothesis and conclude that the coffee breaks in Departments A and G do not differ significantly in length.

Only in very special circumstances would one encounter a situation in which one knew the standard deviation of each of the populations from which two samples had allegedly been drawn. It is not unusual, however, to encounter situations in which two samples are alleged to have come from the same population, a population for which σ is assumed to be known. The discussion of berry packaging at Duravit Corporation deals with just such a situation. There we found a machine putting strawberries into packages intended to contain 16 ounces of frozen strawberries and syrup. The package weights were known to be normally distributed with a standard deviation of 0.40 ounces. In Chapter 9, we discussed two samples of 16 packages each drawn by the quality control inspector. The first sample had a mean content weight ($\bar{x}$) of 15.80 ounces and the second had a mean content weight of 16.20 ounces. The inspector was more anxious to detect deviations of the average weight below 16 ounces than above 16.00 ounces. With a one-sided test and an α of 0.05, the first sample indicated a significant deviation of the average weight *below* 16.00 ounces. The other sample was judged not to show a significant deviation of the average weight above 16.00 ounces ($\alpha = 0.02$, one-sided test). The inspector has been wondering if these two samples would have been recognized as coming from different populations. He suggests a seven percent significance level for the test (the sum of the single tail rejection regions used previously). Then, we wish to test

$$H_0{:}D_\mu = 0 \qquad\qquad H_a{:}D_\mu \neq 0$$
$$\alpha = 0.07 \text{ (two tail)} \qquad z_\alpha = 1.81$$

using as data,

$$\sigma = 0.40 \qquad n_1 = n_2 = 16 \qquad \bar{x}_1 = 16.20 \qquad \bar{x}_2 = 15.80$$

by 11.23,

$$\sigma_{d_{\bar{x}}} = 0.40 \sqrt{\frac{1}{16} + \frac{1}{16}}$$
$$= 0.10 \sqrt{2}$$
$$= \mathbf{0.14}$$

Substituting into 11.24,

$$z = \frac{0.40 - 0}{0.14}$$
$$= \mathbf{2.86}$$

Since $z > z_\alpha$ (2.86 > 1.81), the *null* hypothesis is rejected, and it is concluded that the two samples did come from different populations.

A Test by Analysis of Variance.   We have seen that it is possible to test the equality of two population means with observations from two random samples. A further method for testing the difference between the two means is basically a process which relies upon a partitioning of the total variance present into components as estimates of the variability arising from each of the several sources. The technique involves using ratios of variance estimates (F ratios) and the F distribution to determine if the variance estimate derived by consideration of differences associated with different values of a particular variable is significantly large in relation to a basic estimate of the population variance—a technique known as the *analysis of variance*. This process has the advantage that it can be extended to tests involving many (k) means of the general form:

$$H_0 : \mu_1 = \mu_2 = \cdot \; \cdot \; \cdot = \mu_k$$
H_a:at least two of the means are unequal

This method of analysis can also be extended to consider the effects of more than one factor (variable) simultaneously in one experiment. We can do no more than begin to describe this very useful technique here.

Consider once again the problem of the different coffee break times. We tested the allegation of differences in average times by direct reference to the sampling distribution of the difference between means of random samples. We can test the same hypothesis with a special case of one-way analysis of variance. To do so may help us to understand the more general technique. We have two samples (we will use the two larger samples), supposedly from the same population. Because the items in each sample were randomly selected and the population from which they were drawn shows variability, the items in each sample vary around their mean. If both samples come from the same population, a good estimate of the variability in that population would be obtained by considering all of the information contained in the two samples. We can estimate this *total* variance contained in the two samples directly as the variance of all items in *both* samples about the overall *mean* of all those items. That is, the estimate of variance based on the *total* variance observed in the samples would be:

11.30 $\hat{\sigma}_T{}^2 = \dfrac{\displaystyle\sum_{j=1}^{2} \sum_{i=1}^{n_j} (x_{ji} - \bar{\bar{x}})^2}{n_1 + n_2 - 1}$

where

$\bar{x}$ = the overall mean of the two samples
x_{ji} = observation i in sample j
n_j = total number of observations in sample j
j = 1 or 2, the number of the samples

A computationally easier form of 11.30 would be to substitute x_{ji} for X and $\bar{x}$ for $\bar{X}$ in 5.02, substitute into 8.02 and obtain,

$$\hat{\sigma}_T{}^2 = \left[\frac{\sum\limits_{j=1}^{k} \sum\limits_{i=1}^{n_j} x_{ji}{}^2}{n} - (\bar{x})^2 \right] \frac{n}{n-1}$$

which can be simplified as

11.31 $\quad \hat{\sigma}_T{}^2 = \dfrac{\sum\limits_{j=1}^{k} \sum\limits_{i=1}^{n_j} x_{ji}{}^2 - n(\bar{x})^2}{n-1}$

Substituting into 11.31 values from Table 11.1, the work table developed from this problem,

$$\begin{aligned}
\hat{\sigma}_T{}^2 &= \frac{(6117 + 6812) - 50(15.9)^2}{50 - 1} \\
&= \frac{12929 - 12640.5}{49} \\
&= \frac{288.5}{49} \\
&= \mathbf{5.89}
\end{aligned}$$

Another way to obtain an estimate of the variance present in the two samples is to average out the individual sample estimates. For each sample, an estimate of the population variance can be obtained by combining 8.01 and 8.02 to obtain

11.32 $\quad \hat{\sigma}_j{}^2 = \left[\dfrac{n_j}{n_j - 1} \right] \dfrac{1}{n_j} \sum\limits_{i=1}^{n_j} (x_{ji} - \bar{x}_j)^2$

TABLE 11.1

Work Table for Analyzing Differences between Coffee Break Times, Samples of $n = 25$ from Departments A and G

DEPARTMENT A		DEPARTMENT G	
Observations (Minutes)	Squared Observations	Observations (Minutes)	Squared Observations
17	289	13	169
13	169	19	361
19	361	15	225
11	121	17	289
14	196	14	196
12	144	16	256
16	256	19	361
15	225	18	324
20	400	15	225
18	324	16	256
14	196	18	324
18	324	16	256
12	144	14	196
15	225	15	225
13	169	17	289
17	289	19	361
16	256	19	361
21	441	16	256
19	361	14	196
17	289	19	361
16	256	18	324
12	144	15	225
13	169	16	256
12	144	18	324
15	225	14	196
385	6117	410	6812

which can be simplified to obtain

11.33 $\quad \hat{\sigma}^2 = \dfrac{\sum\limits_{i=1}^{n} x_i^2 - n(\bar{x})^2}{n-1}$

Then, a good estimate of σ^2 would be the weighted average of the two sample estimates or the sum of the two weighted estimates obtained by applying 11.33 divided by 2, the number of sample estimates averaged. Generally, then, if $\hat{\sigma}_W^2$ is the estimate of variance based on the *within-samples* variability,

11.34 $$\hat{\sigma}_W^2 = \frac{\sum\limits_{j=1}^{k} n_j \left[\sum\limits_{i=1}^{n_j} x_{ji}^2 - n_j(\bar{x}_j)^2 \right]}{\sum\limits_{j=1}^{k} (n_j - 1)}$$

Note that $n_1 = n_2 = n_j$ (both samples are the same size) in our example, and 11.34 can be simplified as

$$\hat{\sigma}_W^2 = \frac{\sum\limits_{j=1}^{k} \left[\sum\limits_{i=1}^{n} x_{ji}^2 - n(\bar{x}_j)^2 \right]}{k(n - 1)}$$

For our example, the appropriate values as shown in Table 11.1 are

$$\sum_{i=1}^{25} x_A^2 = 6117 \qquad \sum_{i=1}^{25} x_G^2 = 6812 \qquad k = 2$$

$$\bar{x}_A = 15.4 \qquad\qquad \bar{x}_G = 16.4 \qquad n_j = 25$$

Substituting these values into 11.34, the within-samples estimate of population variance would be:

$$\hat{\sigma}_W^2 = \frac{[6117 - 25(15.4)^2] + [6812 - 25(16.4)^2]}{2(24)}$$
$$= \frac{6117 - 5929 + 6812 - 6724}{48}$$
$$= \frac{276}{48}$$
$$= \mathbf{5.75}$$

Variation in the population is also reflected in the difference between the two samples means. The deviations of these means around the population mean would serve as an estimate of the sampling variance $(\sigma_{\bar{x}}^2)$ for the distribution of the means of all possible pairs of samples of sizes n_1, n_2 from this population. Since we know (from 8.23) that

$\sigma_{\bar{x}}^2 = \sigma^2/n$, it follows that

11.35 $\sigma^2 = n\sigma_{\bar{x}}^2$

and

11.36 $\hat{\sigma}^2 = n\hat{\sigma}_{\bar{x}}^2$

which means that we can obtain an estimate of the population variance based on the observed variance *between* the samples.

To obtain $\hat{\sigma}_{\bar{x}}^2$, we apply the actual variance formula to the deviations of the sample means $(\bar{x}_j)$ about the overall mean $(\bar{\bar{x}})$ since the overall mean is our best estimate of μ.

11.37 $\hat{\sigma}_{\bar{x}}^2 = \dfrac{\displaystyle\sum_{j=1}^{k} (\bar{x}_j - \bar{\bar{x}})^2}{k - 1}$

Combining 11.36 and 11.37, we obtain an estimate of the variance based on the variability *between* the samples.

11.38 $\hat{\sigma}_B^2 = \dfrac{n_j \left[\displaystyle\sum_{j=1}^{k} (\bar{x}_j - \bar{\bar{x}})^2 \right]}{k - 1}$

The computing form of 9.38 would be

11.39 $\hat{\sigma}_B^2 = \dfrac{n_j \left[\displaystyle\sum_{j=1}^{k} \bar{x}_j^2 - k(\bar{\bar{x}})^2 \right]}{k - 1}$

In this way we obtain an estimate of the population variance based on the difference *between* the sample means. The symbol $\hat{\sigma}_B^2$ is used to indicate the between-samples variance estimate.

Applying 11.39 to our coffee break times,

$$\hat{\sigma}_B^2 = \frac{25[(15.4)^2 + (16.4)^2 - 2(15.9)^2]}{2 - 1}$$
$$= 25[237.16 + 268.96 - 2(252.81)]$$
$$= 25(0.50)$$
$$= \mathbf{12.5}$$

If these two samples did come from the same population or from two populations with equal means and variances, this last estimate (the between-sample variance) should not differ significantly from the within-sample variance obtained earlier. To test this proposition, we can compute the F ratio

11.40 $$F = \frac{\text{var. (between)}}{\text{var. (within)}}$$

$$= \frac{\hat{\sigma}_B{}^2}{\hat{\sigma}_W{}^2}$$

If our hypothesis of equal means (samples from the same population or from two populations with equal parameters) is tenable, this ratio should be close to 1.0. If it is significantly larger than 1.0, then the difference between the means has been large enough to produce a variance estimate so large as to make it unreasonable to attribute the difference to sampling error. Substituting into 11.40 from our example,

$$F = \frac{12.5}{5.75}$$
$$= 2.17$$

Referring to Table B-13, for one and 49 degrees of freedom, we observe that this value has more than ten chances in 100 (the upper 10 percent value is about 4.07) of being a chance occurrence. If we again use the ten percent level of significance for our test, we should accept the hypothesis of no difference between the means.

The data generated in such an analysis as this are often organized into a table such as Table 11.2. Such a table makes it clear why we say

TABLE 11.2

VARIANCE ANALYSIS TABLE FOR DIFFERENCE IN AVERAGE TIMES OF
DEPARTMENTS A AND G

Source of Variation	Sum of Squares	Degrees of Freedom	Variance Estimate
Between samples	12.50	1	12.50
Within samples	276.00	48	5.75
Total	288.50	49	5.89

that the variance analysis technique *partitions the variance* among the several "sources." The "sources" in this situation are indicated in the first column of Table 11.2. The second column of Table 11.2 shows the sums of the squared deviations arising from the particular partitioning process. Thus, if we refer back to the calculation of the total variance, $\hat{\sigma}_T^2$, on page 366, we see that the numerator of 11.31 is the sum of the squared deviations around the overall mean, or 288.5. The denominator of 11.31 tells us the degrees of freedom present in this computation $(n - 1)$. We find this value (49) in column three of Table 11.2. The sums of squares for the between-samples estimate is computed in the numerator of 11.38, the associated degree of freedom appear in the denominator of that same formula. Similarly, the within-samples sum of squares and degrees of freedom are found in 11.34.

Note that the total sum of squares is equal to the sum of the sums of squares computed from between the samples and within the samples. The total degrees of freedom is also the sum of the degrees of freedom for the between-samples and the within-samples estimates of population variance. This fact indicates one reason for Table 11.2, to provide a check on these relationships in order to reduce the chance for arithmetic errors in the computations.

The reader is undoubtedly wondering why the within-samples variance estimate was used as the divisor in the test of the difference between the two means. The reason is simple. The between-samples variance estimate should be compounded of variability present because of the random selection of sample values from a many-valued population *and* any variance due to the difference between coffee break times in the two departments. The within-samples variance estimate, on the other hand, contains only variance due to the random selection of sample values from a many-valued population (remember our assumption of either a single population or two populations with equal variance). Note that the total variance estimate is compounded of all these things, between-samples *and* within-samples variability. The ratio we have computed, $\hat{\sigma}_B^2/\hat{\sigma}_W^2$, assuming a difference between coffee break times in the two departments, is

$$F = \frac{\text{(sampling variance)} + \text{(variance due to department)}}{\text{sampling variance}}$$

Our conclusion was that the value of F was not large enough to indicate the presence of anything other than sampling variance in the numerator.

It should be emphasized that in the comparisons between means carried out for Mr. Newboss above, both of the tests we applied rested on three assumptions about the samples from which the means were calculated. *First,* it was assumed that the two samples are *independent,* that is, that items in one sample do not influence items in the other. *Second,* it was assumed that the two samples came either from the same population or from two different populations with equal means *and* variances. *Third,* both methods assumed that the parent population(s) is (are) normally distributed. The first assumption seems to be met in our situations, but is taken up again below. The third assumption also will be more fully considered in a later section of this chapter. A method for testing for difference between two variances is developed after the testing of differences of means from paired samples.

Testing the Difference between Two Means—Paired Samples

At one point in the analysis of the two methods of operating the bearing gauge, we ran into difficulty because our samples (one observation per method for each inspector) were *not* independent. It is not uncommon to have such "paired" samples where each observation in the first sample can be related to a specific observation in the second sample. In testing training techniques, operating methods, and so forth, subjects are often paired by age, sex, previous education, or other characteristics.

Suppose that we return to the Den Products Company and their problem of training stitching machine operators. As a further test of the new training method, 25 experienced operators are chosen for retraining. The third and fourth columns of Table 11.3 present the before and after production rates for each of the 25 operators.

To test whether the means of the paired samples really differ, we subtract the second observation for each operator from the first observation for that operator. The resulting differences (the Δ's in the fourth column of Table 11.3) are a sample of the differences for all operators. Such samples should *average* zero if the retraining has no effect. That is, μ_Δ should equal zero. Our test procedure tests this hypothesis, that is, we test the hypothesis:

$$H_0:\mu_\Delta = 0 \qquad H_a:\mu_\Delta < 0$$

which is equivalent to the hypothesis:

$$H_0:\mu_1 = \mu_2 \qquad H_a:\mu_1 \neq \mu_2$$

Since we are dealing with sample means, the test will utilize the t distribution ($\hat{\sigma}_{\bar{\Delta}}$ must be estimated from the sample). We consider the given observations (the 25 differences) of observations (x_Δ) and compute the mean ($\bar{x}_\Delta$) and standard error of the mean ($\hat{\sigma}_{\bar{x}_\Delta}$) from the given sample

TABLE 11.3

Average Production Rates for 25 Stitching Machine Operators at
Den Products before and after Retraining by
New Training Method

Operator Number	Average Before Retraining	Average After Retraining	Difference (Δ)	Difference Squared (Δ^2)
1	126	136	-10	100
2	130	138	-8	64
3	155	154	1	1
4	160	163	-3	9
5	162	161	1	1
6	162	173	-11	121
7	164	158	6	36
8	165	179	-14	196
9	167	172	-5	25
10	167	176	-9	81
11	169	165	4	16
12	170	180	-10	100
13	171	172	-1	1
14	173	181	-8	64
15	174	181	-7	49
16	175	179	-4	16
17	177	185	-12	144
18	178	170	8	64
19	180	173	-9	81
20	180	173	7	49
21	181	180	1	1
22	182	182	0	0
23	188	194	-6	36
24	192	200	-8	64
25	202	195	7	49
Totals	4250	4342	-92	1378
$\bar{x}$	170	173.68	-3.68	—

values. Thus, by 8.24 and 5.02 and 8.02,

$$\hat{\sigma}_{\bar{x}_\Delta} = \frac{\hat{\sigma}_{x_\Delta}}{\sqrt{n}}$$

$$= \sqrt{\frac{\Sigma x_\Delta{}^2 - n(\bar{x}_\Delta)^2}{n(n-1)}}$$

and, by 8.41,

$$t = \frac{\bar{x}_\Delta - \mu_\Delta}{\hat{\sigma}_{\bar{x}_\Delta}}$$

Substituting from our example,

$$\hat{\sigma}_{\bar{x}_\Delta} = \sqrt{\frac{1378 - 25(3.68)^2}{25(24)}}$$

$$= \sqrt{\frac{1378 - 338.56}{600}}$$

$$= \sqrt{1.7341}$$

$$= 1.32$$

and

$$t = \frac{-3.68 - 0}{1.32}$$

$$= 2.73$$

Returning to Table B-12 for 24 degrees of freedom, $t_{0.02} = 2.492$, and $t_{0.01} = 2.797$ indicating that if $\mu_\Delta = 0$, such a difference would occur by chance more than one time in 100, but not as many as two times in 100. It seems safe to assume that the new training does improve operator skills.

Testing the Difference between Two Variances

The second assumption we made in testing the means using independent samples was that the samples came from populations with equal variances. If the samples come from the *same* population, this assertion *must* be true. If the samples come from different populations, this *may* be true, but cannot be expected to be true for every pair of populations. The tests we have applied are valid only if we have one such pair of populations.

It should be obvious why one of the above assumptions about the variances must hold true. Both of the testing techniques rely on a ratio comparing a value ($d_{\bar{x}}$ or $\hat{\sigma}_B{}^2$) computed from the difference between the means to a "pooled" or average estimate of variance ($\hat{\sigma}_{d_{\bar{x}}}$ or $\hat{\sigma}_W{}^2$) derived by combining the variance information contained within each of the samples. Obviously, it would be inappropriate to "pool" the variance information from populations with different variances, since, if this were done, it would be impossible to specify a general sampling distribution for either the z ratio or the F ratio.

It has already been demonstrated that the ratio of variances computed from pairs of samples drawn from a normally distributed population will be distributed as F. Obviously, this fact can be used to test the assumption of equality of variances. To recapitulate, if as 11.10 specifies,

$$F = \frac{\hat{\sigma}_1^2}{\hat{\sigma}_2^2}$$

then the resulting ratio is distributed as F with $n_1 - 1$ and $n_2 - 1$ degrees of freedom.

Returning to our coffee break example, we consider the smaller samples first. Suppose we decide to test

$$H_0:\sigma_A^2 = \sigma_G^2 \qquad H_a:\sigma_A^2 \neq \sigma_G^2 \qquad \alpha = 0.10 \text{ (two tail)}$$

using the sample data,

$$n_A = n_G = 9 \qquad \hat{\sigma}_A^2 = 9.45 \qquad \hat{\sigma}_G^2 = 3.99$$

We compute the F ratio by 11.10,

$$F = \frac{9.45}{3.99}$$
$$= 2.37$$

To test the hypothesis at the 0.10 level of significance, we look in Table B-13 and find $F_{0.10(8,8)} = 3.44$, the tabled value for $F_{0.05(8,8)}$. Since $F < F_{0.10(8,8)}$, $(2.37 < 3.44)$, we conclude that the two sample variances are not sufficiently different for us to believe that the samples come from populations with different variances.

Applying the same test to the larger samples where

$$n_A = n_G = 25 \qquad \hat{\sigma}_A^2 = 7.83 \qquad \hat{\sigma}_G^2 = 3.67$$

and, $F_{0.10(24,24)} = 1.98$ (two tail). Using 11.10,

$$F = \frac{7.83}{3.67}$$
$$= 2.13$$

In this case $2.13 > 1.98$ or $F > F_{0.10(24,24)}$ (two tail) and we find that the sample variances are sufficiently different for us to conclude that the samples come from populations with different variances. Therefore, the tests for differences between means applied above are inappropriate because one basic assumption of each of the techniques is violated. If this test had been applied first, we would have had to advise Mr. Newboss that coffee break times in the two departments have different variances and the means may differ as well although our simple tests cannot say.

Testing the Differences between Two Proportions

There are many decision problems in business which involve a selection between two actions or strategies based on which of two proportions is larger. For example, suppose that Lossless Grocery Stores is analyzing the effectiveness of its sales promotion efforts. One advertising activity of the company is to sponsor each week a local television program featuring movies made on trips by travelers from the Bigtown area. The company also sponsors a weekly television report on or recap of the games of Bigtown U. The question has arisen as to whether the advertising message is reaching the proper audience. One specific question to be answered is whether women (or men) are attracted more by one show than the other. In a recent survey of Bigtown area homes while the travel program was on, of the 540 adults watching the show, 227 were women and 313 men. The football show that week was watched by 238 women and 372 men. That is, if we let p_T be the proportion of travel show watchers who were women and p_F the proportion of women among those adults watching the football show,

$$p_T = p_1 = \frac{227}{540} = 0.42, \text{ and}$$

$$p_F = p_2 = \frac{238}{610} = 0.39$$

One hypothesis to be tested with these sample results is:

$$H_0 : P_1 = P_2 \quad \text{or } D_P = 0$$
$$H_a : P_1 \neq P_2 \quad \text{or } D_P \neq 0$$

where

P_1 = the proportion of women in Bigtown who watch the travel show
P_2 = the proportion of women in Bigtown who watch the football show

Suppose we have decided on an α of 0.15 for testing the above hypothesis after analysis of the costs of errors of rejection and acceptance.

The hypothesis can be tested in the two ways which are discussed below. The first technique uses the normal probability distribution for testing the difference between the two proportions. The second method also assumes that sample proportions are essentially normally distributed, but utilizes the chi-square distribution as the sampling distribution. This latter technique is easily extended to more than two proportions as will be explained in a later section.

Normal Approximation for Large Samples.   On the assumption that the two random samples indicated above are independent it can be demonstrated that

11.50 $E(p_1 - p_2) = P_1 - P_2 = D_P$

where

$p_i = \dfrac{x_i}{n_i}$, the proportion of "successes" in the sample of size n_i from

population i

P_i = the proportion of successes in population i

If we symbolize the difference between the sample proportion as d_p, that is,

11.51 $d_P = p_1 - p_2$

The variance of the distribution of differences between the sample proportions $(\sigma_{d_p}{}^2)$ would be the sum of the individual variances of the sample proportions. That is,

11.52 $\sigma_{d_p}{}^2 = \dfrac{P_1(1 - P_1)}{n_1} + \dfrac{P_2(1 - P_2)}{n_2}$

The *standard error of the difference between two proportions* would be the positive square root of 11.52. That is,

11.53 $\sigma_{d_p} = \sqrt{\dfrac{P_1(1 - P_1)}{n_1} + \dfrac{P_2(1 - P_2)}{n_2}}$

The familiar ratio of the difference between the sample statistic (d_p) and the (hypothesized) population value (D_P) to the standard error can be considered a standard normal deviate *if the samples are large.* That is,

$$11.54 \quad z_{d_p} = \frac{d_p - D_P}{\sigma_{d_p}}$$

is (approximately) a standard normal deviate if the samples are large ($n_i \geq 30$).

We are operating under the basic assumption that $P_1 = P_2$, that is, that the two samples are either from the same population or two different populations with equal parameters. If this is true, $P_1 = P_2 = P$ and 11.53 reduces to

$$11.55 \quad \sigma_{d_p} = \sqrt{P(1 - P) \frac{n_1 + n_2}{n_1 n_2}}$$

Generally, P would be unknown and its value estimated from the two samples as,

$$11.56 \quad \hat{P} = \frac{x_1 + x_2}{n_1 + n_2}$$

Substituting into 11.56 from our example,

$$\hat{P} = \frac{227 + 238}{540 + 610}$$
$$= \frac{465}{1150}$$
$$= 0.404$$

Substituting $\hat{P}$ into 11.55 (we are dealing with large samples from very large populations and can ignore the finite population correction),

$$\hat{\sigma}_{d_p} = \sqrt{(0.404)(0.596) \frac{540 + 610}{(540)(610)}}$$
$$= \sqrt{(0.2408) \frac{1150}{329,400}}$$
$$= \sqrt{0.000841}$$
$$= 0.029$$

We now have all the values we need except the critical value of the test statistic, z_α. If $\alpha = 0.15$ as was stated, then $z_\alpha = 1.44$. Substituting into 11.54,

$$z_{d_p} = \frac{0.03 - 0}{0.029}$$
$$= 1.03$$

Since $1.03 < 1.44$ $(z_{d_p} < z_{d_p(\alpha)})$, we conclude that the two proportions are not enough different from one another to indicate that women prefer the travel show to the football show.

Chi-square Test.   Once again, if the two samples are independent, random, and sufficiently large, we can obtain an estimate of the population proportion of successes $(\hat{P})$ by application of 11.56. Then, by modifying 11.13, we define the statistic,

$$11.57 \quad \chi^2 = \sum_{i=1}^{h} \sum_{j=1}^{k} \left[\frac{(f_{o_{ij}} - f_{e_{ij}})^2}{f_{e_{ij}}} \right]$$

where

> $f_{o_{ij}}$ = observed frequency of successes $(n_j p_j)$ or nonsuccesses $n_j(1 - p_j)$ in sample j
>
> $f_{e_{ij}}$ = expected frequency of successes $(n_j \hat{P})$ or nonsuccesses $n_j(1 - \hat{P})$ for sample j
>
> h = number of rows (classifications) or 2
>
> k = number of columns (samples) or 2

This statistic is distributed as chi square with one degree of freedom.

What we are doing is setting up two tables. The first has four cells showing observed frequencies of successes and nonsuccesses for the two samples. The second table shows the expected numbers (frequencies) of successes and nonsuccesses in the two samples computed on the basis of the assumption that $P_1 = P_2$. We then relate the squared differences between frequencies in corresponding cells, that is, between observed and expected frequencies, to expected frequencies. If this ratio gets too large, the differences in the numerator cannot be attributed to the chance selection of items into the two samples. That is, if computed χ^2 exceeds $\chi^2_{\alpha(n-1)}$, then the difference between proportions is judged to be statistically significant as the α level of significance.

Returning to our example of the surveys of TV viewers in Bigtown watching shows sponsored by Lossless Grocery Stores, the sample results (observed frequencies) are as shown in Table 11.4, Part A. The expected

TABLE 11.4

DATA FOR CHI-SQUARE ANALYSIS OF DIFFERENCE BETWEEN PROPORTIONS OF
WOMEN IN ADULTS WATCHING TWO TV PROGRAMS

Part A. Observed Frequencies ($f_{o_{ij}}$)

Watchers	Travel Show	Football Show	Totals
Women	227	238	465
Men	313	372	685
Totals	540	610	1150

Part B. Expected Frequencies ($f_{e_{ij}}$)

Watchers	Travel Show	Football Show	Totals
Women	218	247	465
Men	322	363	685
Totals	540	610	1150

Part C. Differences between Observed and Expected Frequencies
   $(f_{o_{ij}} - f_{e_{ij}})$

Watchers	Travel Shows	Football Shows
Men	9	−9
Women	−9	9

frequencies on the assumption that $P_1 = P_2 = \hat{P}$ are shown in part B of the table. The differences between observed and expected frequencies are shown in Part C.

Part B of Table 11.4 was derived by applying the estimated population ($\hat{P}$) and its complement ($1 - \hat{P}$) to the two sample sizes to obtain the expected cell frequencies. Thus, $540(0.404) = \textbf{218.4}$; $540(0.596) = \textbf{321.6}$. When these values are rounded, we obtain the cell values shown in Part B. Substituting the differences shown in Part C into 11.57,

$$\chi^2 = \frac{(9)^2}{218} + \frac{(-9)^2}{322} + \frac{(-9)^2}{247} + \frac{(9)^2}{363}$$
$$= 0.372 + 0.252 + 0.324 + 0.223$$
$$= 1.17$$

Since we have used an estimate of P derived from the samples $(\hat{P})$ and the two samples sizes $(n_1$ and $n_2)$ in computing the expected frequencies, we have lost three degrees of freedom and have made our estimate of χ^2 with only one degree of freedom. From Table B-10, the value of χ^2 for one degree of freedom would equal or exceed 2.71 ten percent of the time if no difference existed between the observed and expected frequencies. It therefore seems reasonable to believe that the difference observed here is attributable to the chance selection of viewers into the samples.

COMPARING MANY POPULATIONS

One Way Analysis of Variance Comparing Many Means. Earlier in this chapter, in discussing the use of variance analysis to test the difference between two means, we mentioned that this method could easily be extended to testing the differences between many means. In the earlier section, the test for a difference between the means of two populations consisted of drawing a sample from each population and, on the assumption that the two populations are normally distributed and have equal variances, obtaining two estimates of the variance value. One estimate, $\hat{\sigma}_B^2$, was based on the observed difference *between* the two sample means. The other estimate, $\hat{\sigma}_W^2$ was based on the variance found within the two samples. That is, the ratio of the variance estimate influenced by the difference between populations (departments in our example) *and* the expected variability between the sample means due to sampling variability was compared to the variance estimate containing only the expected variability due to sampling variability. If the ratio of the between-samples variance estimate to the within-samples variance estimate was enough larger than one (1.0), the difference between the two means was considered to be too large to be considered a chance occurrence.

The formulas for computing these variance estimates are given in

11.31 (Total), 11.34 (Within), and 11.39 (Between). The formulas are actually quite general. When we used them for two samples, we implicitly restricted the number of samples (k) to two. Remove this restriction and the three formulas apply to any number of samples.

TABLE 11.5

TIMES REQUIRED BY INSPECTORS FOR EXAMINING SAMPLES OF
BALL BEARINGS ON AUTOMATIC BEARING GAUGE

Part A. Observed Data
    (Time in seconds)

Sample Number	Inspector 1	Inspector 2	Inspector 3	Inspector 4
1	11	14	12	16
2	13	15	14	16
3	12	14	13	15
4	13	13	13	16
5	12	15	14	15
Totals	61	71	66	78
Means	12.2	14.2	13.2	15.6

Part B. Coded Data
    (Time in seconds minus 10)

Sample Number	Inspector 1	Inspector 2	Inspector 3	Inspector 4
1	1	4	2	6
2	3	5	4	6
3	2	4	3	5
4	3	3	3	6
5	2	5	4	5
Totals	11	21	16	28
Means	2.2	4.2	3.2	5.6

To illustrate the application of the one-way analysis of variance in testing the difference between several means, let us consider a problem faced by the quality control supervisor at Big Corporation. He is attempting to develop work standards for his inspectors. The data in Part A of Table 11.5 are the times in seconds required by inspectors to check five ball bearings for roundness on a gauge which automatically measures and displays the amount of out-of-round present on each ball. It is suspected that some inspectors are faster than others in testing samples on this gauge. If this is so, then the supervisor desires to determine why and establish a training program to reduce these time discrepancies as much as possible in order to make "standard" times more reliable for use in planning and controlling inspector activities.

The calculations for this analysis are carried out in Table 11.6. The

TABLE 11.6

WORK TABLE FOR ANALYSIS OF VARIANCE OF INSPECTOR TIMES ON
BEARING GAUGE (UNCODED VALUES)

Sample	Inspectors									
	1		2		3		4		Totals	
Number	x	x^2	x	x^2	x	x^2	x	x^2	x	x^2
1	11	121	14	196	12	144	16	256	53	717
2	13	169	15	225	14	196	16	256	58	846
3	12	144	14	196	13	169	15	225	54	734
4	13	169	13	169	13	169	16	256	55	763
5	12	144	15	225	14	196	15	225	56	790
Total	61	474	71	1011	66	874	78	1218	276	3850
$\bar{x}$	12.2		14.2		13.2		15.6		13.8 (190.44)	
$\bar{x}^2$	148.84		201.64		174.24		243.36		768.08	

$$\hat{\sigma}_T^2 = \frac{3850 - 20(190.44)}{20 - 1} = \frac{3850 - 3808.80}{19} = \frac{41.20}{19} = \textbf{2.17}$$

$$\hat{\sigma}_B^2 = \frac{5[768.08 - 4(190.44)]}{4 - 1} = \frac{5(6.32)}{3} = \frac{31.60}{3} = \textbf{10.53}$$

$$\hat{\sigma}_W^2 = \frac{747 - 5(148.84) + 1011 - 5(201.64) + 874 - 5(174.24) + 1218 - 5(243.36)}{4(5 - 1)}$$

$$= \frac{3850 - 3840.40}{16} = \frac{9.60}{16} = \textbf{0.60}$$

variance estimates are developed also in a standard variance analysis table (Table 11.7). Substituting the between-samples and within-samples estimates into 11.40,

$$F = \frac{10.53}{0.60}$$
$$= \textbf{17.55}$$

TABLE 11.7

VARIANCE ANALYSIS TABLE FOR DIFFERENCES IN AVERAGE TIMES OF
INSPECTORS ON BEARING GAUGE

Source of Variance	Sum of Squares	Degrees of Freedom	Variance Estimate
Between samples	31.60	3	10.53
Within samples	9.60	16	0.60
Total	41.20	19	2.17

Checking Table B-13 for three and sixteen degrees of freedom, we see that there is less than one chance in 100 of such a value occurring by chance ($F_{0.01(3,16)} = 5.29$). It seems reasonable to conclude that there is a difference in average time between inspectors. The supervisor should therefore set up a study to determine why these differences exist and should work to reduce them.

The calculations carried out in Table 11.6 were not really difficult but they could be simplified. Fortunately, the value of the F ratio is not altered if all the sample observations are multiplied or divided by the same constant, or if a constant is added to or subtracted from each and every sample observation. Actually, any combination of the above procedures can be used. Part B of Table 11.5 and the calculations with the coded values in Table 11.8 are shown to illustrate the ease and advantage of such coding. Note that the variance estimates derived from the reduced (coded values) are exactly the same as when using the uncoded values.

Two-Way Analysis of Variance—One Observation per Cell. The quality control supervisor is disturbed by the differences between inspectors just demonstrated. He studies the methods used by each inspector and finds that there are two basic sets of movements in use, with inspectors 1 and 3 using one (call it M_1) and inspectors 2 and 4 using the other (call it M_2). He wants to know if this difference might account for the differences noted. It would appear that the inspectors (1 and 3) using M_1 are more efficient than those (2 and 4) using M_2. Unfortunately, the data we already have are insufficient to determine if this difference is really due to the method used (assuming it to be significant). In order to sort out the effect of the method from the effect of the inspector, we need to see if all inspectors do better with one method than with the other. The supervisor has already had inspectors 2 and 4 shift to M_1 and has collected one reading on each inspector after they seem to have learned the procedure well enough for their times to stabilize. These times for all four inspectors are shown in the first line of Part A of Table 11.9. The times in the second line of that table were obtained by switching all

TABLE 11.8

WORK TABLE FOR ANALYSIS OF VARIANCE OF INSPECTOR TIMES ON
BEARING GAUGE (CODED VALUES)

Sample Number	| Inspectors |								| Totals |	
	1		2		3		4			
	x	x^2	x	x^2	x	x^2	x	x^2	x	x^2
1	1	1	4	16	2	4	6	36	13	57
2	3	9	5	25	4	16	6	36	18	86
3	2	4	4	16	3	9	5	25	14	54
4	3	9	3	9	3	9	6	36	15	63
5	2	4	5	25	4	16	5	25	16	70
Total	11	27	21	91	16	54	28	158	76	330
$\bar{x}$	2.2		4.2		3.2		5.6		3.8	(14.44)
$\bar{x}^2$	4.84		17.64		10.24		31.36		64.08	

$$\hat{\sigma}_T^2 = \frac{330 - 20(14.44)}{20 - 1} = \frac{330 - 288.80}{19} = \frac{41.20}{19} = 2.17$$

$$\hat{\sigma}_B^2 = \frac{5[64.08 - 4(14.44)]}{4 - 1} = \frac{5(6.32)}{3} = \frac{31.60}{3} = 10.53$$

$$\hat{\sigma}_W^2 = \frac{27 - 5(4.84) + 91 - 5(17.64) + 54 - 5(10.24) + 158 - 5(31.36)}{4(5 - 1)}$$

$$= \frac{330 - 320.40}{16} = \frac{9.60}{16} = 0.60$$

inspectors to M_2 for a period of time and then obtaining a similar reading. These values have been coded in Part B and the basic calculations (Σx, Σx^2, $\bar{x}$'s, $\bar{x}^2$'s, $\Sigma\bar{x}^2$'s) carried out with the coded values. (Note that the method of calculation provides checks on the arithmetic accuracy of the Σx_{ij} and Σx_{ij}^2.)

The simple model we used above divided the total variation into two parts, between-inspectors samples + within-inspector sample = total. Here, however, we find that we have a more complicated arrangement in that there is also between-method and within-method variation. We are interested in determining the between-method and between-inspector variances and comparing them to the sampling variance to determine the significance of inspector and method effects.

TABLE 11.9

INSPECTOR TIMES ON BEARING GAUGE USING TWO DIFFERENT OPERATING METHODS

Part A. Original Values

		Inspector		
Method	1	2	3	4
M_1	12	14	13	14
M_2	13	15	14	16

Part B. Coded Values and Basic Calculations (Original values minus 13)

	Inspector								Totals			
	1		2		3		4					
Method	x	x^2	x	x^2	x	x^2	x	x^2	x	x^2	$\bar{x}$	$\bar{x}^2$
M_1	-1	1	1	1	0	0	1	1	1	3	$\frac{1}{4}$	$\frac{1}{16}$
M_2	0	0	2	4	1	1	3	9	6	14	$\frac{3}{2}$	$\frac{9}{4}$
Totals	-1	1	3	5	1	1	4	10	7	17	$(\frac{7}{4})$	$(\frac{37}{16})$
$\bar{x}$	$-\frac{1}{2}$	—	$\frac{3}{2}$	—	$\frac{1}{2}$	—	2	—	(3.5)	17	0.875	—
$\bar{x}^2$	$\frac{1}{4}$	—	$\frac{9}{4}$	—	$\frac{1}{4}$	—	4	—	(6.75)	—	0.766	—

First of all, let us compute the total variance. If we let x_{ij} stand for the observation for method (row) i and inspector (column) j, then, for this two-way analysis of variance with one observation per cell,

11.60 $$\hat{\sigma}_T^2 = \frac{\sum\limits_{i=1}^{h} \sum\limits_{j=1}^{k} (x_{ij} - \bar{\bar{x}})^2}{n - 1}$$

where

h = the number of rows
k = the number of columns
n = the number of cells (hk)

The computing form of 9.60 (applying 5.02 and 8.02) would be:

$$11.61 \quad \hat{\sigma}_T^2 = \frac{\sum\limits_{i=1}^{h}\sum\limits_{j=1}^{k} x_{ij}^2 - n(\bar{\bar{x}})^2}{n - 1}$$

(Remember that the numerator of 11.61 is the total sum of squares.) Substituting the values from Table 11.9,

$$\hat{\sigma}_T^2 = \frac{17 - 8(0.766)}{8 - 1}$$

$$= \frac{10.87}{7}$$

$$= 1.55$$

Turning to the variance between methods (rows) and using $\hat{\sigma}_{\text{row}}^2$ as our symbol, then applying the logic of computing the variance between the row means ($\hat{\sigma}_{\bar{x}}^2$) and multiplying by sample size for each mean (number of values per row or number of columns),

$$11.62 \quad \hat{\sigma}_{\text{row}}^2 = k \left[\frac{\sum\limits_{i=1}^{h} (\bar{x}_i - \bar{\bar{x}})^2}{h - 1} \right]$$

Simplifying to obtain "sum of squares" over "degrees of freedom," this becomes,

$$11.63 \quad \hat{\sigma}_{\text{row}}^2 = \frac{k \left[\sum\limits_{i=1}^{h} \bar{x}_i^2 - h(\bar{\bar{x}})^2 \right]}{h - 1}$$

Substituting into 11.63 from Table 11.9,

$$\hat{\sigma}_{\text{row}}^2 = \frac{4[{}^{37}\!/_{16} - 2(0.766)]}{2 - 1}$$

$$= \frac{4(0.780)}{1}$$

$$= 3.12$$

To obtain the variance estimate based on variance between inspectors (columns), we would apply the same logic and compute:

$$11.64 \quad \hat{\sigma}_{\text{col}}^2 = h \left[\frac{\sum_{j=1}^{k} (\bar{x}_j - \bar{\bar{x}})^2}{k - 1} \right]$$

In the "sum of squares" over "degrees of freedom" form this would be,

$$11.65 \quad \hat{\sigma}_{\text{col}}^2 = \frac{h \left[\sum_{j=1}^{k} \bar{x}_j^2 - k(\bar{\bar{x}})^2 \right]}{k - 1}$$

Substituting into 11.65 from our example,

$$\hat{\sigma}_{\text{col}}^2 = \frac{2[6.750 - 4(0.766)]}{4 - 1}$$
$$= \frac{2(3.686)}{3}$$
$$= \frac{7.37}{3}$$
$$= 2.46$$

Let us examine the relationship between the sums of squares we have computed:

Row sum of squares	3.12
Column sum of squares	7.37
Total	**10.49**
Total sum of squares	10.87
Sum of squares unaccounted for	**0.38**

The "residual" sum of squares is not unexpected. The *row* variance is an estimate of the sampling variance of the data plus the effect (if there is any) of the particular factor involved in the rows (method). The *column* variance is a combination of sampling variance and *column* (inspector) effects. What is left over after taking out row effects and column effects must be simply *sampling* variance. Can we demonstrate that the *residual* sum of squares above is the amount left over? The effect of sampling variance alone on any single observation would be $(x_{ij} - \bar{\bar{x}}) - (\bar{x}_i - \bar{\bar{x}}) - (\bar{x}_j - \bar{\bar{x}})$, that is, the deviation of the observation from the overall mean less the average deviation due to row effects and the average deviation due to column effects. Eliminating the parentheses and combining terms, the sampling (*residual*) variance could be obtained as

$$11.66 \quad \hat{\sigma}_{res}^2 = \frac{\sum\limits_{i=1}^{h} \sum\limits_{j=1}^{k} (x_{ij} - \bar{x}_i - \bar{x}_j + \bar{\bar{x}})^2}{(h-1)(k-1)}$$

Note that we lose a degree of freedom from each row and each column. The last value in each row (column) would be determined if all but one were given.

For our example, the numerator of 11.66 would yield as the *residual* sum of squares

$$
\begin{aligned}
\text{\textit{Residual} sum of squares} &= (-1 + \tfrac{1}{2} - \tfrac{1}{4} + \tfrac{7}{8})^2 \\
&\quad + (1 - \tfrac{3}{2} - \tfrac{1}{4} + \tfrac{7}{8})^2 + \cdots \\
&\quad + (3 - 2 - \tfrac{3}{2} + \tfrac{7}{8})^2 \\
&= (\tfrac{1}{8})^2 + (\tfrac{1}{8})^2 + \cdots + (\tfrac{3}{8})^2 \\
&= \tfrac{3}{8} \\
&= \mathbf{0.38}
\end{aligned}
$$

Since the two methods yield the same result, it would be easier to obtain the *residual* sum of squares as the difference between the total sum of squares and the sum of the row and column sums of squares. Then the *residual*-variance estimate would be:

$$11.67 \quad \sigma_{res}^2 = \frac{\text{total sum of squares} - (\text{row sum of squares} + \text{column sum of squares})}{(h-1)(k-1)}$$

The values computed from our example have been assembled in Table 11.10 for performing the variance analysis. The F ratios of interest would be

$$11.68 \quad F_{row} = \frac{\hat{\sigma}_{row}^2}{\hat{\sigma}_{res}^2}$$

and

$$11.69 \quad F_{col} = \frac{\hat{\sigma}_{col}^2}{\hat{\sigma}_{res}^2}$$

TABLE 11.10

TABLE FOR ANALYSIS OF VARIANCE OF INSPECTOR OPERATING
TIMES FOR TWO METHODS OF OPERATING BEARING GAUGE

Source of Variation	Sum of Squares	Degrees of Freedom	Variance Estimate
Between methods (rows)	3.12	1	3.12
Among inspectors (cols)	7.38	3	2.46
Residual (error)	0.38	3	0.13
Total	10.87	7	1.55

Making the necessary substitutions,

$$F_{\text{row}} = \frac{3.12}{0.13}$$
$$= 24.0$$
$$F_{\text{col}} = \frac{2.46}{0.13}$$
$$= 18.9$$

Both F ratios are significant at the five percent level.

At this point, the quality control supervisor raises a point that may have disturbed the reader. Doesn't this method of analysis assume that method and inspector (row and column) effects are independent of one another? Isn't it possible that each inspector finds one of the methods more suitable to his particular skills? If this latter situation exists, might we not attribute the combined effects of method *and* inspector to method or to inspector (or both)? The supervisor's fears are well grounded. Our method does assume no "interaction" between method and inspector. Since it seems reasonable that such "interaction" might exist in this situation, we cannot really say whether method (or inspector) alone has caused the result we attribute to method (or inspector). The technique we have illustrated does not have application to *this* problem; it can be applied only when it can be demonstrated (or safely assumed) that confounding interactions are not present. For example, this method could be used to test whether the sales of a commodity to various income classes within the population have changed over time where income classes are defined in terms of percentages of the total population (for example, upper 25 percent, upper middle 25 percent, lower middle

25 percent, lower 25 percent). However, we usually find that the variables of classification cannot be assumed to be completely independent.

Two-Way Analysis of Variance—Multiple Observations per Cell. To get around the difficulty raised above, we need to be able to isolate the "interaction" of the two variables acting together. That is, multiple observations must be taken of each inspector using each method. Such results are shown in Table 11.11. The *interaction* variance can now be

TABLE 11.11

INSPECTOR TIMES ON BEARING GAUGE USING TWO DIFFERENT METHODS, THREE OBSERVATIONS PER CELL

Part A. Original Values

Method	Inspector			
	1	2	3	4
M_1	12, 11, 13	14, 14, 13	12, 14, 13	14, 14, 15
M_2	13, 13, 12	14, 15, 15	14, 13, 14	16, 15, 16

Part B. Coded Values and Basic Calculations (Original values minus 14)

Method	Inspector				Totals			
	1	2	3	4	Σx_{ijg}	$\bar{x}_i$	$\bar{x}_i^2$	Σx_{ijg}^2
M_1	−2, −3, −1	0, 0, −1	−2, 0, −1	0, 0, 1	−9	−0.75	0.562	21
	(−6)(14)	(−1)(1)	(−3)(5)	(1)(1)				
M_2	−1, −1, −2	0, 1, 1	0, −1, 0	2, 1, 1	1	0.083	0.007	15
	(−4)(6)	(2)(2)	(−1)(1)	(4)(6)				
Σx_{ijg}	−10	1	−4	5	−8	—	(0.569)	—
$\bar{x}_j$	−1.67	0.17	−0.67	0.83	—	−0.333	—	—
$\bar{x}_j^2$	2.789	0.029	0.445	0.694	(3.957)	—	0.111	—
Σx_{ijg}^2	20	3	6	7	—	—	—	36

found by multiplying the *residual* variance of the previous example (11.66) by the number of observations in each cell (m). That is,

$$11.70 \quad \hat{\sigma}_{\text{int}}^2 = \frac{m \sum_{j=1}^{k} \sum_{i=1}^{h} (\bar{x}_{ij} - \bar{x}_i - \bar{x}_j + \bar{\bar{x}})^2}{(h-1)(k-1)}$$

If there is no interaction, $\bar{x}_{ij}$ should be equal to $\bar{x}_i + \bar{x}_j - \bar{x}$ and the interaction variance computed by 11.70 would equal zero. The cell mean, $\bar{x}_{ij}$, will differ more from $\bar{x}_j + \bar{x}_j - \bar{x}$ as the interaction increases and the interaction variance will be increased.

The estimate of sampling variance is now computed from the variance found within each of the cells. If we use x_{ijg} as the gth observation in cell ij, the *residual* (sampling) variance estimate becomes

$$11.71 \quad \hat{\sigma}_{\text{res}}^2 = \frac{\displaystyle\sum_{i=1}^{h}\sum_{j=1}^{k}\sum_{g=1}^{m}(x_{ijg} - \bar{x}_{ij})^2}{hk(m-1)}$$

Converting 11.71 to the "sum of squares over degrees of freedom" form,

$$11.72 \quad \hat{\sigma}_{\text{res}}^2 = \frac{\displaystyle\sum_{i=1}^{h}\sum_{j=1}^{k}\left[\sum_{g=1}^{m}x_{ijg}^2 - m\bar{x}_{ij}^2\right]}{hk(m-1)}$$

The row variance (between methods) would be the same as in the one observation case except that in order to be weighted by all items represented, the summed value must be multiplied by mk, not just k.

$$11.73 \quad \hat{\sigma}_{\text{row}}^2 = \frac{mk\left[\displaystyle\sum_{i=1}^{h}\bar{x}_i^2 - h(\bar{\bar{x}})^2\right]}{h-1}$$

Similarly, the *column* variance (between inspectors) would be the same as before except for adding m to the multiplier

$$11.74 \quad \hat{\sigma}_{\text{col}}^2 = \frac{mh\left[\displaystyle\sum_{j=1}^{k}\bar{x}_j^2 - k(\bar{\bar{x}})^2\right]}{k-1}$$

The total variance in this situation would be computed in the same general manner as before, by considering all the individual observations as one large sample.

$$11.75 \quad \hat{\sigma}_T^2 = \frac{\displaystyle\sum_{i=1}^{h}\sum_{j=1}^{k}\sum_{g=1}^{m}x_{ijg}^2 - n(\bar{\bar{x}})^2}{n-1}$$

Returning to our example and substituting the value from Part 8 of Table 11.11, the *total* variance is computed by 11.75.

$$\hat{\sigma}_T{}^2 = \frac{36 - 25(0.111)}{24 - 1}$$

$$= \frac{33.34}{23}$$

$$= 1.45$$

The *row* variance is computed by 11.73.

$$\hat{\sigma}_{\text{row}}{}^2 = \frac{3(4)[0.569 - 2(0.111)]}{2 - 1}$$

$$= \frac{12(0.347)}{1}$$

$$= 4.16$$

The *column* variance is calculated with 11.74.

$$\hat{\sigma}_{\text{col}}{}^2 = \frac{3(2)[3.957 - 4(0.111)]}{4 - 1}$$

$$= \frac{6(3.513)}{3}$$

$$= \frac{21.08}{3}$$

$$= 7.03$$

The *residual* variance would be estimated with 11.72.

$$\hat{\sigma}_{\text{res}}{}^2 = \frac{36 - 3[14 - (-2)^2 + 1 - (-\frac{1}{3})^2 + \cdots + 6 - (\frac{4}{3})^2]}{(2)(4)(3 - 1)}$$

$$= \frac{36 - 28}{16}$$

$$= \frac{8.00}{16}$$

$$= 0.50$$

The *interaction* variance is most easily computed by obtaining the interaction sum of squares as the remainder after subtracting the *row, column,* and *residual* sums of squares from the *total* sum of squares and dividing by the degrees of freedom $(h - 1)(k - 1)$. That is,

11.76 $\hat{\sigma}_{int}^2 = $ (total sums of squares $-$ *row* sums of squares $-$ column sums of squares $-$ *residual* sums of squares)$/(h - 1)(k - 1)$

Then, by 11.76

$$\hat{\sigma}_{int}^2 = \frac{33.34 - (4.16 + 21.08 + 8.00)}{(2 - 1)(4 - 1)}$$

$$= \frac{0.10}{3}$$

$$= 0.03$$

The above calculations are summarized in the standard variance analysis form in Table 11.12. The appropriate F ratios for the two-way

TABLE 11.12

VARIANCE ANALYSIS TABLE FOR DIFFERENCES IN INSPECTOR TIMES ON
BEARING GAUGE USING TWO DIFFERENT OPERATING METHODS
(MULTIPLE OBSERVATIONS PER CELL)

Source of Variation	Sum of Squares	Degrees of Freedom	Variance Estimate
Methods (rows)	4.16	1	4.16
Inspectors (columns)	21.08	3	7.03
Method and inspector interaction	0.10	3	0.03
Residual (sampling)	8.00	16	0.50
Total	33.34	23	1.45

analysis of variance with an equal number of multiple observations per cell relate the variance associated with the factors of interest to the *residual* or sampling variance.

11.77 $F_{int} = \dfrac{\hat{\sigma}_{int}^2}{\hat{\sigma}_{res}^2}$ $[(h - 1)(k - 1)$ and $hk(m - 1)d.f.]$

$F_{row} = \dfrac{\hat{\sigma}_{row}^2}{\hat{\sigma}_{res}^2}$ $[h - 1$ and $hk(m - 1)d.f.]$

$F_{col} = \dfrac{\hat{\sigma}_{col}^2}{\hat{\sigma}_{res}^2}$ $[k - 1$ and $hk(m - 1)d.f.]$

Substituting into 11.77,

$$F_{int} = \frac{0.03}{0.50} = \mathbf{0.06} \ (3, \ 16 \ d.f.)$$

$$F_{row} = \frac{4.16}{0.50} = \mathbf{8.32} \ (1, \ 16 \ d.f.)$$

$$F_{col} = \frac{7.03}{0.50} = \mathbf{14.06} \ (3, \ 16 \ d.f.)$$

The *interaction* $F(0.06)$ is much smaller than even $F_{0.10(3,16)} = 2.46$, indicating that there is no significant interaction between method and inspector using the method. That is, *all* inspectors tend to perform better with method M_1 and worse with method M_2. Since interaction is *not* significant, we can determine whether row (method) and column (inspector) effects are significant.

From Table B-13, $F_{0.05(1,16)} = 4.49$ and $F_{0.01(1,16)} = 8.53$, indicating that the value we have obtained for F_{row} should occur only slightly more than one time in 100 due to chance sampling variability. It seems reasonable to conclude that row (method) variance is significantly different from sampling variance. That is, the method used by the inspectors to operate the bearing gauge affects the time required to test the bearings.

Table B-13 shows that $F_{col} = 14.04$ is much larger than $F_{0.01(3,16)} = 5.29$ so that we conclude that column variance is also significantly larger than sampling variance. This means that there is enough difference between the abilities of these four inspectors to affect the time required to operate the bearing gauge regardless of the method of operation.

This brief introduction to variance analysis indicates that it is a powerful tool. When carrying out experiments involving several independent variables or classifications, we can test for effects of the several variables singly and in combination. We do not have the space to illustrate the full range of problems which can be analyzed with variance analysis, but the student should recognize that the process can be extended fairly easily to cases involving more than two classifications or (variables).

Comparison of Many Proportions

The Compacto Company has three plants each with a number of stamping machines of identical or very similar nature. Each machine has a counting device attached to it to record the number of revolutions made by the machine. Plant supervisors are responsible for keeping the machines fully utilized and for discovering and rectifying correctable causes of lost time on the machines. The number of working hours and rated machine speeds allow the company statistician to compute total potential machine revolutions. The data in Table 11.13 were taken from

TABLE 11.13

DATA ON MACHINE USAGE IN THREE PLANTS OF COMPACTO COMPANY

| Plant | Machine Revolutions per Plant (000's) | | |
	Available	Used	Unused
1	359.3	320.9	38.4
2	421.1	388.6	32.5
3	392.0	361.3	30.7
Totals	1172.4	1070.8	101.6

usage reports for last month sent by the plant superintendents. The statistician wishes to find out whether the lost revolutions are approximately the same in all plants.

The basic hypothesis to be tested is that the proportion of revolutions lost is equal for all plants. That is,

$$H_0 : P_1 = P_2 = \cdots = P_k \qquad H_a : P_j \neq P_m \text{ for some } j \text{ and } m$$

where

k = number of populations examined
j and m are different integers $\leq k$ (there may be more than one pair of P's which are unequal)

Note that in our example, $k = 3$.

The first step toward testing the above hypothesis is to develop the *expected* proportion of revolutions lost in *all* plants. To obtain this estimate of P, the assumed true proportion for all plants, we combine the information for all the samples (plants). This is accomplished by generalizing the formula devised for estimating P in the two-sample case (11.56).

11.78 $$\hat{P} = \frac{\sum_{j=1}^{k} x_j}{\sum_{j=1}^{k} n_j}$$

Substituting from our example,

$$\hat{P} = \frac{101.6}{1172.4}$$
$$= 0.087$$

and

$$1 - \hat{P} = 1 - 0.087 = 0.913$$

Applying $\hat{P}$ and $1 - \hat{P}$ to each of the plant totals we obtain the expected frequencies (f_e's) shown in Table 11.14. For example, $359.3(0.913) = 328.1$ provides the expected number of lost revolutions in Plant 1. By summing the ratios $(f_0 - f_e)^2/f_e$ shown in Table 11.14, we obtain the value of χ^2 (we are applying 11.13).

$$\chi^2 = 0.23 + 2.40$$
$$= 2.63$$

To determine the degrees of freedom with which this estimate was obtained, we must find the number of restrictions taken from the sample to obtain the expected frequencies: $\hat{P}$, obviously, and also the total numbers of revolutions available to which this proportion was applied. There are three plant totals and the $\hat{P}$ value used to make a total of four degrees of freedom lost. We started with six values, so we end with $6 - 4 = 2$ degrees of freedom. Note that this is equal to the number of rows minus one times the number of columns minus one. That is, for such a cross-classified table, if we let r = number of rows and c = number of columns,

11.79   Degrees of freedom = $(r - 1)(c - 1)$

Suppose the company management has weighted the consequences of the two possible errors that can be made in this test and settled upon 0.10 as the appropriate value of α. Referring to Table B-10, we see that $\chi^2_{0.10(2d.f.)} = 4.61$. Since the computed χ^2 (2.63) is less than χ_α^2, we advise the company that the proportions of lost revolutions in the three plants cannot be demonstrated to be unequal at the chosen level of significance and should be considered equal.

TABLE 11.14

BASIC CALCULATIONS FOR χ^2 ANALYSIS OF DIFFERENCE BETWEEN PROPORTIONS OF AVAILABLE MACHINE REVOLUTIONS USED IN COMPACTO PLANTS

Plants	Available	MACHINE REVOLUTIONS PER PLANT (000's)									
		Used					Not Used				
		f_o	f_e	$f_o - f_e$	$(f_o - f_e)^2$	$\dfrac{(f_o - f_e)^2}{f_e}$	f_o	f_e	$f_o - f_e$	$(f_o - f_e)^2$	$\dfrac{(f_o - f_e)^2}{f_e}$
1	359.3	320.9	328.1	−7.2	51.84	0.16	38.4	31.2	7.2	51.84	1.66
2	421.1	388.6	384.7	3.9	15.21	0.04	32.5	36.4	−3.9	15.21	0.42
3	392.0	361.3	358.0	3.3	10.89	0.03	30.7	34.0	−3.3	10.89	0.32
Total	1172.4	1070.8	1070.8	—	—	0.23	101.6	101.6	—	—	2.40

TESTING FOR ASSOCIATION
BETWEEN CLASSIFICATIONS OR VARIABLES

In the previous section, we used nonparametric chi square to test for differences between proportions. In that application, chi square was used as a measure of the lack of agreement between observed and expected frequencies. In 11.13, χ^2 was defined as

$$\chi^2 = \sum \left[\frac{(f_0 - f_e)^2}{f_0} \right]$$

This is a general formula which can be applied in a variety of situations as described below to test for association between classification of data.

Contingency Analysis

The usage reports prepared by plant superintendents of Compacto also classify the lost revolutions by cause. The total and observed frequency (f_o) columns of Table 11.15 are taken directly from the report

TABLE 11.15

OBSERVED AND EXPECTED BREAKDOWNS BY CAUSE IN COMPACTO PLANTS

UNUSED MACHINE REVOLUTIONS PER PLANT (000's)

Plant	Total	Machine Breakdown		Operator Error		Lack of Materials		Reloading Machine	
		f_o	f_e	f_o	f_e	f_o	f_e	f_o	f_e
1	38.4	9.2	9.6	14.5	13.4	8.8	10.0	5.9	5.4
2	32.5	9.6	8.1	10.5	11.4	7.3	8.4	5.1	4.6
3	30.7	6.6	7.7	10.6	10.8	10.3	8.0	3.2	4.2
Total	101.6	25.4	25.4	35.6	35.6	26.4	26.4	14.2	14.2

which provided the data in Table 11.13. The company statistician wants to determine if there is any real difference in cause of lost time by plant.

The hypothesis here is that the two classifications, plant and cause of lost time, are *independent*. That is, being in the Plant 1 row does not influence the proportion of total lost revolutions falling into each cause class. Similarly, being in a particular cause category, say operator error, does not influence the proportion of lost revolutions found in each plant.

The expected frequencies shown in the cells of Table 11.15 were obtained by applying to each plant total the ratio of *total by cause* to *grand total* for each cause. For example,

row 1, column 1: $f_e = \dfrac{25.4}{101.6}(38.4) = 9.6$

row 2, column 2: $f_e = \dfrac{35.6}{101.6}(32.5) = 11.4$

To obtain the value of χ^2, the following process may be used:

$$\chi^2 = \frac{(9.2 - 9.6)^2}{9.6} + \frac{(14.5 - 13.4)^2}{13.4} + \cdots + \frac{(3.2 - 4.2)^2}{4.2}$$
$$= 0.017 + 0.090 + \cdots + 0.238$$
$$= \mathbf{1.904}$$

From Table B-10, we see that for $(r-1)(c-1) = (3-1)(4-1) = 6$ degrees of freedom, $\chi_{0.10}^2 = 10.64$. Since the computed χ^2 (1.904) is less than 10.64, we conclude that the distribution of lost time by cause is not associated with the plant considered.

Testing Goodness of Fit

The same technique used to test contingency can be used to test for goodness of fit of any observed set of frequencies to a corresponding set of expected frequencies. For example, it was assumed in Chapter 9 (see Table 9.5 and related discussion) that the distribution of net weights of packages of frozen strawberries was normal and in Exercise 1, Chapter 7, the distribution presented was specified *not* to be normal (actually, it was expected to be Poisson). Finally, in discussing variance analysis earlier in this chapter, we were faced with the problem of an assumption of a normally distributed population which we would like to test. Chi square can be used in making such tests. Due to limited space, we will demonstrate only the fitting of the normal distribution and testing the *goodness of fit* of the observed and expected frequencies.

Fitting a Normal Distribution to Grouped Data.   As the first example, let us return to the Duravit strawberry packaging example of Chapter 9.

TABLE 11.16

FITTING A NORMAL DISTRIBUTION TO OBSERVED FREQUENCIES OF
AVERAGE WEIGHTS OF NET WEIGHTS OF PACKAGES OF FROZEN
STRAWBERRIES AT DURAVIT CORPORATION

Class Intervals of Package Weights (Ounces)	Obs. Freq. (f_o)	Class Midpoints (m)	Deviations of Class Midpoints from Mean $\dfrac{m - \bar{\mu}_R}{\sigma_{\mu_R}}$	Values from Table B-16 $\left[e - \dfrac{(m - \bar{\mu}_R)^2}{2\sigma^2} \right]$	Exp. Freq. (f_e)
15.77–15.79	0	15.78	3.14	0.0072	1
15.79–15.81	1	15.80	2.86	0.0167	2
15.81–15.83	4	15.82	2.57	0.0368	4
15.83–15.85	10	15.84	2.29	0.0726	8
15.85–15.87	13	15.86	2.00	0.1353	15
15.87–15.89	30	15.88	1.71	0.2318	26
15.89–15.91	42	15.90	1.43	0.3597	41
15.91–15.93	60	15.92	1.14	0.5221	60
15.93–15.95	76	15.94	0.85	0.6968	79
15.95–15.97	98	15.96	0.57	0.8501	97
15.97–15.99	109	15.98	0.28	0.9616	110
15.99–16.01	111	16.00	0	1.0000	114
16.01–16.03	106	16.02	−.28	0.9616	110
16.03–16.05	95	16.04	−.57	0.8501	97
16.05–16.07	82	16.06	−.85	0.6968	79
16.07–16.09	61	16.08	−1.14	0.5221	60
16.09–16.11	42	16.10	−1.43	0.3597	41
16.11–16.13	25	16.12	−1.71	0.2318	26
16.13–16.15	16	16.14	−2.00	0.1353	15
16.15–16.17	10	16.16	−2.29	0.0726	8
16.17–16.19	5	16.18	−2.57	0.0368	4
16.19–16.21	3	16.20	−2.86	0.0167	2
16.21–16.23	1	16.22	−3.14	0.0072	1
Total	1000	—	—	—	1000

The observed frequency distribution of Table 9.5 is reproduced in the
first two columns of Table 11.16. The expected frequencies in the final
column were calculated by determining the height at the class midpoints
of a normal distribution with the same mean and standard deviation.
The midpoint values are shown in the third column of Table 11.16. The

formula used to obtain the height at each midpoint was given in Chapter 5

$$H(X) = \frac{1}{20566\sigma} 2.71828^{-\frac{(X-\mu)^2}{2\sigma^2}} \tag{5.30}$$

This formula gives the ordinate (height) at a point, what we need is the area (actually the number of values) in an interval represented by that point. Thus, for the number of values (f) to be found in each interval for a distribution containing N values arranged in classes of width i and with midpoint m,

11.80 $\quad f(m) = \frac{Ni}{2.5066\sigma} 2.71828^{-\left[\frac{(X-\mu)^2}{2\sigma^2}\right]}$

For the interval of width i centered on μ, 11.80 reduces to

$$f(m - \mu) = \frac{Ni}{2.5066\sigma} 2.71828^{-\left[\frac{(0)^2}{2\sigma^2}\right]}$$

or

11.81 $\quad f(m = \mu) = \frac{Ni}{2.5066\sigma}$

Substituting into 11.81 from our example where $\mu = \mu_0 = 16.00$, $\sigma = \sigma_{\mu_R} = 0.07$, $N = 1000$, and $i = 0.02$,

$$f(m = 16.00) = \frac{1000(0.02)}{2.5066(0.07)}$$
$$= 114$$

To obtain the value at any other class midpoint, we just substitute this value back into 11.80

11.82 $\quad f(m \neq \mu) = f(m = \mu)2.71828^{-\left[\frac{(m-\mu)^2}{2\sigma^2}\right]}$

To ease the burden of these calculations, Table B-16 provides the values of

$$2.71828^{-\left[\frac{(X-\mu)^2}{2\sigma^2}\right]}$$

for the different values of $(X - \mu)/\sigma$, that is, for the deviation of the particular X (m in this case) from the mean expressed in standard deviation units. The midpoints expressed as deviations from the mean are found in the fourth column of Table 11.16. The values in the next column of the table are from Table B-16. The final column contains the expected frequencies developed from the frequency of the mean class (114) multiplied by each of the values from Table B-16.

In order to meet one assumption upon which the chi-square test of differences between the observed and expected frequencies is based, we must combine the values in the three extreme classes on each end of the distribution. Remember that chi-square analysis assumes that the expected frequencies are large, which is interpreted in practice to mean that each expected frequency is at least equal to five.

To compute the degrees of freedom for the chi-square test, we count the number of cells *after* combining the end classes and subtract the number of restrictions taken from the sample (observed data) to compute the expected frequencies. Referring to 11.81 and 11.82, we see that we used: (1) the mean of the observed values, (2) the standard deviation estimated from the observed values, and (3) the number of values in the distribution. Therefore, we lost three degrees of freedom. This means that the total degrees of freedom would be $19 - 3$ or 16.

After making the combinations of three classes on each end of the distribution, the value of chi square is computed as

$$\chi^2 = \frac{(5-7)^2}{7} + \frac{(10-8)^2}{8} + \frac{(13-15)^2}{15} + \cdots + \frac{(10-8)^2}{8} + \frac{(9-7)^2}{7}$$
$$= 0.571 + 0.500 + 0.267 + \cdots + 0.500 + 0.571$$
$$= \mathbf{3.706}$$

From Table B-10, we see that $\chi_{0.995}^2$ for 16 $d.f.$ (5.14) is larger than the computed χ^2. It seems obvious that we conclude that the observed distribution is essentially normal.

Fitting a Normal Distribution to Ungrouped Data. When working with variance analysis earlier in this chapter, we were concerned about the question of whether or not the distribution of times spent on coffee breaks by employees in two departments (A and G) were normally distributed. Suppose we had drawn the 100 values shown in Table 11.17 as a random sample of coffee break times for employees in Department A. Are these times normally distributed?

In order to test the hypothesis that the basic distribution is normal,

TABLE 11.17

RANDOM SAMPLE OF 100 OBSERVATIONS OF COFFEE BREAK TIMES IN DEPARTMENT A AND CALCULATIONS OF BASIC STATISTICS

Obs. f_o	Squared Obs. $f_o{}^2$	Obs. f_o	Squared Obs. $f_o{}^2$	Obs. f_o	Squared Obs. $f_o{}^2$	Obs. f_o	Squared Obs. $f_o{}^2$
15	225	16	256	21	441	19	361
12	144	19	361	15	225	15	225
18	324	17	289	12	144	13	169
13	169	13	169	19	361	17	289
14	196	17	289	16	256	14	196
20	400	13	169	13	169	18	324
15	225	16	256	17	289	14	196
13	169	15	225	12	144	16	256
17	289	19	361	18	324	18	324
19	361	16	256	14	196	13	169
11	121	17	289	20	400	16	256
14	196	15	225	12	144	16	256
15	225	13	169	15	225	15	225
17	289	11	121	14	196	13	169
16	256	18	324	15	225	19	361
18	324	18	324	14	196	14	196
14	196	13	169	19	361	18	324
15	225	16	256	17	289	12	144
12	144	19	361	15	225	17	289
18	324	15	225	19	361	13	169
14	196	14	196	13	169	16	256
18	324	19	361	16	256	18	324
20	400	13	169	14	196	12	144
15	225	16	256	16	256	15	225
16	256	17	289	20	400	18	324

$$\Sigma x = 1559 \qquad \hat{\sigma}^2 = \frac{25086 - 100(15.59)^2}{100 - 1} = \frac{25086 - 24304.81}{99}$$

$$\Sigma x^2 = 25086 \qquad\qquad = \frac{781.19}{99} = \mathbf{7.89}$$

$$\bar{x} = 15.59 \qquad \hat{\sigma} = \mathbf{2.81}$$

we must organize the data of Table 11.17 into a frequency distribution. The class limits must be chosen in such a way that no class will be expected to contain less than five values. Also, since the basic data are integers, it would be advisable to have the class interval be at least equal to one ($i \geq 1$).

We found the expected frequency for the distribution of average net weights in the previous section by application of 11.81 and 11.82 and Table B-16. In the current case we will start with 11.81, but use the table of *areas* under the normal curve (Table B-5) to find the range of each class in order that each class contain an equal number of the items.

We can use 11.81 to determine the number of classes we should use so that we can have equal expected frequencies in each class but have the class interval at least equal to 1. Substituting $i = 1$ into 11.81 for the class centered on the mean,

$$f_e(m = 15.59) = \frac{100(1)}{2.5066(2.81)}$$

$$= \frac{100}{7.043546}$$

$$= 14.2$$

Since 14.2 is about $\frac{1}{7}$ of 100, we can use seven classes with equal expected frequencies of $\frac{100}{7} = 14.29$. To obtain the class limits shown in Table 11.18 we use the fact, for example, that the z value of the lower limit of the class containing the mean will be the z from Table B-5 including $0.1429/2 = 0.07145$ of the total area between that limit and the mean. Entering the body of Table B-5 with 0.07145, we find the corresponding z value to be (interpolating) -0.180. Similarly, the upper limit must be $+0.180\hat{\sigma}$ from μ. Column 2 of Part A of Table 11.18 shows the proportion of the total distribution that must fall between $\hat{\mu}$ and the extreme limit of each class in order to obtain the expected frequencies shown. The corresponding z values from Table B-5 are shown in column 3. The resulting class limits are shown in the column 4. Part B of Table 11.18 presents the calculations necessary to the development of the estimated chi-square value so that the hypothesis of normality can be tested.

Since the assumption that the basic population is normally distributed is not a critical assumption, suppose we decide that we are willing to reject the assumption of normality only about one time in one hundred when the assumption is true. Since we used three values from the sample $(n, \bar{x}, \hat{\sigma})$ in computing the expected frequencies in Table 11.18, the degrees of freedom for the chi square estimated will be $7 - 4 = 3$ *d.f.* From Table B-10, $\chi_{0.01}^2(3 \ d.f.) = 11.34$. From Table 11.18 we see that $\chi^2 = 15.210$. Since $\chi^2 > \chi_\alpha^2$, we conclude that we should reject the hypothesis that the population distribution of coffee break times in Department A are normally distributed.

TABLE 11.18

FITTING DISTRIBUTION AND COMPUTING χ^2 FOR TESTING HYPOTHESIS
THAT COFFEE BREAK TIMES IN DEPARTMENT A ARE
NORMALLY DISTRIBUTED

Part A. Fitting Normal with Equal Frequencies; $\hat{\mu} = 15.59$, $\hat{\sigma} = 2.81$

(1) Expected Frequencies f_e	(2) Proportion of Distribution Between μ and Extreme Class Limit (L_e)	(3) Corresponding z Value From Table B-5	(4) Extreme Class Limit (Minutes) L_e
14.28	-0.5000	—	$-\infty$
14.29	-0.3572	-1.069	12.59
14.29	-0.2144	-0.566	14.00
14.29	± 0.07145	± 0.180	15.085–16.095
14.29	$+0.2144$	$+0.566$	17.18
14.29	$+0.3572$	$+1.069$	18.59
14.28	$+0.5000$	—	$+\infty$
100.01			

Part B. Calculation of Chi-Square Value

Class Limits (Minutes)	f_o	f_e	$f_o - f_e$	$(f_o - f_e)^2$	$\dfrac{(f_o - f_e)^2}{f_e}$
12.58 and Under	9	14.28	-5.28	27.880	1.952
12.59–13.99	13	14.29	-1.29	1.664	0.116
14.00–15.08	27	14.29	12.71	163.544	11.445
15.09–16.09	14	14.29	-0.29	0.084	0.006
16.10–17.18	10	14.29	-4.29	18.404	1.288
17.19–18.59	12	14.29	-2.29	5.244	0.367
18.60 and Over	15	14.28	0.72	0.518	0.036
	100	100.01	-0.01		15.210

Correlation between Variables

A measure of the extent to which two variables vary together (are associated) is the *coefficient of correlation*. Two versions of this useful coefficient will be described here. In Chapter 9 we dealt with a problem of the Den Products Company concerned with evaluating a new training method for stitching machine operators. This activity is part of a larger effort aimed at improving the selection and training of operators. In addition to the new training method, for some time, the company has been administering an aptitude test to applicants. Management wants to know if the aptitude test scores are related to final levels of performance. A question has also arisen concerning the association of individual test scores in the before-and-after retraining data examined in a test of difference between means of paired samples performed above.

Product-Moment Correlation Coefficient. Suppose that the data in Table 11.19 had been obtained for a random sample of stitching machine operators who, after having taken an aptitude test, had been hired, trained, and were operating machines for a long enough time to assume that their average daily performance over the last two weeks could be considered an adequate indication of their final performance abilities. Are the test scores and performance levels associated?

Suppose we were to express each value as a deviation from the mean of its distribution and then multiply the paired deviations ($x - \bar{x}$ and $y - \bar{y}$) for each operator. We might then compute the mean of these cross products. That is, we compute

$$\frac{1}{n} \sum_{i=1}^{n} (x_i - \bar{x})(y_i - \bar{y})$$

where i is the pairs (operator) number and n is the total number of pairs of observations (number of operators). This mean is a sample statistic which estimates the *covariance of x and y*.

Note that if the x and y values each deviate in the same direction from their respective means, all of the products being summed will be positive. Conversely, if the x values always deviate in the opposite direction from the deviation of the y values, the products will be negative. If there is no consistent relationship either direct or inverse between the deviations of the two variables, the products may be either positive or negative and their sum will be near zero.

The covariance is an obvious measure of the extent to which the x and y values are associated, but it has the weakness that it is stated in the same units as the cross-products themselves, which may be meaningless. In the present example, the x values are aptitude test scores and the y values are average units produced per day. The units in which their covariance would be stated are meaningless. The x and y units can be made comparable by expressing them in standard deviation units. The expected value of these *standardized* values can then be used as a

TABLE 11.19

SCORES ON APTITUDE TEST AND AVERAGE UNITS PRODUCED PER
DAY FOR 25 STITCHING MACHINE OPERATORS

Operator	Aptitude Score x	Average Units/Day y	Squared Score x^2	Squared Units/Day y^2	Cross-Product xy
1	48	139	2304	19321	6672
2	53	135	2809	18225	7155
3	61	153	3721	23409	9333
4	67	162	4489	26244	10854
5	74	162	5476	26244	11988
6	79	172	6241	29584	13588
7	87	159	7569	25281	13833
8	92	178	8464	31684	16376
9	95	173	9025	29929	16435
10	96	175	9216	30625	16800
11	101	169	10001	28561	17069
12	104	181	10816	32761	18824
13	105	176	11025	30976	18480
14	112	183	12544	33489	20496
15	113	182	12769	33124	20566
16	116	180	13456	32400	20880
17	120	184	14400	33856	22080
18	121	179	14641	32041	21659
19	124	189	15376	35721	23436
20	125	183	15625	33489	22875
21	125	180	15625	32400	22500
22	131	196	17161	38416	25676
23	136	201	18496	40401	27336
24	140	193	19600	37249	27020
25	147	206	21609	42436	30282
Totals	2572	4390	282658	777866	462213
Means	102.9	175.6	—	—	—

measure of the association between the variables. That is, we compute

$$r = \frac{1}{n} \sum_{i=1}^{n} \frac{(x_i - \bar{x})}{\hat{\sigma}_x} \frac{(y_i - \bar{y})}{\hat{\sigma}_y}$$

which reduces to

11.83 $r = \dfrac{\sum\limits_{i=1}^{n} (x_i - \bar{x})(y_i - \bar{y})}{n \hat{\sigma}_x \hat{\sigma}_y}$

The ratio, r, is a sample estimate of the true *correlation coefficient*,

11.84 $\rho = \dfrac{\sum\limits_{i=1}^{N} (x_i - \mu_x)(y_i - \mu_y)}{N \sigma_x \sigma_y}$

Computation of the sample estimate can be simplified by substituting a computing form based on the sums given in Table 11.19.

11.85 $r = \dfrac{\sum\limits_{i=1}^{n} x_i y_i - n \bar{x} \bar{y}}{n \hat{\sigma}_x \hat{\sigma}_y}$

Substituting into 11.85 from Table 11.19 and using the computing form of the sums of squares in computing the standard deviations,

$$r = \frac{462{,}213 - (25)(102.9)(175.6)}{25 \sqrt{\dfrac{282{,}658 - 25(102.9)^2}{25 - 1}} \sqrt{\dfrac{777{,}866 - 25(175.6)^2}{25 - 1}}}$$

$$= \frac{462{,}213 - 451{,}731}{25 \sqrt{747.8229} \sqrt{290.9167}}$$

$$= \frac{+10{,}482}{25(27.3)(17.0)}$$

$$= \frac{+10{,}482}{11{,}602.5}$$

$$= +0.903$$

Note the sign of r, which indicates whether x and y vary directly together or inversely in opposite directions.

Basic assumptions in correlation analysis are that the two population variables (X and y) comprise a *bivariate normal* population. It is also assumed that each observation of a set of paired observations is independent of all other such observations, that is, that a random sample of paired observations has been drawn from the basic bivariate population.

Before we can leave this analysis, we must determine the meaning of the r value we have calculated. First of all, it must be recognized that the population value ρ and the sample estimate r vary only between -1 and $+1$. If $\rho = 0$, there is no association between the two variables. The covariance would be zero, and therefore ρ would be zero. The closer the association between X and y, the closer ρ would be to ± 1. If the association were perfectly *positive*, then $\rho = +1$; if the association were perfectly *inverse*, then $\rho = -1$. Since r is only a sample estimate of ρ, it is possible for r to be different from ρ. To test whether r is significantly different from the value assumed or hypothesized for ρ, we need to know the sampling distribution of r and how to compute the standard error of r (σ_r). The existence of correlation in the sample indicated by an $r \neq 0$ may be due only to chance selection of the sample rather than the presence of correlation in the bivariate normal population and r reflecting a $\rho \neq 0$.

Unfortunately, the sample correlation coefficient does not follow any of the basic probability distributions which we have been using. However, if n is large enough, the distribution of r about ρ is *approximately* normal if $\rho = 0$. In such situations, a convenient test procedure utilizing the t distribution can be used. Then, t can be computed with $n - 2$ degrees of freedom as

11.86 $t = \dfrac{r \sqrt{n - 2}}{\sqrt{1 - r^2}}$ $(d.f. = n - 2)$

In our example, this would be

$$t = \frac{0.903 \sqrt{25 - 2}}{\sqrt{1 - 0.8154}}$$
$$= \frac{0.903(4.80)}{0.429}$$
$$= \mathbf{10.10}$$

Assuming that the appropriate value of α is 0.05, t_α (23 d.f.) = 2.069, and we conclude that there is a significant correlation between the aptitude test scores before hiring and the later production rates of stitching machine operators at the Den Products Company.

A simple but generally applicable method of testing hypotheses about r

is to convert r into a normally distributed statistic,

11.87 $z_r = 1.1503 \, [\log (1 + r) - \log (1 - r)]$

The transformed r (z_r) has the estimated standard error

11.88 $\sigma_{z_r} = \dfrac{1}{\sqrt{n-3}}$

For our example,

$$
\begin{aligned}
z_r &= 1.1503(\log 1.903 - \log 0.097) \\
&= 1.1503[10.27944 - 10 - (8.98677 - 10)] \\
&= 1.1503(1.29267) \\
&= \mathbf{1.4288}
\end{aligned}
$$

Fortunately, tables exist which make such lengthy calculations unnecessary. Table 14 in Appendix B is such a table.

$$
\begin{aligned}
\sigma_{z_r} &= \frac{1}{\sqrt{25 - 3}} \\
&= \frac{1}{4.69} \\
&= \mathbf{0.213}
\end{aligned}
$$

Substituting z_r and σ_{z_r} into 5.32 with $\rho = 0$, the normal deviate is computed.

$$
\begin{aligned}
z &= \frac{1.4288 - 0}{0.213} \\
&= \mathbf{6.71}
\end{aligned}
$$

Since $z_{0.05} = 1.96$ this test again leads to the conclusion that there is some association between the two variables. Note that the 0 substituted into 5.32 is the z_r corresponding to $\rho = 0$. This same method would apply even if we hypothesized that ρ were equal to some value other than 0. The hypothesized value of ρ would be converted to the corresponding z_r *before* substituting into 5.32.

Testing Association between Ranks.   In examining the effects of the new training method for stitching machine operators at Den Products

Company, we tested the difference between the performance levels of 25 experienced operators before and after retraining by the new method. At that time we decided that the paired samples did indicate an improvement in performance after testing. The testing supervisor notes that some operators actually did not improve. He wonders if the retraining can be judged to be relatively consistent in its effects. One way to test this proposition is to determine if the rankings of the operators on the two tests are approximately the same. That is, have enough individual operators changed their position in the group to an extent that it must be concluded that the retraining has different effects on different operators? If the latter situation exists, then it may be that the retaining acts adversely on some group of workers.

The production rates of the stitching machine operators used in the previous test (Table 11.3) have been converted into ranks in Table 11.20 (lowest score is given the rank of 1; highest score is given the rank of 25; tied scores are given the average rank for the successive number of ranks that would otherwise be assigned; for example, operators 9 and 10 were tied on the first test and were given the rank of $(9 + 10)/2 = 9.5$). The formula for the coefficient of simple correlation was given in 11.85. Symbolizing the rank on test 1 of operator i as R_{1i}, and the rank on test 2 of operator i as R_{2i}, 11.85 can be used to obtain an estimate of the rank correlation coefficient.

11.89 $$r_R = \frac{\sum\limits_{i=1}^{n} R_{1i}R_{2i} - n\bar{R}_1\bar{R}_2}{n\hat{\sigma}_{R_1}\hat{\sigma}_{R_2}}$$

Substituting from Table 11.20,

$$
\begin{aligned}
r_R &= \frac{5310.75 - 25(13.0)(13.0)}{25\sqrt{\dfrac{5524.50 - 25(13.0)^2}{25 - 1}}\sqrt{\dfrac{5522.50 - 25(13.0)^2}{25 - 1}}} \\[2ex]
&= \frac{5310.75 - 4225.00}{25\sqrt{54.1458}\sqrt{54.0625}} \\[2ex]
&= \frac{1085.75}{25(7.36)(7.35)} \\[2ex]
&= \frac{1085.75}{1352.40} \\[2ex]
&= \mathbf{0.803}
\end{aligned}
$$

TABLE 11.20

RANKS OF PRODUCTION RATES OF STITCHING MACHINE OPERATORS
BEFORE AND AFTER RETRAINING BY NEW TRAINING METHOD PLUS
BASIC CALCULATIONS FOR CORRELATION ANALYSIS

Operator Number	Ranks		Squared Ranks		Cross Product of Ranks $R_{1i}R_{2i}$	Difference between Ranks	
	Before (R_{1i})	After (R_{2i})	Before (R_{1i}^2)	After (R_{2i}^2)		d_R	d_R^2
1	1	1	1.00	1.00	1.00	0	0
2	2	2	4.00	4.00	4.00	0	0
3	3	3	9.00	9.00	9.00	0	0
4	4	6	16.00	36.00	24.00	−2.0	4.00
5	5.5	5	30.25	25.00	27.50	0.5	0.25
6	5.5	11.5	30.25	132.25	63.25	−6.0	36.00
7	7	4	49.00	16.00	28.00	3.0	9.00
8	8	16	64.00	256.00	128.00	−8.0	64.00
9	9.5	9.5	90.25	90.25	90.25	0	0
10	9.5	13	90.25	169.00	123.50	−3.5	12.25
11	11	7	121.00	49.00	77.00	4.0	16.00
12	12	16	144.00	256.00	192.00	−4.0	16.00
13	13	9.5	169.00	90.25	123.50	3.5	12.25
14	14	18.5	196.00	342.25	259.00	−4.5	20.25
15	15	18.5	225.00	342.25	277.50	−3.5	12.25
16	16	14	256.00	196.00	224.00	2.0	4.00
17	17	21	289.00	441.00	357.00	−4.0	16.00
18	18	8	324.00	64.00	144.00	10.0	100.00
19	19.5	22	380.25	484.00	429.00	−2.5	6.25
20	19.5	11.5	380.25	132.25	224.25	8.0	64.00
21	21	16	441.00	256.00	336.00	5.0	25.00
22	22	20	484.00	400.00	440.00	2.0	4.00
23	23	23	529.00	529.00	529.00	0	0
24	24	25	576.00	625.00	600.00	−1.0	1.00
25	25	24	625.00	576.00	600.00	1.0	1.00
Totals	325.0	325.0	5524.50	5522.50	5310.75	0	423.50
Means	13.0	13.0	—	—	—	—	—

If the two sets of ranks contain no ties, it can be demonstrated[4] that

11.90 If $d_R = R_{1i} - R_{2i}$,

$$r_R = 1 - \frac{6\Sigma d_R^2}{n(n^2 - 1)}$$

[4] See, for example, Robert Ferber, *Statistical Techniques in Market Research*, New York: McGraw-Hill Book Company, Inc., 1949, pp. 450–451.

In actual practice, ties are often ignored and this simpler formula for the rank correlation coefficient is used. The basic calculations have been carried out in the last two columns of Table 11.20. Substituting into 11.90 from Table 11.20,

$$r_R = 1 - \frac{6(423.50)}{25(25^2 - 1)}$$
$$= 1 - \frac{2531.00}{15600}$$
$$= 1 - 0.162$$
$$= \mathbf{0.838}$$

Note that this value of r_R is slightly larger than the value obtained from the product moment formula. For r_R to be a good estimate of ρ, the true correlation of the variables in a bivariate normal population, ρ must be close to zero and the sample must be large. A most basic assumption of correlation is that the paired observations are drawn from a bivariate normal distribution.

Since the ranks cannot be considered to be normally distributed variables, the exact sampling distribution of r_R is different from that of the ordinary r computed from a sample of paired observations drawn from a bivariate normal population. However, the hypothesis of independence between the ranks can be tested by utilizing t if the sample is large enough. Actually, if n is at least equal to 10, the test is fairly reliable at the 0.01 and 0.05 levels of significance. The test is the same as the large sample test for the simple correlation coefficient given in 11.86, with r_R substituted for the simple correlation coefficient, r.

11.91 $t = \dfrac{r_R \sqrt{n - 2}}{\sqrt{1 - r_R^2}}$

Substituting into 11.91 from our example,

$$t = \frac{0.838 \sqrt{25 - 2}}{\sqrt{1 - (0.838)^2}}$$
$$= \frac{(0.838)(4.796)}{\sqrt{0.2978}}$$
$$= \frac{4.059}{0.546}$$
$$= \mathbf{7.43}$$

From Table B-12 we see that for $\alpha = 0.05$ and 23 degrees of freedom, $t = 2.069$. We therefore conclude that there is some association between the two rankings. It does *not* seem reasonable that the retraining generally has differential effects on high and low performers among the stitching machine operators.

SUMMARY

Experiments are performed in business in order to obtain information about relationships or associations between variables or populations.

TABLE 11.21

CLASSIFICATION OF STATISTICAL INFERENCE PROBLEMS TREATED IN CHAPTER 11, SHOWING THE TEST STATISTIC AND PROBABILITY DISTRIBUTION TO USE FOR EACH PROBLEM

PROBLEM	TEST STATISTIC AND PROBABILITY DISTRIBUTION
I. Testing Difference between:	
A. Two *means*	(1) σ known: z (normal)
	(2) σ estimated: t (approximated by z, normal, for $n \geq 30$)
	(3) One-way analysis of variance (F)
B. More than two *means*	One-way analysis of variance (F)
C. *Values* in classes (Multiple observations per cell)	Two-way analysis of variance (F)
D. Two *variances*	Ratio of estimated variances (F)
E. Two *proportions*	(1) Binomial or Poisson
	(2) Use z (normal) approximation for $n \geq 30$
	(3) Use nonparametric chi square, minimum $f_e \geq 5$, large samples
F. Many *proportions*	Nonparametric chi square
II. Testing Association between:	
A. Two frequency distributions	Nonparametric chi square
1. *Contingency* analysis (counts by classes)	
2. *Goodness of fit*	
B. Two bivariate-normal variables	
1. Simple correlation (r)	(1) z (normal) with Fisher's z_r transform
	(2) t with $n \geq 25$ for testing H_0: $\rho = 0$
2. Rank Correlation (r_R)	t with $n \geq 10$ for testing H_0: $\rho_R = 0$

The techniques of statistical hypothesis testing can be of assistance in such analyses. One of the most common problems involves comparison of parameters from two populations on the basis of sample information. This process is analagous to ordinary hypothesis testing if a hypothesis concerning the *size* of the true difference between the two populations is stated and subjected to a test involving analysis of the deviation of an observed difference between sample statistics from the hypothesized true population difference. Processes for testing differences between means, variances, and proportions were developed in the first part of this chapter.

One method for testing the difference between two population means (variance analysis) was extended to obtain a test for many means and also for differences resulting from two-way classifications of numerical results (values occurring in classes).

Similarly, one method for testing for difference between two population proportions (chi-square analysis) was extended to several proportions and two-way classifications of qualitative variables (counts by class). Nonparametric chi square is also useful for testing for association between frequency distributions in contingency analysis and testing the goodness of fit of fitted frequency distributions.

Finally, the simple correlation coefficient is useful for testing for association between two normally distributed variables (r) or between the ranks of such variables (r_R).

The types of problems analyzed in this chapter, the test statistic(s) appropriate to each test, and the appropriate probability distribution for assessing the significance of each test statistic are shown in Table 11.21.

DISCUSSION QUESTIONS

1. Define the following in your own words. (Do *not* use symbols or verbal formulas.)

   (a) analysis of variance
   (b) an experiment
   (c) confounding variable
   (d) association between variables
   (e) contingency
   (f) contingency analysis
   (g) between-samples variance
   (h) within-samples variance
   (i) interaction

   (j) residual variance
   (k) contingency table
   (l) correlation
   (m) coefficient of correlation
   (n) interaction variance
   (o) independence of classification
   (p) paired samples
   (q) paired observations

2. What assumptions are made when:
   (a) Testing the significance of the difference between two means using z?
   (b) Testing the significance of the difference between means using variance analysis?
   (c) Testing the significance of the difference between two proportions using χ^2?
   (d) Testing the association of two classifications using χ^2?
   (e) Measuring association between two variables with r?
   (f) Testing the significance of the association between two variables using r?
   (g) When applying χ^2 to the analysis of the difference between two frequency distributions?
   (h) Testing the significance of the difference between two means using t?
3. What conclusions should be reached when a hypothesis is rejected using analysis of variance?
   Hints: (1) What specific hypothesis (hypotheses) can be tested by variance analysis?
   (2) What does it mean to reject *any* statistical hypothesis?
4. What conclusions should be reached when a hypothesis is accepted using analysis of variance?
   Hint: See hints for question 3.
5. If a hypothesis about the difference between two means which is being tested by analysis of variance is rejected, can any further analysis be carried out? Explain.
6. If the assumption of equal variances for two populations is rejected, can any information on the difference between populations means be obtained from the sample data? Explain.
7. Is a lack of correlation between two variables adequate indication that they are statistically independent?
8. Can two statistically independent variables be correlated?
9. Can you think of an example of two sets of observations on the same individuals (two sets of samples values from the same set of elementary units) being independent? Explain.
   Hint: Physical and psychological characteristics of humans are often independent.
10. How does an experimental design with ability to detect interactions differ from one that can detect only between-samples and within-samples variations? Why is it desirable to be able to detect interactions?

11. What agreements in concept are there between simple correlation analysis and variance analysis?

Hint: Do both deal with ratios of variances?

DISCUSSION PROBLEMS

Show your method on all solutions.

1. Compacto Company is considering shifting to a new production process. A decision to make the shift will mean a sizable capital outlay to the company. To determine the effect of the new production process on the life and uniformity of its product the Compacto Company tested samples of 50 items from the old process and 50 items from a pilot model of the new process available at the suppliers plant and obtained the following results:

<table>
<tr><td>*Old Process*</td><td>*New Process*</td></tr>
<tr><td>$n = 50$</td><td>$n = 50$</td></tr>
<tr><td>$\bar{x} = 140$ hours</td><td>$\bar{x} = 146$ hours</td></tr>
<tr><td>$s = 35$ hours</td><td>$s = 28$ hours</td></tr>
</table>

(a) Which process produces the more uniform product? What significance level did you use? Why?

Hint: Note that if $n_1 = n_2 = n$, then $\dfrac{\left[s_1 \left(\dfrac{n}{n-1} \right) \right]^2}{\left[s_2 \left(\dfrac{n}{n-1} \right) \right]^2}$ reduces to $\dfrac{s_1^2}{s_2^2}$

(b) Compute the standard error of the mean for each process.

Hint: Note that $\dfrac{s^2 \left(\dfrac{n}{n-1} \right)}{n}$ reduces to $\dfrac{s^2}{n-1}$

(c) What is the standard error of the difference between the means?

(d) Does the new process produce a product with a longer life? What significance level did you use? Why?

2. Assume you have values for each of the following available from samples of 50 items each:

$$\hat{P} \quad \hat{\sigma}_{d_p} \quad p_1 \quad p_2 \quad \hat{\sigma}_{\bar{x}_1} \quad \hat{\sigma}_1 \quad \bar{x}_1 \quad \bar{x}_2 \quad \hat{\sigma}_{\bar{x}_2} \quad \hat{\sigma}_{d_{\bar{z}}} \quad r_R \quad n_1 \quad n_2 \quad z_r \quad r$$

Indicate by use of the symbols given the formula for computing the appropriate t ratio, F ratio, z ratio, or χ^2 statistic for each situation below.

(a) To determine if the mean of the first population is significantly greater than the mean of the second population.

(b) To determine if it is reasonable to believe that sample 2 came from a population where $\mu_2 = \mu_0$.

(c) To determine if the two samples come from populations where $\sigma_1 = \sigma_2$.

(d) To determine if there is any association between paired observations from the two populations.

Note: There are two possible answers here.

(e) To determine if the proportion of customers preferring brand 1 is greater than 0.35.

(f) To determine if the proportion of persons preferring brand 1 is the same for both populations.

Note: There are two possible answers here.

(g) To determine if the true correlation between the two populations (ρ) is less than 0.90.

3. The Big Corporation is experimenting with two machines for the assembly of a new product component. In a test run, 100 assemblies are made on pilot models of the two machines with the following results:

Design 1: 90 perfect assemblies, five with shield mounted backward, five with cracked brace.

Design 2: 84 perfect assemblies, seven with shield mounted backward, nine with cracked brace.

What can you conclude about the two designs?

Hint: You can determine more than just whether the proportion of total defectives produced on each machine is the same.

4. Exercise 9 of Chapter 4 was concerned with the association between TV ownership and family income. Suppose the probabilities given there were developed from a sample of 1500 families in Midtown.

(a) Construct a 3-by-3 table with income in the heading (in columns) and TV ownership in the stub (in rows) showing the frequencies of responses in each category.

(b) Use chi square to test for association between the two characteristics. Use the 0.02 level of significance. What do you conclude?

(c) Does your conclusion on the basis of chi square agree with the conclusion you reached for Exercise 9 in Chapter 4?

5. Quest, Inc., has made a survey of student expenditures at Your U. On returning to the home office, Quest tabulated the following results:

$$n = 64 \qquad \text{Time required per interview}$$
$$\bar{x} = \$2200 \qquad \bar{x}_I = 1 \text{ hour}$$
$$\hat{\sigma}_{\bar{x}} = \$60 \qquad \hat{\sigma}_I = 10 \text{ minutes}$$

The client for whom Quest made the survey is dissatisfied and insists on an error of no more than $80 in the mean estimate with a confidence level of approximately 95 percent. Quest offers to pay $150 to hire you and two friends to make the additional interviews required to reduce the error to the desired level.

(a) What should be the revised standard error of the mean to meet the client's requirements?

Hint: Why would it be better to assume $z = 2$ rather than $z = 1.96$?

(b) How many *additional* interviews are required?

Hint: Remember that $\sigma^2 = n\sigma_{\bar{x}}^2$.

(c) How much per hour could *each* of you (assume 3) expect to earn if you took the job?

    (1) as an average hourly wage?

    (2) as an approximate *minimum* wage per hour? (Assume interview times to be normally distributed.)

Hint: (1) What is the *expected* total time for the additional requirements?

    (2) You must decide what probability you will accept of actually falling below the minimum you estimated.

(d) Assume that you had decided to take the required interviews and obtained the following results:

$$\bar{x} = \$2125$$
$$\hat{\sigma}_{\bar{x}} = 41$$
$$n = \text{(additional interviews required)}$$

Quest expresses dissatisfaction with these results, implying that you and your friends have done something to bias the results. Do you agree that this is a reasonable conclusion, assuming the original sample of 64 is unbiased? Justify the level of significance you use.

Hint: Do the two sample estimates of the mean and variance differ sufficiently to indicate that the samples come from different populations?

(e) As a further test of the above assertion, you have developed the information below:

	Mean	Sum of Squares around Mean	Number of Interviews
You	2075	3,535,500	26
Friend 1	2050	3,600,210	26
Friend 2	2100	3,455,710	26
Total group	2075	10,623,920	78

Hints: (1) Do not forget to check for equal variances.

(2) Use 11.38 to compute $\hat{\sigma}_B^2$ and 11.34 to compute $\hat{\sigma}_W^2$.

(3) Note that total sum of squares equals 10,623,920.

(f) The statistician for Quest asserts that the test performed in (e) indicates that there is no difference in the means between interviewers. He claims that the basis of the problem is the suspicious lack of difference between the interviewer means. To test whether this statement has substance, you should check to see if the ratio of between-interviewer variance to within-interviewer variance is significantly small.

Hint: Use 11.12; take care to use the degrees of freedom correctly.

6. The distribution below was developed by the statistician for Softy Tires. It shows the distribution of lifetimes of a test sample of their new Tredsoft Tires. The statistician is checking to determine if the lifetimes are normally distributed.

Lifetimes (Thousands of Miles)	Observed Frequencies
Under 21	2
21–22	6
22–23	8
23–24	18
24–25	23
25–26	17
26–27	10
27–28	11
28–29	5
29 and over	1
$\bar{x} = 24.8$	$\hat{\sigma} = 1.95$

(a) Plot the above data as a first check on whether this distribution appears normal. What is your reaction? Explain.

(b) What is the height of the ordinate erected at the mean if this is a normal distribution?

(c) Fit a normal curve to the data and plot the computed curve on your graph. What is your reaction now? Explain.

(d) Check the goodness of fit of your computed distribution using chi square. What do you conclude? What level of significance did you use? Why?

Note: You *cannot* say that you are $1 - \alpha$ percent sure that the *null* hypothesis is true if you do not reject H_0. Why?

(e) *Optional:* A useful type of graph paper is available which makes it easier to recognize normal distributions from their plots. This is called *probability graph paper* and is so scaled that any normal distribution plots on it as a straight line. The reader may find it interesting to obtain some probability paper and plot the observed and computed distributions for this problem. The computed distribution should plot as a straight line.

7. Some statisticians *insist* that there be no ties in ranks if the short-cut formula for the rank correlation coefficient (11.90) is to be used. Consideration of the decimal data from which the rates in Table 11.3 were developed made it possible to break the ties shown in Table 11.20. The untied ranks are shown below:

Revised Ranks with Ties Broken for Production Rates of Stitching Machine Operators before and after Retraining by New Method

i	R_{1i}	R_{2i}	i	R_{1i}	R_{2i}
1	1	1	14	14	19
2	2	2	15	15	18
3	3	3	16	16	14
4	4	6	17	17	21
5	5	5	18	18	8
6	6	11	19	19	22
7	7	4	20	20	12
8	8	16	21	21	17
9	9	9	22	22	20
10	10	13	23	23	23
11	11	7	24	24	25
12	12	15	25	25	24
13	13	10			

Compute r_R and compare it to the r_R computed in the chapter discussion by both the regular product-moment and short-cut formulas (11.89 and 11.90). Note that the value of r_R you have computed has been influenced by the manner in which the breaks in ties occurs.

8. Mr. Seller of Hardsell Corporation is convinced that the number of customer contacts in a given period definitely affects the number of sales. He gives you the information below and asks you to test his belief.

Customer Contacts and Number of Sales Last Week

Salesman	Customer Contacts	Number of Sales
A	110	40
B	130	56
C	120	52
D	140	52
Totals	500	200

Hint: Note that you must develop the number of contacts not result-ing in sales. Otherwise, the degrees of freedom would be negative. Why?

9. Mr. Bigone, the president of Hardsell, believes that the differences in number of customer contacts made by the salesmen each week are only chance variations. Use the data of Problem 8 to check this belief. Hint: Mr. Bigone's belief indicates that the number of contacts made by each salesman is equal to the number of contacts by any other salesman.

10. The Bigtown Transit Company is studying the time distribution on different transportation routes at different times of day. Average elapsed times (in minutes) are shown below.

Months of the Year	Route Number 1	2	3	4	5	6
January	8	10	7	7	9	14
	7	9	8	6	10	18
	9	11	7	9	10	12
April	8	8	6	8	7	7
	7	5	4	6	8	9
	6	7	5	6	6	11
July	12	13	12	9	11	10
	10	12	11	9	12	10
	10	11	11	10	11	10
October	12	15	13	15	12	16
	12	15	13	15	12	15
	11	16	14	15	15	16

The company wants to know if the times vary by route or by time of year.

(a) Is time influenced by route or time of year?

(b) Is there any interaction between route and time of year?

Hint: Apply two-way analysis of variance.

EXERCISES

Show your method on all solutions.

1. Mr. Seller of Hardsell Corporation continues to study the relation-ship of number of customer contacts per week and sales per week. The data below were developed from data for last quarter.

Data for Analysis of Association between Sales Performance and
Customer Contacts

Salesman	Average Number of Contacts per Week	Total Amount of Sales ($000)	Average Number of Sales per week
1	96	152	36
2	108	160	38
3	116	181	41
4	120	182	42
5	126	180	40
6	130	186	45
7	133	184	44
8	137	191	53
9	140	208	55
10	142	200	54

(a) Do these data indicate that total amount of sales is associated with number of contacts?

(b) Is amount of sales associated with number of sales?

(c) Is amount of sales more closely associated with number of sales or number of contacts? Is the observed difference in association significant?

(d) Is number of contacts more closely associated with number of sales than amount of sales? Explain fully.

(e) What level of significance did you use in parts (c) and (d)? Why?

2. Notite Container Corporation is developing a new container for NoSuds soap powder. As a test, counters were set up in supermarkets where NoSuds was sold in addition to other soap powders. NoSuds was offered in boxes of three different sizes: large, super-large, and gigantic. Only one size of NoSuds was offered in each store. The locations of NoSuds and the other soap powders were randomly ordered on the counters and the test conducted at many randomly selected stores over a week's period. At the end of the period the following results were reported:

	Large	Super-Large	Gigantic	Totals
Number of Customers:				
Buying soap chips	1000	1500	2000	4500
Buying NoSuds	275	305	320	900
Not buying NoSuds	725	1195	1680	3600

Does size of package influence sales of NoSuds? Explain carefully.

3. The Lectro-Vu Corporation has developed an "improved" model of their famous Bright Eye TV picture tube. As a publicity stunt, 9 of the "old" model and 9 of the "improved" model are put through a life test. The 9 "old" tubes burn an average of 2000 hours with a sample standard deviation (s) of 150 hours. The 9 "improved" tubes burn an average of 2200 hours with a sample standard deviation (s) of 200 hours. Lectro-Vu cites this as "proof" of the superiority of the "improved" tube. Do you agree? Explain carefully.

4. In trying to determine whether one of their products is superior to that of a competitor, Dry-Cell Corporation performed a life test on samples of 50 of each brand with the following results:

Dry-Cell Product	Competitor's Product
$n = 50$	$n = 50$
$\bar{x} = 503$ minutes	$\bar{x} = 478$ minutes
$\hat{\sigma} = 21$ minutes	$\hat{\sigma} = 18$ minutes

(a) Is the Dry-Cell product significantly more variable than the competitor's product?

(b) Does the Dry-Cell product have a significantly longer life than the competitor's product?

5. The Hardy Tire Company has just completed a mileage test from which the data below were developed. The question is whether there is any association between tire position and tire wear.

Locations of 300 Tires Scrapped during a
Mileage Test

	Front	Rear	Total
Left	86	49	135
Right	94	71	165
Total	180	120	300

Does position influence tire wear? Explain fully. What level of significance did you use? Why?

6. The Krumly Company employs two professional "tasters" who aid in the selection of the exact recipe for each type of cooky produced by Krumly. Two of the judges have just ranked 10 variations of one recipe as to tastiness. The rankings are reproduced below. Is there any association between the rankings? Can you test the hypothesis that $\rho_R = 0$? If so, do so. If not, explain.

RANKINGS OF TEN RECIPES BY TWO TASTERS

	RANKINGS	
Recipe	Taster 1	Taster 2
1	3	4
2	6	5
3	4	6
4	8	8
5	9	7
6	10	9
7	2	1
8	5	3
9	1	2
10	7	10

7. The Washer Company's Kleen-O washers are nationally advertised. As an experiment, Washer has also used local newspaper advertising in Bigtown, but not in Largetown. The two cities are almost identical in size, age composition of their populations, and family income distribution. Samples of potential Kleen-O customers in the two cities reveal the following:

	Bigtown	Largetown
Number of persons interviewed	2000	3000
Number planning to buy a washer	360	840
Number planning to buy Kleen-O	60	120

   (a) What are the 90 percent confidence limits for the population proportion preferring Kleen-O in Bigtown? in Largetown?
   (b) Is there a significant difference in the preference for Kleen-O in the two cities? (Use *two* methods for this test and compare the results.)

8. The Big Corporation has five lines in one factory producing the same type of article. An hour's production of the factory consists of five lots, each lot being from a different assembly line. A sample of four articles has been taken at random from each lot and a certain characteristic of each article measured. Are the five assembly lines operating at different levels of the characteristic in question? Explain.

		Assembly Line		
A	B	C	D	E
3	3	5	4	7
4	3	6	4	6
4	1	6	4	6
3	2	6	6	8

9. The sales manager for Big-Way Department Stores holds a theory that sex has a significant effect on customer preference for Tartar tooth brushes. Before advising all clerks in the drug chain that it is easier to sell a substitute brand to women than to men, he wishes to have a test made of his theory. What answer can you give the manager from the following data?

	Men	Women	Total
Refused a substitute	133	196	329
Accepted a substitute	42	99	141
Total	175	295	470

10. Suppose the data presented for testing the hypothesis that there is no significant difference between the sexes as to brand loyalty for the Tartar tooth brush were as follows:

Reaction When Tartar Was Not Available	Men	Women	Total
Accepted substitute with reluctance or evident displeasure	13	45	58
Accepted substitute pleasantly	31	52	83
Refused substitute with evident displeasure	28	72	100
Refused substitute pleasantly	103	126	229
Total	175	295	470

Should the sales manager advise the drug clerks that it is easier to sell a substitute to women than to men? Explain.

11. The Allcap Company is attempting to improve one of its products. A critical factor is the breaking strength of the cap. A change has been made in the production line after one sample was taken; a second sample is then drawn. The results are:

Old Method	New Method
$n = 64$	$n = 64$
$\bar{x} = 200$	$\bar{x} = 220$
$\hat{\sigma} = 36$	$\hat{\sigma} = 32$

Is cap strength for the new method significantly greater than for the older? (The new method uses slightly more machine time and materials and requires the company to increase its price in order to recapture this additional cost if the new method is adopted.

Management is willing to increase price only if the product is really improved.) What level of significance seems appropriate? Explain.

12. The credit manager of the Lessloss Department Stores has been examining the accounts receivable statistics for the five stores in the East Division. He notes that there is little difference between the average size of account in the stores, but the proportions of accounts six or more months delinquent seems to vary. He develops the information shown below and asks for assistance in analyzing it.

Number of Accounts Receivable

Store	Delinquent at Least 6 Months	Not Delinquent 6 Months	Total
A	25	230	255
B	10	179	189
C	14	214	228
D	9	158	167
E	9	109	118
Totals	67	890	957

Does the rate of delinquency for accounts receivable vary between stores in East Division? Explain carefully.

13. For each of the sample pairs below:
   (a) Test for a significant difference in the variance of the populations from which the samples were drawn. (Use $\alpha = 0.01$.)
   (b) Test for a significant difference in the means of the populations from which the samples were drawn. (Use $\alpha = 0.01$.)

Sample Pair	Sample Number	Sample Statistics Mean	$\hat{\sigma}$	s	n
A	1	80	16		16
	2	90	20		25
B	1	88	16		16
	2	76	20		16
C	1	100	16		16
	2	90		20	65
D	1	88	16		90
	2	76	20		9
E	1	88		16	10
	2	76		20	10
F	1	100		17	17
	2	90	20		64
G	1	100	16		16
	2	90	20		64

14. For each of the sample pairs below, test for a difference in the population proportions at the 0.05 level of significance.

Sample Statistics

Sample Pair	Sample Numbers	Proportion	n
A	1	0.50	16
	2	0.375	16
B	1	0.50	36
	2	0.44	36
C	1	0.41	17
	2	0.50	36
D	1	0.40	5
	2	0.60	5

15. For each of the sample pairs below, test for a difference in the population proportions at the 0.05 level of significance.

Sample Statistics

Sample Pair	Sample Number	Number of Successes	n
A	1	6	16
	2	8	16
B	1	3	4
	2	2	4
C	1	40	50
	2	35	50

16. The work methods group at Big Corporation is investigating four
methods of performing a particular milling operation. Three operators
are being used in performing the tests, and the results are shown
below in coded form.

Methods

Operators	A	B	C	D
a	3	0	2	0
	−2	3	0	2
	−5	1	0	0
	0	3	−2	4
	−1	1	1	4
b	−1	1	−2	4
	−6	0	1	3
	−2	2	2	3
	−4	3	−1	1
	−3	2	0	2
c	1	−2	−1	−3
	−1	−2	1	−1
	−2	−4	−3	2
	−2	1	2	−3
	1	0	−1	−3

(a) Are the methods equally effective? (Measurements are basically the time required to perform the operation; the lower the time, the better the method.)

(b) Do the operators differ in their abilities to perform the operation?

(c) Is there any interaction between operator and method?

(d) What is your recommendation to the work methods group based on your analysis?

17. The office manager at the Madave Agency is considering the purchase of one of three brands of electric typewriters. He decides to have each of a group of four typists try each machine during the test periods, with three timed tests for each typist on each machine. The values below are obtained. They are stated as deviations from a standard operating rate.

MACHINE BRAND

Typist	A	B	C
Smith	12, 13, 10	13, 12, 13	18, 22, 20
Jones	24, 20, 22	8, 12, 7	−2, 0, +2
Brown	10, 8, 7	18, 19, 23	−16, −22, −22
Green	28, 29, 26	4, 8, 9	−5, −2, −3

What can you tell the office manager at Madave about the relationships of operators and machines? Make a complete analysis.

18. The supervisor in one of the departments at Den Products Company is considering switching to a new seaming machine, which is supposed to sew faster. The supervisor has analyzed the costs involved in the decision and has come to the conclusion that unless the machine can sew one of the "average" seams 15 seconds faster than the old machine, he cannot afford to buy the new machine. He can afford only a ten percent chance of buying if the new machine is not better. Since the speed at which the machine sews is partly controlled by the operator, the supervisor decides on a paired sample experiment. Each of 20 operators with established times on the old machine are trained on the new machine and timed in sewing the test seam on it. The data below are collected.

Time Required to Sew Test Seam

Operator	Old Machine	New Machine
1	68	53
2	71	56
3	84	62
4	86	70
5	84	68
6	96	72
7	78	63
8	85	71
9	84	64
10	69	58
11	82	67
12	74	59
13	94	72
14	92	74
15	87	73
16	86	70
17	79	65
18	87	61
19	76	60
20	83	63
Total	1645	1298

Would you advise the supervisor to buy the new machine? Explain fully.

19. The advertising manager of Lessloss Department Stores is considering a change in the merchandise sale flyers enclosed with the monthly statements of regular charge customers. Previously, the flyers have been printed in black and white with line-drawing representations of merchandise. The new flyers will include color pictures of the merchandise. Since the new flyers are more expensive, the manager does not wish to use them unless they clearly are more effective. To provide data for testing this proposition, a test mailing to two randomly selected samples of 1000 customers each is made. One sample receives the flyer prepared with black and white line drawings. The other sample receives the same flyer with color pictures of the merchandise in place of the line drawings. A total of 92 orders is received from the test mailing, 52 from those receiving flyers containing color pictures. The advertising manager has indicated that he is willing to take no more than 10 chances in 100 of switching to the color pictures if the line drawings pull just as well. What do you advise him to do? Explain clearly.

20. One of the bolt-cutting machines in the Dimbo Company plant is supposed to operate so that half the bolts are slightly longer than the planned length and the other half slightly shorter. The distribution of longer bolts in the last 100 samples of 10 bolts each is shown below.

Number of Longer Bolts in Sample of 10	Number of Samples Observed
0	1
1	2
2	5
3	10
4	23
5	27
6	18
7	9
8	4
9	1
10	0
	100

(a) Fit a curve to these data on the basis of the hypothesis that the samples come from a population where $P = 0.50$.
(b) Graph the observed and theoretical distributions.
(c) Test the hypothesis that these samples come from a population where $P = 0.50$. Justify the level of significance chosen for the test.

12
relationships
and decisions

INTRODUCTION

It is not uncommon to find that a definite relationship exists between two or more variables in a business situation. For example, total dollar volume of sales by a company may be closely related to the level of disposable personal income of the families in the company's sales area; performance on the job may be related to the amount and type of education and/or experience a worker has had; the hardness of a piece of metal may be closely related to its specific gravity. The problem of defining the exact nature of such relationships so that the resulting functions can be used in prediction of variables such as sales, job performance, and so forth, is called *regression* analysis. It is the subject of the present chapter and involves the expression of relationships between variables in the form of mathematical equations connecting the variables.

Functional Relationships

If one variable is determined by the behavior of some other variable, we say that the first variable is a *function of* the second. Thus, we might say that the amount of sales by a company in a given area over a given time period is a function of the level of disposable income in the area. Such functional relationships are normally expressed in an equation

describing the curve (in the case of more than two variables, the plane
or solid) that traces the intersection of the variables on a set of coordinate
axis. For example, the average level of sales per week of each of the
Lessloss Department stores and a measure of disposable income per
family in each store's sales area are plotted in Figure 12.1. Sales per week
are measured along the vertical axis, coded disposable personal income
per family per year is shown on the horizontal axis. Figure 12.1 is a picture

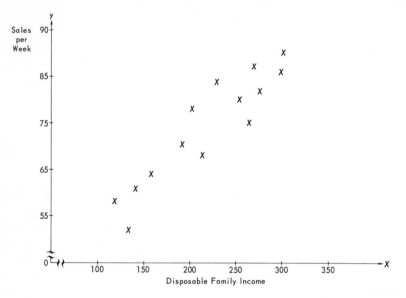

FIG. 12.1.   Scatter diagram of relationship between average weekly sales for
Lessloss store and average disposable family income in the store area
for last twelve months.

of a relationship. This relationship is not a true functional relationship,
however. Each value of X (income) is not considered to be associated
with a unique value of y (sales). For example, two different sales levels
could be related to an income level of $300. Rather, since we believe that
sales levels in Lessloss stores are determined (at least in part) by the
disposable income per family of the families in their sales area, we are
saying that

$$S = A \text{ regression function of } I$$

where

S = average weekly sales per store

I = average disposable income per family in each store's sales area

The above relation is read "average weekly sales per store are a *regression function* of average disposable income per family in each store's sales area." The value of the y variable is said to be *dependent* upon (at least in part) the value of the X variable. Thus y is termed the *dependent* variable. The values of X are not influenced by y, and X is called the *independent* variable. The relationship we have graphed is an example of a *regression* relationship which does not require y to be determined by X, but only that the two variables are associated and y is influenced by X.

The Scatter Diagram

The graph in Figure 12.1 is called a *scatter diagram*. It shows how the paired observations of sales and disposable income "scatter." Such a diagram is useful for examining the general nature (linear, curvilinear, strong, weak) of the relationship by exhibiting the pattern of the "scatter." If the relationship appears to be a strong one, then further mathematical analysis may be justified. The "strength" of the relationship is indicated by how well the plotted points tend to trace a recognizable pattern. Possible types of patterns are discussed at greater length below.

Regression Analysis

The general "drift" of the plotted points in Figure 12.1 seems to follow a straight line sloping upward to the right. That is, a line of the general form

12.00 $Y_i = A + B(X_i)$

where

Y = values on the vertical axis

X = values on the horizontal axis

A and B = constants in the equation

Returning to our example,

$$S_i = A + B(I_i)$$

where

S_i = average sales for store i

I_i = disposable income per family for families in the area served by store i

The constant A in the above equation tells us the value of S when $I = 0$, that is, the level at which the line would cross the vertical axis,

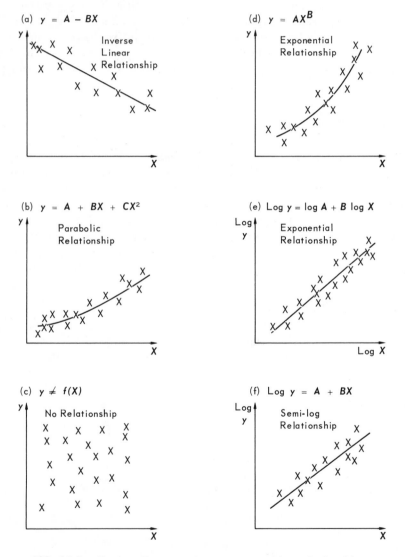

FIG. 12.2. Scatter diagrams for some regression relationships.

commonly called the *Y intercept*. The constant *B* tells us the *slope* of the line, that is, the change in *S* associated with a one-unit change in *I*.

The straight-line relationship illustrated by our example is only one of many possible forms of such relationships. Figure 12.2 represents several other commonly encountered scatter diagrams. Note the change of scales in *e* and *f*. The reader should also realize that the graphs in Figure 12.2 represent only a small portion of the possible forms of relationship between two variables.

The mathematical procedures involved in identifying the nature of the relationship between two or more variables by estimating the constants in an equation describing the relationship is called *regression analysis*. Relationships involving only two variables (a dependent variable and *one* independent variable) are called *simple regression relationships*. The line depicting such relationships is called the *regression* line.

It is possible that additional variables may exert an influence on a variable of interest. Thus, the average sales of each Lessloss store may be influenced not only by the average disposable income of families in the store's area, but also by the number of families in the area. Relationships involving more than one *independent* or causal variable are called *multiple regression* relationships. The surface depicting the impact of the two or more explanatory (*independent*) variables on the explained (*dependent*) variable is called the *regression surface*.

The Regression Equation

The mathematical equation expressing a regression relationship is called the *regression equation*. If there is only one independent variable, the equation is called a *simple regression equation*. A simple regression equation may describe a linear relationship (a straight line) or a curvilinear relationship (a parabola, a log relationship, or any other function not a straight line). When there are two or more independent variables, the equation is called a *multiple regression equation*. Again, multiple regression equations may describe either linear or curvilinear relationships, or they may reflect a combination of linear and curvilinear relationships.

SIMPLE LINEAR REGRESSION ANALYSIS

In the previous section, we introduced a relationship between average weekly sales in Lessloss stores and the average disposable family income of families in the area served by the store. The scatter diagram for these two variables is given in Figure 12.1. The values of the variables are

TABLE 12.1

AVERAGE WEEKLY SALES OF LESSLOSS STORES AND AVERAGE DISPOSABLE
FAMILY INCOME IN THE STORE AREA, LAST TWELVE MONTHS AND
BASIC CALCULATIONS FOR REGRESSION ANALYSIS

Store Number i	Average Weekly Sales ($000) y_i	Average Disposable Family Income (Coded) X_i	Squared Values		Cross-Products $X_i y_i$
			y_i^2	X_i^2	
1	90	301	8,100	90,601	27,090
2	87	267	7,569	71,289	23,229
3	86	297	7,396	88,209	25,542
4	84	227	7,056	51,529	19,068
5	82	273	6,724	74,529	22,386
6	80	253	6,400	64,009	20,240
7	78	203	6,084	41,209	15,834
8	75	263	5,625	69,169	19,725
9	70	190	4,900	36,100	13,300
10	68	212	4,624	44,944	14,416
11	64	157	4,096	24,649	10,048
12	61	141	3,721	19,881	8,601
13	58	119	3,364	14,161	6,902
14	52	133	2,704	17,689	6,916
Totals	1,035	3,036	78,363	707,968	233,297
Means	73.93	216.86			

given in the second and third columns of Table 12.1. These data will be
utilized in illustrating simple linear regression.

The first step is to fit the regression equation. That is, to estimate the
values of A and B in 12.00. What we wish to do is to find the values of
a and b to use in the estimator:

12.10 $\hat{\mu}_{y_i} = a + bX_i$

The value of $\hat{\mu}_{y_i}$ is the estimated average value of y when $X = X_i$. It is
the estimated y coordinate of that point on the regression line which is
directly above X_i.

Note also that the y symbol in 12.10 is a lower-case letter, while the
X symbol is a capital letter. This differentiation reflects one basic assumption of regression analysis, that the X values are *known* values, not
subject to any error or random fluctuations. The values of the dependent

variable, on the other hand, are largely determined by the relationship between y and X. Unless this relationship is a functional relationship, that is, unless the value of each y is completely and fully dependent upon the associated X value, there is some unexplained, (assumed random) fluctuation in y. That is, in regression analysis we assume the relationship is,

12.11 $y_i = A + BX_i + e_i$

where e_i = a random residual in y_i not explained by reference to X_i. Thus the y_i's are a sample of observations and y is therefore a random variable, but X is a known variable.

The constants in the regression equation are called *regression coefficients*. Obviously, the estimated values of these coefficients (a and b) are random variables whose exact value is determined by the particular sample of paired observations considered in the analysis.

It would be desirable to estimate the coefficients of the regression equation in such a fashion that the line would follow the drift of the data and reflect the *average* relationship between y and X. It sounds as if we would like some sort of arithmetic average (mean) line. We obtain such a line by using the *method of least squares,* a method which estimates the coefficients for the regression line in such a way that the sum of the squares of the vertical deviations around the line are minimized. This method requires that we solve simultaneously the following two *normal equations* for the estimates of the constants A and B.

12.12   I. $\Sigma y = na + b\Sigma X$
II. $\Sigma Xy = a\Sigma X + b\Sigma X^2$

An intuitively understandable explanation of the source of the equations goes as follows:

Each value of y is determined by a relation:

$$y_i = a + bX_i$$

that is,

$$(1) \quad \begin{aligned} y_1 &= a + bX_1 \\ y_2 &= a + bX_2 \\ &\cdots \\ &\cdots \\ &\cdots \\ y_n &= a + bX_n \end{aligned}$$

If we multiply each equation by the coefficient of a, which is one (1), and then sum, we obtain

$$\Sigma y_i = na + b\Sigma X_i \qquad \text{(first normal equation)}$$

To obtain the second equation, we multiply each equation in (1) by X_i, the coefficient of b, and sum them.

$$
\begin{aligned}
(2) \quad X_1 y_1 &= aX_1 + bX_1^2 \\
X_2 y_2 &= aX_2 + bX_2^2 \\
& \vdots \\
X_n y_n &= aX_n + bX_n^2
\end{aligned}
$$

summing,

$$\Sigma X_i y_i = a\Sigma X_i + b\Sigma X_i^2 \qquad \text{(second normal equation)}$$

These two equations can then be solved for the two unknowns, a and b.

The normal equations can also be obtained by specifying the desired criterion for the least squares method—that the sum of the squared vertical deviations around the regression values be a minimum—and use the differential calculus.[1] If we let G stand for the sum of the squared vertical deviations from the regression line,

$$G = \Sigma(y_i - (a + bX_i))^2$$

where

y_i = observed value of y paired with the particular value of X (X_i)
a = estimated value of A
b = estimated value of B

Obtaining the first derivatives of the expression for G with respect to a and b, we obtain

$$1. \quad \frac{\partial G}{\partial a} = -2\Sigma(y_i - a - bX_i)$$

$$2. \quad \frac{\partial G}{\partial b} = -2\Sigma X_i(y_i - a - bX_i)$$

---

[1] The appendix to Chapter 2 presents a brief introduction to differential calculus.

Setting these partial derivatives equal to zero and simplifying, we obtain

$$1'. \quad \Sigma y_i = na + b\Sigma X_i$$
$$2'. \quad \Sigma X_i y_i = a\Sigma X_i + b\Sigma X_i^2$$

Equations $1'$ and $2'$ are the two normal equations introduced earlier. Solving 12.12 for a and b, we obtain

12.13 $\quad a = \dfrac{\Sigma X_i^2 \Sigma y_i - \Sigma X_i \Sigma X_i y_i}{n\Sigma X_i^2 - (\Sigma X_i)^2}$

12.14 $\quad b = \dfrac{n\Sigma X_i y_i - \Sigma X_i \Sigma y_i}{n\Sigma X_i^2 - (\Sigma X_i)^2}$

Since a is the value of y when $X = 0$ and the line fitted by the method of least squares must pass through the point whose coordinates are $\bar{X}, \bar{y}$, the value of a can also be computed as

12.15 $\quad a = \bar{y} - b\bar{X}$

This relationship should also be clear from equation $1'$ given above. Substituting into 12.13 and 12.14 from Table 12.1, we obtain

$$a = \frac{707{,}968(1035) - 3036(233{,}297)}{14(707{,}968) - (3036)^2}$$

$$= \frac{24{,}457{,}188}{694{,}256}$$

$$= \mathbf{35.23}$$

$$b = \frac{14(233{,}297) - 3036(1035)}{14(707{,}968) - (3036)^2}$$

$$= \frac{123{,}898}{694{,}256}$$

$$= \mathbf{0.1785}$$

Checking on a by applying 12.15,

$$a = 73.93 - 0.1785(216.86)$$
$$= \mathbf{35.22}$$

Thus, we conclude that $\hat{\mu}_{y_i} = 35.23 + 0.1785X_i$ is the estimated regression equation expressing the relationship between average sales and family income in the store area.

The Standard Deviation of Regression

Not all points in Figure 12.1 will fall on a line computed by use of the equation computed. This is clearly illustrated in Figure 12.3, where the heavy solid line is the regression line plotted on the scatter diagram of Figure 12.1. We measure the dispersion of the observed values about the regression with a measure called the *standard deviation of regression.* Its computation is essentially the same as the computation of any other standard deviation except that we are measuring deviation away from a

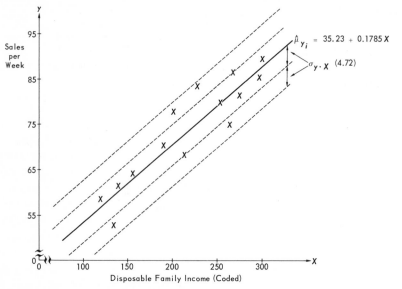

FIG. 12.3. Regression of average store sales on disposable family income in the store area, Lessloss stores.

line rather than deviation away from a single point. If we symbolize the standard deviation of regression by $\sigma_{y \cdot x}$, its formula would be

12.16 $$\sigma_{y \cdot x} = \sqrt{\frac{\Sigma(y_i - \mu_{y_i})^2}{n}}$$

Since μ_{y_i} can only be estimated, an unbiased estimate of $\sigma_{y \cdot x}$ would be obtained from

12.17 $$\hat{\sigma}_{y \cdot x} = \sqrt{\frac{\Sigma(y_i - \hat{\mu}_{y_i})^2}{n - 2}}$$

Note that this formula represents the square root of a variance with the variance computed in the familiar fashion as sum of squares over degrees of freedom. The loss of two degrees of freedom arises from the use of the sample estimates a and b in obtaining the values of $\hat{\mu}_{y_i}$.

The computing form of 12.17 is obtained by substituting $a + bX_i$ for $\hat{\mu}_{y_i}$, squaring, and summing to obtain

12.18 $\hat{\sigma}_{y \cdot x} = \sqrt{\dfrac{\Sigma y_i^2 - a\Sigma y_i - b\Sigma X_i y_i}{n - 2}}$

Substituting from Table 12.2 and earlier calculations into 12.18,

$$\hat{\sigma}_{y \cdot x} = \sqrt{\frac{78{,}363 - (35.23)1035 - 0.1785(233{,}297)}{14 - 2}}$$

$$= \sqrt{\frac{267.57}{12}}$$

$$= \sqrt{22.30}$$

$$= 4.72$$

The standard deviation of regression is used in much the same way as any other standard deviation. It is an absolute measure of the extent to which the regression equation has failed to explain all the variability in the dependent (y) variable. It is basically the standard deviation of the distribution of e_i's in our complete regression model (12.11). Since we assume these e's to be random and to have the same standard deviation for all values of X, $\hat{\sigma}_{y \cdot x}$ is a gross estimate of the standard deviation of the e_i's. Note also that the e_i's for every X_i are assumed to be normally distributed with a mean of zero. If this is true, then 68.27 percent of the observed y's should fall within the range of one standard deviation about the regression line, 95.5 percent within two standard deviations, and so forth. In other words, nine or ten of the fourteen observations in our example should be within the range of one standard deviation of regression about the regression line. The one- and two-standard deviation limits are indicated by the dashed lines on Figure 12.3. It can be seen that nine of the observed values of y_i do fall within the range of one standard deviation about the regression line. However, all (100 percent) of the values fall within two standard deviations of the regression line.

Forecasting with the Regression Equation

The obvious purpose of the kind of regression analysis carried out above is to use the observed relationship as the basis for predictions of the value of the dependent variable. For example, Lessloss may be considering opening a new store in an area for which reliable information (possibly sample estimates) of family income is available. The equation derived above can be used to estimate the average level of weekly sales for the proposed store. However, we must determine the amount of error involved in such an estimate. To answer this question, we must review the assumptions underlying the regression technique and develop estimates of the sampling errors present in estimates derived from the equation.

Basic Assumptions of Least Squares Method.   The basic assumptions of the least squares regression method have been stated rather loosely.

12.19   The assumptions of simple linear least squares regression are:
  (a) $y_i = A + BX_i + e_i$, that is, the regression of y on X is linear.
  (b) The X_i's are selected nonrandomly (known) and are not subject to errors of observation.
  (c) The y_i's are a random sample of the y's for each X_i.
  (d) $\sigma_{y_1}{}^2 = \sigma_{y_2}{}^2 = \ldots = \sigma_{y_n}{}^2 = \sigma_{y \cdot x}{}^2$, that is, the variances of the populations of y's associated with each of the values of X are equal. (This is called the assumption of homoscedasticity.)

Point (d) is illustrated by Figure 12.4, where the assumed distribution of y values about the regression line is illustrated by the ridge following the regression line. If the ridge is cut through parallel to the y axis at any point, the face of the cut forms a normal distribution whose standard

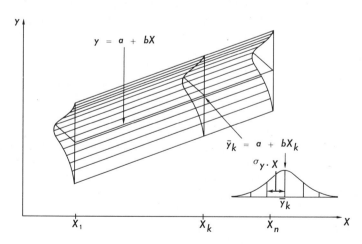

FIG. 12.4.   Conditional probability distributions of y_i assumed in regression analysis.

deviation $= \sigma_{y\cdot x}$, as is indicated by the inset below the main figure. The title of Figure 12.4 is chosen to indicate that each possible X_i has associated with it a distribution of y_i whose mean is μ_{y_i}. Thus, if X_i is given, a distribution of y_i can be specified by knowing the true regression equation and the standard deviation of regression. The true regression equation, $\mu_{y_i} = A + BX_i$, gives the value of μ_{y_i} (the value on the line at that point), and $\sigma_{y\cdot x}$ indicates the scatter of the y_i distribution around the line.

Note once again that the regression technique assumes that the X's are known without error, but the y's are sample values, with each y_i drawn from a distribution of y's associated with the corresponding X_i. The coefficients in the *estimated regression equation*, $\hat{\mu}_{y_i} = a + bX_i$, are derived from the sample of observed y_i values. We therefore consider them sample estimates subject to ordinary sampling error. The measures of that sampling error are developed in the next section.

Sampling Errors in Regression.   The equation ($\hat{\mu}_{y_i} = 35.23 + 1785X_i$) derived by application of 12.13 and 12.14 above is obtained from sample data. Estimates obtained from its application are therefore subject to sampling variability. This variability derives from three sources. First, there is the "equation error" (lack of precision in the equation itself). This arises from the fact that the regression relationship does not explain all the variability in the observed values of the dependent variable (y_i). This error is estimated by $\hat{\sigma}_{y\cdot x}$.

A second source of error is the sampling variability present in the estimate of the y intercept, a. This intercept indicates the *height* of the regression line. It is analagous to a mean, and the error in its computation is reflected in the error in the estimate of each average value of y_i ($\hat{\mu}_{y_i}$). The $\hat{\mu}_{y_i}$ are sample means (see 12.19), and the standard error of these estimates would be the standard error of the mean of μ_{y_i}. The measure of variability for the y_i distributions is $\sigma_{y\cdot x}$. Thus, our best estimate of the error in the y intercept, a, would look like the standard error of a mean where the mean is a $\hat{\mu}_{y_i}$ on the regression line. That is,

12.20 $\sigma_a = \dfrac{\sigma_{y\cdot x}}{\sqrt{n}}$

but, $\sigma_{y\cdot x}$ must be estimated and our best estimate of σ_a would be:

12.21 $\hat{\sigma}_a = \dfrac{\hat{\sigma}_{y\cdot x}}{\sqrt{n}}$

For example,

$$\hat{\sigma}_{\hat{\mu}_{y_i}} = \frac{4.72}{\sqrt{n}}$$
$$= 1.26$$

The third source of error in the estimated regression equation is the sampling error involved in the estimate of b, the slope coefficient. The standard error of the slope coefficient, σ_b, is given by

12.22 $\sigma_b = \dfrac{\sigma_{y \cdot x}}{\sqrt{\Sigma(X_i - \bar{X})^2}}$

Note that σ_b will vary directly with the size of the population standard deviation of regression and inversely with the number of observations (since adding more squared deviations would increase the denominator and, therefore, reduce the size of the total ratio). Finally, the greater the range in the X values, the less the sampling error in the estimate of b. Since we know only the estimated value of the standard deviation of regression, σ_b can only be estimated. In addition, a computationally simpler form for the sum of the squared deviations in the denominator can be used.

12.23 $\hat{\sigma}_b = \dfrac{\hat{\sigma}_{y \cdot x}}{\sqrt{\Sigma X_i^2 - n \bar{X}^2}}$

Applying 12.23 to our example using values from Table 12.1,

$$\hat{\sigma}_b = \frac{4.72}{\sqrt{707,968 - (14)(216.86)^2}}$$
$$= \frac{4.72}{\sqrt{49,586.37}}$$
$$= \frac{4.72}{223}$$
$$= 0.0211 \text{ or } 0.021$$

The standard error of the slope coefficient is useful in determining whether there really is a relationship between X and y. If there is no relationship, then the true value of the slope would be zero $(B = 0)$. By application of the technique of hypothesis testing developed in preceding chapters, we can test the hypothesis of no relationship by computing the t ratio. Since sample size is determined, we can control only the probability of Type I error, the error of deciding there is a relationship between X and y when, in reality, there is not. It would seem reasonable to keep the probability of that error low. Therefore, we will use the following test:

$$H_0:B = 0 \qquad H_a:B \neq 0 \qquad \alpha = 0.05$$

Computing the t ratio,

$$
\begin{aligned}
t &= \frac{b - 0}{\hat{\sigma}_b} \\
&= \frac{0.1785}{0.021} \\
&= \mathbf{8.50}
\end{aligned}
$$

Since t_α for twelve degrees of freedom equals only 2.18, it seems reasonable to believe that there is a relationship between store sales and family income in the area.

Note that b is a normally distributed sample statistic and the ratio

$$z = \frac{b - B}{\sigma_b}$$

is a standard normal deviate. If the standard error of b were obtained from 12.22, the z ratio would be used rather than the t ratio. Also, if $n - 2 \geq 30$, the z could be used as an approximation for t.

Confidence Interval Estimates from the Regression Equation. The values computed from the regression equation, $\hat{\mu}_{y_i}$, are point estimates subject to sampling error. More information would be provided by confidence interval estimates. The general process by which confidence interval estimates can be derived was developed in Chapter 8. Let us look at the particular forms they assume here.

Estimating an average y $(\mu_{y \cdot x})$ *for a given value of* X. In order to obtain a confidence interval estimate for a particular μ_{y_i}, we must develop the standard error of the sample statistic $\hat{\mu}_{y \cdot x_0}$ (the $\hat{\mu}_{y_i}$ value when $X = X_0$). For example, suppose average family income in the area where the new Lessloss store, mentioned earlier, is to be located is (after coding) equal to 200. Then,

$$\hat{\mu}_{y \cdot 200} = 35.23 + 0.1785(200)$$
$$= 35.23 + 35.70$$
$$= \textbf{70.93 or 70.9}$$

What is the standard error of this statistic? It should reflect the error in a (see 12.21) and the error in b (see 12.23). An estimator for the standard error of estimate of the average value of y_i given X_0 is given by:

12.24 $\hat{\sigma}_{\hat{\mu}_y \cdot x_0} = \hat{\sigma}_{y \cdot x} \sqrt{\dfrac{1}{n} + \dfrac{(X_0 - \bar{X})^2}{\Sigma X_i^2 - n\bar{X}^2}}$

The first part of the expression under the radical reflects the error in a; the second part reflects the error in b. Note that the estimated error increases as the deviation of X_0 from $\bar{X}$ increases. It is a minimum and is equal to the $\hat{\sigma}_a$ when $X_0 = \bar{X}$. $\left(\text{Note that } \sqrt{\dfrac{1}{n}} = \dfrac{1}{\sqrt{n}}.\right)$ For example,

$$\hat{\sigma}_{\hat{\mu}_y \cdot 200} = 4.72 \sqrt{\frac{1}{14} + \frac{(200 - 216.9)^2}{707,968 - 14(216.86)^2}}$$
$$= 4.72 \sqrt{\frac{1}{14} + \frac{(-16.9)^2}{49,586.37}}$$
$$= 4.72 \sqrt{0.071429 + \frac{285.61}{49,586.37}}$$
$$= 4.72 \sqrt{0.077482}$$
$$= 4.72(0.2784)$$
$$= \textbf{1.31}$$

Suppose we wish to calculate a symmetrical 90 percent confidence interval for $\hat{\mu}_{y \cdot 200}$. Then, referring to Table B-12 for $t_{0.90}$,

$$\text{confidence interval} = \hat{\mu}_{y \cdot 200} \pm t_{0.90}\hat{\sigma}_{\hat{\mu}_y \cdot 200}$$
$$= 70.93 \pm 1.78(1.31)$$
$$= 70.93 \pm 2.33$$
$$= \textbf{68.6 to 73.3}$$

We can be 90 percent *confident* that the interval from 68.6 to 73.3 contains the true value of $\mu_{y \cdot 200}$.

Note that the interval does not specify where the actual average sales of the store being considered will fall, but merely assesses our belief about where the average sales of the average store will occur if family income is (coded) at 200.

Note also that $\hat{\mu}_{y \cdot x_i}$ is considered a normally distributed statistic. If $\sigma_{y \cdot x}$ were known, we would use z_C instead of t_C in calculating the limits of the confidence interval.

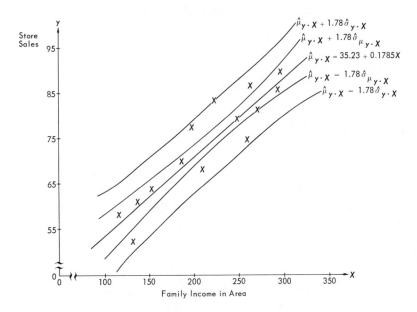

FIG. 12.5.   Ninety percent confidence intervals for $\mu_{y \cdot x}$ and y_1 Lessloss stores.

The 90 percent confidence limits for $\hat{\mu}_{y \cdot x_0}$ are shown in Figure 12.5. Note how the width of the interval increases as X_0 deviates further from $\bar{X}$ (216.9).

Estimating an individual value of y *for a given value of* X.   The statistic estimated in the previous section is the value on the regression line when $X = X_0$. Our interest often centers more on the range of values y_i can be expected to assume given a particular value of X (X_0). In the example we are considering, Lessloss executives obviously would like to know the range within which the average weekly sales of the specific store under consideration might be expected to fall. We could miss the true value with our estimating equation not only because of the sampling error in the estimates of coefficients in the equation, but also because the model itself is deficient. The equation used to estimate the standard error of an individual y value must include three elements; the error in the equation, the error in the intercept, and the error in the slope, b.

12.25 $\hat{\sigma}_{\hat{y} \cdot x_0} = \hat{\sigma}_{y \cdot x} \sqrt{1 + \dfrac{1}{n} + \dfrac{(X_0 - \bar{X})^2}{\Sigma X_i^2 - n\bar{X}^2}}$

Substituting into 12.25 from our example for $X = 200$,

$$\begin{aligned}
\hat{\sigma}_{\hat{y} \cdot 200} &= 4.72 \sqrt{1 + \dfrac{1}{14} + \dfrac{(200 - 216.86)^2}{707,968 - (14)(216.86)^2}} \\
&= 4.72 \sqrt{1.077482} \\
&= 4.72(1.038) \\
&= \mathbf{4.90}
\end{aligned}$$

Suppose we wish to determine a confidence interval for the average weekly sales volume of the proposed store in the area where disposable income is (coded) 200. It seems reasonable to ask for an interval such that there are no more than five chances in one hundred that average weekly sales volume would fall outside the interval at either the upper or the lower end. This would be the symmetrical 90 percent confidence interval. Then,

$$\begin{aligned}
\text{confidence interval} &= \hat{\mu}_{y \cdot 200} \pm t_{0 \cdot 90} \hat{\sigma}_{\hat{y} \cdot 200} \\
&= 70.93 \pm 1.78(4.90) \\
&= 70.93 \pm 8.72 \\
&= \mathbf{62.2} \text{ to } \mathbf{79.6}
\end{aligned}$$

The 90 percent confidence limits for $\hat{\mu}_{y \cdot x}$ and $\hat{y}_i$ are shown in Figure 12.5. Note how the intervals widen as X_0 moves further from the mean of X.

MULTIPLE LINEAR REGRESSION

The dependent variable in regression analysis is often assumed or known to depend on more than one other variable. The linear multiple regression model is similar to the simple linear model.

$$y = f(X_1, X_2, \cdots, X_k)$$

Basic Assumptions of the Linear Multiple Regression Model

The basic assumptions are similar to those for simple linear regression.

12.30 The basic assumptions of multiple linear regression:
   (a) $y_i = A + B_1X_{1i} + B_2X_{2i} + \cdots + B_kX_{ki} + e_i$; that is, the function is linear.
   (b) The X_{ji}'s (independent variables) are selected nonrandomly (known) and are not subject to errors of observation.
   (c) Each X_{ji} is independent of all other X_{ji}; that is, the independent variables are not correlated with one another and the individual values of a particular independent variable are not correlated with one another (serially autocorrelated).
   (d) Each y_i is selected randomly from the population of y_i's generated by the ith set of X_j's.
   (e) $\sigma_{y_1}^2 = \sigma_{y_2}^2 = \cdots = \sigma_{y_n}^2 = \sigma_{y \cdot jk}^2$; that is, the variances of the populations of y's associated with each set of the values of independent variables are equal (homoscedasticity).

In multiple regression, as in simple regression, the first step in the analysis is to determine the nature of the existing relationships by preparing scatter diagrams for the paired observations of the dependent variable, y, and each independent variable, X_j. Suppose, for example, that the data on number of families within the area served by each of the fourteen Lessloss stores were known. It might be that the addition of this variable to the relationship would improve our ability to estimate average store sales. The scatter diagram for average sales and number of families is given in Figure 12.6. Since both this relationship and the relationship of store sales and average disposable income appear to be linear, it can be assumed that the multiple relationship is a linear one. Thus, we fit the function:

$$\hat{\mu}_{y_i} = a + b_1X_{1_i} + b_2X_{2_i}$$

where

$\hat{\mu}_{y_i}$ = the average value of y associated with the ith set of observations of the independent variables

a = the value of y when all independent variables equal zero

b_j = the *partial regression* coefficient of X_j, which indicates the effects of X_j alone on y

X_{j_i} = the ith observation of the jth independent variable

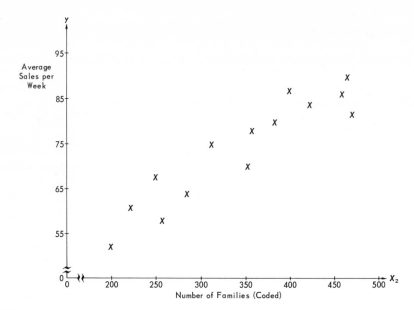

FIG. 12.6. Scatter diagram of average weekly sales of Lessloss stores and number of families (coded) in each store's area.

Note that with the definitions given immediately above, the regression function can be expanded to include more independent variables.

12.31 $\hat{\mu}_{y_i} = a + b_1 X_{1_i} + b_2 X_{2_i} + \cdots + b_k X_{k_i}$ $(i = 1, n)$

where

k = the number of independent variables
n = the number of sets of observations

The *partial regression coefficients* are estimated by the method of least squares from sets of *normal equations* which are merely extensions of the two normal equations for the two-variable case.

12.32 The normal equations for k independent variables:

I. $\Sigma y = na + b_1 \Sigma X_1 + b_2 \Sigma X_2 + \cdots + b_k \Sigma X_k$
II. $\Sigma X_1 y = a\Sigma X_1 + b_1 \Sigma X_1{}^2 + b_2 \Sigma X_1 X_2 + \cdots + b_k \Sigma X_1 X_k$
III. $\Sigma X_2 y = a\Sigma X_2 + b_1 \Sigma X_1 X_2 + b_2 \Sigma X_2{}^2 + \cdots + b_k \Sigma X_2 X_k$

$(K + 1)$ $\Sigma X_k y = a\Sigma X_k + b_1 \Sigma X_1 X_k + b_2 \Sigma X_2 X_k + \cdots + b_k \Sigma X_k{}^2$

The first normal equation is found by multiplying each equation,

$$y_i = a + b_1 X_{1i} + b_2 X_{2i} + \cdots + b_k X_{ki},$$

through by 1, the coefficient of a, and summing over the sample of observations. The second normal equation is found by multiplying the above equation by X_{1i}, the coefficient of b_1, and summing over the sample of observations. Generally the gth normal equation is found by multiplying the equation above by the coefficient of the gth coefficient (counting a as the first coefficient, b_1 as the second, and so forth) and summing over the n observations.

To obtain estimates of a and the b_j's from the normal equations given in 12.32 is a lengthy procedure of systematic elimination of unknowns. The calculation of the partial regression coefficients, the standard deviation of regression, and other statistics is a time-consuming process. Generally, such results are obtained along with several other informative statistics as the output from an electronic computer program designed for the purpose. Such programs are generally available at any computer installation. The major jobs in using multiple regression are to decide on the nature of the regression relationship (linear, logarithmic, semilogarithmic, and so forth), to enter the data properly into the computer along with an appropriate program, and then to interpret the results properly. The sections below describe the major statistics available in multiple regression analysis and illustrate their interpretation and use. The values of those statistics as obtained in computer output from the BMD 03R regression program for the Lessloss example are given in Table 12.2.

Partial Regression Coefficients

The coefficients in the regression equation have the following meanings:

a = the value of y when $X_1 = X_2 = 0$; when both X_1 and X_2 are zero, $y = \mathbf{30.18}$.

b_1 = the change in y which results from a one-unit change in X_1; if X_1 changes from 150 to 151, y increases by $\mathbf{+0.0922}$.

b_2 = the change in y which results from a one-unit change in X_2; if X_2 changes from 300 to 301, y increases by $\mathbf{+0.0695}$.

The estimates of the partial regression coefficients (b_j's) are subject to sampling error. The standard error of each of the b_j's is indicated in Table 12.2. Hypotheses concerning the true values, the B_j's, can be tested using the familiar t ratio.

TABLE 12.2

MULTIPLE REGRESSION RESULTS, LESSLOSS STORES†

(y = average weekly sales per store; X_1 = average disposable income in store area; X_2 = number of families in store area)

Sums:	$\Sigma y = 1{,}035$	$\Sigma X_1 = 3{,}036$	$\Sigma X_2 = 4{,}784$
	$\Sigma y^2 = 78{,}363$	$\Sigma X_1{}^2 = 707{,}968$	$\Sigma X_2{}^2 = 1{,}739{,}774$
		$\Sigma X_1 y = 233{,}297$	$\Sigma X_2 y = 366{,}648$
			$\Sigma X_1 X_2 = 1{,}098{,}995$
Correlation Coefficients:		$R_{y \cdot 12}{}^2 = 0.9300$	$R_{y \cdot 12} = 0.9644$
	$r_{y X_1} = 0.9247$	$r_{y X_2} = 0.9316$	$r_{X_1 X_2} = 0.8529$
Intercept $(a) = 30.18$		$\hat{\sigma}_{y \cdot 12}{}^2 = 11.7527$	$\hat{\sigma}_{y \cdot 12} = 3.43$

Variable	Mean	Standard Deviation	Regression Coefficient	Standard Error of b	Computed t Value	Partial Correl. Coeff.
X_1	216.86	61.76	0.0922	0.0295	3.13	0.6859
X_2	341.74	89.88	0.0695	0.0203	3.43	0.7189
y	73.93	11.92				

Analysis of Variance for the Multiple Linear Regression

Source of Variation	Sum of Squares	Degrees of Freedom	Mean Squares	F Value
Due to regression	1717.6494	2	858.8247	73.07
About regression	129.2793	11	11.7527	
Total	1846.9287	13		

† This table is adapted from the output of BMD 03R, see "Multiple Regression with Case Combinations," *Biomedical Computer Programs*, Health Sciences Computing Facility, School of Medicine, University of California, Los Angeles, January 1964, pp. 258–275.

Standard Deviation of Multiple Regression

Another useful statistic is the *estimated standard deviation of multiple regression*, $\hat{\sigma}_{y \cdot jk}$. It corresponds to the estimated standard deviation of simple regression introduced earlier (12.17). Its interpretation is parallel to that of $\hat{\sigma}_{y \cdot x}$; it is the standard deviation of the conditional distribution of the dependent variable about the regression surface. Its primary uses are in judging the closeness of the relationship, in obtaining estimates of the sampling error involved in computing the partial regression coefficients, and in obtaining pure measures of the closeness of the relationship. The basic formula is the same as that for $\hat{\sigma}_{y \cdot x}$.

Confidence interval estimates of the dependent variable are obtained in multiple regression in the same general fashion as that used in simple regression. However, the statement of the formulas for the confidence limits is beyond the scope of this book. Reasonably precise estimates of these limits for large samples can be obtained by use of the t distribution and the estimated standard deviation of regression. For example, for our sample problem, the statistics in Table 12.2 indicate that

$$\hat{\mu}_{y \cdot 12} = 30.18 + 0.0922X_1 + 0.0695X_2$$
$$\hat{\sigma}_{y \cdot 12} = 3.43$$
$$d.f. = 14 - 3 = 11$$

and a 90 percent confidence interval estimate for store sales given a coded income value of 200 (X_1) and 300 (X_2) as the scaled number of families in the store area would be

$$\hat{\mu}_{y \cdot 200,300} = 30.18 + 0.0922(200) + 0.0695(300)$$
$$= \mathbf{69.47}$$
$$t_{0.90}(11 \ d.f.) = 1.80$$
90 percent confidence limits for $y = \hat{\mu}_{y \cdot 12} \pm t_{0.90}\sigma_{y \cdot 12}$
$$= 69.47 \pm 1.80(3.43)$$
$$= \mathbf{63.3 \text{ to } 75.6}$$

REGRESSION AND CORRELATION

In Chapter 11, we considered the situation in which random samples were drawn from a bivariate normal population. In estimating relationships with regression, we often find ourselves dealing with independent variables which are not specified but are randomly selected (along with a corresponding dependent variable). In order to use the methods described in previous sections, we indicated that the assumptions given in 12.19 are necessary. However, the least squares regression line can be used to predict $\mu_{y \cdot x}$ (or $\mu_{y \cdot ij}$) by making somewhat different assumptions.

12.40 The assumptions of simple linear correlation:
   (a) $(x_1, y_1), (x_2, y_2), \cdots, (x_n, y_n)$ are n randomly selected pairs from a bivariate normal population.
   (b) The means $E(y|x)$ and $E(x|y)$ each lie on a straight line.
   (c) The variance of y given x, $\sigma_{y \cdot x}^2$, is the same for all x (and $\sigma_{x \cdot y}^2$ is the same for all y).

When estimating y as a function of x, tests of hypothesis about and confidence intervals for $\mu_{y \cdot x}$ and y are the same for both 12.40 and 12.19.
   The preceding comments can be extended to cover the multivariate

as well as the bivariate case. Note, however, that the correlation model assumes only covariation (association) between the variables and does not say anything about causal relationships. The regression model does assume that causation runs from X to y.

The above relationship between the correlation and the regression models makes it possible to compute correlation measures to indicate the strength of the relationship between the two (or more) variables. A simple extension of the correlation concept allows the use of a form of variance analysis for drawing inferences about the strengths of the observed relationship.

Simple Linear Correlation

The calculation of r, the estimated simple linear correlation coefficient, is usually performed differently in estimation situations than when merely testing for association with the product moment measure as introduced in Chapter 11 (11.85). Figure 12.7 will be used as an aid in describing the logic of this technique.

If we knew nothing about a relationship with X (or x), our best (minimum variance) estimate of y for any situation would be the mean of y, $\bar{y}$. But using $\bar{y}$ as the estimate of y misses a great deal of the variation in y. In Figure 12.7 the deviations of each y from the corresponding estimate, $\bar{y}$, is shown by the line from each y to $\bar{y}$. We measure this total variability with σ_y^2, the variance of y. When we fit the regression equation to the x and y values, we *explain* part of the *total* variation from our previous best estimate. In our example, as in most situations, even the regression line does not explain all of the variation around $\bar{y}$. The remaining *unexplained* variation is indicated by the vertical line segments between each observed y and the regression line in Figure 12.7. The ends of these line segments are indicated by the ends of the curved arcs in Figure 12.7. This unexplained variation is what was previously described (see Figure 12.4 and related discussion) as the conditional distributions of the y's for each given X. The variance of these distributions is $\sigma_{y \cdot x}^2$, the square of the standard deviation of regression.

The above observations indicate that $\hat{\sigma}_y^2$ is an estimate of the *total variance* in y which is *to be explained*. The variance remaining *unexplained* after fitting the regression line is estimated by $\hat{\sigma}_{y \cdot x}^2$. An estimate of the *proportion of variance explained* must be the estimated *total* variance *minus* the estimated *unexplained* variance *over* the estimated *total* variance, that is,

$$\frac{\hat{\sigma}_y^2 - \hat{\sigma}_{y \cdot x}^2}{\hat{\sigma}_y^2}$$

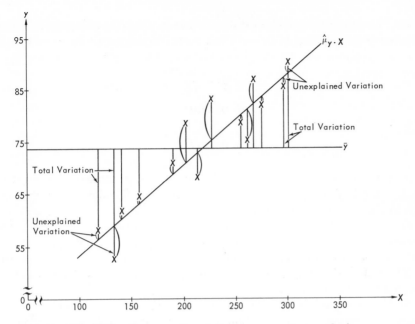

FIG. 12.7. Sources of variation in regression analysis.

Simplifying this ratio, we obtain

12.41 $r^2 = 1 - \dfrac{\hat{\sigma}_{y \cdot x}^2}{\hat{\sigma}_y^2}$

This value, r^2, is known as the *coefficient of determination*. Its square root, r, is the *coefficient of correlation*. The sign of r is the same as the sign of the slope coefficient, b, in the regression equation and reflects the *direction* of the relationship. The r computed by this method is the same statistic as the simple linear correlation coefficient in Chapter 11.

Using the data in Table 12.1,

$$\hat{\sigma}_y^2 = \frac{\Sigma y^2 - n\bar{y}^2}{n - 1}$$

$$= \frac{78,363 - 14(73.93)^2}{13}$$

$$= 142.07$$

The unexplained variance has been estimated as

$$\hat{\sigma}_{y \cdot x}^2 = 22.30$$

Then, the proportion of the total variance in y explained by the relationship between X and y is

$$r^2 = 1 - \frac{22.30}{142.07}$$

$$= 0.8550$$

and

$$r = \sqrt{0.8550}$$

$$= 0.9247$$

Note that the sign of r is positive in this instance, indicating a positive or direct relationship between x and y. Its sign is taken from the sign of b in the regression equation.

As was stated in Chapter 11, r can vary only between -1 and $+1$, and a value close to $+1$ or -1 indicates a strong association. The r value for our example indicates a strong positive relationship between X and y. The value of r^2 indicates that 85 percent of the variance in y is "explained" by the relationship.

The r computed in simple linear regression can be subjected to the inference testing and estimation procedures discussed in Chapter 11. (See Exercise 1 at the end of this chapter.)

Correlation in Multiple Linear Regression

Correlation can be computed and used in multiple linear regression in essentially the same manner as in simple linear regression. Several correlation values can be computed and used in the analysis.

12.42   *The multiple linear correlation coefficient, $R_{y \cdot jk}$.* (Usually used in its squared form as the coefficient of multiple determination to indicate the proportion of variance in the dependent variable explained by the regression.) The basic formula is:

$$R^2 = 1 - \frac{\hat{\sigma}_{y \cdot jk}^2}{\hat{\sigma}_y^2}$$

For our example, $R_{y \cdot 12}^2 = 0.9300$, indicating that 93 percent of the variance in store sales is associated with variance in the two independent variables.

12.43   The *partial correlation coefficients, $r_{yj \cdot k}$,* each of which indicates the strength of the linear relationship between y and x_j with the effects of all other x's (the x's identified by the k's to the right of the dot in the subscript) "held constant."

The relative importance of the individual independent variables is directly reflected in the relative sizes of the associated partial correlation coefficients.

The basic formula is:

$$r_{yj \cdot k}{}^2 = 1 - \frac{\hat{\sigma}_{y \cdot jk}{}^2}{\hat{\sigma}_{y \cdot k}{}^2}$$

Specifically, for the case of two independent variables,

$$r_{y1 \cdot 2}{}^2 = 1 - \frac{\hat{\sigma}_{y \cdot 12}{}^2}{\hat{\sigma}_{y \cdot 2}{}^2}$$

and

$$r_{y2 \cdot 1}{}^2 = 1 - \frac{\hat{\sigma}_{y \cdot 12}{}^2}{\hat{\sigma}_{y \cdot 1}{}^2}$$

That is, the proportion of variance explained after adding the additional variable, X_j, is indicated by $r_{yj \cdot k}{}^2$. For our example, X_2 (number of families in the store area) is most closely related to y (store sales), but only slightly; $r_{y2 \cdot 1}$ is 0.7189 and $r_{y1 \cdot 2}$ is slightly smaller at 0.6859. Note that these partial coefficients are *not* equal to the *simple* linear correlation coefficients.

Statistical Inference in Multiple Regression and Correlation

The degree of multiple and partial correlation can be used in inference tests. Both coefficients are sample statistics and are subject to sample variation which can be estimated by use of appropriate formulas. However, an easier method of testing if the degree of the association indicated by the regression is significantly different from zero is based on the partitioning of the variance used in determining the correlation present. We have already seen that the total variance in y, the dependent variable, can be separated into variance explained in the regression and variance unexplained. Both these sources of variation can be used to provide estimates of variance which can then be compared by the F-ratio analysis introduced in Chapter 11. Many computer programs which perform regression analysis report these variances and their ratio and it is then a simple matter to compare the reported F with the tabled values for the appropriate degrees of freedom to discover the significance of the regression relationship. For our multiple regression example, the statistics in Table 12.2 indicate that in the analysis of the significance of deviations due to regression,

$$F = 73.07$$

Table B-13 indicates that for two and eleven degrees of freedom, $F_{0.01}$ is only 7.21. It seems safe to conclude that the regression accounts for a significant proportion of the variance in store sales.

CURVILINEAR REGRESSION AND CORRELATION

Often, the relationship between the variables in simple or multiple regression is not linear. This problem can often be overcome by a suitable transformation of the data. For example, if the relationship appears to involve constant ratios (constant percentage relationships) between the variables the regression relation can be expressed as a linear function of logarithms. For simple regression,

$$\log y = \log a + b \log X$$

is equivalent to

$$y = ax^b$$

Such a relationship would plot as a straight line on logarithmic graph paper. (See Figure 12.2.) For multiple regression, additional logarithmic terms would be present

$$\log y = \log a + b_1 \log X_1 + b_2 \log X_2 + \cdots + b_k \log X_k$$

Another common assumption is of an exponential (or modified exponential) relationship. That is, that

$$y = ab^X$$

in logarithms (the computing form) this would be (notice only y is in logs)

$$\log y = \log a + X \log b$$

When plotted on semilogarithmic graph paper the exponential relationship would show as a straight line.

After such log transformations the linear regression proceeds as before. Caution must be exercised in the interpretation of the results, however. The regression coefficients as estimated by the least squares method minimize the vertical deviations of the y units whatever they may be. In the above transformations, the y units are logarithms. The standard deviation of regression is in logarithms and its antilog measures a *percentage* of deviation, not an *amount* of deviation.

The reader should also be wary of loose interpretations of the correlation coefficients derived from data expressed in logarithms. The squared standard deviation of regression enters into this computation. However, the proportion of unexplained variance involves the same kind of logarithmic based variance estimates in both the denominator and the numerator. The correlation coefficient can be compared with the measures of the degree of relationship from other analyses. It must be remembered, however, that it measures association between logarithms rather than absolute values.

A second method of describing a curvilinear relationship is with higher order polynomials. The coefficients in the linear combination of variables in the equation,

$$y = a + bX + cX^2$$

can be estimated by the least squares method. Again care must be exercised in interpreting the standard deviation of regression and the correlation coefficient.

It is possible to avoid some of the difficulties of interpretation of the standard deviation of regression when the data are transformed in some way to obtain a linear combination of variables for describing the relationship. The standard deviation of regression should be calculated by the basic formula:

12.50 $\hat{\sigma}_{y \cdot jk} = \hat{\sigma}_{y \cdot x} = \sqrt{\dfrac{\Sigma(y - \hat{\mu}_y)^2}{n - c}}$

where c is the number of constants in the regression equation, including the zero intercept, a. This formula is a generalized form of 12.17 with the n reduced by the degrees of freedom lost in the fitting process. Note that there can be one or more X's involved in the equation. We could compute $\hat{\sigma}_{y \cdot x}$ in this fashion for a simple linear logarithmic regression after the estimated y values ($\hat{\mu}_{y \cdot x}$) are obtained in original units, for example.

In curvilinear correlation, the appropriate correlation measure is the *index of correlation* (symbolized by the Greek letter eta).

12.51 $$\eta = \sqrt{1 - \frac{\hat{\sigma}_{y \cdot jk}^2}{\hat{\sigma}_y^2}}$$

where $\hat{\sigma}_{y \cdot jk}^2$ is computed by the method discussed immediately above.

REGRESSION WITH TIME SERIES DATA

There is a large class of regression problems in which the basic data are observed as values of variables occurring over time (as time series). Since time series data usually follow a *trend*, that is, drift in a particular direction over time, some of the assumptions of the least squares regression method are violated. A further problem is that similar trends or other movements in two time series may be due to some third force and thus the observed relation is *spurious* and is not to be relied upon. A major reason for regression and correlation analysis is to obtain predictions of the dependent variable that can be used as a basis for decision making. Unreliable relationships provide a poor basis for prediction.

Effect of Time Series Deficiencies

More succinctly, the regression model assumes

(1) Each pair of observations is independent of other pairs. Most important, the independent variables are not autocorrelated or correlated with each other.
(2) Causation runs only from X to y.

To illustrate the problems with time series, suppose that Lessloss Stores is interested in predicting total annual dollar sales of the chain. Suppose further that a series on gross business activity in the firm's total sales area is available. Both the dependent variable (dollar sales of Lessloss) and the independent variable (business activity in the Lessloss sales area) are time series. It is obvious that sales are autocorrelated; that is, sales in the current year are not independent of sales in the previous (or subsequent) year. Sales in the previous year provide a basis for estimating sales in the current year. Second, the observed parallel movement in the two series is undoubtedly due in part to common outside forces such as population growth (or decline), increasing (or decreasing) industrialization in the area, superior natural resources of the area, and so forth. Finally, Lessloss sales are a part of total business activity in the area. Only if they are an extremely small part of such activity would it be safe to ignore this reverse causality.

If the assumptions of the least squares regression model are violated, the estimates of the regression coefficients are unreliable. Adding an additional set of observations or taking away one set of observations can change the estimates significantly. Concurrent trends act to give high estimates of correlation, but estimates of the dependent variable from such relationships are little, if any, better than simple trend line estimates. This tendency for trends to induce spurious correlation is reinforced by the widespread effects of recessions and booms, major natural catastrophies such as fires, floods, tornados, and so forth, and the seasonal effects of climate and other factors on wide areas of activity.

Using Time Series in Regression

If it is desired to use time series in regression some pre-editing is often desirable. One technique that can be useful is to compute the trend for the series to be used so that the series can be adjusted for trend and the ratios to trend can be used in the regression. Another method used to reduce the effects of autocorrelation in time series is to take first difference of each series and correlate these first differences. First differences are computed as

$$y_{(i+1)} - y_i = d_{(i+1)}$$
$$y_i - y_{(i-1)} = d_i$$

where y is the value of time series and i is the current time period. Even if similar trends are present, only the trend influence over one year will influence the calculations.

Another method of adjusting for the influence of time on the regression is to include time as an independent variable in the regression. This has the advantage of allowing the nontime related influences of the other independent variables to be reflected in the derived relationship. It has the disadvantage that time is only an index of a composite of general forces and the relationship is difficult to interpret explicitly.

Other adjustments which can often reduce the effects of spurious correlation on the analysis include:

(1) Adjusting for the effects of changes in the price level when using sales and income data.

(2) Using the data as per capita or per family, for example, the average family income data used in the Lessloss problem.
(3) Defining and removing common seasonal or any other regular movements along with trend.

SUMMARY

Business decisions often depend on the value of a particular variable such as total sales, net income, job performance, the tensile or bearing strength of a metal rod, and so forth. It is often difficult, if not impossible, to obtain adequate predictions of such variables directly, but it is often possible to find another variable or other variables such as price, production costs, performance in training programs, previous experience, hardness of the metal, and so forth, which are related to the first variable and which are available or can be obtained without undue effort. When one decides that, for two such variables, $y = f(X)$, a causal relationship is postulated in which the variable y is assumed to be the *dependent* variable whose value is determined at least in part by the value of X, the *independent* variable. The paired observations are then plotted on a *scatter diagram* to determine if the relationship actually exists. The scatter diagram also indicates whether the relationship is linear or curvilinear and gives an indication of the type of function to employ in the *regression analysis*. If a curvilinear relation is found, it is often helpful to plot the data on semilogarithmic or logarithmic paper to pinpoint the type of curvilinear relation which exists.

In simple linear regression and correlation (two variables, a straight line relationship) the most important statistical measures to be estimated are:

1. The regression coefficients, that is, the constants in the estimated regression equation $\hat{\mu}_{y_i} = a + bX_i$. (12.13 and 12.14)
2. The standard errors of the regression coefficients, for inference tests to see if a relationship really exists. (12.21 and 12.23)
3. The standard error of values on the regression line, $\hat{\sigma}_{\hat{\mu}_y \cdot x_i}$ (12.24) for developing confidence interval estimates of $\mu_{y \cdot x_i}$.
4. The standard error of estimated individual values of y ($\hat{\sigma}_{\hat{y} \cdot x_i}$) for developing confidence interval estimates. (12.25)
5. The coefficients of determination and correlation to judge the closeness of the relationship. (12.41 and 11.85)
6. The standard error of the correlation coefficient for inference tests of the degree of association. (11.86, 11.87, 11.88)
7. A variance ratio for testing the significance of the regression.

In multiple linear regression and correlation the most important statistical measures to be estimated are:

1. The partial regression coefficients, that is, the constants in the regression equation $\hat{\mu}_{y \cdot jk} = a + b_1 X_1 + \cdots b_k X_k$.
2. The standard errors of the partial regression coefficients for inference estimates and tests concerning the true coefficients.
3. The standard deviation of regression for use in judging the closeness of the total relationship and for use in computing standard errors of the partial regression coefficients and correlation measures.
4. Coefficients of multiple determination and correlation as indications of the strength of the relationship.
5. Coefficients of partial correlation which indicate the relative importance of each independent variable in the regression.
6. Variance ratios for testing the significance of the regression.

The calculations involved in regression and correlation analysis of relationships usually are carried out on an electronic computer. The major problems are to recognize the presence of the relationship and its nature, properly prepare the data for input with a regression program into the computer, and interpret the output. Data preparation is especially important when the data series are time series. Presence of similar trends, seasonals, and other common periodic movements can give high correlations where little or no causal relations exist.

DISCUSSION QUESTIONS

1. Define the following *in your own words* (do *not* use symbols or verbal formulas).
   - (a) function
   - (b) regression analysis
   - (c) regression equation
   - (d) simple regression
   - (e) multiple regression
   - (f) linear regression
   - (g) curvilinear regression
   - (h) regression coefficient
   - (i) partial regression coefficient
   - (j) dependent variable
   - (k) independent variable
   - (l) causal variable
   - (m) scatter diagram
   - (n) standard deviation of regression
   - (o) partial correlation coefficient
   - (p) multiple correlation coefficient
   - (q) coefficient of determination
   - (r) index of correlation
   - (s) autocorrelation
   - (t) time series

2. Why must the regression equation in simple linear regression pass through the point with the coordinates $(\bar{X}, \bar{y})$?

    Hint: The sum of the squared deviations should be a minimum at all points on the curve.

3. What is (are) the difference(s) between correlation and regression problems?

    Hint: Do they have different basic assumptions which make them appropriate to different goals in data analysis?

4. The executives of Magna Corporation wish to determine the growth curve for the industry in which they compete. How would you suggest they proceed? Be specific.

    Hint: You must decide on the type of mathematical function which is appropriate.

5. What is the *null* hypothesis used in testing r or R for significance? What is its meaning? Discuss the various methods for making this test. What are the advantages and limitations of each method?

    Hint: Refer to the sections on correlation in both Chapters 11 and 12. Do not forget to compare the assumptions of each testing method.

6. Argue that correlation analysis, whether simple or multiple, linear or curvilinear, can be considered a branch of variance analysis.

    Hint: Basically, what is F? and the correlation measures?

7. We have two functions containing identical variables:

    (1) $E = 0.0028D^{1.04}(S^{0.22})(P^{-0.37})$

    $R^2_{E \cdot DSP} = 0.985$

    (2) $E = 6.70 + 0.024D + 0.046S - 0.11P$

    $R^2_{E \cdot DSP} = 0.981$

    E = expenditure for electrical appliances per household

    D = disposable personal income per household

    S = number of private residential housing starts

    P = relative price of electrical appliances:

    (index of appliance prices)/(consumer price index)

    (a) What is the meaning of each of the coefficients in the two equations?

    (b) How do you account for the difference in form of the two equations?

    (c) How would you decide which is the better form to use in a problem of analysis?

    Hints: (1) Remember that someone had to decide on the form of the equation.

    (2) Even if the R's had been different, would the higher R necessarily indicate a more correct description of the relationship?

8. What can be done to improve results in functional analysis when two independent variables are highly correlated?

    Hint: Refer to the discussion of time series. Can any of the methods discussed be extended in a general way? Are there any other solutions? Have time series been ruled out by the question?

9. Describe as precisely as possible the relationship between the standard deviation of regression and the standard deviation of y as a basis for determining the strength of the relationship between y and one or more independent variables for the following situations:

    (a) when no correlation is present.

    (b) when correlation is perfect.

    Hint: Examine 12.41 and 12.51.

DISCUSSION PROBLEMS

Show your method on all solutions.

1. The sales manager of the Hardsell Corporation assembles the information given below in a study of characteristics of salesmen related to sales performance for ten of the salesmen in his department.

Salesman Number	Amount of Sales per Week (thousands of $)	No. of Customers Contacted per Week	Years Employed by Hardsell
1	10	21	3
2	12	23	7
3	11	20	1
4	14	22	16
5	13	24	8
6	15	25	3
7	16	24	4
8	18	27	6
9	17	29	19
10	19	33	5

The Sales Manager proposes to use these data to test the assertions that (1) number of customer contacts is closely related to levels of sales, and (2) experience is a major factor in determining the level of sales.

(a) Do you have any reservations about using the above data for the purposes indicated? Explain briefly but fully each such reservation.

    Hint: Do the proposed independent variables measure what the sales manager is interested in? Where did they come from?

(b) Prepare a scatter diagram for each of the two relationships of interest. Be sure your charts are complete in all respects.

Working only from your scatter diagram (no computations)

(1) For each of the two relationships: Is the correlation positive or negative? closer to $+1$, zero, or -1?

(2) Draw a freehand approximation to the *linear* regression line on the scatter diagram for sales and customer contacts only.

Hint: It may be helpful to plot a line between averages for the highest three and lowest three observations.

(3) Using *only* your freehand linear regression line, estimate the values of the coefficients in the regression equation. Clearly indicate your method on the scatter diagram.

Hint: (1) Graphically, what is a? b?

(2) Do you have a zero line for X on your graph? Do you need one to find a? (see 12.15)

(c) For the relation between sales and customer contacts *only*, define the following:

(1) the population being sampled

(2) the sample being used

(3) the random variable (or variables) involved

(4) State a suitable null hypothesis to be tested. Be specific (use symbols). Explain your choice.

(5) For the hypothesis you have chosen, what is the Type I error?

2. If the correlation of A with B is $+1$ and A with C is -1, what is the correlation of B with C?

(a) Draw rough graphs of the three relationships as part of your answer.

(b) Must the correlation lines in the graphs have slopes of $+1$ and -1?

Hint: Does $r = b$?

3. The Instate Company has analyzed its sales experience by county and has information available concerning the relationships between its sales and total disposable personal income by county. The available information includes:

A regression equation with sales (S) in thousands of dollars and disposable income (D) in millions of dollars:

$$S = 8.2 + 3.5D$$

The additional information given below:

$$n = 50 \qquad \hat{\sigma}_{y \cdot x} = 2.5 \qquad \bar{D} = 5.4 \qquad \Sigma D^2 = 1057.60$$

The company is expanding into two neighboring states and intends to open a branch in each state next year. Two counties in each state are being considered as possible locations for the new operations. Disposable incomes are as given below:

State	County	Disposable Income (Millions)
Eaststate	A	3.4
	B	3.8
Weststate	C	4.5
	D	6.0

(a) What is the possible range of sales that Instate can expect in each county with 19 chances in 20 of being correct?
Hint: You must estimate y and must use 12.25 in the confidence interval calculation.

(b) What is the possible range of average sales in counties like A in Eaststate which would not be exceeded more than ten times in 100?
Hint: You must estimate $\hat{\mu}_{y \cdot x}$ and, therefore, should use 12.24 in the confidence interval calculation.

(c) Instate estimates that minimum sales of 14 million dollars are necessary in order to show a reasonable profit on such an operation. Should they expect to break even in each of the above counties?

(d) Instate executives have previously stated a policy of not going into a new area unless there are at least 75 chances in 100 of exceeding the breakeven point by $50,000. What would you advise?
Hint: Note that the executives have specified a one-sided confidence interval.

4. Using annual observations for 16 years, the statistician for Sellmore Real Estate Corporation developed the following information:

$$y = -50.8 + 76.8X_1 + 53.7X_3$$

where

y = index of expenditures on construction of new dwelling units, adjusted for price change (1957–59 = 100)
X_1 = index of rent prices (1957–59 = 100)
X_2 = index of building material prices (1957–59 = 100)

$\hat{\sigma}_{y \cdot 12} = 8.2$	$r(y, X_1) = +0.92$	$r_{y1 \cdot 2} = +0.50$
$R_{y \cdot 12} = 0.96$	$r(y, X_2) = +0.95$	$r_{y2 \cdot 1} = +0.72$
$\hat{\sigma}_{b_1} = 36.4$	$\hat{\sigma}_{b_2} = 7.8$	$\hat{\sigma}_y^2 = 11717.89$

Evaluate the above model, indicating:

(a) Whether each of the individual independent variables appears to be related to the dependent variable.

Hint: Are the B_i's significantly different from zero? and the partial correlation coefficients?

(b) Does the model account for a significant proportion of the variance in the dependent variable?

Hint: What is the proportion of variance explained?

(c) Does the model appear realistic in its assumptions of relationship?

Hint: Is it reasonable to expect linear relationships? Causation from the X_i's to y?

EXERCISES

Show your method on all solutions.

1. Using Fisher's z_r transformation introduced in Chapter 11, test the hypothesis that the value of ρ for the relationship between average store sales of Lessloss stores and average family income is:
   (a) no greater than 0.80
   (b) at least 0.95
   Explain your answers fully.

2. Given the results in Table 12.2, are store sales more closely related to average family income or number of families? Explain in detail.

3. The data below were developed in a study of the relationship between the breaking strength in pounds and the density (measured by weight in grams) of a part produced by a new molding process. Two hundred of the parts were tested and weighed.

$$\text{breaking strength} = -1800.0 + 25.0(\text{weight})$$
$$\hat{\sigma}_{y \cdot x} = 8 \qquad \bar{X} = 90 \qquad \Sigma X^2 = 1,625,000 \qquad \hat{\sigma}_x = 4.8 \qquad \hat{\sigma}_y = 17$$

The observations appear to be normally distributed about the regression line. If a breaking strength of less than 300 pounds is considered unsatisfactory,

(a) What is the probability that the breaking strength will be unsatisfactory if the part weighs:

   (1) 85.0 grams?   (2) 86 grams?

(b) Would you recommend that the new process be used? Explain fully.

4. A study was made in 1967 in an attempt to predict new automobile sales in 1968 and 1969. The following model was developed from data for the period 1949–1965 ($n = 17$):

$$y_0 = -12.6 + 0.112X_1 + 0.782X_2$$

where

y = annual new car registrations (in hundreds of thousands of cars)
X_1 = per capita disposable personal income (in terms of dollars)
X_2 = average annual civilian employment (in millions of people)

Other information derived included:

$$r_{y1 \cdot 2} = +0.09 \qquad R_{y \cdot 12} = 0.82 \qquad r_{yX_1} = +0.82$$
$$r_{y2 \cdot 1} = +0.10 \qquad \hat{\sigma}_{y \cdot 12} = 8.07 \qquad r_{yX_2} = +0.83$$

(a) Identify the value of and explain (in words) the meaning of each of the following:

(1) b_1 (3) $R_{y \cdot 12}$ (5) $R_{y \cdot 12}{}^2$
(2) $r_{y2 \cdot 1}$ (4) $\hat{\sigma}_{y \cdot 12}$ (6) $r_{y \cdot X_1}$

(b) What is the value of b_2? What does it mean?
(c) Suppose the following are forecast for 1968:
per capita disposable income (dollars) = \$2600
average annual civilian employment (thousands of persons) = 98,600
(1) Estimate annual new car registrations for 1968.
(2) Does this seem like a reasonable estimate for 1968? Explain.
(3) What confidence do you have in your estimate?
(d) Considering *all* of the information developed, what is your evaluation of this forecasting equation? Be exhaustive.

5. The research department of Compacto, Inc., is involved in a study of the relationship between the impact strength of a container produced from compressed wood chips and its density (measured by weight per square yard). An examination of 100 containers yields the following information:

$$\hat{\mu}_{y \cdot x} = -100 + 12.5X \qquad\qquad \hat{\sigma}_{y \cdot x} = 10$$
$$\bar{X} = 90 \qquad\qquad \Sigma(X - \bar{X})^2 = 180$$

where y represents impact strength in pounds and X represents weight in ounces.

(a) If an impact strength under 930 pounds is considered unsatisfactory, how likely is it that the impact strength will be unsatisfactory if the material weighs 80 ounces per yard?

(b) Does this study involve a regression or a correlation problem? Explain *briefly*.

6. Refer to the data in Table 11.19 and develop a regression equation for predicting the average level of performance from the test score. Make a complete analysis of this relationship and fully explain the results.

7. In the manufacture of a certain stamping, the angle between two sides was required to be held to 90 degrees plus or minus $\frac{1}{3}$ degree. The factory reported that this angular tolerance could not be held due to the variation in the thickness of the stock. In order to determine whether this claim was correct, a number of stampings were checked for both angle and thickness and the results entered as below. The question involved is whether the tolerance of the angle could be held despite the variation in stock thickness.

(a) Plot a scatter diagram of these data with Angle as dependent variable and Thickness as the independent variable.

(b) Working from your scatter diagram *only*, what can you conclude about the initial adjustment of the dies and of the relationship between angular tolerance and thickness of stock? Be exhaustive. Explain fully.

Angle (Deviation from 90°)	Thickness (Mils)	Angle (Deviation from 90°)	Thickness (Mils)
−0.2	77.0	−0.1	78.0
−0.4	79.0	0.1	76.0
−0.5	80.0	−0.1	76.5
−0.4	78.0	−0.3	79.5
−0.3	78.0	0.0	76.5
0.1	76.5	−0.4	80.5
−0.4	79.5	−0.2	77.5
−0.2	78.5	−0.1	77.5
0.0	77.0	−0.5	81.0
−0.3	79.0	−0.3	78.5
−0.2	79.0	−0.1	77.0
0.0	77.5	0.0	78.0
−0.2	78.0	−0.3	80.0
−0.3	77.5	−0.1	78.5
−0.1	79.0	−0.3	77.0

8. The Big Corporation has a factory producing springs. The quality control inspector at the spring factory wishes to know if the initial (relaxed) angular position of the legs of a torsion spring can be used as an index of the pressure generated by the flexed spring when it is in use. The data below were generated by measuring the angle formed by the legs of the spring, loading the spring into a testing device and measuring the ounces of pressure generated when the flexing of the spring in use was simulated.

Pressure Produced by Spring	Initial Angle between Spring Arms	Pressure Produced by Spring	Initial Angle between Spring Arms
87.0	68.0	88.9	69.5
92.0	77.0	92.0	80.0
91.5	80.0	88.1	72.2
91.0	79.0	89.0	71.7
89.6	73.3	91.1	78.9
91.7	77.0	90.9	75.6
90.3	77.5	89.5	74.1
90.1	78.7	91.6	77.0
90.4	76.8	89.8	75.0
90.6	74.4	91.4	75.3
91.4	78.2	90.5	73.6
91.2	78.5	90.0	76.4
91.3	77.4	90.6	75.3
92.9	80.5	92.5	79.0
92.3	79.4	92.6	80.3
97.0	94.8	96.7	91.9
92.7	79.9	93.5	80.8
92.3	81.0	96.5	86.2
95.5	88.0	96.0	85.6
93.3	87.0	93.0	79.0
94.4	82.2	94.6	83.0
93.5	81.0	95.5	86.3
94.7	86.5	93.8	82.8
94.4	82.0	95.0	83.0
93.0	84.9	95.4	85.2
94.2	80.0	95.1	83.2

(a) Plot the data on a scatter diagram. What do you conclude about a possible relationship? Explain fully.

(b) The sums and cross products of the above data are: (y = ounces of pressure; X = initial angle in degrees)

$$\Sigma y = 4{,}801.9 \qquad \Sigma X = 4{,}143.9 \qquad \Sigma XY = 383{,}242.59$$
$$\Sigma y^2 = 443{,}703.77 \qquad \Sigma X^2 = 331{,}647.83 \qquad n = 52$$

Compute the correlation coefficient between the two series. Does its value support the advice given in (a)? Explain fully.

(c) Compute the linear regression equation for the two variables. Explain its meaning.

(d) What would you estimate would be the pressure generated by a spring whose initial angle was 80 degrees? (Allow only five chances in 100 of being wrong.)

(e) Is the slope coefficient in the regression equation significantly different from zero? Explain fully.

9. In a study of sales ability involving 24 salesmen, data for sales (y), the salesman's score on a sales aptitude test (X_1), his years of experience as a salesman (X_2), and the average income of the area served by the salesman (X_3) were put through the computer in linear multiple regression analysis. The following results (among others) were reported:

(1) Simple linear correlations among the variables:

$$r_{y1} = 0.8578 \qquad r_{y2} = -0.1306 \qquad r_{y3} = 0.1416$$
$$r_{12} = 0.2892 \qquad r_{13} = 0.3398 \qquad r_{23} = 0.3339$$

(2) Multiple linear correlation:

$$R_{y\cdot123} = 0.9464$$

(3) Sums of squares:

$$\text{attributable to regression} = 4372.19$$
$$\text{about regression} = 509.64$$

(4) Regression results:

Variable	Regression Coefficient	Std. Error of Reg. Coeff.	Computed t Value	Partial Correl. Coeff.
X_1	0.8764	0.0691	12.6852	0.9431
X_2	-0.7263	0.1431	-5.0745	-0.7502
X_3	-0.3263	0.4078	-0.8002	-0.1761

(a) Which of the variables are significantly closely correlated? (Use r's).

(b) Which of the variables are important to the regression relationship? Explain fully.

(c) Does the multiple regression account for a significant proportion of the variance in y? Explain fully.

(d) What do you recommend to the researcher about predicting sales results for salesmen after examining the results of this study? Be specific in your recommendations, indicating which line or lines of further examination might be most useful. Justify your recommendations.

section 4
decision making with mixed models

13
queues, probability, and simulation

THE PROBLEM

Mr. Bigone, the president of Hardsell Corporation, has a barber come to his office once each week to cut his hair. Tom Boss, his office manager, goes out to a small one-chair barbershop in the next block. The barber who visits Mr. Bigone also visits other executives of Hardsell as well as executives of other firms with offices in the same building as Hardsell. The barber sometimes has to wait for Mr. Bigone to finish a meeting or other business before he can give him his weekly haircut. Tom Boss often finds that he must wait for his barber to finish a customer or two who arrived ahead of him.

These situations have some characteristics in common; they are members of a class of problems called *waiting line problems*. They involve:

(1) a *service* (the haircut)
(2) a service *facility* (the barber and his tools)
(3) *customers* requiring service (persons needing a haircut)
(4) a *discipline* which determines the order in which customers are to be serviced (Mr. Bigone's barber works from an appointment book; Tom's barber operates on a first-come, first-served basis)

These situations also involve some conflicts in goals. Mr. Bigone's barber would prefer *not* to be kept waiting, although his fee is scaled high enough to cover the possibility of being made to wait and thus not being able to service as many *customers* as he would if he never had to wait. With better scheduling he could cut his time per customer and service more customers. Mr. Bigone is willing to pay this higher fee so that he will *not* have to wait for the barber's services. Tom Boss and his barber have a different relationship, but a similar conflict. Tom does not like to have to wait. Waiting for other *customers* to be serviced uses time that could be spent more profitably or enjoyably in other ways. Tom knows that he could go to a larger barbershop across the street where more barbers are available and waiting time is usually less. However, haircuts at the bigger barbershop are more expensive. Tom's barber, on the other hand, likes to have the next customer immediately available when he finishes the current customer. With customers waiting he loses none of his productive time.

These two situations also illustrate other characteristics of waiting-line problems. Mr. Bigone's barber knows that some of his customers like him to do his job as quickly and quietly as possible. Others tend to look on their haircut as a pleasant break in a busy schedule, a chance to relax and swap stories or ball scores with the barber. Thus, the service time is not constant for all customers. Tom Boss's barber also does not complete all customers in the same length of time for similar reasons. In addition, the time required by both barbers varies according to whether other customers are waiting for service. If Mr. Bigone's barber has an appointment in another office a short time later, he will work faster. Tom's barber will work faster when he has other customers waiting in the shop.

Finally, if we observed these two barbers for a few weeks, we would soon notice that customers tend to call for service in "bunches." That is, many of the customers of both barbers like to get their haircuts on Thursday or Friday so they will look well-groomed on the next weekend. Also, few customers ask the barber to visit (or visit the barber) very early in the day. Tom's barber finds his shop tends to fill up at noontime and again in the late afternoon. Mr. Bigone's barber finds the demand for his services are light during the luncheon hours. These observations lead us to conclude that the situations we are studying also involve some other interesting characteristics:

(5) *arrival rates* (how frequently customers arrive or call for service)
(6) *waiting time* (how long a customer must wait before receiving service)
(7) *service time* (how long it takes to service one customer)

(8) *facility utilization rate* (the proportion of time which the facility has available for service which is so utilized)

Examples of waiting line (*queuing*) problems are numerous. All of us are familiar with this basic type of problem. We wait in lines for haircuts, shoeshines, all kinds of tickets, stamps, traffic lights, free telephone circuits, and to pay for our purchases in self-service stores. Not so many of us are familiar with the waiting lines formed by shop workers lining up to get tools at a factory tool crib, machines waiting for service by maintenance workers, letters waiting to be typed in the typing pool, and jobs waiting to be processed by an electronic computer. The waiting lines that develop could be reduced by providing more chairs and barbers in the barber shop, more ticket or stamp windows and clerks to staff them, more underpasses and overpasses on the highways, more telephone lines, larger tool cribs holding more tools and using more tool clerks, computers with greater speed and capacity and greater ability to accept inputs and produce outputs. All of these solutions cost money. In addition, the extra facilities may not be fully utilized and profits per unit may fall for the business enterprise furnishing these services. The costs associated with waiting must be matched against the costs of preventing waiting to find a position where the two kinds of costs just offset one another. Such an analysis would allow the business enterprise to determine the optimum number of *servers* (barbers, clerks, telephone line, computers, and so forth) for each service provided.

The purpose of this chapter is to present an elementary introduction to two methods of analyzing such problems. One is a method involving mathematical analysis, *formal queuing theory*. The other is more of a trial-and-error process, *simulation*.

QUEUING MODELS

Types of Queuing Models

The total body of queuing theory is too large and too mathematically sophisticated for presentation here. However, we can indicate the major types of models that have been considered and for which solutions have been found.

Perhaps the simplest model is for the single service facility where customers arrive at fixed intervals and service times are constant. Then, with proper scheduling and enough service capacity, so long as customers do not arrive while the facility is closed, no waiting line will develop. Some conveyor-belt problems are of this type; mass production assembly lines are an example of arrivals at fixed intervals with fixed service times (forced by the line speed).

The next simplest model may be one in which customers arrive randomly at one service facility where service times are fixed. Automobiles being serviced at an automatic car wash would be an example of such a facility. This situation is slightly complicated by the addition of multiple service facilities, for example, two wash lines at the car wash.

Another level of complication is to add facilities in tandem. For example, the car is washed, dried, and then spray waxed in separate but related facilities. Two or more wash-dry lines may feed one spray wax line.

Mathematical solutions exist for the models mentioned so far, at least as long as the population of customers is infinite and arrivals are random. In such cases the distribution of arrivals is Poisson. Adding the complication of random (exponential) service times leads to some cases for which solutions have not been developed. If both arrival and service times vary randomly and there are several *stages* (levels) of service facilities with more than one service facility at each stage, solutions exist only for special cases.

Only in the case of one service facility is a general solution available regardless of the nature of the arrival and service time distributions. In all the more complicated cases solutions exist only for special cases other than where the population is infinite and the arrivals random. We will restrict our attention to models assuming an infinite population of customers and random arrival and service times.

The reader must recognize that we have said nothing about varying *queue disciplines*. We will assume a "first-come, first-served" discipline. More complicated disciplines involving priorities are not uncommon in the real world, but are not generally solved except for special cases.

Solution for Simple Models

A Single-Service Facility—Random Arrivals and Service Times. Let us assume the following:

(1) A one-chair barber shop provides men's haircuts only (a single server).
(2) Customers arrive randomly from an infinite population and arrivals are independent of one another.
(3) Arrivals are served on a first-come, first-served basis.
(4) Waiting time will be determined in the system.

(5) Service times are distributed randomly and are independent from service to service.
(6) Facility utilization rates will be determined in the system.

We would like to determine:

1. The probability of various numbers of customers in the facility (in the waiting line or being serviced) at any given moment.
2. The average time a customer will spend in the system.
3. The usage rate for the service facility (the proportion of time it will be in use).
4. The effect of adding more servers.

Let us assume our barber can take care of an average of six customers per hour. We will call this average service rate, μ; here, $\mu = 6$. Let us assume that customers arrive at an *average* rate of four per hour (once every fifteen minutes on the average). We will call this arrival rate λ; here, $\lambda = 4$. Now, let us think of a *moment* in time, say 9:00 A.M. when the barber opens his shop. Let us call this moment in time t. Then, if we think of a small increment of time ahead of t (Δt), we arrive at a second moment in time at $t + \Delta t$. If Δt is a small enough time interval, and we assume it is, no more than one arrival or departure could take place in that interval. But the probability of an arrival or departure in that interval will be quite small. If we assume that an arrival is as likely to occur during the given interval of time (9:00 A.M. to 9:00 $+ \Delta t$ A.M.) as during any other time interval of length Δt, and that successive arrivals are independent, the probability distribution of number of arrivals in one hour can be considered Poisson, and we can use the Poisson distribution to determine the probability of any given number of arrivals in the basic time interval of one hour. Substituting the mean number of arrivals in time t (λt) for c in the Poisson formula (5.43),

13.00 $P(A = n) = \dfrac{(\lambda t)^n e^{-\lambda t}}{n!}$

where A stands for the number of arrivals in time interval t. For our example of the single-chair barber shop, $\lambda = 4$, $t = 1$ hour and the probability of seven customers arriving in one hour, one of the ways a waiting line will form, is computed as

$$P(A = 7) = \frac{4^7 e^{-4}}{7!}$$

Substituting the value of e^{-4} from Table B-7 and the value of 7! from Table B-1,

$$P(A = 7) = \frac{16384(0.01832)}{5040}$$
$$= 0.0596$$

This value can also be obtained from Table B-8 where we find

$$P(A \geq 7) = 0.1107$$
$$P(A \geq 8) = 0.0511$$

The difference between these values,

$$0.1107 - 0.0511 = 0.0596$$

is the probability of seven arrivals in one hour.

It is often preferable to describe the pattern of arrivals by the distribution of the time intervals *between* arrivals. For arrivals which are Poisson distributed, such an *interarrival distribution* is described by the *exponential distribution*. The probability that the time between arrivals falls between any two arbitrary values, say a and b, is found by multiplying the probability of *zero* arrivals up to time a (in the interval of length a) by the probability of *one or more* arrivals in the time interval of length $b - a$. From 13.00, it can be seen that

$$P(A = 0 \text{ in time } a) = e^{-\lambda a}$$
$$P(A \geq 1 \text{ in time } b - a) = 1 - e^{-\lambda(b-a)}$$

Multiplying these values together and simplifying, we obtain

13.01 $P(a \geq I \geq b) = e^{-\lambda a} - e^{-\lambda b}$

where I stands for the *interarrival* time. The graph of the distribution of interarrival times for our example is given in Figure 13.1. The probability of obtaining a value between 10 and 12 (of there being an interval of ten to twelve minutes between arrivals) is shown by the shaded area under the curve (the total area under the curve is equal to one). Suppose we compute the total area under the curve during the interval

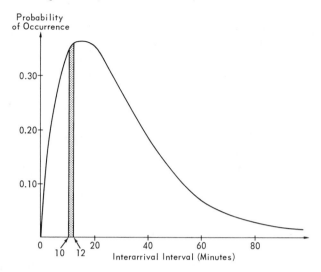

FIG. 13.1.   Probability distribution of interarrival times, average interval is 15 minutes.

from ten to twelve minutes. We will use 13.01, substituting $^{10}\!\!/_{60}$ or $\frac{1}{6}$ for a and $^{12}\!\!/_{60}$ or $\frac{1}{5}$ for b and obtaining values of e^{-x} from Table B-7.

$$P(10 \leq I \leq 12) = e^{-4(\frac{1}{6})} - e^{-4(\frac{1}{5})}$$
$$= e^{-0.67} - e^{-0.8}$$
$$= 0.5417 - 0.4493$$
$$= \mathbf{0.062}$$

So we see that there is a probability of 0.062 that ten to twelve minutes will elapse between arrivals at the barbershop.

From the ratio of arrival rate to service rate we can determine what proportion of the capacity of the service facility is utilized. That is, the *utilization factor, u,* is

13.02 $u = \dfrac{\lambda}{\mu}$

For the one-chair barbershop,

$$u = \text{⁴⁄₆} = \mathbf{0.667}$$

and we see that the barber will operate at an average level of two thirds of capacity. Note that unless $u < 1$, the queue will grow infinitely long.

Now we would like to know how many customers we might expect to find in the shop at any moment. This could be computed as the sum of the series of products, one times the probability of one customer in the shop, two times the probability of two customers in the shop, and so on.

The probability distribution for interarrival times can also be used to describe random service times (times required for providing the required service). In cases where service times can be considered exponential, several important relationships can be demonstrated. First, the average number of customers in the system at any time is given by

13.03 $E(x_s) = \dfrac{\lambda}{\mu - \lambda}$

If x_w is the number of customers in the waiting line (waiting for service),

13.04 $E(x_w) = \dfrac{\lambda^2}{\mu(\mu - \lambda)}$

Letting t_s be the average time a customer spends in the system,

13.05 $E(t_s) = \dfrac{1}{\mu - \lambda}$

If t_w is the time a customer spends waiting for service, then

13.06 $E(t_w) = \dfrac{\lambda}{\mu(\mu - \lambda)}$

Note the logic of 13.06. The expected length of the waiting line has been divided by the arrival rate.

Finally, the probability that the number of customers in the system will be larger than n is given by

13.07 $P(x_s > n) = \left(\dfrac{\lambda}{\mu}\right)^{n+1}$

For our single-chair barbershop, we know that

$$\lambda = 4 \qquad \mu = 6 \qquad \text{and } u = \tfrac{2}{3}$$

Therefore, applying formulas 13.03 through 13.06,

$$E(x_s) = \frac{4}{6 - 4} = \frac{4}{2} = \textbf{2 customers} \tag{13.03}$$

$$E(x_w) = \frac{4^2}{6(6 - 4)} = \frac{16}{12} = \textbf{1.33 customers} \tag{13.04}$$

$$E(t_s) = \frac{1}{6 - 4} = \textbf{½ hour} \tag{13.05}$$

$$E(t_w) = \frac{4}{6(6 - 4)} = \frac{4}{16} = \textbf{¼ hour} \tag{13.06}$$

So the average customer using this shop can expect to find two customers in the shop when he arrives, be forced to wait 15 minutes for service, and spend a total of 30 minutes getting his haircut.

What does it cost Tom Boss to use this barber? Suppose he pays $2.00 for the haircut and values his time at $5.00 per hour. Then, it is costing him $4.50 ($2.00 + ½($5.00)), on the average, to obtain each haircut. If he were to go to the bigger shop down the street, it might be cheaper in total cost although his out-of-pocket costs would be higher. It would depend upon the relative sizes of the value of the shorter waiting time and the greater cost of the haircut.

The usefulness of this kind of analysis to the businessman is obvious. Mr. Little of Little Grocery has one checkstand in his store and employs a woman to operate it. Sometimes, a line forms at the stand and some customers have complained about the poor service. A stop-watch study of the operation indicates that the arrivals and service times are random, so we assume Poisson arrivals and exponential service times. Note that these assumptions (hypotheses) could be checked by chi-square analysis as explained in Chapter 11. Suppose the stop-watch study gives the following values:

Average arrival rate: $\lambda = 12$ per hour
Average service rate: $\mu = 15$ per hour

Then, we obtain the following analytical results: the utilization factor, $u = \frac{12}{15} = \textbf{0.80}$. The number of customers expected to be involved in checking out at any time is (by 13.03)

$$E(x_s) = \frac{12}{15 - 12} = \textbf{4}$$

The expected length of the waiting line is (by 13.04)

$$E(x_w) = \frac{(12)^2}{15(15 - 12)} = \frac{144}{45} = \textbf{3.2}$$

The expected total time a customer spends in checking out is (by 13.05)

$$E(t_s) = \frac{1}{15 - 12} = \text{⅓ \textbf{hour} or \textbf{20 minutes}}$$

This seems rather high. Many customers would spend significantly more than 20 minutes and may not return if this situation continues. Customers object most to the lost time in waiting for service. This is (by 13.06)

$$E(t_w) = \frac{12}{15(15 - 12)} = \frac{12}{45} = \textbf{0.267 hour} \text{ or } \textbf{16.0 minutes}$$

which means that customers are, on the average, spending sixteen minutes simply waiting in line to get to the checkstand.

Mr. Little talks to a sample of his customers and reaches the conclusion that at least 80 percent of the customers who find themselves waiting over ten minutes eventually will go elsewhere for groceries.

The expected total cost per hour would be estimated as follows. Each customer takes an average of four minutes for processing at the checkstand, which means that on the average of 2.5 persons can be processed in ten minutes. Therefore, if more than 2.5 persons are in the system, someone is waiting more than ten minutes. The probability that the number of persons in the system will exceed 2.5 is (by 13.07)

$$P(x > 2.5) = \left(\frac{12}{15}\right)^{(2.5+1)}$$
$$= 0.80^{3.5}$$
$$= \textbf{0.458 or 0.46}$$

If an average of twelve customers arrive each hour, an average of twelve must be serviced each hour since the service rate is greater than twelve. If each customer brings in an average gross margin of $2 per visit, the possible hourly loss associated with the waiting line is

$$(0.46)(12)(0.80)(\$2) = \textbf{\$8.83}$$

It is doubtful that the cost of another checkstand and cashier would be as great as $8.83 per hour, and Mr. Little should install a second check-stand. When it is recognized that reducing the waiting time probably will attract additional customers, installation of the second checkstand becomes even more attractive.

We will evaluate the expected results with an additional checkstand after we present the appropriate formulas for multiple facilities (servers).

Multiple Service Facilities—Random Arrivals and Service Times. We were also interested in the effects of adding more servers (chairs and barbers) to our barbershop. We want to study the effect of two chairs, of three chairs, and so forth. To do so, we need to know how to analyze systems with more than one service facility. The explanation of how the analysis is developed is beyond the level of this text, but we can present some of the basic equations which are used to analyze multiple server situations.

We shall assume that there is one waiting line for the C channels (service facilities). All channels have the same service rate. The important pieces of information for cost analysis of the system are the time each customer will spend waiting and the length of the waiting line. Before we can obtain these pieces of information, we must be able to calculate the probability of the system containing any given number of customers.

13.10 $P(x = 0) = P_0 = \left[\dfrac{(\lambda/\mu)^C}{C! \left(1 - \dfrac{\lambda/\mu}{C} \right)} + 1 + \dfrac{(\lambda/\mu)}{1!} + \cdots + \dfrac{(\lambda/\mu)^{C-1}}{(C-1)!} \right]^{-1}$

and

13.11 $P(x = n) = P_0 \dfrac{(\lambda/\mu)^n}{n!}$ if $n \le C$

13.12 $P(x = n) = P_0 \dfrac{(\lambda/\mu)^n}{C! C^{n-c}}$ if $n > C$

where, in both 13.11 and 13.12, P_0 stands for

$$P(x = 0).$$

The expected number of customers waiting for service (in the queue) would be:

13.13 $E(x_w) = \dfrac{(\lambda/\mu)^{C+1}}{C C! \left(1 - \dfrac{\lambda/\mu}{C} \right)^2} P_0$

The expected waiting time for a new arrival is logically computed as the expected length of the queue over the arrival rate, the same as in the single server case.

13.14 $E(t_w) = \dfrac{E(x_w)}{\lambda}$

Turning to our barbershop example, we assume a single waiting line, two chairs (servers), each server operating at a service rate of six customers per hour. Customers are served on a first-come, first-served basis and do not desert the queue when forced to wait. Finally, we assume that the presence of two chairs does not increase the arrival rate from four per hour (we will change this later).

Then,

$$\lambda = 4 \qquad \mu = 6 \text{ per server}$$
$$u = \tfrac{4}{6} \qquad C = 2$$

and, by 13.10

$$P_0 = \left[\frac{1}{\dfrac{(\tfrac{4}{6})^2}{2\left(1 - \dfrac{\tfrac{4}{6}}{2}\right)} + 1 + \dfrac{\tfrac{4}{6}}{1}} \right]$$

$$= \frac{1}{\dfrac{\tfrac{4}{9}}{2 - \tfrac{4}{6}} + 1\tfrac{4}{6}}$$

$$= \tfrac{1}{2} = \mathbf{0.50}$$

Substituting into 13.13, the expected length of the waiting line is

$$E(x_w) = \frac{(\tfrac{4}{6})^3}{(2)(2)\left(1 - \dfrac{\tfrac{4}{6}}{2}\right)^2} (\tfrac{1}{2})$$

$$= \frac{64}{768} = \mathbf{0.08}$$

or very close to zero.

According to 13.14, expected waiting time would be

$$E(t_w) = \frac{0.08}{4} = \mathbf{0.02 \ hour \ or \ 1.2 \ minutes}$$

If we make the reasonable assumption that two chairs and no waiting time would attract additional customers, say λ increases to 6, then, by 13.10,

$$P_0 = \cfrac{1}{\cfrac{(6/6)^2}{2(1 - 1/2)} + 1 + 1/1} = 1/3 = \textbf{0.333}$$

by 13.13,

$$E(x_w) = \frac{(6/6)^3}{(2)(2)(1 - 1/2)^2} \, 1/3 = 1/3 = \textbf{0.333}$$

and, by 13.14,

$$E(t_w) = 0.333/6 = \textbf{0.0555 hour} \text{ or } \textbf{3.33 minutes}$$

and we still have a great improvement over the original situation.

Returning to Mr. Little's problem, suppose he adds a second check-stand beside the first in such a manner that they share a common waiting line. Then,

$$C = 2 \qquad \lambda = 12 \qquad \mu = 15 \qquad u = \textbf{0.80}$$

By 13.10,

$$P_0 = \cfrac{1}{\cfrac{0.8^2}{2(1 - 0.8/2)} + 1 + 0.8/1}$$
$$= \textbf{0.43}$$

The average length of the queue is (by 13.13)

$$E(x_w) = \frac{(0.8)^3}{(2)(2)(1 - 0.8/2)^2} \, 0.43$$
$$= \frac{(0.512)(0.43)}{4(0.36)} = \frac{0.22}{1.44}$$
$$= \textbf{0.15}$$

The average waiting time to be expected by a new arrival would be:

$$E(t_w) = 0.15/12 = \textbf{0.0125 hour} \text{ or } \textbf{0.75 minute}$$

We have made an important hidden assumption in all of the above analysis. It is that the system has settled down to its long run average. For operations such as the barbershop and the grocery store where the operation is intermittent (the shop and the store are only open during part of each day), this may not be an entirely realistic assumption. The closer the utilization factor is to one, the longer it takes for the system to reach its stable state. As mentioned previously, queuing analysis is a complicated subject and its techniques should not be widely practiced by the amateur. A safer practice is to *simulate* the process and manipulate the resulting model to observe the effects of different actions or policies. The remainder of this chapter introduces the simulation technique.

SIMULATION

Seldom does a real-life situation correspond exactly to the analytical mathematical models of management science. For example, the queuing models we have just been using make some assumptions which are difficult to match in the real world. In many cases some sort of *simulation* is useful as a way of experimenting with the system. For simulation, we need a model which represents the real situation, at least, as we see it. In addition, we need a mechanism which reflects the characteristics of the model and can be manipulated to study the way in which the model (system) operates. For example, aircraft manufacturers build models (small replicas) of flight mechanisms and "fly" them in wind tunnels in order to study characteristics such as their life, drag, and stability during flight. Simulation is particularly useful in situations for which analytical models are not available or are unable to represent the complex situation adequately.

There are two basic *simulation* models used in management science. The first is the *Monte Carlo model*, which is used in essence to represent samplings of variable phenomena. The other major type of simulation model might be called *structural* models. Structural models may or may not include stochastic (uncertain) elements which use Monte Carlo methods in their representation.

Monte Carlo Methods

In Chapter 6 we used a table of random digits to aid us in selecting a random sample. This table can be used to aid us in other ways. For example, in Chapter 7 we worked with the Neet-Lawn Company and its problem of how many crews to call for service each day. In Table 7.2 we showed the relative frequency with which particular demands had been realized in past periods. These probabilities of various levels of demand were then used to compute the expected (average) return when using a strategy of calling some particular number of crews on the following day. But other strategies are possible. What if, for example, the manager were to call the number of crews used on the previous day? What would be the effect of such a policy? In order to judge the effect, we need to have a method of generating demands in the same manner as the real world. All we know is what is given in Table 7.2 and reproduced below in Table 13.1; the probability of a demand for five crews, for

TABLE 13.1

RELATIVE FREQUENCY OF DEMANDS FOR NEET-LAWN SERVICE CREWS
AND CORRESPONDING TWO-DIGIT RANDOM NUMBERS

Demand Level Number of Crews	Probability of Demand Level	Corresponding Two-Digit Random Numbers
5	0.02	01–02
6	0.05	03–07
7	0.12	08–19
8	0.17	20–36
9	0.26	37–62
10	0.18	63–80
11	0.15	81–95
12	0.05	96–99 and 00

example, is 0.02. Note that we assume also that there is no apparent pattern in the demands, that is, that individual demand levels are independent.

Suppose we choose pairs of random digits from Table B-9. There would then be 100 distinguishable pairs (00, 01, 02, . . . , 98, 99). We can then assume that every time we draw a two-digit pair, we experience the demand level corresponding to the random digit pair drawn as the corresponding pairs are identified in Table 13.1. Note that two of the 100 random numbers are assigned to the event "demand is for five crews," five numbers to the event "demand is for six crews," and so forth.

We are now prepared to simulate the demand process. This is done in Table 13.2 for a period of 25 days. Both the demands and the returns

TABLE 13.2

SIMULATION OF DEMAND FOR NEET-LAWN SERVICE CREWS AND
EXPECTED RESULTS OF TWO STRATEGIES

| | | | | RETURN FOR STRATEGY OF | |
| | | | | Call Number of Crews Needed on Previous Day | |
Day Number	Random Number	Level of Demand	Call 9 Crews	Crews Called	Return
1	12	7	$106	—	—
2	68	10	162	7	$126
3	68	10	162	10	180
4	69	10	162	10	180
5	01	5	10	10	−30
6	78	10	162	5	90
7	55	9	162	10	142
8	68	10	162	9	162
9	86	11	162	10	180
10	98	12	162	11	198
11	00	12	162	12	216
12	38	9	162	12	102
13	47	9	162	9	162
14	06	6	48	9	48
15	80	10	162	6	108
16	00	12	162	10	180
17	46	9	162	12	102
18	79	10	162	9	162
19	27	8	124	10	104
20	75	10	162	8	144
21	12	7	86	10	66
22	03	6	48	7	88
23	17	7	86	6	108
24	21	8	124	7	126
25	82	11	162	8	144
Total		228	$3,386		$3,088
Average		9.02	$135.44		$123.52

are simulated in the table. From this analysis, it would appear that the strategy, "call nine crews each day" is superior to the strategy "each day call the number of crews that was needed on the previous day." This is to be expected, since the model assumes that demands on subsequent days are independent. What if, however, it appeared from past data that demand each day has a 0.6 probability of being the same as on the previous day? Then the probability of each demand level would change from day to day. This latter possibility could be incorporated in a Monte Carlo model. Each time a demand is realized, the probability for each demand level would change. We will not work out such an example here, but it would be possible to do so. One of the advantages of these simulation models is their flexibility.

Monte Carlo simulation is also used for studying forms of business activity other than demand. It can be used to simulate complicated queuing situations where the time between arrivals and the time required for each service are determined according to some arbitrary probability distribution by proper reference to a table of random digits. Problems involving multiple stages of service with multiple channels at each stage are most likely to be studied in this way.

Monte Carlo simulation is often used to study inventory policies. Sales per day and the length of the time required to obtain an order can be determined according to some empirical probability distribution and reorder points, reorder amounts, and other variables manipulated to determine strategy for obtaining minimum inventory investment and/or maximum profits.

Other Simulation Techniques

Simulation has become such a widely used tool for guiding business decisions that special computer languages have been developed to aid in structuring such problems for computer solution. Examples of such languages are Simscript, General Purpose System Simulator, and Dynamo. Each of these languages reflects a particular way of looking at business problems. Generally, they allow business activities to be described in terms of standard activities within systems.

Other simulators, called *business games*, reproduce the environment within which a firm or a group of firms operate. Participants in the "game" then assume the roles of executives for the firm or firms and guide the activities of the firm with almost immediate feedback on the results of their general policies and specific actions.

All of these simulation techniques require the use of an electronic computer for real problems of a size large enough to be interesting. The task of doing the necessary calculations to reflect the outcome of a decision or a sequence of decisions is prohibitive without electronic assistance.

SUMMARY

We have seen in this chapter that queuing problems involving randomly distributed *arrivals* and *service times* generally can be handled by *queuing models* which assume the time between arrivals (*interarrival times*) and the *service times* (times required to service *customers* at the *service facility*) are exponentially distributed. Such models make it possible to balance the loss from waiting in the queue against the cost of providing additional service facilities.

More complicated queuing situations involving multiple stages of service and multiple servers are most often studied by the use of *simulation*. Simulation involves building a structural mathematical model of a situation and manipulating it to study the effects of various policies and practices.

DISCUSSION QUESTIONS

1. Define the following in *your own words*. Do not use symbols or verbal formulas.

   (a) queuing model
   (b) waiting line
   (c) service facility
   (d) server
   (e) utilization factor
   (f) arrivals
   (g) interarrival time
   (h) service time

   (i) simulation
   (j) Monte Carlo model
   (k) customer
   (l) queue discipline
   (m) arrival rate
   (n) service rate
   (o) channel

2. Would it be possible for the arrival rate to exceed the service rate for a single server waiting line situation? Explain fully.
   Hint: Might there be factors in the real world not included in the models dealt with here?

3. Would it be possible for systems where $\lambda > \mu$ to have a steady state?
   Hint: Two answers are required, one for theory and one for practice where customers refuse to enter or will leave too-long queues.

4. In a multiple *channel* queuing problem, can $\lambda > \mu$? Is it better that $\lambda > \mu$? Explain fully.

DISCUSSION PROBLEMS

Show your method on all solutions.

1. The Den Products Company has a large number of automatic weaving machines which occasionally require the services of an operator. The average number of machines requiring attention in one hour is 20. On the average, each machine requiring attention can be "fixed" in ten minutes. If the value of the production of one machine in one hour is $15 and the operator costs $4 per hour, how many operators should Den Products employ?

Hints: (1) Note that $\lambda = 20$ and $\mu = 6$.
      (2) Try 3, 4, and 5 operators.
      (3) Use 13.10 and 13.13.

2. One of the plants of the Big Corporation has an inventory problem. Electric motors for one product must be purchased from a supplier over 1000 miles away. The motors are relatively expensive, costing $1250 per motor. It costs Big Corporation $1 per day to carry a motor in inventory. The cost of placing an order for motors is $20 and the cost of being out of motors when they are required is $25 per motor. The probability distribution of numbers of motors used per day and of delivery times from the motor manufacturer are given below.

PROBABILITY DISTRIBUTIONS FOR USAGE AND DELIVERY TIME

USAGE		DELIVERY TIMES	
Units	Probability	Days	Probability
0	0.01	1	0.00
1	0.02	2	0.05
2	0.11	3	0.16
3	0.13	4	0.30
4	0.19	5	0.21
5	0.19	6	0.14
6	0.15	7	0.09
7	0.11	8	0.05
8	0.05		
9	0.03		
10	0.01		

(a) Evaluate the inventory plan for a reordering when inventory falls to 15 using an order quantity of 25. Assume a beginning inventory of 25.

Hints: (1) Set up a table with the headings in the following order from left to right: day, random number for usage, random number for delivery time, usage, receipts, inventory balance, inventory carrying cost, order cost, shortage cost.

     (2) Draw enough random numbers to simulate 50 days experience and fill in the table.

     (3) Add up the last three columns and evaluate the average experience.

(b) Does 50 days experience seem adequate for evaluating these operating rules? Explain.

(c) Students should compare their individual results. Does the combination of results for several students seem adequate for evaluating these operating rules?

Note: This problem should indicate why one usually uses a computer for such simulation.

3. Refer to Problem 1 of Chapter 2 and apply the model developed there to the data for Problem 2 just above, assuming that use is constant at the weekly average amount (7 times the daily average).

(a) What does the model indicate should be the reorder amount?

(b) Does this appear reasonable in light of your simulation results? Explain.

4. For the single server with random arrivals and service times, verify algebraically that the average service *time* $1/\mu$ is the difference between the average time a customer spends in the system and the average time the customer spends waiting for service.

5. For a single channel system with a Poisson arrival distribution and an exponential service time distribution, verify algebraically that the fraction of time the system is in use (u) is directly related to the difference between the average number of customers in the system at a given time and the average length of the waiting line.

EXERCISES

Show your method on all solutions.

1. Refer to Discussion Problem 1 and assume that the value of the output of one machine in one hour is only $10. How many operators should Den Products employ?

2. Refer to Discussion Problem 2 and rework the problem, using the reorder quantity derived in Problem 3. What do you conclude?

3. Arrivals of workers for supplies at a small stores supply room for workers in Plant 4 of the Big Corporation follow the Poisson distribu-

tion with an average interarrival time of 5 minutes. Service times are exponentially distributed with an average of 3 minutes. Workers are handled on a first come, first served basis. Find:

(a) the average number of workers in the system at any time

(b) the average length of the waiting line

(c) the average time a shop worker spends waiting for service

(d) the average time a shop worker spends in the system

4. If the daily cost of operating the system in Exercise 3 were $60 (assume one 8 hour shift) and shop workers in the system represent a cost of $10 per hour in lost production and wages:

(a) What is the total cost of operating the supply room with one attendant?

(b) What would be the cost of the system if the current attendant were replaced with a man whose average service time was only 2 minutes but who cost $1 more per hour?

5. The main terminal of the Interstate Bus Company is located in Bigtown. The company has one reservations clerk who does nothing but take telephone reservations. If a caller requests a reservation or information on a possible reservation, the telephone operator transfers the call to the reservations clerk. If the clerk is busy, the operator puts the caller to hold. Whenever the clerk completes a call, the operator transfers the caller who has been waiting for the longest time. Assume that the arrival of calls follows the Poisson distribution with a mean arrival rate of 15 per hour. Service times are exponential with a mean service time of three minutes.

(a) What is the utilization factor for the clerk?

(b) What is the average time a caller would be expected to wait for the clerk?

(c) What is the expected length of the waiting line?

6. Suppose Interstate Bus Company (Exercise 5) executives are considering adding a second reservations clerk.

(a) What would be the average length of the waiting line with two clerks?

(b) What would be the expected waiting time of a customer with two clerks?

(c) Suppose the goodwill cost of making a customer wait is 15 cents per minute of waiting and the cost of a second reservation desk is $30 per day. What will be the expected net return from the second desk?

(d) At what good will cost per minute should Interstate be indifferent between adding a second reservations clerk or staying with one? Explain.

7. Letters arrive at the central stenograph pool of the Big Corporation in a random manner at the rate of 8 per hour. One stenographer can prepare an average of 3 letters per hour. How many stenographers should Big Corporation have in the central pool if the policy is to have a letter wait no more than 30 minutes before one of the stenographers starts to type it?

8. In a study of the use of fork lift trucks in a factory assembling heavy industrial machinery, the following data were collected from the two major assembly bays of the factory

	East Bay	West Bay
Number of minutes observed	2340	2460
Number of calls for fork trucks	117	197
Average service time per call (minutes)	4.44	4.80

Individual arrivals and individual service times both appear to be random and independent. The cost of a fork lift truck and operator is $10 per hour. If a shop worker has to wait for a fork lift to move a piece of work, the company loses $2.80 per hour. How many fork lifts should be used in each bay? Explain.

appendix a
answers to odd-numbered exercises

Chapter 2

1. (a) $MR = 4 - 16x$ (b) $x = -1$ (c) $P = -16x - 8x^2 - 8$
   $MC = 20$
3. (a) $Q = 2$ $\partial^2R/\partial Q^2 = -8$ $\partial^2R/\partial Q\partial A = \partial^2R/\partial A\partial Q = 0$
   $A = 2$ $\partial^2R/\partial A^2 = -12$ $(-8)(-12) > (0)(0)$
   (b) $Q = 2$ (c) $A = (20 - 5Q)/5 = 4 - Q$
   $A = 2$ or $Q = (20 - 5A)/5 = 4 - A$
   $\lambda = 0$
5. (a) sales = \$500,000 (b) sales = \$577,777.78
7. (a) 625,000 sq ft. (b) \$6,240.25

Chapter 3

1. Solution values: $Z = \$76,000$; deluxe $= 16,000$; standard $= 0$
   Unused capacities: assembly $= 8,000$; warehouse $= 2,000$; painting $=$
   1,000
   Binding constraint: machining; shadow price $= -1.9$
3. Solution values: $Z = \$4,401.20$; cycle $= 35.92$; scooter $= 65.13$; Form-
   ing and welding slack $= 154.93$ hours; shadow prices: Assembly $=$
   $-\$7.63$, painting $= -\$6.58$.
5. (a) Supra $= 5,000$; Prima $= 5,000$; Eclipse $= 25,741$ (rounded)
   (b) Maximum profit $= \$204,444.45$

501

(c) Binding constraint: assembly, shadow price = −$22.22,
  Minimum production Supra, shadow price $5.56 (Note sign)
  Minimum production Prima, shadow price $7.78 (Note sign)
7. Minimum cost = $6,960.165
  Production mix: (Hours per shop)

	Job 1	Job 2	Job 3	Job 4	Hours Used	Hours Unused
Shop 1	0	15	11	0	26	14
Shop 2	12	0	0	5	17	23

  Shadow prices depend upon structure of problem.
9. Maximum profit = $952.84
  Strawberry = 600; peach = 60; blueberry = 50; corn = 800;
  Raspberry = 320; spinach = 100; green beans = 888.6; peas = 200;
  Lima beans = 500; carrots and peas = 900
  Slack: space = 507.71 sq. ft.
  Binding constraints and associated shadow prices: cash (0.037); peach
  minimum (0.249); blueberry min. (0.006); spinach min. (0.021); peas
  min. (0.044); strawberry maximum (0.227); raspberry max. (0.145);
  corn max. (0.073); carrots and peas max. (0.002); lima beans max.
  (0.003). (Watch the signs on the shadow prices.)

Chapter 4

1. (a) 136/220   (b) 1/220   (c) 84/220   (d) 108/220
   (e) 108/220
3. 13/21
5. (a) 19/396   (b) 19/396
7. (b) 0.01   (c) 0.035
9. (a) 0.81   (b) 0.03   (c) 0.20
11. (a) 0.061   (c) 0.009

Chapter 5

1. (a) 0.285   (b) 0.0668
3. (a) 0.5987   (b) 0.0746   (c) 0.9139   (d) 0.4013
5. −0.167
7. (a) 3/95   (b) 70/323   (c) 1/969   (d) 232/323
   (e) 241/969   (f) 91/323   (g) 938/969
9. (a) 0.3874   (b) 0.6513   (c) 0.7361   (d) 0.1937   (e) 0.9298
11. (a) 4.42 mo.   (b) (1) 71   (2) 100   (3) 100
13. (a) 3500 parts per week

Chapter 7

1. (a) $24 = \$2.996$; $20 = \$3.218$; $16 = \$2.998$
   (b) Opt. inventory $= 19 = \$3.282$ (c) \$.691   (e) (1) 1.88
       (2) 17.32   (3) 6.72   (4) .96
3. Loc. $C = \$25,000$
5. \$1183.67
7. \$39,090
9. (c) Bonds $= \$1570$

Chapter 8

1. (a) \$3076   (b) \$4172
3. Cost $= \$3307.50$
7. Assume allowable error $= 0.08$, $C = 90$ percent, $n = 89$
   Assume allowable error $= 0.08$, $C = 95$ percent, $n = 132$
   Assume allowable error $= 0.10$, $C = 98$ percent, $n = 115$
9. 0.0039
11. 0.0020

Chapter 9

1. Probability of fine $= P\left(z \leq \dfrac{38 - 39.6}{0.8}\right) = 0.02275$
3. (a) $n = 102$; $p^* = 0.33$
5. (a) $H_0{:}P \leq 0.07$ (Indifferent between two acts at $P = 0.07$)
   (c) Now three acts: (1) sell to Lossless as is, $E(\text{ret.}) = \$3246.75$
       (2) sell to Apple Shippers as is, $E(\text{ret.}) = \$2600.00$ (3) resort
       and sell to Lossless, $E(\text{ret.}) = \$2858.40$
7. (a) Reject if $\alpha \geq 0.0015$ (one tail)   (b) \$9427.58
9. (a) 19711.82 miles   (c) $z = \dfrac{\mu_b - \mu_H}{\sigma_{\bar{x}}} \doteq 17$
11. (a) $\hat{z} = -5$ (b) $\hat{z} = -1$ (c) $\hat{z} = -1.58$
13. (a)

P_i	$P'(P_i)$
0.30	0.01
0.35	0.10
0.40	0.41
0.45	0.36
0.50	0.11
0.55	0.01
	1.00

   (b) $P(P \geq 0.45) \doteq 0.48$

Chapter 10

1. $5.91

3 An illustrative sample of values:

CONDITIONAL PROBABILITIES OF ERROR

P	Run As Is		Reset Before Continuing	
	$n = 10, x^* = 1$	$n = 20, x^* = 2$	$n = 10, x^* = 1$	$n = 20, x^* = 2$
0.03	(no error)	(no error)	0.2626	0.1198
0.05	(no error)	(no error)	0.4013	0.2642
0.08	0.4344	0.5169	(no error)	(no error)
0.10	0.3487	0.3917	(no error)	(no error)

5. (a)

Rule	*TUEOL*
$n = 10, x^* = 1$	$1.17
$n = 20, x^* = 2$	1.53
from Exercise 4	2.54

7. (a) An illustrative sample of values:

CONDITIONAL PROBABILITY OF ERROR

μ	σ	$\bar{x}$ rule	$\acute{\sigma}$ rule	Combined Rule
			(approx.)	(approx.)
195	16	0.0062	0.10	0.11
195	20	0.0228	0.50	0.51
200	16	0.1736	0.10	0.26
200	20	0.2266	0.50	0.61
205	16	0.2660	0.10	0.34
205	20	0.3085	0.50	0.65
210	16	0.0143	0.10	0.11
210	20	0.0401	0.50	0.52

9. (a)

Acts	*Expected Net Returns*
Produce and market	$850,000
Sell concept	$930,000

Chapter 11

1. (a) $r_{CA} = 0.8470$; $z_r = 1.244$; $\sigma_{z_r} = 0.378$; $z = 3.29$
   (b) $r_{NA} = 0.8135$; $z_r = 1.138$; $\sigma_{z_r} = 0.378$; $z = 3.01$

(c) Assume $\sigma_{\text{diff.}} = \sqrt{\sigma_{z_{r_1}}{}^2 + \sigma_{z_{r_2}}{}^2} = 0.378$; $t_{\text{diff.}} = 0.28$

(d) $r_{CN} = 0.7993$; $t_{\text{diff.}} = 0.394$

3. $\hat{\sigma}_{d_{\bar{z}}} = 88.4$; $t = 2.26$

5. $\chi^2 = 1.40$

7. (a) Bigtown $= 0.153 - 0.181$; Largetown $= 0.133 - 0.153$

   (b) $\hat{\sigma}_{d_p} = 0.033$; $z = 0.73$

9. $\chi^2 = 4.78$

11. $\hat{\sigma}_{d_{\bar{z}}} = 6.02$; $z = 3.32$

13.

Sample Pair	A	B	C	D	E	F	G
F (variances)	1.56	1.56	1.59	1.56	1.56	1.30	1.56
t (means)	1.76	1.87	3.33	1.74	1.56	2.03	2.12

15. (a) $\chi^2 = 3.84$; (b) No available test (consult Table B-4);

    (c) $\chi^2 = 1.33$; $\hat{\sigma}_{d_p} = .087$; $z = 1.15$

17.

Source	Sum of Squares	d.f.	Variance Estimate
Typists	662.84	3	220.95
Brands	2,123.04	2	1,061.52
Interaction	2,780.53	6	463.42
Residual	108.51	24	4.52
	5,674.92	35	

19. $\chi^2 = 1.64$

Chapter 12

1. (a) $z = 1.73$ (b) $z = -0.70$

3. (a) (1) $\hat{\mu}_{y \cdot 85} = 325$; $\hat{\sigma}_{\hat{y} \cdot x} = 8.02$; $z = 3.12$

     (2) $\hat{\mu}_{y \cdot 86} = 350$; $\hat{\sigma}_{\hat{y} \cdot x} = 8.02$; $z = 6.22$

5. (a) $\hat{\mu}_{y \cdot 80} = 900$; $\hat{\sigma}_{\hat{y} \cdot x} = 12.5$; $P(X \leq 930) = 0.9918$

Chapter 13

1. $C = 5$ Total expected cost $\doteq \$21.96$

3. (a) 1.5; (b) 0.9; (c) 4.5 minutes; (d) 7.5 minutes

5. (a) 0.75; (b) 9 minutes (c) 2.56

7. 4

appendix b
statistical tables

Table B-1.   Factorials and Logarithms of Factorials

n	$n!$	$\log_{10} n!$	n	$n!$	$\log_{10} n!$
			50	3.0414×10^{64}	64.48307
1	1.0000	0.00000	51	1.5511×10^{66}	66.19064
2	2.0000	0.30103	52	8.0658×10^{67}	67.90665
3	6.0000	0.77815	53	4.2749×10^{69}	69.63092
4	2.4000×10	1.38021	54	2.3084×10^{71}	71.36332
5	1.2000×10^{2}	2.07918	55	1.2696×10^{73}	73.10368
6	7.2000×10^{2}	2.85733	56	7.1100×10^{74}	74.85187
7	5.0400×10^{3}	3.70243	57	4.0527×10^{76}	76.60774
8	4.0320×10^{4}	4.60552	58	2.3506×10^{78}	78.37117
9	3.6288×10^{5}	5.55976	59	1.3868×10^{80}	80.14202
10	3.6288×10^{6}	6.55976	60	8.3210×10^{81}	81.92017
11	3.9917×10^{7}	7.60116	61	5.0758×10^{83}	83.70550
12	4.7900×10^{8}	8.68034	62	3.1470×10^{85}	85.49790
13	6.2270×10^{9}	9.79428	63	1.9826×10^{87}	87.29724
14	8.7178×10^{10}	10.94041	64	1.2689×10^{89}	89.10342
15	1.3077×10^{12}	12.11650	65	8.2477×10^{90}	90.91633
16	2.0923×10^{13}	13.32062	66	5.4434×10^{92}	92.73587
17	3.5569×10^{14}	14.55107	67	3.6471×10^{94}	94.56195
18	6.4024×10^{15}	15.80634	68	2.4800×10^{96}	96.39446
19	1.2165×10^{17}	17.08509	69	1.7112×10^{98}	98.23331
20	2.4329×10^{18}	18.38612	70	1.1979×10^{100}	100.07841
21	5.1091×10^{19}	19.70834	71	8.5048×10^{101}	101.92966
22	1.1240×10^{21}	21.05077	72	6.1234×10^{103}	103.78700
23	2.5852×10^{22}	22.41249	73	4.4701×10^{105}	105.65032
24	6.2045×10^{23}	23.79271	74	3.3079×10^{107}	107.51955
25	1.5511×10^{25}	25.19065	75	2.4809×10^{109}	109.39461
26	4.0329×10^{26}	26.60562	76	1.8855×10^{111}	111.27543
27	1.0889×10^{28}	28.03698	77	1.4518×10^{113}	113.16192
28	3.0489×10^{29}	29.48414	78	1.1324×10^{115}	115.05401
29	8.8418×10^{30}	30.94654	79	8.9462×10^{116}	116.95164
30	2.6525×10^{32}	32.42366	80	7.1569×10^{118}	118.85473
31	8.2228×10^{33}	33.91502	81	5.7971×10^{120}	120.76321
32	2.6313×10^{35}	35.42017	82	4.7536×10^{122}	122.67703
33	8.6833×10^{36}	36.93869	83	3.9455×10^{124}	124.59610
34	2.9523×10^{38}	38.47016	84	3.3142×10^{126}	126.52038
35	1.0333×10^{40}	40.01423	85	2.8171×10^{128}	128.44980
36	3.7199×10^{41}	41.57054	86	2.4227×10^{130}	130.38430
37	1.3764×10^{43}	43.13874	87	2.1078×10^{132}	132.32382
38	5.2302×10^{44}	44.71852	88	1.8548×10^{134}	134.26830
39	2.0398×10^{46}	46.30959	89	1.6508×10^{136}	136.21769
40	8.1592×10^{47}	47.91165	90	1.4857×10^{138}	138.17194
41	3.3453×10^{49}	49.52443	91	1.3520×10^{140}	140.13098
42	1.4050×10^{51}	51.14768	92	1.2438×10^{142}	142.09476
43	6.0415×10^{52}	52.78115	93	1.1568×10^{144}	144.06325
44	2.6583×10^{54}	54.42460	94	1.0874×10^{146}	146.03638
45	1.1962×10^{56}	56.07781	95	1.0330×10^{148}	148.01410
46	5.5026×10^{57}	57.74057	96	9.9168×10^{149}	149.99637
47	2.5862×10^{59}	59.41267	97	9.6193×10^{151}	151.98314
48	1.2414×10^{61}	61.09391	98	9.4269×10^{153}	153.97437
49	6.0828×10^{62}	62.78410	99	9.3326×10^{155}	155.97000
			100	9.3326×10^{157}	157.97000

Source: R. S. Burington and D. C. May, *Handbook of Probability and Statistics with Tables*, 1953, McGraw-Hill Book Company, Inc., by permission of the publisher.

Table B-2.   Table of Common Logarithms

0–50

N	0	1	2	3	4	5	6	7	8	9
0	− ∞	00 000	30 103	47 712	60 206	69 897	77 815	84 510	90 309	95 424
1	00 000	04 139	07 918	11 394	14 613	17 609	20 412	23 045	25 527	27 875
2	30 103	32 222	34 242	36 173	38 021	39 794	41 497	43 136	44 716	46 240
3	47 712	49 136	50 155	51 851	53 148	54 407	55 630	56 820	57 978	59 106
4	60 206	61 278	62 325	63 347	64 345	65 321	66 276	67 210	68 124	69 020
5	69 897	70 757	71 600	72 428	73 239	74 036	74 819	75 587	76 343	77 085
6	77 815	78 533	79 239	79 934	80 618	81 291	81 954	82 607	83 251	83 885
7	84 510	85 126	85 733	86 332	86 923	87 506	88 081	88 649	89 209	89 763
8	90 309	90 849	91 381	91 908	92 428	92 942	93 450	93 952	94 448	94 939
9	95 424	95 904	96 379	96 848	97 313	97 772	98 227	98 677	99 123	99 564
10	00 000	00 432	00 860	01 284	01 703	02 119	02 531	02 938	03 342	03 743
11	04 139	04 532	04 922	05 308	05 690	06 070	06 446	06 819	07 188	07 555
12	07 918	08 279	08 636	08 991	09 342	09 691	10 037	10 380	10 721	11 059
13	11 394	11 727	12 057	12 385	12 710	13 033	13 354	13 672	13 988	14 301
14	14 613	14 922	15 229	15 534	15 836	16 137	16 435	16 732	17 026	17 319
15	17 609	17 898	18 184	18 469	18 752	19 033	19 312	19 590	19 866	20 140
16	20 412	20 683	20 952	21 219	21 484	21 748	22 011	22 272	22 531	22 789
17	23 045	23 300	23 553	23 805	24 055	24 304	24 551	24 797	25 042	25 285
18	25 527	25 768	26 007	26 245	26 482	26 717	26 951	27 184	27 416	27 646
19	27 875	28 103	28 330	28 556	28 780	29 003	29 226	29 447	29 667	29 885
20	30 103	30 320	30 535	30 750	30 963	31 175	31 387	31 597	31 806	32 015
21	32 222	32 428	32 634	32 838	33 041	33 244	33 445	33 646	33 846	34 044
22	34 242	34 439	34 635	34 830	35 025	35 218	35 411	35 603	35 793	35 984
23	36 173	36 361	36 549	36 736	36 922	37 107	37 291	37 475	37 658	37 840
24	38 021	38 202	38 382	38 561	38 739	38 917	39 094	39 270	39 445	39 620
25	39 794	39 967	40 140	40 312	40 483	40 654	40 824	40 993	41 162	41 330
26	41 497	41 664	41 830	41 996	42 160	42 325	42 488	42 651	42 813	42 975
27	43 136	43 297	43 457	43 616	43 775	43 933	44 091	44 248	44 404	44 560
28	44 716	44 871	45 025	45 179	45 332	45 484	45 637	45 788	45 939	46 090
29	46 240	46 389	46 538	46 687	46 835	46 982	47 129	47 276	47 422	47 567
30	47 712	47 857	48 001	48 144	48 287	48 430	48 572	48 714	48 855	48 996
31	49 136	49 276	49 415	49 554	49 693	49 831	49 969	50 106	50 243	50 379
32	50 515	50 651	50 786	50 920	51 055	51 188	51 322	51 455	51 587	51 720
33	51 851	51 983	52 114	52 244	52 375	52 504	52 634	52 763	52 892	53 020
34	53 148	53 275	53 403	53 529	53 656	53 782	53 908	54 033	54 158	54 283
35	54 407	54 531	54 654	54 777	54 900	55 023	55 145	55 267	55 388	55 509
36	55 630	55 751	55 871	55 991	56 110	56 229	56 348	56 467	56 585	56 703
37	56 820	56 937	57 054	57 171	57 287	57 403	57 519	57 634	57 749	57 864
38	57 978	58 092	58 206	58 320	58 433	58 546	58 659	58 771	58 883	58 995
39	59 106	59 218	59 329	59 439	59 550	59 660	59 770	59 879	59 988	60 097
40	60 206	60 314	60 423	60 531	60 638	60 746	60 853	60 959	61 066	61 172
41	61 278	61 384	61 490	61 595	61 700	61 805	61 909	62 014	62 118	62 221
42	62 325	62 428	62 531	62 634	62 737	62 839	62 941	63 043	63 144	63 246
43	63 347	63 448	63 548	63 649	63 749	63 849	63 949	64 048	64 147	64 246
44	64 345	64 444	64 542	64 640	64 738	64 836	64 933	65 031	65 128	65 225
45	65 321	65 418	65 514	65 610	65 706	65 801	65 896	65 992	66 087	66 181
46	66 276	66 370	66 464	66 558	66 652	66 745	66 839	66 932	67 025	67 117
47	67 210	67 302	67 394	67 486	67 578	67 669	67 761	67 852	67 943	68 034
48	68 124	68 215	68 305	68 395	68 485	68 574	68 664	68 753	68 842	68 931
49	69 020	69 108	69 197	69 285	69 373	69 461	69 548	69 636	69 723	69 810
50	69 897	69 984	70 070	70 157	70 243	70 329	70 415	70 501	70 586	70 672
N	0	1	2	3	4	5	6	7	8	9

Table B-2. Table of Common Logarithms (*Continued*)

50–100

N	0	1	2	3	4	5	6	7	8	9
50	69 897	69 984	70 070	70 157	70 243	70 329	70 415	70 501	70 586	70 672
51	70 757	70 842	70 927	71 012	71 096	71 181	71 265	71 349	71 433	71 517
52	71 600	71 684	71 767	71 850	71 933	72 016	72 099	72 181	72 263	72 346
53	72 428	72 509	72 591	72 673	72 754	72 835	72 916	72 997	73 078	73 159
54	73 239	73 320	73 400	73 480	73 560	73 640	73 719	73 799	73 878	73 957
55	74 036	74 115	74 194	74 273	74 351	74 429	74 507	74 586	74 663	74 741
56	74 819	74 896	74 974	75 051	75 128	75 205	75 282	75 358	75 435	75 511
57	75 587	75 664	75 740	75 815	75 891	75 967	76 042	76 118	76 193	76 268
58	76 343	76 418	76 492	76 567	76 641	76 716	76 790	76 864	76 938	77 012
59	77 085	77 159	77 232	77 305	77 379	77 452	77 525	77 597	77 670	77 743
60	77 815	77 887	77 960	78 032	78 104	78 176	78 247	78 319	78 390	78 462
61	78 533	78 604	78 675	78 746	78 817	78 888	78 958	79 029	79 099	79 169
62	79 239	79 309	79 379	79 449	79 518	79 588	79 657	79 727	79 796	79 865
63	79 934	80 003	80 072	80 140	80 209	80 277	80 346	80 414	80 482	80 550
64	80 618	80 686	80 754	80 821	80 889	80 956	81 023	81 090	81 158	81 224
65	81 291	81 358	81 425	81 491	81 558	81 624	81 690	81 757	81 823	81 889
66	81 954	82 020	82 086	82 151	82 217	82 282	82 347	82 413	82 478	82 543
67	82 607	82 672	82 737	82 802	82 866	82 930	82 995	83 059	83 123	83 187
68	83 251	83 315	83 378	83 442	83 506	83 569	83 632	83 696	83 759	83 822
69	83 885	83 948	84 011	84 073	84 136	84 198	84 261	84 323	84 386	84 448
70	84 510	84 572	84 634	84 696	84 757	84 819	84 880	84 942	85 003	85 065
71	85 126	85 187	85 248	85 309	85 370	85 431	85 491	85 552	85 612	85 673
72	85 733	85 794	85 854	85 914	85 974	86 034	86 094	86 153	86 213	86 273
73	86 332	86 392	86 451	86 510	86 570	86 629	86 688	86 747	86 806	86 864
74	86 923	86 982	87 040	87 099	87 157	87 216	87 274	87 332	87 390	87 448
75	87 506	87 564	87 622	87 679	87 737	87 795	87 852	87 910	87 967	88 024
76	88 081	88 138	88 195	88 252	88 309	88 366	88 423	88 480	88 536	88 593
77	88 649	88 705	88 762	88 818	88 874	88 930	88 986	89 042	89 098	89 154
78	89 209	89 265	89 321	89 376	89 432	89 487	89 542	89 597	89 653	89 708
79	89 763	89 818	89 873	89 927	89 982	90 037	90 091	90 146	90 200	90 255
80	90 309	90 363	90 417	90 472	90 526	90 580	90 634	90 687	90 741	90 795
81	90 849	90 902	90 956	91 009	91 062	91 116	91 169	91 222	91 275	91 328
82	91 381	91 434	91 487	91 540	91 593	91 645	91 698	91 751	91 803	91 855
83	91 908	91 960	92 012	92 065	92 117	92 169	92 221	92 273	92 324	92 376
84	92 428	92 480	92 531	92 583	92 634	92 686	92 737	92 788	92 840	92 891
85	92 942	92 993	93 044	93 095	93 146	93 197	93 247	93 298	93 349	93 399
86	93 450	93 500	93 551	93 601	93 651	93 702	93 752	93 802	93 852	93 902
87	93 952	94 002	94 052	94 101	94 151	94 201	94 250	94 300	94 349	94 399
88	94 448	94 498	94 547	94 596	94 645	94 694	94 743	94 792	94 841	94 890
89	94 939	94 988	95 036	95 085	95 134	95 182	95 231	95 279	95 328	95 376
90	95 424	95 472	95 521	95 569	95 617	95 665	95 713	95 761	95 809	95 856
91	95 904	95 952	95 999	96 047	96 095	96 142	96 190	96 237	96 284	96 332
92	96 379	96 426	96 473	96 520	96 567	96 614	96 661	96 708	96 755	96 802
93	96 848	96 895	96 942	96 988	97 035	97 081	97 128	97 174	97 220	97 267
94	97 313	97 359	97 405	97 451	97 497	97 543	97 589	97 635	97 681	97 727
95	97 772	97 818	97 864	97 909	97 955	98 000	98 046	98 091	98 137	98 182
96	98 227	98 272	98 318	98 363	98 408	98 453	98 498	98 543	98 588	98 632
97	98 677	98 722	98 767	98 811	98 856	98 900	98 945	98 989	99 034	99 078
98	99 123	99 167	99 211	99 255	99 300	99 344	99 388	99 432	99 476	99 520
99	99 564	99 607	99 651	99 695	99 739	99 782	99 826	99 870	99 913	99 957
100	00 000	00 043	00 087	00 130	00 173	00 217	00 260	00 303	00 346	00 389
N	0	1	2	3	4	5	6	7	8	9

Table B-3.   Basic Values for Using the Binomial Distribution

Part A.   Binomial Coefficients

n	$\binom{n}{0}$	$\binom{n}{1}$	$\binom{n}{2}$	$\binom{n}{3}$	$\binom{n}{4}$	$\binom{n}{5}$	$\binom{n}{6}$	$\binom{n}{7}$	$\binom{n}{8}$	$\binom{n}{9}$	$\binom{n}{10}$
0	1										
1	1	1									
2	1	2	1								
3	1	3	3	1							
4	1	4	6	4	1						
5	1	5	10	10	5	1					
6	1	6	15	20	15	6	1				
7	1	7	21	35	35	21	7	1			
8	1	8	28	56	70	56	28	8	1		
9	1	9	36	84	126	126	84	36	9	1	
10	1	10	45	120	210	252	210	120	45	10	1
11	1	11	55	165	330	462	462	330	165	55	11
12	1	12	66	220	495	792	924	792	495	220	66
13	1	13	78	286	715	1287	1716	1716	1287	715	286
14	1	14	91	364	1001	2002	3003	3432	3003	2002	1001
15	1	15	105	455	1365	3003	5005	6435	6435	5005	3003
16	1	16	120	560	1820	4368	8008	11440	12870	11440	8008
17	1	17	136	680	2380	6188	12376	19448	24310	24310	19448
18	1	18	153	816	3060	8568	18564	31824	43758	48620	43758
19	1	19	171	969	3876	11628	27132	50388	75582	92378	92378
20	1	20	190	1140	4845	15504	38760	77520	125970	167960	184756

Table B-3. Basic Values for Using the Binomial Distribution
(*Continued*)

Part B. Products of P and $1 - P$

P	\multicolumn{10}{c}{$1 - P$}

P	0.05	0.10	0.15	0.20	0.25	0.30	0.35	0.40	0.45	0.50
.05	.0025	.0050	.0075	.0100	.0125	.0150	.0175	.0200	.0225	.0250
.10		.0100	.0150	.0200	.0250	.0300	.0350	.0400	.0450	.0500
.15			.0225	.0300	.0375	.0450	.0525	.0600	.0675	.0750
.20				.0400	.0500	.0600	.0700	.0800	.0900	.1000
.25					.0625	.0750	.0875	.1000	.1125	.1250
.30						.0900	.1050	.1200	.1350	.1500
.35							.1225	.1400	.1575	.1750
.40								.1600	.1800	.2000
.45									.2025	.2250
.50										.2500

Table B-3. Basic Values for Using the Binomial Distribution
(*Continued*)

Part B. Products of P and $1 - P$ (continued)

P	\multicolumn{9}{c}{$1 - P$}

P	0.55	0.60	0.65	0.70	0.75	0.80	0.85	0.90	0.95
.05	.0275	.0300	.0325	.0350	.0375	.0400	.0425	.0450	.0475
.10	.0550	.0600	.0650	.0700	.0750	.0800	.0850	.0900	.0950
.15	.0825	.0900	.0975	.1050	.1125	.1200	.1275	.1350	.1425
.20	.1100	.1200	.1300	.1400	.1500	.1600	.1700	.1800	.1900
.25	.1375	.1500	.1625	.1750	.1875	.2000	.2125	.2250	.2375
.30	.1650	.1800	.1950	.2100	.2250	.2400	.2550	.2700	.2850
.35	.1925	.2100	.2275	.2450	.2625	.2800	.2975	.3150	.3325
.40	.2200	.2400	.2600	.2800	.3000	.3200	.3400	.3600	.3800
.45	.2475	.2700	.2925	.3150	.3375	.3600	.3825	.4050	.4275
.50	.2750	.3000	.3250	.3500	.3750	.4000	.4250	.4500	.4750
.55	.3025	.3300	.3575	.3850	.4125	.4400	.4675	.4950	.5225
.60		.3600	.3900	.4200	.4500	.4800	.5100	.5400	.5700
.65			.4225	.4550	.4875	.5200	.5525	.5850	.6175
.70				.4900	.5250	.5600	.5950	.6300	.6650
.75					.5625	.6000	.6375	.6750	.7125
.80						.6400	.6800	.7200	.7600
.85							.7225	.7650	.8075
.90								.8100	.8550
.95									.9025

Table B-4.   Cumulative Binomial Distribution
$$P(x \geq x^*|n,P)$$

x* \ P	.01	.02	.03	.04	n = 2 .05	.06	.07	.08	.09	.10
1	.0199	.0396	.0591	.0784	.0975	.1164	.1351	.1536	.1719	.1900
2	.0001	.0004	.0009	.0016	.0025	.0036	.0049	.0064	.0081	.0100

x* \ P	.11	.12	.13	.14	.15	.16	.17	.18	.19	.20
1	.2079	.2256	.2431	.2604	.2775	.2944	.3111	.3276	.3439	.3600
2	.0121	.0144	.0169	.0196	.0225	.0256	.0289	.0324	.0361	.0400

x* \ P	.21	.22	.23	.24	.25	.30	.35	.40	.45	.50
1	.3759	.3916	.4071	.4224	.4375	.5100	.5775	.6400	.6975	.7500
2	.0441	.0484	.0529	.0576	.0625	.0900	.1225	.1600	.2025	.2500

x* \ P	.01	.02	.03	.04	n = 3 .05	.06	.07	.08	.09	.10
1	.0297	.0588	.0873	.1153	.1426	.1694	.1956	.2213	.2464	.2710
2	.0003	.0012	.0026	.0047	.0073	.0104	.0140	.0182	.0228	.0280
3				.0001	.0001	.0002	.0003	.0005	.0007	.0010

x* \ P	.11	.12	.13	.14	.15	.16	.17	.18	.19	.20
1	.2950	.3185	.3415	.3639	.3859	.4073	.4282	.4486	.4686	.4880
2	.0336	.0397	.0463	.0533	.0608	.0686	.0769	.0855	.0946	.1040
3	.0013	.0017	.0022	.0027	.0034	.0041	.0049	.0058	.0069	.0080

x* \ P	.21	.22	.23	.24	.25	.30	.35	.40	.45	.50
1	.5070	.5254	.5435	.5610	.5781	.6570	.7254	.7840	.8336	.8750
2	.1138	.1239	.1344	.1452	.1563	.2160	.2818	.3520	.4253	.5000
3	.0093	.0106	.0122	.0138	.0156	.0270	.0429	.0640	.0911	.1250

x* \ P	.01	.02	.03	.04	n = 4 .05	.06	.07	.08	.09	.10
1	.0394	.0776	.1147	.1507	.1855	.2193	.2519	.2836	.3143	.3439
2	.0006	.0023	.0052	.0091	.0140	.0199	.0267	.0344	.0430	.0523
3			.0001	.0002	.0005	.0008	.0013	.0019	.0027	.0037
4									.0001	.0001

x* \ P	.11	.12	.13	.14	.15	.16	.17	.18	.19	.20
1	.3726	.4003	.4271	.4530	.4780	.5021	.5254	.5479	.5695	.5904
2	.0624	.0732	.0847	.0968	.1095	.1228	.1366	.1509	.1656	.1808
3	.0049	.0063	.0079	.0098	.0120	.0144	.0171	.0202	.0235	.0272
4	.0001	.0002	.0003	.0004	.0005	.0007	.0008	.0010	.0013	.0016

Source: *Tables of the Cumulative Binomial Probability Distribution*, The Annals of the Computation Laboratory of Harvard University, 35, 1955.

Table B-4.   Cumulative Binomial Distribution (*Continued*)

n = 4

P	.21	.22	.23	.24	.25	.30	.35	.40	.45	.50
x*										
1	.6105	.6298	.6485	.6664	.6836	.7599	.8215	.8704	.9085	.9375
2	.1963	.2122	.2285	.2450	.2617	.3483	.4370	.5248	.6090	.6875
3	.0312	.0356	.0403	.0453	.0508	.0837	.1265	.1792	.2415	.3125
4	.0019	.0023	.0028	.0033	.0039	.0081	.0150	.0256	.0410	.0625

n = 5

P	.01	.02	.03	.04	.05	.06	.07	.08	.09	.10
x*										
1	.0490	.0961	.1413	.1846	.2262	.2661	.3043	.3409	.3760	.4095
2	.0010	.0038	.0085	.0148	.0226	.0319	.0425	.0544	.0674	.0815
3		.0001	.0003	.0006	.0012	.0020	.0031	.0045	.0063	.0086
4						.0001	.0001	.0002	.0003	.0005

P	.11	.12	.13	.14	.15	.16	.17	.18	.19	.20
x*										
1	.4416	.4723	.5016	.5296	.5563	.5818	.6061	.6293	.6513	.6723
2	.0965	.1125	.1292	.1467	.1648	.1835	.2027	.2224	.2424	.2627
3	.0112	.0143	.0179	.0220	.0266	.0318	.0375	.0437	.0505	.0579
4	.0007	.0009	.0013	.0017	.0022	.0029	.0036	.0045	.0055	.0067
5					.0001	.0001	.0001	.0001	.0002	.0002	.0003

P	.21	.22	.23	.24	.25	.30	.35	.40	.45	.50
x*										
1	.6923	.7113	.7293	.7464	.7627	.8319	.8840	.9222	.9497	.9688
2	.2833	.3041	.3251	.3461	.3672	.4718	.5716	.6630	.7438	.8125
3	.0659	.0744	.0836	.0933	.1035	.1631	.2352	.3174	.4069	.5000
4	.0081	.0097	.0114	.0134	.0156	.0308	.0540	.0870	.1312	.1875
5	.0004	.0005	.0006	.0008	.0010	.0024	.0053	.0102	.0185	.0313

n = 6

P	.01	.02	.03	.04	.05	.06	.07	.08	.09	.10
x*										
1	.0585	.1142	.1670	.2172	.2649	.3101	.3530	.3936	.4321	.4686
2	.0015	.0057	.0125	.0216	.0328	.0459	.0608	.0773	.0952	.1143
3		.0002	.0005	.0012	.0022	.0038	.0058	.0085	.0118	.0159
4				.0001	.0002	.0003	.0005	.0008	.0013
5										.0001

P	.11	.12	.13	.14	.15	.16	.17	.18	.19	.20
x*										
1	.5030	.5356	.5664	.5954	.6229	.6487	.6731	.6960	.7176	.7379
2	.1345	.1556	.1776	.2003	.2235	.2472	.2713	.2956	.3201	.3446
3	.0206	.0261	.0324	.0395	.0473	.0560	.0655	.0759	.0870	.0989
4	.0018	.0025	.0034	.0045	.0059	.0075	.0094	.0116	.0141	.0170
5	.0001	.0001	.0002	.0003	.0004	.0005	.0007	.0010	.0013	.0016
6										.0001

Table B-4. Cumulative Binomial Distribution (*Continued*)

n = 6

x* P	.21	.22	.23	.24	.25	.30	.35	.40	.45	.50
1	.7569	.7748	.7916	.8073	.8220	.8824	.9246	.9533	.9723	.9844
2	.3692	.3937	.4180	.4422	.4661	.5798	.6809	.7667	.8364	.8906
3	.1115	.1250	.1391	.1539	.1694	.2557	.3529	.4557	.5585	.6563
4	.0202	.0239	.0280	.0326	.0376	.0705	.1174	.1792	.2553	.3438
5	.0020	.0025	.0031	.0038	.0046	.0109	.0223	.0410	.0692	.1094
6	.0001	.0001	.0001	.0002	.0002	.0007	.0018	.0041	.0083	.0156

n = 7

x* P	.01	.02	.03	.04	.05	.06	.07	.08	.09	.10
1	.0679	.1319	.1920	.2486	.3017	.3515	.3983	.4422	.4832	.5217
2	.0020	.0079	.0171	.0294	.0444	.0618	.0813	.1026	.1255	.1497
3		.0003	.0009	.0020	.0038	.0063	.0097	.0140	.0193	.0257
4				.0001	.0002	.0004	.0007	.0012	.0018	.0027
5								.0001	.0001	.0002

x* P	.11	.12	.13	.14	.15	.16	.17	.18	.19	.20
1	.5577	.5913	.6227	.6521	.6794	.7049	.7286	.7507	.7712	.7903
2	.1750	.2012	.2281	.2556	.2834	.3115	.3396	.3677	.3956	.4233
3	.0331	.0416	.0513	.0620	.0738	.0866	.1005	.1154	.1313	.1480
4	.0039	.0054	.0072	.0094	.0121	.0153	.0189	.0231	.0279	.0333
5	.0003	.0004	.0006	.0009	.0012	.0017	.0022	.0029	.0037	.0047
6					.0001	.0001	.0001	.0002	.0003	.0004

x* P	.21	.22	.23	.24	.25	.30	.35	.40	.45	.50
1	.8080	.8243	.8395	.8535	.8665	.9176	.9510	.9720	.9848	.9922
2	.4506	.4775	.5040	.5298	.5551	.6706	.7662	.8414	.8976	.9375
3	.1657	.1841	.2033	.2231	.2436	.3529	.4677	.5801	.6836	.7734
4	.0394	.0461	.0536	.0617	.0706	.1260	.1998	.2898	.3917	.5000
5	.0058	.0072	.0088	.0107	.0129	.0288	.0556	.0963	.1529	.2266
6	.0005	.0006	.0008	.0011	.0013	.0038	.0090	.0188	.0357	.0625
7					.0001	.0002	.0006	.0016	.0037	.0078

n = 8

x* P	.01	.02	.03	.04	.05	.06	.07	.08	.09	.10
1	.0773	.1492	.2163	.2786	.3366	.3904	.4404	.4868	.5297	.5695
2	.0027	.0103	.0223	.0381	.0572	.0792	.1035	.1298	.1577	.1869
3	.0001	.0004	.0013	.0031	.0058	.0096	.0147	.0211	.0289	.0381
4			.0001	.0002	.0004	.0007	.0013	.0022	.0034	.0050
5							.0001	.0001	.0003	.0004

Table B-4. Cumulative Binomial Distribution (*Continued*)

n = 8

x* \ P	.11	.12	.13	.14	.15	.16	.17	.18	.19	.20
1	.6063	.6404	.6718	.7008	.7275	.7521	.7748	.7956	.8147	.8322
2	.2171	.2480	.2794	.3111	.3428	.3744	.4057	.4366	.4670	.4967
3	.0487	.0608	.0743	.0891	.1052	.1226	.1412	.1608	.1815	.2031
4	.0071	.0097	.0129	.0168	.0214	.0267	.0328	.0397	.0476	.0563
5	.0007	.0010	.0015	.0021	.0029	.0038	.0050	.0065	.0083	.0104
6		.0001	.0001	.0002	.0002	.0003	.0005	.0007	.0009	.0012
7									.0001	.0001

x* \ P	.21	.22	.23	.24	.25	.30	.35	.40	.45	.50
1	.8483	.8630	.8764	.8887	.8999	.9424	.9681	.9832	.9916	.9961
2	.5257	.5538	.5811	.6075	.6329	.7447	.8309	.8936	.9368	.9648
3	.2255	.2486	.2724	.2967	.3215	.4482	.5722	.6846	.7799	.8555
4	.0659	.0765	.0880	.1004	.1138	.1941	.2936	.4059	.5230	.6367
5	.0129	.0158	.0191	.0230	.0273	.0580	.1061	.1737	.2604	.3633
6	.0016	.0021	.0027	.0034	.0042	.0113	.0253	.0498	.0885	.1445
7	.0001	.0002	.0002	.0003	.0004	.0013	.0036	.0085	.0181	.0352
8						.0001	.0002	.0007	.0017	.0039

n = 9

x* \ P	.01	.02	.03	.04	.05	.06	.07	.08	.09	.10
1	.0865	.1663	.2398	.3075	.3698	.4270	.4796	.5278	.5721	.6126
2	.0034	.0131	.0282	.0478	.0712	.0978	.1271	.1583	.1912	.2252
3	.0001	.0006	.0020	.0045	.0084	.0138	.0209	.0298	.0405	.0530
4			.0001	.0003	.0006	.0013	.0023	.0037	.0057	.0083
5						.0001	.0002	.0003	.0005	.0009
6										.0001

x* \ P	.11	.12	.13	.14	.15	.16	.17	.18	.19	.20
1	.6496	.6835	.7145	.7427	.7684	.7918	.8131	.8324	.8499	.8658
2	.2599	.2951	.3304	.3657	.4005	.4348	.4685	.5012	.5330	.5638
3	.0672	.0833	.1009	.1202	.1409	.1629	.1861	.2105	.2357	.2618
4	.0117	.0158	.0209	.0269	.0339	.0420	.0512	.0615	.0730	.0856
5	.0014	.0021	.0030	.0041	.0056	.0075	.0098	.0125	.0158	.0196
6	.0001	.0002	.0003	.0004	.0006	.0009	.0013	.0017	.0023	.0031
7						.0001	.0001	.0002	.0002	.0003

Table B-4. Cumulative Binomial Distribution. (*Continued*)

n = 9

x* P	.21	.22	.23	.24	.25	.30	.35	.40	.45	.50
1	.8801	.8931	.9048	.9154	.9249	.9596	.9793	.9899	.9954	.9980
2	.5934	.6218	.6491	.6750	.6997	.8040	.8789	.9295	.9615	.9805
3	.2885	.3158	.3434	.3713	.3993	.5372	.6627	.7682	.8505	.9102
4	.0994	.1144	.1304	.1475	.1657	.2703	.3911	.5174	.6386	.7461
5	.0240	.0291	.0350	.0416	.0489	.0988	.1717	.2666	.3786	.5000
6	.0040	.0051	.0065	.0081	.0100	.0253	.0536	.0994	.1658	.2539
7	.0004	.0006	.0008	.0010	.0013	.0043	.0112	.0250	.0498	.0898
8			.0001	.0001	.0001	.0004	.0014	.0038	.0091	.0195
9							.0001	.0003	.0008	.0020

n = 10

x* P	.01	.02	.03	.04	.05	.06	.07	.08	.09	.10
1	.0956	.1829	.2626	.3352	.4013	.4614	.5160	.5656	.6106	.6513
2	.0043	.0162	.0345	.0582	.0861	.1176	.1517	.1879	.2254	.2639
3	.0001	.0009	.0028	.0062	.0115	.0188	.0283	.0401	.0540	.0702
4			.0001	.0004	.0010	.0020	.0036	.0058	.0088	.0128
5					.0001	.0002	.0003	.0006	.0010	.0016
6									.0001	.0001

x* P	.11	.12	.13	.14	.15	.16	.17	.18	.19	.20
1	.6882	.7215	.7516	.7787	.8031	.8251	.8448	.8626	.8784	.8926
2	.3028	.3417	.3804	.4184	.4557	.4920	.5270	.5608	.5932	.6242
3	.0884	.1087	.1308	.1545	.1798	.2064	.2341	.2628	.2922	.3222
4	.0178	.0239	.0313	.0400	.0500	.0614	.0741	.0883	.1039	.1209
5	.0025	.0037	.0053	.0073	.0099	.0130	.0168	.0213	.0266	.0328
6	.0003	.0004	.0006	.0010	.0014	.0020	.0027	.0037	.0049	.0064
7			.0001	.0001	.0001	.0002	.0003	.0004	.0006	.0009
8									.0001	.0001

x* P	.21	.22	.23	.24	.25	.30	.35	.40	.45	.50
1	.9053	.9166	.9267	.9357	.9437	.9718	.9865	.9940	.9975	.9990
2	.6536	.6815	.7079	.7327	.7560	.8507	.9140	.9536	.9767	.9893
3	.3526	.3831	.4137	.4442	.4744	.6172	.7384	.8327	.9004	.9453
4	.1391	.1587	.1794	.2012	.2241	.3504	.4862	.6177	.7340	.8281
5	.0399	.0479	.0569	.0670	.0781	.1503	.2485	.3669	.4956	.6230
6	.0082	.0104	.0130	.0161	.0197	.0473	.0949	.1662	.2616	.3770
7	.0012	.0016	.0021	.0027	.0035	.0106	.0260	.0548	.1020	.1719
8	.0001	.0002	.0002	.0003	.0004	.0016	.0048	.0123	.0274	.0547
9						.0001	.0005	.0017	.0045	.0107
10								.0001	.0003	.0010

Table B-4. Cumulative Binomial Distribution (*Continued*)

n = 11

P	.01	.02	.03	.04	.05	.06	.07	.08	.09	.10
x*										
1	.1047	.1993	.2847	.3618	.4312	.4937	.5499	.6004	.6456	.6862
2	.0052	.0195	.0413	.0692	.1019	.1382	.1772	.2181	.2601	.3026
3	.0002	.0012	.0037	.0083	.0152	.0248	.0370	.0519	.0695	.0896
4		.0002	.0007	.0016	.0030	.0053	.0085	.0129	.0185
5					.0001	.0003	.0005	.0010	.0017	.0028
6								.0001	.0002	.0003

P	.11	.12	.13	.14	.15	.16	.17	.18	.19	.20
x*										
1	.7225	.7549	.7839	.8097	.8327	.8531	.8712	.8873	.9015	.9141
2	.3452	.3873	.4286	.4689	.5078	.5453	.5811	.6151	.6474	.6779
3	.1120	.1366	.1632	.1915	.2212	.2521	.2839	.3164	.3494	.3826
4	.0256	.0341	.0442	.0560	.0694	.0846	.1013	.1197	.1397	.1611
5	.0042	.0061	.0087	.0119	.0159	.0207	.0266	.0334	.0413	.0504
6	.0005	.0008	.0012	.0018	.0027	.0037	.0051	.0068	.0090	.0117
7		.0001	.0001	.0002	.0003	.0005	.0007	.0010	.0014	.0020
8							.0001	.0001	.0002	.0002

P	.21	.22	.23	.24	.25	.30	.35	.40	.45	.50
x*										
1	.9252	.9350	.9436	.9511	.9578	.9802	.9912	.9964	.9986	.9995
2	.7065	.7333	.7582	.7814	.8029	.8870	.9394	.9698	.9861	.9941
3	.4158	.4488	.4814	.5134	.5448	.6873	,7999	.8811	.9348	.9673
4	.1840	.2081	.2333	.2596	.2867	.4304	.5744	.7037	.8089	.8867
5	.0607	.0723	.0851	.0992	.1146	.2103	.3317	.4672	.6029	.7256
6	.0148	.0186	.0231	.0283	.0343	.0782	.1487	.2465	.3669	.5000
7	.0027	.0035	.0046	.0059	.0076	.0216	.0501	.0994	.1738	.2744
8	.0003	.0005	.0007	.0009	.0012	.0043	.0122	.0293	.0610	.1133
9			.0001	.0001	.0001	.0006	.0020	.0059	.0148	.0327
10							.0002	.0007	.0022	.0059
11									.0002	.0005

n = 12

P	.01	.02	.03	.04	.05	.06	.07	.08	.09	.10
x*										
1	.1136	.2153	.3062	.3873	.4596	.5241	.5814	.6323	.6775	.7176
2	.0062	.0231	.0486	.0809	.1184	.1595	.2033	.2487	.2948	.3410
3	.0002	.0015	.0048	.0107	.0196	.0316	.0468	.0652	.0866	.1109
4		.0001	.0003	.0010	.0022	.0043	.0075	.0120	.0180	.0256
5				.0001	.0002	.0004	.0009	.0016	.0027	.0043
6							.0001	.0002	.0003	.0005
7										.0001

Table B-4. Cumulative Binomial Distribution (*Continued*)

n = 12

x* P	.11	.12	.13	.14	.15	.16	.17	.18	.19	.20
1	.7530	.7843	.8120	.8363	.8578	.8766	.8931	.9076	.9202	.9313
2	.3867	.4314	.4748	.5166	.5565	.5945	.6304	.6641	.6957	.7251
3	.1377	.1667	.1977	.2303	.2642	.2990	.3344	.3702	.4060	.4417
4	.0351	.0464	.0597	.0750	.0922	.1114	.1324	.1552	.1795	.2054
5	.0065	.0095	.0133	.0181	.0239	.0310	.0393	.0489	.0600	.0726
6	.0009	.0014	.0022	.0033	.0046	.0065	.0088	.0116	.0151	.0194
7	.0001	.0002	.0003	.0004	.0007	.0010	.0015	.0021	.0029	.0039
8					.0001	.0001	.0002	.0003	.0004	.0006
9										.0001

x* P	.21	.22	.23	.24	.25	.30	.35	.40	.45	.50
1	.9409	.9493	.9566	.9629	.9683	.9862	.9943	.9978	.9992	.9998
2	.7524	.7776	.8009	.8222	.8416	.9150	.9576	.9804	.9917	.9968
3	.4768	.5114	.5450	.5778	.6093	.7472	.8487	.9166	.9579	.9807
4	.2326	.2610	.2904	.3205	.3512	.5075	.6533	.7747	.8655	.9270
5	.0866	.1021	.1192	.1377	.1576	.2763	.4167	.5618	.6956	.8062
6	.0245	.0304	.0374	.0453	.0544	.1178	.2127	.3348	.4731	.6128
7	.0052	.0068	.0089	.0113	.0143	.0386	.0846	.1582	.2607	.3872
8	.0008	.0011	.0016	.0021	.0028	.0095	.0255	.0573	.1117	.1938
9	.0001	.0001	.0002	.0003	.0004	.0017	.0056	.0153	.0356	.0730
10						.0002	.0008	.0028	.0079	.0193
11							.0001	.0003	.0011	.0032
12									.0001	.0002

n = 13

x* P	.01	.02	.03	.04	.05	.06	.07	.08	.09	.10
1	.1225	.2310	.3270	.4118	.4867	.5526	.6107	.6617	.7065	.7458
2	.0072	.0270	.0564	.0932	.1354	.1814	.2298	.2794	.3293	.3787
3	.0003	.0020	.0062	.0135	.0245	.0392	.0578	.0799	.1054	.1339
4		.0001	.0005	.0014	.0031	.0060	.0103	.0163	.0242	.0342
5				.0001	.0003	.0007	.0013	.0024	.0041	.0065
6						.0001	.0001	.0003	.0005	.0009
7									.0001	.0001

Table B-4.   Cumulative Binomial Distribution (Continued)

n = 13

x* \ P	.11	.12	.13	.14	.15	.16	.17	.18	.19	.20
1	.7802	.8102	.8364	.8592	.8791	.8963	.9113	.9242	.9354	.9450
2	.4270	.4738	.5186	.5614	.6017	.6396	.6751	.7080	.7384	.7664
3	.1651	.1985	.2337	.2704	.3080	.3463	.3848	.4231	.4611	.4983
4	.0464	.0609	.0776	.0967	.1180	.1414	.1667	.1939	.2226	.2527
5	.0097	.0139	.0193	.0260	.0342	.0438	.0551	.0681	.0827	.0991
6	.0015	.0024	.0036	.0053	.0075	.0104	.0139	.0183	.0237	.0300
7	.0002	.0003	.0005	.0008	.0013	.0019	.0027	.0038	.0052	.0070
8			.0001	.0001	.0002	.0003	.0004	.0006	.0009	.0012
9								.0001	.0001	.0002

x* \ P	.21	.22	.23	.24	.25	.30	.35	.40	.45	.50
1	.9533	.9604	.9666	.9718	.9762	.9903	.9963	.9987	.9996	.9999
2	.7920	.8154	.8367	.8559	.8733	.9363	.9704	.9874	.9951	.9983
3	.5347	.5699	.6039	.6364	.6674	.7975	.8868	.9421	.9731	.9888
4	.2839	.3161	.3489	.3822	.4157	.5794	.7217	.8314	.9071	.9539
5	.1173	.1371	.1585	.1816	.2060	.3457	.4995	.6470	.7721	.8666
6	.0375	.0462	.0562	.0675	.0802	.1654	.2841	.4256	.5732	.7095
7	.0093	.0120	.0154	.0195	.0243	.0624	.1295	.2288	.3563	.5000
8	.0017	.0024	.0032	.0043	.0056	.0182	.0462	.0977	.1788	.2905
9	.0002	.0004	.0005	.0007	.0010	.0040	.0126	.0321	.0698	.1334
10			.0001	.0001	.0001	.0007	.0025	.0078	.0203	.0461
11						.0001	.0003	.0013	.0041	.0112
12								.0001	.0005	.0017
13										.0001

n = 14

x* \ P	.01	.02	.03	.04	.05	.06	.07	.08	.09	.10
1	.1313	.2464	.3472	.4353	.5123	.5795	.6380	.6888	.7330	.7712
2	.0084	.0310	.0645	.1059	.1530	.2037	.2564	.3100	.3632	.4154
3	.0003	.0025	.0077	.0167	.0301	.0478	.0698	.0958	.1255	.1584
4		.0001	.0006	.0019	.0042	.0080	.0136	.0214	.0315	.0441
5				.0002	.0004	.0010	.0020	.0035	.0059	.0092
6						.0001	.0002	.0004	.0008	.0015
7									.0001	.0002

Table B-4. Cumulative Binomial Distribution *(Continued)*

n = 14

x* \ P	.11	.12	.13	.14	.15	.16	.17	.18	.19	.20
1	.8044	.8330	.8577	.8789	.8972	.9129	.9264	.9379	.9477	.9560
2	.4658	.5141	.5599	.6031	.6433	.6807	.7152	.7469	.7758	.8021
3	.1939	.2315	.2708	.3111	.3521	.3932	.4341	.4744	.5138	.5519
4	.0594	.0774	.0979	.1210	.1465	.1742	.2038	.2351	.2679	.3018
5	.0137	.0196	.0269	.0359	.0467	.0594	.0741	.0907	.1093	.1298
6	.0024	.0038	.0057	.0082	.0115	.0157	.0209	.0273	.0349	.0439
7	.0003	.0006	.0009	.0015	.0022	.0032	.0046	.0064	.0087	.0116
8		.0001	.0001	.0002	.0003	.0005	.0008	.0012	.0017	.0024
9						.0001	.0001	.0002	.0003	.0004

x* \ P	.21	.22	.23	.24	.25	.30	.35	.40	.45	.50
1	.9631	.9691	.9742	.9786	.9822	.9932	.9976	.9992	.9998	.9999
2	.8259	.8473	.8665	.8837	.8990	.9525	.9795	.9919	.9971	.9991
3	.5887	.6239	.6574	.6891	.7189	.8392	.9161	.9602	.9830	.9935
4	.3366	.3719	.4076	.4432	.4787	.6448	.7795	.8757	.9368	.9713
5	.1523	.1765	.2023	.2297	.2585	.4158	.5773	.7207	.8328	.9102
6	.0543	.0662	.0797	.0949	.1117	.2195	.3595	.5141	.6627	.7880
7	.0152	.0196	.0248	.0310	.0383	.0933	.1836	.3075	.4539	.6047
8	.0033	.0045	.0060	.0079	.0103	.0315	.0753	.1501	.2586	.3953
9	.0006	.0008	.0011	.0016	.0022	.0083	.0243	.0583	.1189	.2120
10	.0001	.0001	.0002	.0002	.0003	.0017	.0060	.0175	.0426	.0898
11						.0002	.0011	.0039	.0114	.0287
12							.0001	.0006	.0022	.0065
13								.0001	.0003	.0009
14										.0001

n = 15

x* \ P	.01	.02	.03	.04	.05	.06	.07	.08	.09	.10
1	.1399	.2614	.3667	.4579	.5367	.6047	.6633	.7137	.7570	.7941
2	.0096	.0353	.0730	.1191	.1710	.2262	.2832	.3403	.3965	.4510
3	.0004	.0030	.0094	.0203	.0362	.0571	.0829	.1130	.1469	.1841
4		.0002	.0008	.0024	.0055	.0104	.0175	.0273	.0399	.0556
5			.0001	.0002	.0006	.0014	.0028	.0050	.0082	.0127
6					.0001	.0001	.0003	.0007	.0013	.0022
7								.0001	.0002	.0003

x* \ P	.11	.12	.13	.14	.15	.16	.17	.18	.19	.20

Table B-4.   Cumulative Binomial Distribution (*Continued*)

n = 15

x*	P .11	.12	.13	.14	.15	.16	.17	.18	.19	.20
1	.8259	.8530	.8762	.8959	.9126	.9269	.9389	.9490	.9576	.9648
2	.5031	.5524	.5987	.6417	.6814	.7179	.7511	.7813	.8085	.8329
3	.2238	.2654	.3084	.3520	.3958	.4392	.4819	.5234	.5635	.6020
4	.0742	.0959	.1204	.1476	.1773	.2092	.2429	.2782	.3146	.3518
5	.0187	.0265	.0361	.0478	.0617	.0778	.0961	.1167	.1394	.1642
6	.0037	.0057	.0084	.0121	.0168	.0227	.0300	.0387	.0490	.0611
7	.0006	.0010	.0015	.0024	.0036	.0052	.0074	.0102	.0137	.0181
8	.0001	.0001	.0002	.0004	.0006	.0010	.0014	.0021	.0030	.0042
9					.0001	.0001	.0002	.0003	.0005	.0008
10									.0001	.0001

x*	P .21	.22	.23	.24	.25	.30	.35	.40	.45	.50
1	.9709	.9759	.9802	.9837	.9866	.9953	.9984	.9995	.9999	1.0000
2	.8547	.8741	.8913	.9065	.9198	.9647	.9858	.9948	.9983	.9995
3	.6385	.6731	.7055	.7358	.7639	.8732	.9383	.9729	.9893	.9963
4	.3895	.4274	.4650	.5022	.5387	.7031	.8273	.9095	.9576	.9824
5	.1910	.2195	.2495	.2810	.3135	.4845	.6481	.7827	.8796	.9408
6	.0748	.0905	.1079	.1272	.1484	.2784	.4357	.5968	.7392	.8491
7	.0234	.0298	.0374	.0463	.0566	.1311	.2452	.3902	.5478	.6964
8	.0058	.0078	.0104	.0135	.0173	.0500	.1132	.2131	.3465	.5000
9	.0011	.0016	.0023	.0031	.0042	.0152	.0422	.0950	.1818	.3036
10	.0002	.0003	.0004	.0006	.0008	.0037	.0124	.0338	.0769	.1509
11			.0001	.0001	.0001	.0007	.0028	.0093	.0255	.0592
12						.0001	.0005	.0019	.0063	.0176
13							.0001	.0003	.0011	.0037
14									.0001	.0005

n = 16

x*	P .01	.02	.03	.04	.05	.06	.07	.08	.09	.10
1	.1485	.2762	.3857	.4796	.5599	.6284	.6869	.7366	.7789	.8147
2	.0109	.0399	.0818	.1327	.1892	.2489	.3098	.3701	.4289	.4853
3	.0005	.0037	.0113	.0242	.0429	.0673	.0969	.1311	.1694	.2108
4		.0002	.0011	.0032	.0070	.0132	.0221	.0342	.0496	.0684
5			.0001	.0003	.0009	.0019	.0038	.0068	.0111	.0170
6					.0001	.0002	.0005	.0010	.0019	.0033
7							.0001	.0001	.0003	.0005
8										.0001

Table B-4. Cumulative Binomial Distribution (*Continued*)

n = 16

x* \ P	.11	.12	.13	.14	.15	.16	.17	.18	.19	.20
1	.8450	.8707	.8923	.9105	.9257	.9386	.9493	.9582	.9657	.9719
2	.5386	.5885	.6347	.6773	.7161	.7513	.7830	.8115	.8368	.8593
3	.2545	.2999	.3461	.3926	.4386	.4838	.5277	.5698	.6101	.6482
4	.0907	.1162	.1448	.1763	.2101	.2460	.2836	.3223	.3619	.4019
5	.0248	.0348	.0471	.0618	.0791	.0988	.1211	.1458	.1727	.2018
6	.0053	.0082	.0120	.0171	.0235	.0315	.0412	.0527	.0662	.0817
7	.0009	.0015	.0024	.0038	.0056	.0080	.0112	.0153	.0204	.0267
8	.0001	.0002	.0004	.0007	.0011	.0016	.0024	.0036	.0051	.0070
9			.0001	.0001	.0002	.0003	.0004	.0007	.0010	.0015
10							.0001	.0001	.0002	.0002

x* \ P	.21	.22	.23	.24	.25	.30	.35	.40	.45	.50
1	.9770	.9812	.9847	.9876	.9900	.9967	.9990	.9997	.9999	1.0000
2	.8791	.8965	.9117	.9250	.9365	.9739	.9902	.9967	.9990	.9997
3	.6839	.7173	.7483	.7768	.8029	.9006	.9549	.9817	.9934	.9979
4	.4418	.4814	.5203	.5583	.5950	.7541	.8661	.9349	.9719	.9894
5	.2327	.2652	.2991	.3341	.3698	.5501	.7108	.8334	.9147	.9616
6	.0992	.1188	.1405	.1641	.1897	.3402	.5100	.6712	.8024	.8949
7	.0342	.0432	.0536	.0657	.0796	.1753	.3119	.4728	.6340	.7728
8	.0095	.0127	.0166	.0214	.0271	.0744	.1594	.2839	.4371	.5982
9	.0021	.0030	.0041	.0056	.0075	.0257	.0671	.1423	.2559	.4018
10	.0004	.0006	.0008	.0012	.0016	.0071	.0229	.0583	.1241	.2272
11	.0001	.0001	.0001	.0002	.0003	.0016	.0062	.0191	.0486	.1051
12						.0003	.0013	.0049	.0149	.0384
13							.0002	.0009	.0035	.0106
14								.0001	.0006	.0021
15									.0001	.0003

n = 17

x* \ P	.01	.02	.03	.04	.05	.06	.07	.08	.09	.10
1	.1571	.2907	.4042	.5004	.5819	.6507	.7088	.7577	.7988	.8332
2	.0123	.0446	.0909	.1465	.2078	.2717	.3362	.3995	.4604	.5182
3	.0006	.0044	.0134	.0286	.0503	.0782	.1118	.1503	.1927	.2382
4		.0003	.0014	.0040	.0088	.0164	.0273	.0419	.0603	.0826
5			.0001	.0004	.0012	.0026	.0051	.0089	.0145	.0221
6					.0001	.0003	.0007	.0015	.0027	.0047
7							.0001	.0002	.0004	.0008
8										.0001

Table B-4. Cumulative Binomial Distribution (*Continued*)

n = 17

x*	P .11	.12	.13	.14	.15	.16	.17	.18	.19	.20
1	.8621	.8862	.9063	.9230	.9369	.9484	.9579	.9657	.9722	.9775
2	.5723	.6223	.6682	.7099	.7475	.7813	.8113	.8379	.8613	.8818
3	.2858	.3345	.3836	.4324	.4802	.5266	.5711	.6133	.6532	.6904
4	.1087	.1383	.1710	.2065	.2444	.2841	.3251	.3665	.4091	.4511
5	.0321	.0446	.0598	.0778	.0987	.1224	.1487	.1775	.2087	.2418
6	.0075	.0114	.0166	.0234	.0319	.0423	.0548	.0695	.0864	.1057
7	.0014	.0023	.0037	.0056	.0083	.0118	.0163	.0220	.0291	.0377
8	.0002	.0004	.0007	.0011	.0017	.0027	.0039	.0057	.0080	.0109
9		.0001	.0001	.0002	.0003	.0005	.0008	.0012	.0018	.0026
10						.0001	.0001	.0002	.0003	.0005
11										.0001

x*	P .21	.22	.23	.24	.25	.30	.35	.40	.45	.50
1	.9818	.9854	.9882	.9906	.9925	.9977	.9993	.9998	1.0000	1.0000
2	.8996	.9152	.9285	.9400	.9499	.9807	.9933	.9979	.9994	.9999
3	.7249	.7567	.7859	.8123	.8363	.9226	.9673	.9877	.9959	.9988
4	.4927	.5333	.5728	.6107	.6470	.7981	.8972	.9536	.9816	.9936
5	.2766	.3128	.3500	.3879	.4261	.6113	.7652	.8740	.9404	.9755
6	.1273	.1510	.1770	.2049	.2347	.4032	.5803	.7361	.8529	.9283
7	.0479	.0598	.0736	.0894	.1071	.2248	.3812	.5522	.7098	.8338
8	.0147	.0194	.0251	.0320	.0402	.1046	.2128	.3595	.5257	.6855
9	.0037	.0051	.0070	.0094	.0124	.0403	.0994	.1989	.3374	.5000
10	.0007	.0011	.0016	.0022	.0031	.0127	.0383	.0919	.1834	.3145
11	.0001	.0002	.0003	.0004	.0006	.0032	.0120	.0348	.0826	.1662
12				.0001	.0001	.0007	.0030	.0106	.0301	.0717
13						.0001	.0006	.0025	.0086	.0245
14							.0001	.0005	.0019	.0064
15								.0001	.0003	.0012
16										.0001

n = 18

x*	P .01	.02	.03	.04	.05	.06	.07	.08	.09	.10
1	.1655	.3049	.4220	.5204	.6028	.6717	.7292	.7771	.8169	.8499
2	.0138	.0495	.1003	.1607	.2265	.2945	.3622	.4281	.4909	.5497
3	.0007	.0052	.0157	.0333	.0581	.0898	.1275	.1702	.2168	.2662
4		.0004	.0018	.0050	.0109	.0201	.0333	.0506	.0723	.0982
5			.0002	.0006	.0015	.0034	.0067	.0116	.0186	.0282
6				.0001	.0002	.0005	.0010	.0021	.0038	.0064
7							.0001	.0003	.0006	.0012
8									.0001	.0002

Table B-4. Cumulative Binomial Distribution (*Continued*)

n = 18

x* \ P	.11	.12	.13	.14	.15	.16	.17	.18	.19	.20
1	.8773	.8998	.9185	.9338	.9464	.9566	.9651	.9719	.9775	.9820
2	.6042	.6540	.6992	.7398	.7759	.8080	.8362	.8609	.8824	.9009
3	.3173	.3690	.4206	.4713	.5203	.5673	.6119	.6538	.6927	.7287
4	.1282	.1618	.1986	.2382	.2798	.3229	.3669	.4112	.4554	.4990
5	.0405	.0558	.0743	.0959	.1206	.1482	.1787	.2116	.2467	.2836
6	.0102	.0154	.0222	.0310	.0419	.0551	.0708	.0889	.1097	.1329
7	.0021	.0034	.0054	.0081	.0118	.0167	.0229	.0306	.0400	.0513
8	.0003	.0006	.0011	.0017	.0027	.0041	.0060	.0086	.0120	.0163
9		.0001	.0002	.0003	.0005	.0008	.0013	.0020	.0029	.0043
10					.0001	.0001	.0002	.0004	.0006	.0009
11								.0001	.0001	.0002

x* \ P	.21	.22	.23	.24	.25	.30	.35	.40	.45	.50
1	.9856	.9886	.9909	.9928	.9944	.9984	.9996	.9999	1.0000	1.0000
2	.9169	.9306	.9423	.9522	.9605	.9858	.9954	.9987	.9997	.9999
3	.7616	.7916	.8187	.8430	.8647	.9400	.9764	.9918	.9975	.9993
4	.5414	.5825	.6218	.6591	.6943	.8354	.9217	.9672	.9880	.9962
5	.3220	.3613	.4012	.4414	.4813	.6673	.8114	.9058	.9589	.9846
6	.1586	.1866	.2168	.2488	.2825	.4656	.6450	.7912	.8923	.9519
7	.0645	.0799	.0974	.1171	.1390	.2783	.4509	.6257	.7742	.8811
8	.0217	.0283	.0363	.0458	.0569	.1407	.2717	.4366	.6085	.7597
9	.0060	.0083	.0112	.0148	.0193	.0596	.1391	.2632	.4222	.5927
10	.0014	.0020	.0028	.0039	.0054	.0210	.0597	.1347	.2527	.4073
11	.0003	.0004	.0006	.0009	.0012	.0061	.0212	.0576	.1280	.2403
12		.0001	.0001	.0002	.0002	.0014	.0062	.0203	.0537	.1189
13						.0003	.0014	.0058	.0183	.0481
14							.0003	.0013	.0049	.0154
15								.0002	.0010	.0038
16									.0001	.0007
17										.0001

n = 19

x* \ P	.01	.02	.03	.04	.05	.06	.07	.08	.09	.10
1	.1738	.3188	.4394	.5396	.6226	.6914	.7481	.7949	.8334	.8649
2	.0153	.0546	.1100	.1751	.2453	.3171	.3879	.4560	.5202	.5797
3	.0009	.0061	.0183	.0384	.0665	.1021	.1439	.1908	.2415	.2946
4		.0005	.0022	.0061	.0132	.0243	.0398	.0602	.0853	.1150
5			.0002	.0007	.0020	.0044	.0085	.0147	.0235	.0352
6				.0001	.0002	.0006	.0014	.0029	.0051	.0086
7						.0001	.0002	.0004	.0009	.0017
8								.0001	.0001	.0003

Table B-4. Cumulative Binomial Distribution (*Continued*)

n = 19

P x*	.11	.12	.13	.14	.15	.16	.17	.18	.19	.20
1	.8908	.9119	.9291	.9431	.9544	.9636	.9710	.9770	.9818	.9856
2	.6342	.6835	.7277	.7669	.8015	.8318	.8581	.8809	.9004	.9171
3	.3488	.4032	.4568	.5089	.5587	.6059	.6500	.6910	.7287	.7631
4	.1490	.1867	.2275	.2708	.3159	.3620	.4085	.4549	.5005	.5449
5	.0502	.0685	.0904	.1158	.1444	.1762	.2107	.2476	.2864	.3267
6	.0135	.0202	.0290	.0401	.0537	.0700	.0891	.1110	.1357	.1631
7	.0030	.0048	.0076	.0113	.0163	.0228	.0310	.0411	.0532	.0676
8	.0005	.0009	.0016	.0026	.0041	.0061	.0089	.0126	.0173	.0233
9	.0001	.0002	.0003	.0005	.0008	.0014	.0021	.0032	.0047	.0067
10				.0001	.0001	.0002	.0004	.0007	.0010	.0016
11							.0001	.0001	.0002	.0003

P x*	.21	.22	.23	.24	.25	.30	.35	.40	.45	.50
1	.9887	.9911	.9930	.9946	.9958	.9989	.9997	.9999	1.0000	1.0000
2	.9313	.9434	.9535	.9619	.9690	.9896	.9969	.9992	.9998	1.0000
3	.7942	.8222	.8471	.8692	.8887	.9538	.9830	.9945	.9985	.9996
4	.5877	.6285	.6671	.7032	.7369	.8668	.9409	.9770	.9923	.9978
5	.3681	.4100	.4520	.4936	.5346	.7178	.8500	.9304	.9720	.9904
6	.1929	.2251	.2592	.2950	.3322	.5261	.7032	.8371	.9223	.9682
7	.0843	.1034	.1248	.1487	.1749	.3345	.5188	.6919	.8273	.9165
8	.0307	.0396	.0503	.0629	.0775	.1820	.3344	.5122	.6831	.8204
9	.0093	.0127	.0169	.0222	.0287	.0839	.1855	.3325	.5060	.6762
10	.0023	.0034	.0047	.0066	.0089	.0326	.0875	.1861	.3290	.5000
11	.0005	.0007	.0011	.0016	.0023	.0105	.0347	.0885	.1841	.3238
12	.0001	.0001	.0002	.0003	.0005	.0028	.0114	.0352	.0871	.1796
13				.0001	.0001	.0006	.0031	.0116	.0342	.0835
14						.0001	.0007	.0031	.0109	.0318
15							.0001	.0006	.0028	.0096
16								.0001	.0005	.0022
17									.0001	.0004

n = 20

P x*	.01	.02	.03	.04	.05	.06	.07	.08	.09	.10
1	.1821	.3324	.4562	.5580	.6415	.7099	.7658	.8113	.8484	.8784
2	.0169	.0599	.1198	.1897	.2642	.3395	.4131	.4831	.5484	.6083
3	.0010	.0071	.0210	.0439	.0755	.1150	.1610	.2121	.2666	.3231
4		.0006	.0027	.0074	.0159	.0290	.0471	.0706	.0993	.1330
5			.0003	.0010	.0026	.0056	.0107	.0183	.0290	.0432
6				.0001	.0003	.0009	.0019	.0038	.0068	.0113
7						.0001	.0003	.0006	.0013	.0024
8								.0001	.0002	.0004
9										.0001

Table B-4. Cumulative Binomial Distribution (*Continued*)

n = 20

x^* \ P	.11	.12	.13	.14	.15	.16	.17	.18	.19	.20
1	.9028	.9224	.9383	.9510	.9612	.9694	.9759	.9811	.9852	.9885
2	.6624	.7109	.7539	.7916	.8244	.8529	.8773	.8982	.9159	.9308
3	.3802	.4369	.4920	.5450	.5951	.6420	.6854	.7252	.7614	.7939
4	.1710	.2127	.2573	.3041	.3523	.4010	.4496	.4974	.5439	.5886
5	.0610	.0827	.1083	.1375	.1702	.2059	.2443	.2849	.3271	.3704
6	.0175	.0260	.0370	.0507	.0673	.0870	.1098	.1356	.1643	.1958
7	.0041	.0067	.0103	.0153	.0219	.0304	.0409	.0537	.0689	.0867
8	.0008	.0014	.0024	.0038	.0059	.0088	.0127	.0177	.0241	.0321
9	.0001	.0002	.0005	.0008	.0013	.0021	.0033	.0049	.0071	.0100
10			.0001	.0001	.0002	.0004	.0007	.0011	.0017	.0026
11						.0001	.0001	.0002	.0004	.0006
12									.0001	.0001

x^* \ P	.21	.22	.23	.24	.25	.30	.35	.40	.45	.50
1	.9910	.9931	.9946	.9959	.9968	.9992	.9998	1.0000	1.0000	1.0000
2	.9434	.9539	.9626	.9698	.9757	.9924	.9979	.9995	.9999	1.0000
3	.8230	.8488	.8716	.8915	.9087	.9645	.9879	.9964	.9991	.9998
4	.6310	.6711	.7085	.7431	.7748	.8929	.9556	.9840	.9951	.9987
5	.4142	.4580	.5014	.5439	.5852	.7625	.8818	.9490	.9811	.9941
6	.2297	.2657	.3035	.3427	.3828	.5836	.7546	.8744	.9447	.9793
7	.1071	.1301	.1557	.1838	.2142	.3920	.5834	.7500	.8701	.9423
8	.0419	.0536	.0675	.0835	.1018	.2277	.3990	.5841	.7480	.8684
9	.0138	.0186	.0246	.0320	.0409	.1133	.2376	.4044	.5857	.7483
10	.0038	.0054	.0075	.0103	.0139	.0480	.1218	.2447	.4086	.5881
11	.0009	.0013	.0019	.0028	.0039	.0171	.0532	.1275	.2493	.4119
12	.0002	.0003	.0004	.0006	.0009	.0051	.0196	.0565	.1308	.2517
13			.0001	.0001	.0002	.0013	.0060	.0210	.0580	.1316
14						.0003	.0015	.0065	.0214	.0577
15							.0003	.0016	.0064	.0207
16								.0003	.0015	.0059
17									.0003	.0013
18										.0002

Table B-4.   Cumulative Binomial Distribution (*Continued*)

n = 25

P x*	.01	.02	.03	.04	.05	.06	.07	.08	.09	.10
1	.2222	.3965	.5330	.6396	.7226	.7871	.8370	.8756	.9054	.9282
2	.0258	.0886	.1720	.2642	.3576	.4473	.5304	.6053	.6714	.7288
3	.0020	.0132	.0380	.0765	.1271	.1871	.2534	.3232	.3937	.4629
4	.0001	.0014	.0062	.0165	.0341	.0598	.0936	.1351	.1832	.2364
5		.0001	.0008	.0028	.0072	.0151	.0274	.0451	.0686	.0980
6			.0001	.0004	.0012	.0031	.0065	.0123	.0210	.0334
7					.0002	.0005	.0013	.0028	.0054	.0095
8						.0001	.0002	.0005	.0011	.0023
9								.0001	.0002	.0005
10										.0001

P x*	.11	.12	.13	.14	.15	.16	.17	.18	.19	.20
1	.9457	.9591	.9692	.9770	.9828	.9872	.9905	.9930	.9949	.9962
2	.7779	.8195	.8543	.8832	.9069	.9263	.9420	.9546	.9646	.9726
3	.5291	.5912	.6483	.7000	.7463	.7870	.8226	.8533	.8796	.9018
4	.2934	.3525	.4123	.4714	.5289	.5837	.6352	.6829	.7266	.7660
5	.1331	.1734	.2183	.2668	.3179	.3707	.4241	.4772	.5292	.5793
6	.0499	.0709	.0965	.1268	.1615	.2002	.2425	.2875	.3347	.3833
7	.0156	.0243	.0359	.0509	.0695	.0920	.1185	.1488	.1827	.2200
8	.0041	.0070	.0113	.0173	.0255	.0361	.0495	.0661	.0859	.1091
9	.0009	.0017	.0030	.0050	.0080	.0121	.0178	.0252	.0348	.0468
10	.0002	.0004	.0007	.0012	.0021	.0035	.0055	.0083	.0122	.0173
11		.0001	.0001	.0003	.0005	.0009	.0015	.0024	.0037	.0056
12				.0001	.0001	.0002	.0003	.0006	.0010	.0015
13							.0001	.0001	.0002	.0004
14										.0001

Table B-4. Cumulative Binomial Distribution (*Continued*)

n = 25

x* \ P	.21	.22	.23	.24	.25	.30	.35	.40	.45	.50
1	.9972	.9980	.9986	.9990	.9992	.9999	1.0000	1.0000	1.0000	1.0000
2	.9789	.9838	.9877	.9907	.9930	.9984	.9997	1.0000	1.0000	1.0000
3	.9204	.9360	.9488	.9593	.9679	.9910	.9979	.9996	.9999	1.0000
4	.8013	.8324	.8597	.8834	.9038	.9668	.9903	.9976	.9995	.9999
5	.6270	.6718	.7134	.7516	.7863	.9095	.9680	.9905	.9977	.9995
6	.4325	.4816	.5298	.5767	.6217	.8065	.9174	.9706	.9914	.9980
7	.2601	.3027	.3471	.3927	.4389	.6594	.8266	.9264	.9742	.9927
8	.1358	.1658	.1989	.2349	.2735	.4882	.6939	.8465	.9362	.9784
9	.0614	.0788	.0993	.1228	.1494	.3231	.5332	.7265	.8660	.9461
10	.0240	.0326	.0431	.0560	.0713	.1894	.3697	.5754	.7576	.8852
11	.0082	.0116	.0163	.0222	.0297	.0978	.2288	.4142	.6157	.7878
12	.0024	.0036	.0053	.0076	.0107	.0442	.1254	.2677	.4574	.6550
13	.0006	.0010	.0015	.0023	.0034	.0175	.0604	.1538	.3063	.5000
14	.0001	.0002	.0004	.0006	.0009	.0060	.0255	.0778	.1827	.3450
15			.0001	.0001	.0002	.0018	.0093	.0344	.0960	.2122
16						.0004	.0029	.0132	.0440	.1148
17						.0001	.0008	.0043	.0174	.0539
18							.0002	.0012	.0058	.0216
19								.0003	.0016	.0073
20									.0004	.0020
21									.0001	.0005
22										.0001

n = 50

x* \ P	.01	.02	.03	.04	.05	.06	.07	.08	.09	.10
1	.3950	.6358	.7819	.8701	.9231	.9547	.9734	.9845	.9910	.9948
2	.0894	.2642	.4447	.5995	.7206	.8100	.8735	.9173	.9468	.9662
3	.0138	.0784	.1892	.3233	.4595	.5838	.6892	.7740	.8395	.8883
4	.0016	.0178	.0628	.1391	.2396	.3527	.4673	.5747	.6697	.7497
5	.0001	.0032	.0168	.0490	.1036	.1794	.2710	.3710	.4723	.5688
6		.0005	.0037	.0144	.0378	.0776	.1350	.2081	.2928	.3839
7		.0001	.0007	.0036	.0118	.0289	.0583	.1019	.1596	.2298
8			.0001	.0008	.0032	.0094	.0220	.0438	.0768	.1221
9				.0001	.0008	.0027	.0073	.0167	.0328	.0579
10					.0002	.0007	.0022	.0056	.0125	.0245
11						.0002	.0006	.0017	.0043	.0094
12							.0001	.0005	.0013	.0032
13								.0001	.0004	.0010
14									.0001	.0003
15										.0001

Table B-4. Cumulative Binomial Distribution (*Continued*)

n = 50

x* \ P	.11	.12	.13	.14	.15	.16	.17	.18	.19	.20
1	.9971	.9983	.9991	.9995	.9997	.9998	.9999	1.0000	1.0000	1.0000
2	.9788	.9869	.9920	.9951	.9971	.9983	.9990	.9994	.9997	.9998
3	.9237	.9487	.9661	.9779	.9858	.9910	.9944	.9965	.9979	.9987
4	.8146	.8655	.9042	.9330	.9540	.9688	.9792	.9863	.9912	.9943
5	.6562	.7320	.7956	.8472	.8879	.9192	.9428	.9601	.9726	.9815
6	.4760	.5647	.6463	.7186	.7806	.8323	.8741	.9071	.9327	.9520
7	.3091	.3935	.4789	.5616	.6387	.7081	.7686	.8199	.8624	.8966
8	.1793	.2467	.3217	.4010	.4812	.5594	.6328	.6996	.7587	.8096
9	.0932	.1392	.1955	.2605	.3319	.4071	.4832	.5576	.6280	.6927
10	.0435	.0708	.1074	.1537	.2089	.2718	.3403	.4122	.4849	.5563
11	.0183	.0325	.0535	.0824	.1199	.1661	.2203	.2813	.3473	.4164
12	.0069	.0135	.0242	.0402	.0628	.0929	.1309	.1768	.2300	.2893
13	.0024	.0051	.0100	.0179	.0301	.0475	.0714	.1022	.1405	.1861
14	.0008	.0018	.0037	.0073	.0132	.0223	.0357	.0544	.0791	.1106
15	.0002	.0006	.0013	.0027	.0053	.0096	.0164	.0266	.0411	.0607
16	.0001	.0002	.0004	.0009	.0019	.0038	.0070	.0120	.0197	.0308
17		.0001	.0003	.0007	.0014	.0027	.0050	.0087	.0144
18			.0001	.0002	.0005	.0010	.0019	.0036	.0063
19				.0001	.0001	.0003	.0007	.0013	.0025
20							.0001	.0002	.0005	.0009
21								.0001	.0002	.0003
22										.0001

Table B-4. Cumulative Binomial Distribution (*Continued*)

n = 50

x* P	.21	.22	.23	.24	.25	.30	.35	.40	.45	.50
1	1.0000	1.0000	1.0000	1.0000	1.0000	1.0000	1.0000	1.0000	1.0000	1.0000
2	.9999	.9999	1.0000	1.0000	1.0000	1.0000	1.0000	1.0000	1.0000	1.0000
3	.9992	.9995	.9997	.9998	.9999	1.0000	1.0000	1.0000	1.0000	1.0000
4	.9964	.9978	.9986	.9992	.9995	1.0000	1.0000	1.0000	1.0000	1.0000
5	.9877	.9919	.9948	.9967	.9979	.9998	1.0000	1.0000	1.0000	1.0000
6	.9663	.9767	.9841	.9893	.9930	.9993	.9999	1.0000	1.0000	1.0000
7	.9236	.9445	.9603	.9720	.9806	.9975	.9998	1.0000	1.0000	1.0000
8	.8523	.8874	.9156	.9377	.9547	.9927	.9992	.9999	1.0000	1.0000
9	.7505	.8009	.8437	.8794	.9084	.9817	.9975	.9998	1.0000	1.0000
10	.6241	.6870	.7436	.7934	.8363	.9598	.9933	.9992	.9999	1.0000
11	.4864	.5552	.6210	.6822	.7378	.9211	.9840	.9978	.9998	1.0000
12	.3533	.4201	.4878	.5544	.6184	.8610	.9658	.9943	.9994	1.0000
13	.2383	.2963	.3585	.4233	.4890	.7771	.9339	.9867	.9982	.9998
14	.1490	.1942	.2456	.3023	.3630	.6721	.8837	.9720	.9955	.9995
15	.0862	.1181	.1565	.2013	.2519	.5532	.8122	.9460	.9896	.9987
16	.0462	.0665	.0926	.1247	.1631	.4308	.7199	.9045	.9780	.9967
17	.0229	.0347	.0508	.0718	.0983	.3161	.6111	.8439	.9573	.9923
18	.0105	.0168	.0259	.0384	.0551	.2178	.4940	.7631	.9235	.9836
19	.0045	.0075	.0122	.0191	.0287	.1406	.3784	.6644	.8727	.9675
20	.0018	.0031	.0054	.0088	.0139	.0848	.2736	.5535	.8026	.9405
21	.0006	.0012	.0022	.0038	.0063	.0478	.1861	.4390	.7138	.8987
22	.0002	.0004	.0008	.0015	.0026	.0251	.1187	.3299	.6100	.8389
23	.0001	.0001	.0003	.0006	.0010	.0123	.0710	.2340	.4981	.7601
24			.0001	.0002	.0004	.0056	.0396	.1562	.3866	.6641
25				.0001	.0001	.0024	.0207	.0978	.2840	.5561
26						.0009	.0100	.0573	.1966	.4439
27						.0003	.0045	.0314	.1279	.3359
28						.0001	.0019	.0160	.0780	.2399
29							.0007	.0076	.0444	.1611
30							.0003	.0034	.0235	.1013
31							.0001	.0014	.0116	.0595
32								.0005	.0053	.0325
33								.0002	.0022	.0164
34								.0001	.0009	.0077
35									.0003	.0033
36									.0001	.0013
37										.0005
38										.0002

Table B-4. Cumulative Binomial Distribution (*Continued*)

n = 100

x*	.01	.02	.03	.04	.05	.06	.07	.08	.09	.10
1	.6340	.8674	.9524	.9831	.9941	.9979	.9993	.9998	.9999	1.0000
2	.2642	.5967	.8054	.9128	.9629	.9848	.9940	.9977	.9991	.9997
3	.0794	.3233	.5802	.7679	.8817	.9434	.9742	.9887	.9952	.9981
4	.0184	.1410	.3528	.5705	.7422	.8570	.9256	.9633	.9827	.9922
5	.0034	.0508	.1821	.3711	.5640	.7232	.8368	.9097	.9526	.9763
6	.0005	.0155	.0808	.2116	.3840	.5593	.7086	.8201	.8955	.9424
7	.0001	.0041	.0312	.1064	.2340	.3936	.5557	.6968	.8060	.8828
8		.0009	.0106	.0475	.1280	.2517	.4012	.5529	.6872	.8828
9		.0002	.0032	.0190	.0631	.1463	.2660	.4074	.5506	.6791
10			.0009	.0068	.0282	.0775	.1620	.2780	.4125	.5487
11			.0002	.0022	.0115	.0376	.0908	.1757	.2882	.4168
12				.0007	.0043	.0168	.0469	.1028	.1876	.2970
13				.0002	.0015	.0069	.0224	.0559	.1138	.1982
14					.0005	.0026	.0099	.0282	.0645	.1239
15					.0001	.0009	.0041	.0133	.0341	.0726
16						.0003	.0016	.0058	.0169	.0399
17						.0001	.0006	.0024	.0078	.0206
18							.0002	.0009	.0034	.0100
19							.0001	.0003	.0014	.0046
20								.0001	.0005	.0020
21									.0002	.0008
22									.0001	.0003
23										.0001

Table B-4. Cumulative Binomial Distribution (*Continued*)

n = 100

x* \ P	.11	.12	.13	.14	.15	.16	.17	.18	.19	.20
1	1.0000	1.0000	1.0000	1.0000	1.0000	1.0000	1.0000	1.0000	1.0000	1.0000
2	.9999	1.0000	1.0000	1.0000	1.0000	1.0000	1.0000	1.0000	1.0000	1.0000
3	.9992	.9997	.9999	1.0000	1.0000	1.0000	1.0000	1.0000	1.0000	1.0000
4	.9966	.9985	.9994	.9998	.9999	1.0000	1.0000	1.0000	1.0000	1.0000
5	.9886	.9947	.9977	.9990	.9996	.9998	.9999	1.0000	1.0000	1.0000
6	.9698	.9848	.9926	.9966	.9984	.9993	.9997	.9999	1.0000	1.0000
7	.9328	.9633	.9808	.9903	.9953	.9978	.9990	.9996	.9998	.9999
8	.8715	.9239	.9569	.9766	.9878	.9939	.9970	.9986	.9994	.9997
9	.7835	.8614	.9155	.9508	.9725	.9853	.9924	.9962	.9982	.9991
10	.6722	.7743	.8523	.9078	.9449	.9684	.9826	.9908	.9953	.9977
11	.5471	.6663	.7663	.8440	.9006	.9393	.9644	.9800	.9891	.9943
12	.4206	.5458	.6611	.7591	.8365	.8939	.9340	.9605	.9773	.9874
13	.3046	.4239	.5446	.6566	.7527	.8297	.8876	.9289	.9567	.9747
14	.2076	.3114	.4268	.5436	.6526	.7469	.8234	.8819	.9241	.9531
15	.1330	.2160	.3173	.4294	.5428	.6490	.7417	.8177	.8765	.9196
16	.0802	.1414	.2236	.3227	.4317	.5420	.6458	.7370	.8125	.8715
17	.0456	.0874	.1492	.2305	.3275	.4338	.5414	.6429	.7327	.8077
18	.0244	.0511	.0942	.1563	.2367	.3319	.4357	.5408	.6403	.7288
19	.0123	.0282	.0564	.1006	.1628	.2424	.3359	.4374	.5403	.6379
20	.0059	.0147	.0319	.0614	.1065	.1689	.2477	.3395	.4391	.5398
21	.0026	.0073	.0172	.0356	.0663	.1121	.1745	.2525	.3429	.4405
22	.0011	.0034	.0088	.0196	.0393	.0710	.1174	.1797	.2570	.3460
23	.0005	.0015	.0042	.0103	.0221	.0428	.0754	.1223	.1846	.2611
24	.0002	.0006	.0020	.0051	.0119	.0246	.0462	.0796	.1270	.1891
25	.0001	.0003	.0009	.0024	.0061	.0135	.0271	.0496	.0837	.1314
26		.0001	.0004	.0011	.0030	.0071	.0151	.0295	.0528	.0875
27			.0001	.0005	.0014	.0035	.0081	.0168	.0318	.0558
28			.0001	.0002	.0006	.0017	.0041	.0091	.0184	.0342
29				.0001	.0003	.0008	.0020	.0048	.0102	.0200
30					.0001	.0003	.0009	.0024	.0054	.0112
31						.0001	.0004	.0011	.0027	.0061
32						.0001	.0002	.0005	.0013	.0031
33							.0001	.0002	.0006	.0016
34								.0001	.0003	.0007
35									.0001	.0003
36										.0001
37										.0001

Table B-4.   Cumulative Binomial Distribution (*Continued*)

n = 100

x* P	.21	.22	.23	.24	.25	.30	.35	.40	.45	.50
1	1.0000	1.0000	1.0000	1.0000	1.0000	1.0000	1.0000	1.0000	1.0000	1.0000
2	1.0000	1.0000	1.0000	1.0000	1.0000	1.0000	1.0000	1.0000	1.0000	1.0000
3	1.0000	1.0000	1.0000	1.0000	1.0000	1.0000	1.0000	1.0000	1.0000	1.0000
4	1.0000	1.0000	1.0000	1.0000	1.0000	1.0000	1.0000	1.0000	1.0000	1.0000
5	1.0000	1.0000	1.0000	1.0000	1.0000	1.0000	1.0000	1.0000	1.0000	1.0000
6	1.0000	1.0000	1.0000	1.0000	1.0000	1.0000	1.0000	1.0000	1.0000	1.0000
7	1.0000	1.0000	1.0000	1.0000	1.0000	1.0000	1.0000	1.0000	1.0000	1.0000
8	.9999	1.0000	1.0000	1.0000	1.0000	1.0000	1.0000	1.0000	1.0000	1.0000
9	.9996	.9998	.9999	1.0000	1.0000	1.0000	1.0000	1.0000	1.0000	1.0000
10	.9989	.9995	.9998	.9999	1.0000	1.0000	1.0000	1.0000	1.0000	1.0000
11	.9971	.9986	.9993	.9997	.9999	1.0000	1.0000	1.0000	1.0000	1.0000
12	.9933	.9965	.9983	.9992	.9996	1.0000	1.0000	1.0000	1.0000	1.0000
13	.9857	.9922	.9959	.9979	.9990	1.0000	1.0000	1.0000	1.0000	1.0000
14	.9721	.9840	.9911	.9953	.9975	.9999	1.0000	1.0000	1.0000	1.0000
15	.9496	.9695	.9823	.9900	.9946	.9998	1.0000	1.0000	1.0000	1.0000
16	.9153	.9462	.9671	.9806	.9889	.9996	1.0000	1.0000	1.0000	1.0000
17	.8668	.9112	.9430	.9647	.9789	.9990	1.0000	1.0000	1.0000	1.0000
18	.8032	.8625	.9074	.9399	.9624	.9978	.9999	1.0000	1.0000	1.0000
19	.7252	.7991	.8585	.9038	.9370	.9955	.9999	1.0000	1.0000	1.0000
20	.6358	.7220	.7953	.8547	.9005	.9911	.9997	1.0000	1.0000	1.0000
21	.5394	.6338	.7189	.7918	.8512	.9835	.9992	1.0000	1.0000	1.0000
22	.4419	.5391	.6320	.7162	.7886	.9712	.9983	1.0000	1.0000	1.0000
23	.3488	.4432	.5388	.6304	.7136	.9521	.9966	.9999	1.0000	1.0000
24	.2649	.3514	.4444	.5386	.6289	.9245	.9934	.9997	1.0000	1.0000
25	.1933	.2684	.3539	.4455	.5383	.8864	.9879	.9994	1.0000	1.0000
26	.1355	.1972	.2717	.3561	.4465	.8369	.9789	.9988	1.0000	1.0000
27	.0911	.1393	.2009	.2748	.3583	.7756	.9649	.9976	.9999	1.0000
28	.0588	.0945	.1429	.2043	.2776	.7036	.9442	.9954	.9998	1.0000
29	.0364	.0616	.0978	.1463	.2075	.6232	.9152	.9916	.9996	1.0000
30	.0216	.0386	.0643	.1009	.1495	.5377	.8764	.9852	.9992	1.0000
31	.0123	.0232	.0406	.0669	.1038	.4509	.8270	.9752	.9985	1.0000
32	.0067	.0134	.0247	.0427	.0693	.3669	.7669	.9602	.9970	.9999
33	.0035	.0074	.0144	.0262	.0446	.2893	.6971	.9385	.9945	.9998
34	.0018	.0039	.0081	.0154	.0276	.2207	.6197	.9087	.9902	.9996
35	.0009	.0020	.0044	.0087	.0164	.1629	.5376	.8697	.9834	.9991

Table B-4. Cumulative Binomial Distribution (*Continued*)

n = 100

x* / P	.21	.22	.23	.24	.25	.30	.35	.40	.45	.50
36	.0004	.0010	.0023	.0048	.0094	.1161	.4542	.8205	.9728	.9982
37	.0002	.0005	.0011	.0025	.0052	.0799	.3731	.7614	.9571	.9967
38	.0001	.0002	.0005	.0013	.0027	.0530	.2976	.6932	.9349	.9940
39		.0001	.0002	.0006	.0014	.0340	.2301	.6178	.9049	.9895
40			.0001	.0003	.0007	.0210	.1724	.5379	.8657	.9824
41				.0001	.0003	.0125	.1250	.4567	.8169	.9716
42				.0001	.0001	.0072	.0877	.3775	.7585	.9557
43					.0001	.0040	.0594	.3033	.6913	.9334
44						.0021	.0389	.2365	.6172	.9033
45						.0011	.0246	.1789	.5387	.8644
46						.0005	.0150	.1311	.4587	.8159
47						.0003	.0088	.0930	.3804	.7579
48						.0001	.0050	.0638	.3069	.6914
49						.0001	.0027	.0423	.2404	.6178
50							.0015	.0271	.1827	.5398
51							.0007	.0168	.1346	.4602
52							.0004	.0100	.0960	.3822
53							.0002	.0058	.0662	.3086
54							.0001	.0032	.0441	.2421
55								.0017	.0284	.1841
56								.0009	.0176	.1356
57								.0004	.0106	.0967
58								.0002	.0061	.0666
59								.0001	.0034	.0443
60									.0018	.0284
61									.0009	.0176
62									.0005	.0105
63									.0002	.0060
64									.0001	.0033
65										.0018
66										.0009
67										.0004
68										.0002
69										.0001

Table B-5. Areas under the Normal Curve

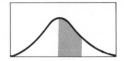

z	0.00	0.01	0.02	0.03	0.04	0.05	0.06	0.07	0.08	0.09
0.0	.00000	.00399	.00798	.01197	.01595	.01994	.02392	.02790	.03188	.03586
0.1	.03983	.04380	.04776	.05172	.05567	.05962	.06356	.06749	.07142	.07535
0.2	.07926	.08317	.08706	.09095	.09483	.09871	.10257	.10642	.11026	.11409
0.3	.11791	.12172	.12552	.12930	.13307	.13683	.14058	.14431	.14803	.15173
0.4	.15542	.15910	.16276	.16640	.17003	.17364	.17724	.18082	.18439	.18793
0.5	.19146	.19497	.19847	.20194	.20540	.20884	.21226	.21566	.21904	.22240
0.6	.22575	.22907	.23237	.23565	.23891	.24215	.24537	.24857	.25175	.25490
0.7	.25804	.26115	.26424	.26730	.27035	.27337	.27637	.27935	.28230	.28524
0.8	.28814	.29103	.29389	.29673	.29955	.30234	.30511	.30785	.31057	.31327
0.9	.31594	.31859	.32121	.32381	.32639	.32894	.33147	.33398	.33646	.33891
1.0	.34134	.34375	.34614	.34850	.35083	.35314	.35543	.35769	.35993	.36214
1.1	.36433	.36650	.36864	.37076	.37286	.37493	.37698	.37900	.38100	.38298
1.2	.38493	.38686	.38877	.39065	.39251	.39435	.39617	.39796	.39973	.40147
1.3	.40320	.40490	.40658	.40824	.40988	.41149	.41309	.41466	.41621	.41774
1.4	.41924	.42073	.42220	.42364	.42507	.42647	.42786	.42922	.43056	.43189
1.5	.43319	.43448	.43574	.43699	.43822	.43943	.44062	.44179	.44295	.44408
1.6	.44520	.44630	.44738	.44845	.44950	.45053	.45154	.45254	.45352	.45449
1.7	.45543	.45637	.45728	.45818	.45907	.45994	.46080	.46164	.46246	.46327
1.8	.46407	.46485	.46562	.46638	.46712	.46784	.46856	.46926	.46995	.47062
1.9	.47128	.47193	.47257	.47320	.47381	.47441	.47500	.47558	.47615	.47670
2.0	.47725	.47778	.47831	.47882	.47932	.47982	.48030	.48077	.48124	.48169
2.1	.48214	.48257	.48300	.48341	.48382	.48422	.48461	.48500	.48537	.48574
2.2	.48610	.48645	.48679	.48713	.48745	.48778	.48809	.48840	.48870	.48899
2.3	.48928	.48956	.48983	.49010	.49036	.49061	.49086	.49111	.49134	.49158
2.4	.49180	.49202	.49224	.49245	.49266	.49286	.49305	.49324	.49343	.49361
2.5	.49377	.49396	.49413	.49430	.49446	.49461	.49477	.49492	.49506	.49520
2.6	.49534	.49547	.49560	.49573	.49585	.49598	.49609	.49621	.49632	.49643
2.7	.49653	.49664	.49674	.49683	.49693	.49702	.49711	.49720	.49728	.49736
2.8	.49744	.49752	.49760	.49767	.49774	.49781	.49788	.49795	.49801	.49807
2.9	.49813	.49819	.49825	.49831	.49836	.49841	.49846	.49851	.49856	.49861
3.0	.49865	.49869	.49874	.49878	.49882	.49886	.49889	.49893	.49897	.49900
3.1	.49903	.49906	.49910	.49913	.49916	.49918	.49921	.49924	.49926	.49929
3.2	.49931	.49934	.49936	.49938	.49940	.49942	.49944	.49946	.49948	.49950
3.3	.49952	.49953	.49955	.49957	.49958	.49960	.49961	.49962	.49964	.49965
3.4	.49966	.49968	.49969	.49970	.49971	.49972	.49973	.49974	.49975	.49976
3.5	.49977	.49978	.49978	.49979	.49980	.49981	.49981	.49982	.49983	.49983
3.6	.49984	.49985	.49985	.49986	.49986	.49987	.49987	.49988	.49988	.49989
3.7	.49989	.49990	.49990	.49990	.49991	.49991	.49992	.49992	.49992	.49992
3.8	.49993	.49993	.49993	.49994	.49994	.49994	.49994	.49995	.49995	.49995
3.9	.49995	.49995	.49996	.49996	.49996	.49996	.49996	.49996	.49997	.49997
4.0	.49997	.49997	.49997	.49997	.49997	.49997	.49998	.49998	.49998	.49998

Table B-6.   Selected Tail Areas under the Normal Curve

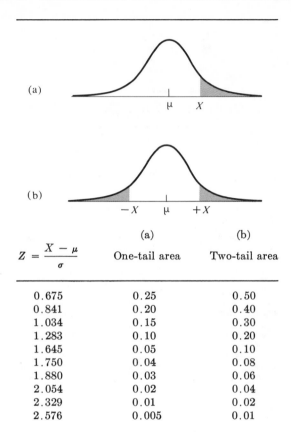

$Z = \dfrac{X - \mu}{\sigma}$	(a) One-tail area	(b) Two-tail area
0.675	0.25	0.50
0.841	0.20	0.40
1.034	0.15	0.30
1.283	0.10	0.20
1.645	0.05	0.10
1.750	0.04	0.08
1.880	0.03	0.06
2.054	0.02	0.04
2.329	0.01	0.02
2.576	0.005	0.01

Table B-7.   Values of e^{-x}

x	e^{-x}	x	e^{-x}	x	e^{-x}	x	e^{-x}
0.00	1.00000	0.50	.60653	1.00	.36788	1.50	.22313
0.01	0.99005	0.51	.60050	1.01	.36422	1.51	.22091
0.02	.98020	0.52	.59452	1.02	.36059	1.52	.21871
0.03	.97045	0.53	.58860	1.03	.35701	1.53	.21654
0.04	.96079	0.54	.58275	1.04	.35345	1.54	.21438
0.05	.95123	0.55	.57695	1.05	.34994	1.55	.21225
0.06	.94176	0.56	.57121	1.06	.34646	1.56	.21014
0.07	.93239	0.57	.56553	1.07	.34301	1.57	.20805
0.08	.92312	0.58	.55990	1.08	.33960	1.58	.20598
0.09	.91393	0.59	.55433	1.09	.33622	1.59	.20393
0.10	.90484	0.60	.54881	1.10	.33287	1.60	.20190
0.11	.89583	0.61	.54335	1.11	.32956	1.61	.19989
0.12	.88692	0.62	.53794	1.12	.32628	1.62	.19790
0.13	.87810	0.63	.53259	1.13	.32303	1.63	.19593
0.14	.86936	0.64	.52729	1.14	.31982	1.64	.19398
0.15	.86071	0.65	.52205	1.15	.31664	1.65	.19205
0.16	.85214	0.66	.51685	1.16	.31349	1.66	.19014
0.17	.84366	0.67	.51171	1.17	.31037	1.67	.18825
0.18	.83527	0.68	.50662	1.18	.30728	1.68	.18637
0.19	.82696	0.69	.50158	1.19	.30422	1.69	.18452
0.20	.81873	0.70	.49659	1.20	.30119	1.70	.18268
0.21	.81058	0.71	.49164	1.21	.29820	1.71	.18087
0.22	.80252	0.72	.48675	1.22	.29523	1.72	.17907
0.23	.79453	0.73	.48191	1.23	.29229	1.73	.17728
0.24	.78663	0.74	.47711	1.24	.28938	1.74	.17552
0.25	.77880	0.75	.47237	1.25	.28650	1.75	.17377
0.26	.77105	0.76	.46767	1.26	.28365	1.76	.17204
0.27	.76338	0.77	.46301	1.27	.28083	1.77	.17033
0.28	.75578	0.78	.45841	1.28	.27804	1.78	.16864
0.29	.74826	0.79	.45384	1.29	.27527	1.79	.16696
0.30	.74082	0.80	.44933	1.30	.27253	1.80	.16530
0.31	.73345	0.81	.44486	1.31	.26982	1.81	.16365
0.32	.72615	0.82	.44043	1.32	.26714	1.82	.16203
0.33	.71892	0.83	.43605	1.33	.26448	1.83	.16041
0.34	.71177	0.84	.43171	1.34	.26185	1.84	.15882
0.35	.70469	0.85	.42741	1.35	.25924	1.85	.15724
0.36	.69768	0.86	.42316	1.36	.25666	1.86	.15567
0.37	.69073	0.87	.41895	1.37	.25411	1.87	.15412
0.38	.68386	0.88	.41478	1.38	.25158	1.88	.15259
0.39	.67706	0.89	.41066	1.39	.24908	1.89	.15107
0.40	.67032	0.90	.40657	1.40	.24660	1.90	.14957
0.41	.66365	0.91	.40252	1.41	.24414	1.91	.14808
0.42	.65705	0.92	.39852	1.42	.24171	1.92	.14661
0.43	.65051	0.93	.39455	1.43	.23931	1.93	.14515
0.44	.64404	0.94	.39063	1.44	.23693	1.94	.14370
0.45	.63763	0.95	.38674	1.45	.23457	1.95	.14227
0.46	.63128	0.96	.38289	1.46	.23224	1.96	.14086
0.47	.62500	0.97	.37908	1.47	.22993	1.97	.13946
0.48	.61878	0.98	.37531	1.48	.22764	1.98	.13807
0.49	.61263	0.99	.37158	1.49	.22537	1.99	.13670

Source: R. S. Burington and D. C. May, *Handbook of Probability and Statistics with Tables*, 1953, McGraw-Hill Book Company, Inc., by permission of the publisher.

Table B-7. Values of e^{-x} (*Continued*)

x	e^{-x}	x	e^{-x}	x	e^{-x}	x	e^{-x}
2.00	.13534	2.40	.09072	2.80	.06081	4.00	.01832
2.01	.13399	2.41	.08982	2.81	.06020	4.10	.01657
2.02	.13266	2.42	.08892	2.82	.05961	4.20	.01500
2.03	.13134	2.43	.08804	2.83	.05901	4.30	.01357
2.04	.13003	2.44	.08716	2.84	.05843	4.40	.01228
2.05	.12873	2.45	.08629	2.85	.05784	4.50	.01111
2.06	.12745	2.46	.08544	2.86	.05727	4.60	.01005
2.07	.12619	2.47	.08458	2.87	.05670	4.70	.00910
2.08	.12493	2.48	.08374	2.88	.05613	4.80	.00823
2.09	.12369	2.49	.08291	2.89	.05558	4.90	.00745
2.10	.12246	2.50	.08208	2.90	.05502	5.00	.00674
2.11	.12124	2.51	.08127	2.91	.05448	5.10	.00610
2.12	.12003	2.52	.08046	2.92	.05393	5.20	.00552
2.13	.11884	2.53	.07966	2.93	.05340	5.30	.00499
2.14	.11765	2.54	.07887	2.94	.05287	5.40	.00452
2.15	.11648	2.55	.07808	2.95	.05234	5.50	.00409
2.16	.11533	2.56	.07730	2.96	.05182	5.60	.00370
2.17	.11418	2.57	.07654	2.97	.05130	5.70	.00335
2.18	.11304	2.58	.07577	2.98	.05079	5.80	.00303
2.19	.11192	2.59	.07502	2.99	.05029	5.90	.00274
2.20	.11080	2.60	.07427	3.00	.04979	6.00	.00248
2.21	.10970	2.61	.07353	3.05	.04736	6.25	.00193
2.22	.10861	2.62	.07280	3.10	.04505	6.50	.00150
2.23	.10753	2.63	.07208	3.15	.04285	6.75	.00117
2.24	.10646	2.64	.07136	3.20	.04076	7.00	.00091
2.25	.10540	2.65	.07065	3.25	.03877	7.50	.00055
2.26	.10435	2.66	.06995	3.30	.03688	8.00	.00034
2.27	.10331	2.67	.06925	3.35	.03508	8.50	.00020
2.28	.10228	2.68	.06856	3.40	.03337	9.00	.00012
2.29	.10127	2.69	.06788	3.45	.03175	9.50	.00007
2.30	.10026	2.70	.06721	3.50	.03020	10.00	.00005
2.31	.09926	2.71	.06654	3.55	.02872		
2.32	.09827	2.72	.06587	3.60	.02732		
2.33	.09730	2.73	.06522	3.65	.02599		
2.34	.09633	2.74	.06457	3.70	.02472		
2.35	.09537	2.75	.06393	3.75	.02352		
2.36	.09442	2.76	.06329	3.80	.02237		
2.37	.09348	2.77	.06266	3.85	.02128		
2.38	.09255	2.78	.06204	3.90	.02024		
2.39	.09163	2.79	.06142	3.95	.01925		

Table B-8. Cumulative Poisson Distribution Function

$$P(X \geq x|c) = \sum_{X=x}^{X=\infty} (e^{-c}c^x/X!)$$

x	0.1	0.2	0.3	0.4	0.5	0.6	0.7	0.8	0.9	1.0
0	1.0000	1.0000	1.0000	1.0000	1.0000	1.0000	1.0000	1.0000	1.0000	1.0000
1	.0952	.1813	.2592	.3297	.3935	.4512	.5034	.5507	.5934	.6321
2	.0047	.0175	.0369	.0616	.0902	.1219	.1558	.1912	.2275	.2642
3	.0002	.0011	.0036	.0079	.0144	.0231	.0341	.0474	.0629	.0803
4	.0000	.0001	.0003	.0008	.0018	.0034	.0058	.0091	.0135	.0190
5	.0000	.0000	.0000	.0001	.0002	.0004	.0008	.0014	.0023	.0037
6	.0000	.0000	.0000	.0000	.0000	.0000	.0001	.0002	.0003	.0006
7	.0000	.0000	.0000	.0000	.0000	.0000	.0000	.0000	.0000	.0001

x	1.1	1.2	1.3	1.4	1.5	1.6	1.7	1.8	1.9	2.0
0	1.0000	1.0000	1.0000	1.0000	1.0000	1.0000	1.0000	1.0000	1.0000	1.0000
1	.6671	.6988	.7275	.7534	.7769	.7981	.8173	.8347	.8504	.8647
2	.3010	.3374	.3732	.4082	.4422	.4751	.5068	.5372	.5663	.5940
3	.0996	.1205	.1429	.1665	.1912	.2166	.2428	.2694	.2963	.3233
4	.0257	.0338	.0431	.0537	.0656	.0788	.0932	.1087	.1253	.1429
5	.0054	.0077	.0107	.0143	.0186	.0237	.0296	.0364	.0441	.0527
6	.0010	.0015	.0022	.0032	.0045	.0060	.0080	.0104	.0132	.0166
7	.0001	.0003	.0004	.0006	.0009	.0013	.0019	.0026	.0034	.0045
8	.0000	.0000	.0001	.0001	.0002	.0003	.0004	.0006	.0008	.0011
9	.0000	.0000	.0000	.0000	.0000	.0000	.0001	.0001	.0002	.0002

x	2.1	2.2	2.3	2.4	2.5	2.6	2.7	2.8	2.9	3.0
0	1.0000	1.0000	1.0000	1.0000	1.0000	1.0000	1.0000	1.0000	1.0000	1.0000
1	.8775	.8892	.8997	.9093	.9179	.9257	.9328	.9392	.9450	.9502
2	.6204	.6454	.6691	.6916	.7127	.7326	.7513	.7689	.7854	.8009
3	.3504	.3773	.4040	.4303	.4562	.4816	.5064	.5305	.5540	.5768
4	.1614	.1806	.2007	.2213	.2424	.2640	.2859	.3081	.3304	.3528
5	.0621	.0725	.0838	.0959	.1088	.1226	.1371	.1523	.1682	.1847
6	.0204	.0249	.0300	.0357	.0420	.0490	.0567	.0651	.0742	.0839
7	.0059	.0075	.0094	.0116	.0142	.0172	.0206	.0244	.0287	.0335
8	.0015	.0020	.0026	.0033	.0042	.0053	.0066	.0081	.0099	.0119
9	.0003	.0005	.0006	.0009	.0011	.0015	.0019	.0024	.0031	.0038
10	.0001	.0001	.0001	.0002	.0003	.0004	.0005	.0007	.0009	.0011
11	.0000	.0000	.0000	.0000	.0001	.0001	.0001	.0002	.0002	.0003
12	.0000	.0000	.0000	.0000	.0000	.0000	.0000	.0000	.0001	.0001

x	3.1	3.2	3.3	3.4	3.5	3.6	3.7	3.8	3.9	4.0
0	1.0000	1.0000	1.0000	1.0000	1.0000	1.0000	1.0000	1.0000	1.0000	1.0000
1	.9550	.9592	.9631	.9666	.9698	.9727	.9753	.9776	.9798	.9817
2	.8153	.8288	.8414	.8532	.8641	.8743	.8838	.8926	.9008	.9084
3	.5988	.6201	.6406	.6603	.6792	.6973	.7146	.7311	.7469	.7619
4	.3752	.3975	.4197	.4416	.4634	.4848	.5058	.5265	.5468	.5665
5	.2018	.2194	.2374	.2558	.2746	.2936	.3128	.3322	.3516	.3712
6	.0943	.1054	.1171	.1295	.1424	.1559	.1699	.1844	.1994	.2149
7	.0388	.0446	.0510	.0579	.0653	.0733	.0818	.0909	.1005	.1107
8	.0142	.0168	.0198	.0231	.0267	.0308	.0352	.0401	.0454	.0511
9	.0047	.0057	.0069	.0083	.0099	.0117	.0137	.0160	.0185	.0214
10	.0014	.0018	.0022	.0027	.0033	.0040	.0048	.0058	.0069	.0081
11	.0004	.0005	.0006	.0008	.0010	.0013	.0016	.0019	.0023	.0028
12	.0001	.0001	.0002	.0002	.0003	.0004	.0005	.0006	.0007	.0009
13	.0000	.0000	.0000	.0001	.0001	.0001	.0001	.0002	.0002	.0003
14	.0000	.0000	.0000	.0000	.0000	.0000	.0000	.0000	.0001	.0001

Source: R. S. Burington and D. C. May, *Handbook of Probability and Statistics with Tables*, 1953, McGraw-Hill Book Company, Inc., by permission of the publisher.

Table B-8. Cumulative Poisson Distribution Function
(Continued)

x	4.1	4.2	4.3	4.4	4.5	4.6	4.7	4.8	4.9	5.0
0	1.0000	1.0000	1.0000	1.0000	1.0000	1.0000	1.0000	1.0000	1.0000	1.0000
1	.9834	.9850	.9864	.9877	.9889	.9899	.9909	.9918	.9926	.9933
2	.9155	.9220	.9281	.9337	.9389	.9437	.9482	.9523	.9561	.9596
3	.7762	.7898	.8026	.8149	.8264	.8374	.8477	.8575	.8667	.8753
4	.5858	.6046	.6228	.6406	.6577	.6743	.6903	.7058	.7207	.7350
5	.3907	.4102	.4296	.4488	.4679	.4868	.5054	.5237	.5418	.5595
6	.2307	.2469	.2633	.2801	.2971	.3142	.3316	.3490	.3665	.3840
7	.1214	.1325	.1442	.1564	.1689	.1820	.1954	.2092	.2233	.2378
8	.0573	.0639	.0710	.0786	.0866	.0951	.1040	.1133	.1231	.1334
9	.0245	.0279	.0317	.0358	.0403	.0451	.0503	.0558	.0618	.0681
10	.0095	.0111	.0129	.0149	.0171	.0195	.0222	.0251	.0283	.0318
11	.0034	.0041	.0048	.0057	.0067	.0078	.0090	.0104	.0120	.0137
12	.0011	.0014	.0017	.0020	.0024	.0029	.0034	.0040	.0047	.0055
13	.0003	.0004	.0005	.0007	.0008	.0010	.0012	.0014	.0017	.0020
14	.0001	.0001	.0002	.0002	.0003	.0003	.0004	.0005	.0006	.0007
15	.0000	.0000	.0000	.0001	.0001	.0001	.0001	.0001	.0002	.0002
16	.0000	.0000	.0000	.0000	.0000	.0000	.0000	.0000	.0001	.0001

x	5.1	5.2	5.3	5.4	5.5	5.6	5.7	5.8	5.9	6.0
0	1.0000	1.0000	1.0000	1.0000	1.0000	1.0000	1.0000	1.0000	1.0000	1.0000
1	.9939	.9945	.9950	.9955	.9959	.9963	.9967	.9970	.9973	.9975
2	.9628	.9658	.9686	.9711	.9734	.9756	.9776	.9794	.9811	.9826
3	.8835	.8912	.8984	.9052	.9116	.9176	.9232	.9285	.9334	.9380
4	.7487	.7619	.7746	.7867	.7983	.8094	.8200	.8300	.8396	.8488
5	.5769	.5939	.6105	.6267	.6425	.6579	.6728	.6873	.7013	.7149
6	.4016	.4191	.4365	.4539	.4711	.4881	.5050	.5217	.5381	.5543
7	.2526	.2676	.2829	.2983	.3140	.3297	.3456	.3616	.3776	.3937
8	.1440	.1551	.1665	.1783	.1905	.2030	.2159	.2290	.2424	.2560
9	.0748	.0819	.0894	.0974	.1056	.1143	.1234	.1328	.1426	.1528
10	.0356	.0397	.0441	.0488	.0538	.0591	.0648	.0708	.0772	.0839
11	.0156	.0177	.0200	.0225	.0253	.0282	.0314	.0349	.0386	.0426
12	.0063	.0073	.0084	.0096	.0110	.0125	.0141	.0160	.0179	.0201
13	.0024	.0028	.0033	.0038	.0045	.0051	.0059	.0068	.0078	.0088
14	.0008	.0010	.0012	.0014	.0017	.0020	.0023	.0027	.0031	.0036
15	.0003	.0003	.0004	.0005	.0006	.0007	.0009	.0010	.0012	.0014
16	.0001	.0001	.0001	.0002	.0002	.0002	.0003	.0004	.0004	.0005
17	.0000	.0000	.0000	.0001	.0001	.0001	.0001	.0001	.0001	.0002
18	.0000	.0000	.0000	.0000	.0000	.0000	.0000	.0000	.0000	.0001

x	6.1	6.2	6.3	6.4	6.5	6.6	6.7	6.8	6.9	7.0
0	1.0000	1.0000	1.0000	1.0000	1.0000	1.0000	1.0000	1.0000	1.0000	1.0000
1	.9978	.9980	.9982	.9983	.9985	.9986	.9988	.9989	.9990	.9991
2	.9841	.9854	.9866	.9877	.9887	.9897	.9905	.9913	.9920	.9927
3	.9423	.9464	.9502	.9537	.9570	.9600	.9629	.9656	.9680	.9704
4	.8575	.8658	.8736	.8811	.8882	.8948	.9012	.9072	.9129	.9182
5	.7281	.7408	.7531	.7649	.7763	.7873	.7978	.8080	.8177	.8270
6	.5702	.5859	.6012	.6163	.6310	.6453	.6594	.6730	.6863	.6993
7	.4098	.4258	.4418	.4577	.4735	.4892	.5047	.5201	.5353	.5503
8	.2699	.2840	.2983	.3127	.3272	.3419	.3567	.3715	.3864	.4013
9	.1633	.1741	.1852	.1967	.2084	.2204	.2327	.2452	.2580	.2709
10	.0910	.0984	.1061	.1142	.1226	.1314	.1404	.1498	.1505	.1695
11	.0469	.0514	.0563	.0614	.0668	.0726	.0786	.0849	.0916	.0985
12	.0224	.0250	.0277	.0307	.0339	.0373	.0409	.0448	.0490	.0534
13	.0100	.0113	.0127	.0143	.0160	.0179	.0199	.0221	.0245	.0270
14	.0042	.0048	.0055	.0063	.0071	.0080	.0091	.0102	.0115	.0128
15	.0016	.0019	.0022	.0026	.0030	.0034	.0039	.0044	.0050	.0057
16	.0006	.0007	.0008	.0010	.0012	.0014	.0016	.0018	.0021	.0024
17	.0002	.0003	.0003	.0004	.0004	.0005	.0006	.0007	.0008	.0010
18	.0001	.0001	.0001	.0001	.0002	.0002	.0002	.0003	.0003	.0004
19	.0000	.0000	.0000	.0000	.0001	.0001	.0001	.0001	.0001	.0001

Table B-8.   Cumulative Poisson Distribution Function
(Continued)

x	7.1	7.2	7.3	7.4	7.5	7.6	7.7	7.8	7.9	8.0
0	1.0000	1.0000	1.0000	1.0000	1.0000	1.0000	1.0000	1.0000	1.0000	1.0000
1	.9992	.9993	.9993	.9994	.9994	.9995	.9995	.9996	.9996	.9997
2	.9933	.9939	.9944	.9949	.9953	.9957	.9961	.9964	.9967	.9970
3	.9725	.9745	.9764	.9781	.9797	.9812	.9826	.9839	.9851	.9862
4	.9233	.9281	.9326	.9368	.9409	.9446	.9482	.9515	.9547	.9576
5	.8359	.8445	.8527	.8605	.8679	.8751	.8819	.8883	.8945	.9004
6	.7119	.7241	.7360	.7474	.7586	.7693	.7797	.7897	.7994	.8088
7	.5651	.5796	.5940	.6080	.6218	.6354	.6486	.6616	.6743	.6866
8	.4162	.4311	.4459	.4607	.4754	.4900	.5044	.5188	.5330	.5470
9	.2840	.2973	.3108	.3243	.3380	.3518	.3657	.3796	.3935	.4075
10	.1798	.1904	.2012	.2123	.2236	.2351	.2469	.2589	.2710	.2834
11	.1058	.1133	.1212	.1293	.1378	.1465	.1555	.1648	.1743	.1841
12	.0580	.0629	.0681	.0735	.0792	.0852	.0915	.0980	.1048	.1119
13	.0297	.0327	.0358	.0391	.0427	.0464	.0504	.0546	.0591	.0638
14	.0143	.0159	.0176	.0195	.0216	.0238	.0261	.0286	.0313	.0342
15	.0065	.0073	.0082	.0092	.0103	.0114	.0127	.0141	.0156	.0173
16	.0028	.0031	.0036	.0041	.0046	.0052	.0059	.0066	.0074	.0082
17	.0011	.0013	.0015	.0017	.0020	.0022	.0026	.0029	.0033	.0037
18	.0004	.0005	.0006	.0007	.0008	.0009	.0011	.0012	.0014	.0016
19	.0002	.0002	.0002	.0003	.0003	.0004	.0004	.0005	.0006	.0006
20	.0001	.0001	.0001	.0001	.0001	.0001	.0002	.0002	.0002	.0003
21	.0000	.0000	.0000	.0000	.0000	.0000	.0001	.0001	.0001	.0001

x	8.1	8.2	8.3	8.4	8.5	8.6	8.7	8.8	8.9	9.0
0	1.0000	1.0000	1.0000	1.0000	1.0000	1.0000	1.0000	1.0000	1.0000	1.0000
1	.9997	.9997	.9998	.9998	.9998	.9998	.9998	.9998	.9999	.9999
2	.9972	.9975	.9977	.9979	.9981	.9982	.9984	.9985	.9987	.9988
3	.9873	.9882	.9891	.9900	.9907	.9914	.9921	.9927	.9932	.9938
4	.9604	.9630	.9654	.9677	.9699	.9719	.9738	.9756	.9772	.9788
5	.9060	.9113	.9163	.9211	.9256	.9299	.9340	.9379	.9416	.9450
6	.8178	.8264	.8347	.8427	.8504	.8578	.8648	.8716	.8781	.8843
7	.6987	.7104	.7219	.7330	.7438	.7543	.7645	.7744	.7840	.7932
8	.5609	.5746	.5881	.6013	.6144	.6272	.6398	.6522	.6643	.6761
9	.4214	.4353	.4493	.4631	.4769	.4906	.5042	.5177	.5311	.5443
10	.2959	.3085	.3212	.3341	.3470	.3600	.3731	.3863	.3994	.4126
11	.1942	.2045	.2150	.2257	.2366	.2478	.2591	.2706	.2822	.2940
12	.1193	.1269	.1348	.1429	.1513	.1600	.1689	.1780	.1874	.1970
13	.0687	.0739	.0793	.0850	.0909	.0971	.1035	.1102	.1171	.1242
14	.0372	.0405	.0439	.0476	.0514	.0555	.0597	.0642	.0689	.0739
15	.0190	.0209	.0229	.0251	.0274	.0299	.0325	.0353	.0383	.0415
16	.0092	.0102	.0113	.0125	.0138	.0152	.0168	.0184	.0202	.0220
17	.0042	.0047	.0053	.0059	.0066	.0074	.0082	.0091	.0101	.0111
18	.0018	.0021	.0023	.0027	.0030	.0034	.0038	.0043	.0048	.0053
19	.0008	.0009	.0010	.0011	.0013	.0015	.0017	.0019	.0022	.0024
20	.0003	.0003	.0004	.0005	.0005	.0006	.0007	.0008	.0009	.0011
21	.0001	.0001	.0002	.0002	.0002	.0002	.0003	.0003	.0004	.0004
22	.0000	.0000	.0001	.0001	.0001	.0001	.0001	.0001	.0002	.0002
23	.0000	.0000	.0000	.0000	.0000	.0000	.0000	.0000	.0001	.0001

x	9.1	9.2	9.3	9.4	9.5	9.6	9.7	9.8	9.9	10
0	1.0000	1.0000	1.0000	1.0000	1.0000	1.0000	1.0000	1.0000	1.0000	1.0000
1	.9999	.9999	.9999	.9999	.9999	.9999	.9999	.9999	1.0000	1.0000
2	.9989	.9990	.9991	.9991	.9992	.9993	.9993	.9994	.9995	.9995
3	.9942	.9947	.9951	.9955	.9958	.9962	.9965	.9967	.9970	.9972
4	.9802	.9816	.9828	.9840	.9851	.9862	.9871	.9880	.9889	.9897
5	.9483	.9514	.9544	.9571	.9597	.9622	.9645	.9667	.9688	.9707
6	.8902	.8959	.9014	.9065	.9115	.9162	.9207	.9250	.9290	.9329
7	.8022	.8108	.8192	.8273	.8351	.8426	.8498	.8567	.8634	.8699
8	.6877	.6990	.7101	.7208	.7313	.7416	.7515	.7612	.7706	.7798
9	.5574	.5704	.5832	.5958	.6082	.6204	.6324	.6442	.6558	.6672

Table B-8.   Cumulative Poisson Distribution Function
(Continued)

					c					
x	9.1	9.2	9.3	9.4	9.5	9.6	9.7	9.8	9.9	10
10	.4258	.4389	.4521	.4651	.4782	.4911	.5040	.5168	.5295	.5421
11	.3059	.3180	.3301	.3424	.3547	.3671	.3795	.3920	.4045	.4170
12	.2068	.2168	.2270	.2374	.2480	.2588	.2697	.2807	.2919	.3032
13	.1316	.1393	.1471	.1552	.1636	.1721	.1809	.1899	.1991	.2084
14	.0790	.0844	.0900	.0958	.1019	.1081	.1147	.1214	.1284	.1355
15	.0448	.0483	.0520	.0559	.0600	.0643	.0688	.0735	.0784	.0835
16	.0240	.0262	.0285	.0309	.0335	.0362	.0391	.0421	.0454	.0487
17	.0122	.0135	.0148	.0162	.0177	.0194	.0211	.0230	.0249	.0270
18	.0059	.0066	.0073	.0081	.0089	.0098	.0108	.0119	.0130	.0143
19	.0027	.0031	.0034	.0038	.0043	.0048	.0053	.0059	.0065	.0072
20	.0012	.0014	.0015	.0017	.0020	.0022	.0025	.0028	.0031	.0035
21	.0005	.0006	.0007	.0008	.0009	.0010	.0011	.0013	.0014	.0016
22	.0002	.0002	.0003	.0003	.0004	.0004	.0005	.0005	.0006	.0007
23	.0001	.0001	.0001	.0001	.0001	.0002	.0002	.0002	.0003	.0003
24	.0000	.0000	.0000	.0000	.0001	.0001	.0001	.0001	.0001	.0001

					c					
x	11	12	13	14	15	16	17	18	19	20
0	1.0000	1.0000	1.0000	1.0000	1.0000	1.0000	1.0000	1.0000	1.0000	1.0000
1	1.0000	1.0000	1.0000	1.0000	1.0000	1.0000	1.0000	1.0000	1.0000	1.0000
2	.9998	.9999	1.0000	1.0000	1.0000	1.0000	1.0000	1.0000	1.0000	1.0000
3	.9988	.9995	.9998	.9999	1.0000	1.0000	1.0000	1.0000	1.0000	1.0000
4	.9951	.9977	.9990	.9995	.9998	.9999	1.0000	1.0000	1.0000	1.0000
5	.9849	.9924	.9963	.9982	.9991	.9996	.9998	.9999	1.0000	1.0000
6	.9625	.9797	.9893	.9945	.9972	.9986	.9993	.9997	.9998	.9999
7	.9214	.9542	.9741	.9858	.9924	.9960	.9979	.9990	.9995	.9997
8	.8568	.9105	.9460	.9684	.9820	.9900	.9946	.9971	.9985	.9992
9	.7680	.8450	.9002	.9379	.9626	.9780	.9874	.9929	.9961	.9979
10	.6595	.7576	.8342	.8906	.9301	.9567	.9739	.9846	.9911	.9950
11	.5401	.6528	.7483	.8243	.8815	.9226	.9509	.9696	.9817	.9892
12	.4207	.5384	.6468	.7400	.8152	.8730	.9153	.9451	.9653	.9786
13	.3113	.4240	.5369	.6415	.7324	.8069	.8650	.9083	.9394	.9610
14	.2187	.3185	.4270	.5356	.6368	.7255	.7991	.8574	.9016	.9339
15	.1460	.2280	.3249	.4296	.5343	.6325	.7192	.7919	.8503	.8951
16	.0926	.1556	.2364	.3306	.4319	.5333	.6285	.7133	.7852	.8435
17	.0559	.1013	.1645	.2441	.3359	.4340	.5323	.6250	.7080	.7789
18	.0322	.0630	.1095	.1728	.2511	.3407	.4360	.5314	.6216	.7030
19	.0177	.0374	.0698	.1174	.1805	.2577	.3450	.4378	.5305	.6186
20	.0093	.0213	.0427	.0765	.1248	.1878	.2637	.3491	.4394	.5297
21	.0047	.0116	.0250	.0479	.0830	.1318	.1945	.2693	.3528	.4409
22	.0023	.0061	.0141	.0288	.0531	.0892	.1385	.2009	.2745	.3563
23	.0010	.0030	.0076	.0167	.0327	.0582	.0953	.1449	.2069	.2794
24	.0005	.0015	.0040	.0093	.0195	.0367	.0633	.1011	.1510	.2125
25	.0002	.0007	.0020	.0050	.0112	.0223	.0406	.0683	.1067	.1568
26	.0001	.0003	.0010	.0026	.0062	.0131	.0252	.0446	.0731	.1122
27	.0000	.0001	.0005	.0013	.0033	.0075	.0152	.0282	.0486	.0779
28	.0000	.0001	.0002	.0006	.0017	.0041	.0088	.0173	.0313	.0525
29	.0000	.0000	.0001	.0003	.0009	.0022	.0050	.0103	.0195	.0343
30	.0000	.0000	.0000	.0001	.0004	.0011	.0027	.0059	.0118	.0218
31	.0000	.0000	.0000	.0001	.0002	.0006	.0014	.0033	.0070	.0135
32	.0000	.0000	.0000	.0000	.0001	.0003	.0007	.0018	.0040	.0081
33	.0000	.0000	.0000	.0000	.0000	.0001	.0004	.0010	.0022	.0047
34	.0000	.0000	.0000	.0000	.0000	.0001	.0002	.0005	.0012	.0027
35	.0000	.0000	.0000	.0000	.0000	.0000	.0001	.0002	.0006	.0015
36	.0000	.0000	.0000	.0000	.0000	.0000	.0000	.0001	.0003	.0008
37	.0000	.0000	.0000	.0000	.0000	.0000	.0000	.0001	.0002	.0004
38	.0000	.0000	.0000	.0000	.0000	.0000	.0000	.0000	.0001	.0002
39	.0000	.0000	.0000	.0000	.0000	.0000	.0000	.0000	.0000	.0001
40	.0000	.0000	.0000	.0000	.0000	.0000	.0000	.0000	.0000	.0001

Table B-9. Table of Random Digits

21923 99446	97749 47608	49463 49930	00846 25596	33278 54499
18948 20924	35354 62093	53114 76964	49227 06394	72015 74211
16110 20934	88646 26581	79223 67028	54422 95573	83624 43706
17691 67281	38079 50747	93250 43657	39761 50177	07883 43309
14766 64469	66659 14594	71769 45249	94860 48362	69057 74931
29848 52953	86270 94119	11436 18407	09464 49685	44659 37345
61444 20635	04972 11624	43178 67983	94876 85506	85855 21421
68449 59781	87662 22401	70652 26505	70821 44267	99787 61438
17061 27930	58298 37674	36144 32528	75961 35142	44040 61184
83150 47159	28921 13544	60808 24481	30359 27434	09271 93599
46632 17790	26799 51917	95608 90094	79720 74497	23920 63704
27778 87347	98620 08830	88659 00569	81648 10858	59166 47736
89391 11778	62918 74777	08105 90081	25341 70456	59260 40198
08526 25088	88178 70760	10484 72234	01239 54013	51569 09444
62490 95716	03530 86091	01130 04106	43691 90049	93873 25859
54639 92395	96951 22749	96622 80525	65739 14312	85026 01216
87368 05050	95651 45008	78899 58905	43080 34790	77286 78588
26753 87863	50225 08223	24086 76297	14074 02319	00520 87894
55714 18744	73575 14282	87944 37768	22375 13536	07157 29655
60420 50182	12903 64160	26327 85455	95589 68010	00472 86060
95935 96469	67484 17867	31609 60210	10385 50685	67636 46988
65722 45170	24641 93567	69602 30656	92997 91278	16516 26176
17075 28625	80639 72795	46906 80247	70992 61507	32565 34694
94180 26263	15523 44330	13112 06103	16838 06266	03126 06428
38322 21687	90943 14484	23312 45012	24277 75876	36780 13654
49421 72582	24282 04230	44745 30476	25317 04918	02361 62389
23156 14332	78440 55721	81506 04999	27570 66982	99175 14792
00818 51959	14953 60005	23089 08637	54310 13528	28818 51115
11290 89619	34592 00017	05704 89045	54043 09931	24011 25976
86941 52660	01437 20272	03528 05770	95802 39919	95385 60873
80674 06262	02508 17437	97927 48224	52456 60063	29986 20602
05895 69682	80949 60742	63115 87392	99110 06329	80405 11850
89804 23264	73942 66074	85732 10993	14855 71231	94284 41786
98993 91858	05221 92243	42316 74866	64176 29079	12166 98474
51205 57266	97808 48397	44510 04630	73891 67666	54807 46286
46788 52190	18902 45576	56604 86458	13686 64341	11270 38599
31101 84348	14363 73653	65258 89411	80722 77750	35931 31891
08520 35640	82136 20692	74161 18520	97797 00423	92239 69512
88287 99676	72179 23769	73187 91627	69774 81817	47697 28849
08544 55568	23496 08304	89290 64704	06729 01524	17406 64292

Table B-9. Table of Random Digits (*Continued*)

23816 11611	10616 48187	28894 09517	48910 51659	96889 22624
48195 70034	72123 21058	95293 77962	92476 02282	63505 04436
35662 74568	90647 85690	14423 97994	23182 07304	08392 50904
59002 88820	74552 41176	72465 75395	73819 34238	00712 95107
09825 35407	43038 74793	16199 86293	14860 44753	15365 21341
52005 63159	38677 34082	55610 86448	23580 36656	10358 43925
90847 09531	20391 60583	86040 51185	43195 34499	83312 53232
00641 31827	27615 89254	16980 82984	95419 63555	17465 68346
06723 37379	69741 18905	97074 33794	69696 78441	44547 33449
25363 01997	55099 40432	07530 17171	38195 94838	83639 39019
66202 75336	02380 29585	02331 12577	18159 51663	97121 94918
98295 95560	35665 42715	49550 69165	76258 65672	82399 81294
97789 90513	35523 54306	26364 31090	58564 46264	09020 02046
69789 39829	78016 61493	47228 01787	52571 04198	18385 92803
79359 14628	61131 96439	35301 04281	77601 90439	93957 13348
38271 54967	58046 22950	97533 61932	05199 65968	69784 25659
74954 11139	32340 00238	54081 63766	66274 09771	17051 60843
07307 64629	26239 48758	23827 43391	20177 40870	98937 29599
18845 62518	18714 46143	95452 76606	30595 72063	83891 79900
24906 00057	96306 59876	69024 96413	38830 89175	78687 45028
68777 10246	14622 24331	37787 30227	64433 07861	28727 34831
78989 32573	83812 49912	85129 29186	44922 35424	13594 92872
54256 26266	51135 60044	85460 84862	47463 12435	15046 79651
96249 23916	76229 14080	06483 14151	98774 00028	18640 64752
07429 76930	53721 34495	38931 78251	95052 16277	47396 46789
24681 48533	22599 90887	98008 60962	24811 34763	66474 03786
03196 98720	46994 17846	94951 88339	05038 93022	95803 12528
17221 11876	29510 05095	78868 31802	20370 89725	67764 44090
39758 24072	57748 12412	30509 81872	18221 20199	82044 70214
21104 58690	70392 78216	44028 03822	50398 56276	90547 71811
86789 09687	07986 47002	13014 63742	02099 75820	82044 69327
63266 27011	59694 98222	81798 34205	87578 17336	31813 82937
07554 10383	37671 45963	05971 95481	16368 86447	79947 20081
98607 46940	73300 96970	84101 79023	46579 59290	66583 90371
23823 78360	11580 40189	45856 61735	62884 03102	02639 03941
73600 63776	87983 53747	06220 48741	68478 52122	62281 28519
61562 34366	11515 33088	49878 32911	17495 68800	53273 67119
04602 61346	37760 91761	58135 50143	93076 11535	33425 96337
42539 10741	57760 68890	70512 01333	45295 71454	07430 64721
33813 32180	85317 63692	26463 01931	48009 77874	92997 78006

Table B-9.   Table of Random Digits (*Continued*)

49344 33448	34945 22704	66567 30722	06148 81139	53308 14483
01565 63683	95791 95254	10324 95952	93544 57515	90896 51772
45906 70975	73203 32961	96695 53678	44046 54054	90040 34785
83459 35685	07769 93214	00710 53857	66118 42274	77031 07622
92735 35048	62889 96468	44148 39783	70408 70499	71823 67041
47019 80469	03538 88628	26423 75962	38536 31216	77099 19365
61368 93270	64631 39496	04404 96681	38984 01883	84856 11917
48072 06002	87096 88383	33341 88461	95866 23735	80950 88576
64913 26273	31344 37751	46301 67602	70440 07056	68791 24448
45104 51726	02912 75688	98726 39605	67033 08026	16081 01095
18833 00839	59643 02764	26120 93217	24393 28615	62828 25217
50036 66634	64327 41672	18148 97047	13655 89572	67320 77405
29840 26164	98840 91773	72584 82187	23688 94165	39714 12687
75637 33488	84531 92203	18124 56614	47340 17734	62161 22768
54581 12473	81761 62984	58169 96305	41467 62127	28160 62715
46718 30101	95947 78632	50692 93664	01953 39231	86649 48634
68347 23612	52831 41755	90630 52182	12860 55284	10109 92970
92684 87323	99855 03427	79473 42282	17108 65655	54995 73161
11944 34009	51650 94274	23127 80111	08532 54826	79951 74711
87793 37576	32387 10209	47829 21125	93110 11206	81644 70227

Source: The Rand Corporation, *A Million Random Digits with 100,000 Normal Deviates*, The Free Press, 1955, pp. 316–317, by permission of the publisher.

Table B-10. Values of Chi Square

Degrees of freedom	Probability that chi-square value will be exceeded									
	0.995	0.990	0.975	0.950	0.900	0.100	0.050	0.025	0.010	0.005
1	0.0^4393	0.0^3157	0.0^3982	0.0^2393	0.0158	2.71	3.84	5.02	6.63	7.88
2	0.0100	0.0201	0.0506	0.103	0.211	4.61	5.99	7.38	9.21	10.60
3	0.072	0.115	0.216	0.352	0.584	6.25	7.81	9.35	11.34	12.84
4	0.207	0.297	0.484	0.711	1.064	7.78	9.49	11.14	13.28	14.86
5	0.412	0.554	0.831	1.145	1.61	9.24	11.07	12.83	15.09	16.75
6	0.676	0.872	1.24	1.64	2.20	10.64	12.59	14.45	16.81	18.55
7	0.989	1.24	1.69	2.17	2.83	12.02	14.07	16.01	18.48	20.28
8	1.34	1.65	2.18	2.73	3.49	13.36	15.51	17.53	20.09	21.96
9	1.73	2.09	2.70	3.33	4.17	14.68	16.92	19.02	21.67	23.59
10	2.16	2.56	3.25	3.94	4.87	15.99	18.31	20.48	23.21	25.19
11	2.60	3.05	3.82	4.57	5.58	17.28	19.68	21.92	24.72	26.76
12	3.07	3.57	4.40	5.23	6.30	18.55	21.03	23.34	26.22	28.30
13	3.57	4.11	5.01	5.89	7.04	19.81	22.36	24.74	27.69	29.82
14	4.07	4.66	5.63	6.57	7.79	21.06	23.68	26.12	29.14	31.32
15	4.60	5.23	6.26	7.26	8.55	22.31	25.00	27.49	30.58	32.80
16	5.14	5.81	6.91	7.96	9.31	23.54	26.30	28.85	32.00	34.27
17	5.70	6.41	7.56	8.67	10.09	24.77	27.59	30.19	33.41	35.72
18	6.26	7.01	8.23	9.39	10.86	25.99	28.87	31.53	34.81	37.16
19	6.84	7.63	8.91	10.12	11.65	27.20	30.14	32.85	36.19	38.58
20	7.43	8.26	9.59	10.85	12.44	28.41	31.41	34.17	37.57	40.00
21	8.03	8.90	10.28	11.59	13.24	29.62	32.67	35.48	38.93	41.40
22	8.64	9.54	10.98	12.34	14.04	30.81	33.92	36.78	40.29	42.80
23	9.26	10.20	11.69	13.09	14.85	32.01	35.17	38.08	41.64	44.18
24	9.89	10.86	12.40	13.85	15.66	33.20	36.42	39.36	42.98	45.56
25	10.52	11.52	13.12	14.61	16.47	34.38	37.65	40.65	44.31	46.93
26	11.16	12.20	13.84	15.38	17.29	35.56	38.89	41.92	45.64	48.29
27	11.81	12.88	14.57	16.15	18.11	36.74	40.11	43.19	46.96	49.64
28	12.46	13.56	15.31	16.93	18.94	37.92	41.34	44.46	48.28	50.99
29	13.12	14.26	16.05	17.71	19.77	39.09	42.56	45.72	49.59	52.34
30	13.79	14.95	16.79	18.49	20.60	40.26	43.77	46.98	50.89	53.67
40	20.71	22.16	24.43	26.51	29.05	51.80	55.76	59.34	63.69	66.77
50	27.99	29.71	32.36	34.76	37.69	63.17	67.50	71.42	76.15	79.49
60	35.53	37.48	40.48	43.19	46.46	74.40	79.08	83.30	88.38	91.95
70	43.28	45.44	48.76	51.74	55.33	85.53	90.53	95.02	100.4	104.22
80	51.17	53.54	57.15	60.39	64.28	96.58	101.9	106.6	112.3	116.32
90	59.20	61.75	65.65	69.13	73.29	107.6	113.1	118.1	124.1	128.3
100	67.33	70.06	74.22	77.93	82.36	118.5	124.3	129.6	135.8	140.2
z_α	-2.58	-2.33	-1.96	-1.64	-1.28	+1.28	+1.64	+1.96	+2.33	+2.58

Source: Adapted from E. S. Pearson and H. O. Hartley, Editors, *Biometrika Tables for Statisticians*, Volume I, Table 18, pp. 160–163, published for the Biometrika Trustees by Cambridge University, 1954, by permission of Professor Pearson and the Trustees of Biometrika.

Table B-11.   Factors for Estimating σ from the Average Range ($\bar{R}$)

$$\hat{\sigma} = \frac{\bar{R}}{d_2}$$

Sample Size† (n)	Factor $d_2 = \dfrac{\bar{R}}{\sigma}$
2	1.128
3	1.693
4	2.059
5	2.326
6	2.534
7	2.704
8	2.847
9	2.970
10	3.078
11	3.178
12	3.258

† For sample sizes larger than 12, it is advisable to use estimates based on direct computations of s or $\hat{\sigma}$.

Source: American Society for Testing Materials, *Manual on Quality Control of Materials*, Philadelphia, Pennsylvania, 1951, by permission of the publisher.

Table B-12. Two-Tail Areas of the t Distribution

Degrees of freedom	Probability												
	0.9	0.8	0.7	0.6	0.5	0.4	0.3	0.2	0.1	0.05	0.02	0.01	0.001
1	0.158	0.325	0.510	0.727	1.000	1.376	1.963	3.078	6.314	12.706	31.821	63.657	636.619
2	0.142	0.289	0.445	0.617	0.816	1.061	1.386	1.886	2.920	4.303	6.965	9.925	31.598
3	0.137	0.277	0.424	0.584	0.765	0.978	1.250	1.638	2.353	3.182	4.541	5.841	12.924
4	0.134	0.271	0.414	0.569	0.741	0.941	1.190	1.533	2.132	2.776	3.747	4.604	8.610
5	0.132	0.267	0.408	0.559	0.727	0.920	1.156	1.476	2.015	2.571	3.365	4.032	6.869
6	0.131	0.265	0.404	0.553	0.718	0.906	1.134	1.440	1.943	2.447	3.143	3.707	5.959
7	0.130	0.263	0.402	0.549	0.711	0.896	1.119	1.415	1.895	2.365	2.998	3.499	5.408
8	0.130	0.262	0.399	0.546	0.706	0.889	1.108	1.397	1.860	2.306	2.896	3.355	5.041
9	0.129	0.261	0.398	0.543	0.703	0.883	1.100	1.383	1.833	2.262	2.821	3.250	4.781
10	0.129	0.260	0.397	0.542	0.700	0.879	1.093	1.372	1.812	2.228	2.764	3.169	4.587
11	0.129	0.260	0.396	0.540	0.697	0.876	1.088	1.363	1.796	2.201	2.718	3.106	4.437
12	0.128	0.259	0.395	0.539	0.695	0.873	1.083	1.356	1.782	2.179	2.681	3.055	4.318
13	0.128	0.259	0.394	0.538	0.694	0.870	1.079	1.350	1.771	2.160	2.650	3.012	4.221
14	0.128	0.258	0.393	0.537	0.692	0.868	1.076	1.345	1.761	2.145	2.624	2.977	4.140
15	0.128	0.258	0.393	0.536	0.691	0.866	1.074	1.341	1.753	2.131	2.602	2.947	4.073
16	0.128	0.258	0.392	0.535	0.690	0.865	1.071	1.337	1.746	2.120	2.583	2.921	4.015
17	0.128	0.257	0.392	0.534	0.689	0.863	1.069	1.333	1.740	2.110	2.567	2.898	3.965
18	0.127	0.257	0.392	0.534	0.688	0.862	1.067	1.330	1.734	2.101	2.552	2.878	3.922
19	0.127	0.257	0.391	0.533	0.688	0.861	1.066	1.328	1.729	2.093	2.539	2.861	3.883
20	0.127	0.257	0.391	0.533	0.687	0.860	1.064	1.325	1.725	2.086	2.528	2.845	3.850
21	0.127	0.257	0.391	0.532	0.686	0.859	1.063	1.323	1.721	2.080	2.518	2.831	3.819
22	0.127	0.256	0.390	0.532	0.686	0.858	1.061	1.321	1.717	2.074	2.508	2.819	3.792
23	0.127	0.256	0.390	0.532	0.685	0.858	1.060	1.319	1.714	2.069	2.500	2.807	3.767
24	0.127	0.256	0.390	0.531	0.685	0.857	1.059	1.318	1.711	2.064	2.492	2.797	3.745
25	0.127	0.256	0.390	0.531	0.684	0.856	1.058	1.316	1.708	2.060	2.485	2.787	3.725
26	0.127	0.256	0.390	0.531	0.684	0.856	1.058	1.315	1.706	2.056	2.479	2.779	3.707
27	0.127	0.256	0.389	0.531	0.684	0.855	1.057	1.314	1.703	2.052	2.473	2.771	3.690
28	0.127	0.256	0.389	0.530	0.683	0.855	1.056	1.313	1.701	2.048	2.467	2.763	3.674
29	0.127	0.256	0.389	0.530	0.683	0.854	1.055	1.311	1.699	2.045	2.462	2.756	3.659
30	0.127	0.256	0.389	0.530	0.683	0.854	1.055	1.310	1.697	2.042	2.457	2.750	3.646
40	0.126	0.255	0.388	0.529	0.681	0.851	1.050	1.303	1.684	2.021	2.423	2.704	3.551
60	0.126	0.254	0.387	0.527	0.679	0.848	1.046	1.296	1.671	2.000	2.390	2.660	3.460
120	0.126	0.254	0.386	0.526	0.677	0.845	1.041	1.289	1.658	1.980	2.358	2.617	3.373
∞	0.126	0.253	0.385	0.524	0.674	0.842	1.036	1.282	1.645	1.960	2.326	2.576	3.291

Source: Table B-12 is reprinted from Table III of Ronald A. Fisher and Frank Yates, *Statistical Tables for Biological, Agricultural, and Medical Research*, 6th ed., Oliver & Boyd, Ltd., Edinburgh, 1963, by permission of the authors and publisher.

Table B-13.   Values of F.

Degrees of freedom for the numerator

Upper 10 per cent points

df for denominator	1	2	3	4	5	6	7	8	9	10	12	15	20	24	30	40	60	120	∞
1	39.86	49.50	53.59	55.83	57.24	58.20	58.91	59.44	59.86	60.20	60.70	61.22	61.74	62.00	62.26	62.53	62.79	63.06	63.33
2	8.53	9.00	9.16	9.24	9.29	9.33	9.35	9.37	9.38	9.39	9.41	9.42	9.44	9.45	9.46	9.47	9.47	9.48	9.49
3	5.54	5.46	5.39	5.34	5.31	5.28	5.27	5.25	5.24	5.23	5.22	5.20	5.18	5.18	5.17	5.16	5.15	5.14	5.13
4	4.54	4.32	4.19	4.11	4.05	4.01	3.98	3.95	3.94	3.92	3.90	3.87	3.84	3.83	3.82	3.80	3.79	3.78	3.76
5	4.06	3.78	3.62	3.52	3.45	3.40	3.37	3.34	3.32	3.30	3.27	3.24	3.21	3.19	3.17	3.16	3.14	3.12	3.10
6	3.78	3.46	3.29	3.18	3.11	3.05	3.01	2.98	2.96	2.94	2.90	2.87	2.84	2.82	2.80	2.78	2.76	2.74	2.72
7	3.59	3.26	3.07	2.96	2.88	2.83	2.78	2.76	2.72	2.70	2.67	2.63	2.59	2.58	2.56	2.54	2.51	2.49	2.47
8	3.46	3.11	2.92	2.81	2.73	2.67	2.62	2.59	2.56	2.54	2.50	2.46	2.42	2.40	2.38	2.36	2.34	2.32	2.29
9	3.36	3.01	2.81	2.69	2.61	2.55	2.51	2.47	2.44	2.42	2.38	2.34	2.30	2.28	2.25	2.23	2.21	2.18	2.16
10	3.28	2.92	2.73	2.61	2.52	2.46	2.41	2.38	2.35	2.32	2.28	2.24	2.20	2.18	2.16	2.13	2.11	2.08	2.06
11	3.23	2.86	2.66	2.54	2.45	2.39	2.34	2.30	2.27	2.25	2.21	2.17	2.12	2.10	2.08	2.05	2.03	2.00	1.97
12	3.18	2.81	2.61	2.48	2.39	2.33	2.28	2.24	2.21	2.19	2.15	2.10	2.06	2.04	2.01	1.99	1.96	1.93	1.90
13	3.14	2.76	2.56	2.43	2.35	2.28	2.23	2.20	2.16	2.14	2.10	2.05	2.01	1.98	1.96	1.93	1.90	1.88	1.85
14	3.10	2.73	2.52	2.39	2.31	2.24	2.19	2.15	2.12	2.10	2.05	2.01	1.96	1.94	1.91	1.89	1.86	1.83	1.80
15	3.07	2.70	2.49	2.36	2.27	2.21	2.16	2.12	2.09	2.06	2.02	1.97	1.92	1.90	1.87	1.85	1.82	1.79	1.76
16	3.05	2.67	2.46	2.33	2.24	2.18	2.13	2.09	2.06	2.03	1.99	1.94	1.89	1.87	1.84	1.81	1.78	1.75	1.72
17	3.03	2.64	2.44	2.31	2.22	2.15	2.10	2.06	2.03	2.00	1.96	1.91	1.86	1.84	1.81	1.78	1.75	1.72	1.69
18	3.01	2.62	2.42	2.29	2.20	2.13	2.08	2.04	2.00	1.98	1.93	1.89	1.84	1.81	1.78	1.75	1.72	1.69	1.66
19	2.99	2.61	2.40	2.27	2.18	2.11	2.06	2.02	1.98	1.96	1.91	1.86	1.81	1.79	1.76	1.73	1.70	1.67	1.63

Table B-13. Values of F (Continued)

Degrees of freedom for the numerator

Upper 10 per cent points

df for denominator	1	2	3	4	5	6	7	8	9	10	12	15	20	24	30	40	60	120	∞
20	2.97	2.59	2.38	2.25	2.16	2.09	2.04	2.00	1.96	1.94	1.89	1.84	1.79	1.77	1.74	1.71	1.68	1.64	1.61
21	2.96	2.57	2.36	2.23	2.14	2.08	2.02	1.98	1.95	1.92	1.87	1.83	1.78	1.75	1.72	1.69	1.66	1.62	1.59
22	2.95	2.56	2.35	2.22	2.13	2.06	2.01	1.97	1.93	1.90	1.86	1.81	1.76	1.73	1.70	1.67	1.64	1.60	1.57
23	2.94	2.55	2.34	2.21	2.11	2.05	1.99	1.95	1.92	1.89	1.85	1.80	1.74	1.72	1.69	1.66	1.62	1.59	1.55
24	2.93	2.54	2.33	2.19	2.10	2.04	1.98	1.94	1.91	1.88	1.83	1.78	1.73	1.70	1.67	1.64	1.61	1.57	1.53
25	2.92	2.53	2.32	2.18	2.09	2.02	1.97	1.93	1.89	1.87	1.82	1.77	1.72	1.69	1.66	1.63	1.59	1.56	1.52
26	2.91	2.52	2.31	2.17	2.08	2.01	1.96	1.92	1.88	1.86	1.81	1.76	1.71	1.68	1.65	1.61	1.58	1.54	1.50
27	2.90	2.51	2.30	2.17	2.07	2.00	1.95	1.91	1.87	1.85	1.80	1.75	1.70	1.67	1.64	1.60	1.57	1.53	1.49
28	2.89	2.50	2.29	2.16	2.06	2.00	1.94	1.90	1.87	1.84	1.79	1.74	1.69	1.66	1.63	1.59	1.56	1.52	1.48
29	2.89	2.50	2.28	2.15	2.06	1.99	1.93	1.89	1.86	1.83	1.78	1.73	1.68	1.65	1.62	1.58	1.55	1.51	1.47
30	2.88	2.49	2.28	2.14	2.05	1.98	1.93	1.88	1.85	1.82	1.77	1.72	1.67	1.64	1.61	1.57	1.54	1.50	1.46
40	2.84	2.44	2.23	2.09	2.00	1.93	1.87	1.83	1.79	1.76	1.71	1.66	1.61	1.57	1.54	1.51	1.47	1.42	1.38
60	2.79	2.39	2.18	2.04	1.95	1.87	1.82	1.77	1.74	1.71	1.66	1.60	1.54	1.51	1.48	1.44	1.40	1.35	1.29
120	2.75	2.35	2.13	1.99	1.90	1.82	1.77	1.72	1.68	1.65	1.60	1.54	1.48	1.45	1.41	1.37	1.32	1.26	1.19
∞	2.71	2.30	2.08	1.94	1.85	1.77	1.72	1.67	1.63	1.60	1.55	1.49	1.42	1.38	1.34	1.30	1.24	1.17	1.00

Source: Adapted from E. S. Pearson and H. O. Hartley, Editors, Biometrika Tables for Statisticians, Volume I, published for the Biometrika Trustees by Cambridge University, 1954, by permission of Professor Pearson and the Trustees of Biometrika.

Table B-13. Values of F (Continued)

Degrees of freedom for the numerator

Upper 5 per cent points

df for denominator	1	2	3	4	5	6	7	8	9	10	12	15	20	24	30	40	60	120	∞
1	161	200	216	225	230	234	237	239	241	242	244	246	248	249	250	251	252	253	254
2	18.5	19.0	19.2	19.2	19.3	19.3	19.4	19.4	19.4	19.4	19.4	19.4	19.4	19.5	19.5	19.5	19.5	19.5	19.5
3	10.1	9.55	9.28	9.12	9.01	8.94	8.89	8.85	8.81	8.79	8.74	8.70	8.66	8.64	8.62	8.59	8.57	8.55	8.53
4	7.71	6.94	6.59	6.39	6.26	6.16	6.09	6.04	6.00	5.96	5.91	5.86	5.80	5.77	5.75	5.72	5.69	5.66	5.63
5	6.61	5.79	5.41	5.19	5.05	4.95	4.88	4.82	4.77	4.74	4.68	4.62	4.56	4.53	4.50	4.46	4.43	4.40	4.37
6	5.99	5.14	4.76	4.53	4.39	4.28	4.21	4.15	4.10	4.06	4.00	3.94	3.87	3.84	3.81	3.77	3.74	3.70	3.67
7	5.59	4.74	4.35	4.12	3.97	3.87	3.79	3.73	3.68	3.64	3.57	3.51	3.44	3.41	3.38	3.34	3.30	3.27	3.23
8	5.32	4.46	4.07	3.84	3.69	3.58	3.50	3.44	3.39	3.35	3.28	3.22	3.15	3.12	3.08	3.04	3.01	2.97	2.93
9	5.12	4.26	3.86	3.63	3.48	3.37	3.29	3.23	3.18	3.14	3.07	3.01	2.94	2.90	2.86	2.83	2.79	2.75	2.71
10	4.96	4.10	3.71	3.48	3.33	3.22	3.14	3.07	3.02	2.98	2.91	2.85	2.77	2.74	2.70	2.66	2.62	2.58	2.54
11	4.84	3.98	3.59	3.36	3.20	3.09	3.01	2.95	2.90	2.85	2.79	2.72	2.65	2.61	2.57	2.53	2.49	2.45	2.40
12	4.75	3.89	3.49	3.26	3.11	3.00	2.91	2.85	2.80	2.75	2.69	2.62	2.54	2.51	2.47	2.43	2.38	2.34	2.30
13	4.67	3.81	3.41	3.18	3.03	2.92	2.83	2.77	2.71	2.67	2.60	2.53	2.46	2.42	2.38	2.34	2.30	2.25	2.21
14	4.60	3.74	3.34	3.11	2.96	2.85	2.76	2.70	2.65	2.60	2.53	2.46	2.39	2.35	2.31	2.27	2.22	2.18	2.13
15	4.54	3.68	3.29	3.06	2.90	2.79	2.71	2.64	2.59	2.54	2.48	2.40	2.33	2.29	2.25	2.20	2.16	2.11	2.07
16	4.49	3.63	3.24	3.01	2.85	2.74	2.66	2.59	2.54	2.49	2.42	2.35	2.28	2.24	2.19	2.15	2.11	2.06	2.01
17	4.45	3.59	3.20	2.96	2.81	2.70	2.61	2.55	2.49	2.45	2.38	2.31	2.23	2.19	2.15	2.10	2.06	2.01	1.96
18	4.41	3.55	3.16	2.93	2.77	2.66	2.58	2.51	2.46	2.41	2.34	2.27	2.19	2.15	2.11	2.06	2.02	1.97	1.92
19	4.38	3.52	3.13	2.90	2.74	2.63	2.54	2.48	2.42	2.38	2.31	2.23	2.16	2.11	2.07	2.03	1.98	1.93	1.88
20	4.35	3.49	3.10	2.87	2.71	2.60	2.51	2.45	2.39	2.35	2.28	2.20	2.12	2.08	2.04	1.99	1.95	1.90	1.84
21	4.32	3.47	3.07	2.84	2.68	2.57	2.49	2.42	2.37	2.32	2.25	2.18	2.10	2.05	2.01	1.96	1.92	1.87	1.81
22	4.30	3.44	3.05	2.82	2.66	2.55	2.46	2.40	2.34	2.30	2.23	2.15	2.07	2.03	1.98	1.94	1.89	1.84	1.78
23	4.28	3.42	3.03	2.80	2.64	2.53	2.44	2.37	2.32	2.27	2.20	2.13	2.05	2.01	1.96	1.91	1.86	1.81	1.76
24	4.26	3.40	3.01	2.78	2.62	2.51	2.42	2.36	2.30	2.25	2.18	2.11	2.03	1.98	1.94	1.89	1.84	1.79	1.73
25	4.24	3.39	2.99	2.76	2.60	2.49	2.40	2.34	2.28	2.24	2.16	2.09	2.01	1.96	1.92	1.87	1.82	1.77	1.71
26	4.23	3.37	2.98	2.74	2.59	2.47	2.39	2.32	2.27	2.22	2.15	2.07	1.99	1.95	1.90	1.85	1.80	1.75	1.69
27	4.21	3.35	2.96	2.73	2.57	2.46	2.37	2.31	2.25	2.20	2.13	2.06	1.97	1.93	1.88	1.84	1.79	1.73	1.67
28	4.20	3.34	2.95	2.71	2.56	2.45	2.36	2.29	2.24	2.19	2.12	2.04	1.96	1.91	1.87	1.82	1.77	1.71	1.65
29	4.18	3.33	2.93	2.70	2.55	2.43	2.35	2.28	2.22	2.18	2.10	2.03	1.94	1.90	1.85	1.81	1.75	1.70	1.64
30	4.17	3.32	2.92	2.69	2.53	2.42	2.33	2.27	2.21	2.16	2.09	2.01	1.93	1.89	1.84	1.79	1.74	1.68	1.62
40	4.08	3.23	2.84	2.61	2.45	2.34	2.25	2.18	2.12	2.08	2.00	1.92	1.84	1.79	1.74	1.69	1.64	1.58	1.51
60	4.00	3.15	2.76	2.53	2.37	2.25	2.17	2.10	2.04	1.99	1.92	1.84	1.75	1.70	1.65	1.59	1.53	1.47	1.39
120	3.92	3.07	2.68	2.45	2.29	2.18	2.09	2.02	1.96	1.91	1.83	1.75	1.66	1.61	1.55	1.50	1.43	1.35	1.25
∞	3.84	3.00	2.60	2.37	2.21	2.10	2.01	1.94	1.88	1.83	1.75	1.67	1.57	1.52	1.46	1.39	1.32	1.22	1.00

Table B-13.   Values of F (*Continued*)

Degrees of freedom for the numerator

Upper 1 per cent points

df for denominator	1	2	3	4	5	6	7	8	9	10	12	15	20	24	30	40	60	120	∞
1	4052	5000	5403	5625	5764	5859	5928	5982	6023	6056	6106	6157	6209	6235	6261	6287	6313	6339	6366
2	98.5	99.0	99.2	99.2	99.3	99.3	99.4	99.4	99.4	99.4	99.4	99.4	99.4	99.5	99.5	99.5	99.5	99.5	99.5
3	34.1	30.8	29.5	28.7	28.2	27.9	27.7	27.5	27.3	27.2	27.1	26.9	26.7	26.6	26.5	26.4	26.3	26.2	26.1
4	21.2	18.0	16.7	16.0	15.5	15.2	15.0	14.8	14.7	14.5	14.4	14.2	14.0	13.9	13.8	13.7	13.7	13.6	13.5
5	16.3	13.3	12.1	11.4	11.0	10.7	10.5	10.3	10.2	10.1	9.89	9.72	9.55	9.47	9.38	9.29	9.20	9.11	9.02
6	13.7	10.9	9.78	9.15	8.75	8.47	8.26	8.10	7.98	7.87	7.72	7.56	7.40	7.31	7.23	7.14	7.06	6.97	6.88
7	12.2	9.55	8.45	7.85	7.46	7.19	6.99	6.84	6.72	6.62	6.47	6.31	6.16	6.07	5.99	5.91	5.82	5.74	5.65
8	11.3	8.65	7.59	7.01	6.63	6.37	6.18	6.03	5.91	5.81	5.67	5.52	5.36	5.28	5.20	5.12	5.03	4.95	4.86
9	10.6	8.02	6.99	6.42	6.06	5.80	5.61	5.47	5.35	5.26	5.11	4.96	4.81	4.73	4.65	4.57	4.48	4.40	4.31
10	10.0	7.56	6.55	5.99	5.64	5.39	5.20	5.06	4.94	4.85	4.71	4.56	4.41	4.33	4.25	4.17	4.08	4.00	3.91
11	9.65	7.21	6.22	5.67	5.32	5.07	4.89	4.74	4.63	4.54	4.40	4.25	4.10	4.02	3.94	3.86	3.78	3.69	3.60
12	9.33	6.93	5.95	5.41	5.06	4.82	4.64	4.50	4.39	4.30	4.16	4.01	3.86	3.78	3.70	3.62	3.54	3.45	3.36
13	9.07	6.70	5.74	5.21	4.86	4.62	4.44	4.30	4.19	4.10	3.96	3.82	3.66	3.59	3.51	3.43	3.34	3.25	3.17
14	8.86	6.51	5.56	5.04	4.70	4.46	4.28	4.14	4.03	3.94	3.80	3.66	3.51	3.43	3.35	3.27	3.18	3.09	3.00
15	8.68	6.36	5.42	4.89	4.56	4.32	4.14	4.00	3.89	3.80	3.67	3.52	3.37	3.29	3.21	3.13	3.05	2.96	2.87
16	8.53	6.23	5.29	4.77	4.44	4.20	4.03	3.89	3.78	3.69	3.55	3.41	3.26	3.18	3.10	3.02	2.93	2.84	2.75
17	8.40	6.11	5.19	4.67	4.34	4.10	3.93	3.79	3.68	3.59	3.46	3.31	3.16	3.08	3.00	2.92	2.83	2.75	2.65
18	8.29	6.01	5.09	4.58	4.25	4.01	3.84	3.71	3.60	3.51	3.37	3.23	3.08	3.00	2.92	2.84	2.75	2.66	2.57
19	8.18	5.93	5.01	4.50	4.17	3.94	3.77	3.63	3.52	3.43	3.30	3.15	3.00	2.92	2.84	2.76	2.67	2.58	2.49
20	8.10	5.85	4.94	4.43	4.10	3.87	3.70	3.56	3.46	3.37	3.23	3.09	2.94	2.86	2.78	2.69	2.61	2.52	2.42
21	8.02	5.78	4.87	4.37	4.04	3.81	3.64	3.51	3.40	3.31	3.17	3.03	2.88	2.80	2.72	2.64	2.55	2.46	2.36
22	7.95	5.72	4.82	4.31	3.99	3.76	3.59	3.45	3.35	3.26	3.12	2.98	2.83	2.75	2.67	2.58	2.50	2.40	2.31
23	7.88	5.66	4.76	4.26	3.94	3.71	3.54	3.41	3.30	3.21	3.07	2.93	2.78	2.70	2.62	2.54	2.45	2.35	2.26
24	7.82	5.61	4.72	4.22	3.90	3.67	3.50	3.36	3.26	3.17	3.03	2.89	2.74	2.66	2.58	2.49	2.40	2.31	2.21
25	7.77	5.57	4.68	4.18	3.86	3.63	3.46	3.32	3.22	3.13	2.99	2.85	2.70	2.62	2.54	2.45	2.36	2.27	2.17
26	7.72	5.53	4.64	4.14	3.82	3.59	3.42	3.29	3.18	3.09	2.96	2.82	2.66	2.58	2.50	2.42	2.33	2.23	2.13
27	7.68	5.49	4.60	4.11	3.78	3.56	3.39	3.26	3.15	3.06	2.93	2.78	2.63	2.55	2.47	2.38	2.29	2.20	2.10
28	7.64	5.45	4.57	4.07	3.75	3.53	3.36	3.23	3.12	3.03	2.90	2.75	2.60	2.52	2.44	2.35	2.26	2.17	2.06
29	7.60	5.42	4.54	4.04	3.73	3.50	3.33	3.20	3.09	3.00	2.87	2.73	2.57	2.49	2.41	2.33	2.23	2.14	2.03
30	7.56	5.39	4.51	4.02	3.70	3.47	3.30	3.17	3.07	2.98	2.84	2.70	2.55	2.47	2.39	2.30	2.21	2.11	2.01
40	7.31	5.18	4.31	3.83	3.51	3.29	3.12	2.99	2.89	2.80	2.66	2.52	2.37	2.29	2.20	2.11	2.02	1.92	1.80
60	7.08	4.98	4.13	3.65	3.34	3.12	2.95	2.82	2.72	2.63	2.50	2.35	2.20	2.12	2.03	1.94	1.84	1.73	1.60
120	6.85	4.79	3.95	3.48	3.17	2.96	2.79	2.66	2.56	2.47	2.34	2.19	2.03	1.95	1.86	1.76	1.66	1.53	1.38
∞	6.63	4.61	3.78	3.32	3.02	2.80	2.64	2.51	2.41	2.32	2.18	2.04	1.88	1.79	1.70	1.59	1.47	1.32	1.00

Table B-14.   Values of the Simple Linear Correlation Coefficient, r, for Values of Fisher's z_r

(Tabled values are r values)

z	·00	·01	·02	·03	·04	·05	·06	·07	·08	·09	Mean Diff.
·0	·0000	·0100	·0200	·0300	·0400	·0500	·0599	·0699	·0798	·0898	100
·1	·0997	·1096	·1194	·1293	·1391	·1489	·1586	·1684	·1781	·1877	98
·2	·1974	·2070	·2165	·2260	·2355	·2449	·2543	·2636	·2729	·2821	94
·3	·2913	·3004	·3095	·3185	·3275	·3364	·3452	·3540	·3627	·3714	89
·4	·3800	·3885	·3969	·4053	·4136	·4219	·4301	·4382	·4462	·4542	82
·5	·4621	·4699	·4777	·4854	·4930	·5005	·5080	·5154	·5227	·5299	75
·6	·5370	·5441	·5511	·5580	·5649	·5717	·5784	·5850	·5915	·5980	68
·7	·6044	·6107	·6169	·6231	·6291	·6351	·6411	·6469	·6527	·6584	60
·8	·6640	·6696	·6751	·6805	·6858	·6911	·6963	·7014	·7064	·7114	53
·9	·7163	·7211	·7259	·7306	·7352	·7398	·7443	·7487	·7531	·7574	46
1·0	·7616	·7658	·7699	·7739	·7779	·7818	·7857	·7895	·7932	·7969	39
1·1	·8005	·8041	·8076	·8110	·8144	·8178	·8210	·8243	·8275	·8306	33
1·2	·8337	·8367	·8397	·8426	·8455	·8483	·8511	·8538	·8565	·8591	28
1·3	·8617	·8643	·8668	·8692	·8717	·8741	·8764	·8787	·8810	·8832	24
1·4	·8854	·8875	·8896	·8917	·8937	·8957	·8977	·8996	·9015	·9033	20
1·5	·9051	·9069	·9087	·9104	·9121	·9138	·9154	·9170	·9186	·9201	17
1·6	·9217	·9232	·9246	·9261	·9275	·9289	·9302	·9316	·9329	·9341	14
1·7	·9354	·9366	·9379	·9391	·9402	·9414	·9425	·9436	·9447	·9458	12
1·8	·94681	·94783	·94884	·94983	·95080	·95175	·95268	·95359	·95449	·95537	95
1·9	·95624	·95709	·95792	·95873	·95953	·96032	·96109	·96185	·96259	·96331	79
2·0	·96403	·96473	·96541	·96609	·96675	·96739	·96803	·96865	·96926	·96986	65
2·1	·97045	·97103	·97159	·97215	·97269	·97323	·97375	·97426	·97477	·97526	53
2·2	·97574	·97622	·97668	·97714	·97759	·97803	·97846	·97888	·97929	·97970	44
2·3	·98010	·98049	·98087	·98124	·98161	·98197	·98233	·98267	·98301	·98335	36
2·4	·98367	·98399	·98431	·98462	·98492	·98522	·98551	·98579	·98607	·98635	30
2·5	·98661	·98688	·98714	·98739	·98764	·98788	·98812	·98835	·98858	·98881	24
2·6	·98903	·98924	·98945	·98966	·98987	·99007	·99026	·99045	·99064	·99083	20
2·7	·99101	·99118	·99136	·99153	·99170	·99186	·99202	·99218	·99233	·99248	16
2·8	·99263	·99278	·99292	·99306	·99320	·99333	·99346	·99359	·99372	·99384	13
2·9	·99396	·99408	·99420	·99431	·99443	·99454	·99464	·99475	·99485	·99495	11

	·0	·1	·2	·3	·4	·5	·6	·7	·8	·9	
3	·99505	·99595	·99668	·99728	·99777	·99818	·99851	·99878	·99900	·99918	—
4	·99933	·99945	·99955	·99963	·99970	·99975	·99980	·99983	·99986	·99989	—

Source: Reproduced from Table VII of Ronald A. Fisher and Frank Yates, *Statistical Tables for Biological, Agricultural and Medical Research*, 6th ed., Oliver & Boyd, Ltd., Edinburgh, 1963, by permission of the authors and publisher.

Table B-15. Squares, Square Roots, and Reciprocals

N	N^2	$\sqrt{N}$	$\sqrt{10N}$	1000/N	N	N^2	$\sqrt{N}$	$\sqrt{10N}$	1000/N
1	1	1.00 000	3.16 228	1000.00	50	2 500	7.07 107	22.36 07	20.00 00
2	4	1.41 421	4.47 214	500.00 0	51	2 601	7.14 143	22.58 32	19.60 78
3	9	1.73 205	5.47 723	333.33 3	52	2 704	7.21 110	22.80 35	19.23 08
4	16	2.00 000	6.32 456	250.00 0	53	2 809	7.28 011	23.02 17	18.86 79
5	25	2.23 607	7.07 107	200.00 0	54	2 916	7.34 847	23.23 79	18.51 85
					55	3 025	7.41 620	23.45 21	18.18 18
6	36	2.44 949	7.74 597	166.66 7	56	3 136	7.48 331	23.66 43	17.85 71
7	49	2.64 575	8.36 660	142.85 7	57	3 249	7.54 983	23.87 47	17.54 39
8	64	2.82 843	8.94 427	125.00 0	58	3 364	7.61 577	24.08 32	17.24 14
9	81	3.00 000	9.48 683	111.11 1	59	3 481	7.68 115	24.28 99	16.94 92
10	100	3.16 228	10.00 00	100.00 0	60	3 600	7.74 597	24.49 49	16.66 67
11	121	3.31 662	10.48 81	90.90 91	61	3 721	7.81 025	24.69 82	16.39 34
12	144	3.46 410	10.95 45	83.33 33	62	3 844	7.87 401	24.89 98	16.12 90
13	169	3.60 555	11.40 18	76.92 31	63	3 969	7.93 725	25.09 98	15.87 30
14	196	3.74 166	11.83 22	71.42 86	64	4 096	8.00 000	25.29 82	15.62 50
15	225	3.87 298	12.24 74	66.66 67	65	4 225	8.06 226	25.49 51	15.38 46
16	256	4.00 000	12.64 91	62.50 00	66	4 356	8.12 404	25.69 05	15.15 15
17	289	4.12 311	13.03 84	58.82 35	67	4 489	8.18 535	25.88 44	14.92 54
18	324	4.24 264	13.41 64	55.55 56	68	4 624	8.24 621	26.07 68	14.70 59
19	361	4.35 890	13.78 40	52.63 16	69	4 761	8.30 662	26.26 79	14.49 28
20	400	4.47 214	14.14 21	50.00 00	70	4 900	8.36 660	26.45 75	14.28 57
21	441	4.58 258	14.49 14	47.61 90	71	5 041	8.42 615	26.64 58	14.08 45
22	484	4.69 042	14.83 24	45.45 45	72	5 184	8.48 528	26.83 28	13.88 89
23	529	4.79 583	15.16 58	43.47 83	73	5 329	8.54 400	27.01 85	13.69 86
24	576	4.89 898	15.49 19	41.66 67	74	5 476	8.60 233	27.20 29	13.51 35
25	625	5.00 000	15.81 14	40.00 00	75	5 625	8.66 025	27.38 61	13.33 33
26	676	5.09 902	16.12 45	38.46 15	76	5 776	8.71 780	27.56 81	13.15 79
27	729	5.19 615	16.43 17	37.03 70	77	5 929	8.77 496	27.74 89	12.98 70
28	784	5.29 150	16.73 32	35.71 43	78	6 084	8.83 176	27.92 85	12.82 05
29	841	5.38 516	17.02 94	34.48 28	79	6 241	8.88 819	28.10 69	12.65 82
30	900	5.47 723	17.32 05	33.33 33	80	6 400	8.94 427	28.28 43	12.50 00
31	961	5.56 776	17.60 68	32.25 81	81	6 561	9.00 000	28.46 05	12.34 57
32	1 024	5.65 685	17.88 85	31.25 00	82	6 724	9.05 539	28.63 56	12.19 51
33	1 089	5.74 456	18.16 59	30.30 30	83	6 889	9.11 043	28.80 97	12.04 82
34	1 156	5.83 095	18.43 91	29.41 18	84	7 056	9.16 515	28.98 28	11.90 48
35	1 225	5.91 608	18.70 83	28.57 14	85	7 225	9.21 954	29.15 48	11.76 47
36	1 296	6.00 000	18.97 37	27.77 78	86	7 396	9.27 362	29.32 58	11.62 79
37	1 369	6.08 276	19.23 54	27.02 70	87	7 569	9.32 738	29.49 58	11.49 43
38	1 444	6.16 441	19.49 36	26.31 58	88	7 744	9.38 083	29.66 48	11.36 36
39	1 521	6.24 500	19.74 84	25.64 10	89	7 921	9.43 398	29.83 29	11.23 60
40	1 600	6.32 456	20.00 00	25.00 00	90	8 100	9.48 683	30.00 00	11.11 11
41	1 681	6.40 312	20.24 85	24.39 02	91	8 281	9.53 939	30.16 62	10.98 90
42	1 764	6.48 074	20.49 39	23.80 95	92	8 464	9.59 166	30.33 15	10.86 96
43	1 849	6.55 744	20.73 64	23.25 58	93	8 649	9.64 365	30.49 59	10.75 27
44	1 936	6.63 325	20.97 62	22.72 73	94	8 836	9.69 536	30.65 94	10.63 83
45	2 025	6.70 820	21.21 32	22.22 22	95	9 025	9.74 679	30.82 21	10.52 63
46	2 116	6.78 233	21.44 76	21.73 91	96	9 216	9.79 796	30.98 39	10.41 67
47	2 209	6.85 565	21.67 95	21.27 66	97	9 409	9.84 886	31.14 48	10.30 93
48	2 304	6.92 820	21.90 89	20.83 33	98	9 604	9.89 949	31.30 50	10.20 41
49	2 401	7.00 000	22.13 59	20.40 82	99	9 801	9.94 987	31.46 43	10.10 10
50	2 500	7.07 107	22.36 07	20.00 00	100	10 000	0.00 000	31.62 28	10.00 00
N	N^2	$\sqrt{N}$	$\sqrt{10N}$	1000/N	N	N^2	$\sqrt{N}$	$\sqrt{10N}$	1000/N

Source: Griffin, *Statistics: Methods and Applications*, 1962; adopted from Larsen, *Rinehart Mathematical Tables, Formulas and Curves*, revised edition.

Table B-15. Squares, Square Roots, and Reciprocals (*Continued*)

N	N²	√N	√10N	1000/N		N	N²	√N	√10N	1000/N
100	10 000	10.00 00	31.62 28	10.00 000		**150**	22 500	12.24 74	38.72 98	6.66 667
101	10 201	10.04 99	31.78 05	9.90 099		151	22 801	12.28 82	38.85 87	6.62 252
102	10 404	10.09 95	31.93 74	9.80 392		152	23 104	12.32 88	38.98 72	6.57 895
103	10 609	10.14 89	32.09 36	9.70 874		153	23 409	12.36 93	39.11 52	6.53 595
104	10 816	10.19 80	32.24 90	9.61 538		154	23 716	12.40 97	39.24 28	6.49 351
105	11 025	10.24 70	32.40 37	9.52 381		155	24 025	12.44 99	39.37 00	6.45 161
106	11 236	10.29 56	32.55 76	9.43 396		**156**	24 336	12.49 00	39.49 68	6.41 026
107	11 449	10.34 41	32.71 09	9.34 579		157	24 649	12.53 00	39.62 32	6.36 943
108	11 664	10.39 23	32.86 34	9.25 926		158	24 964	12.56 98	39.74 92	6.32 911
109	11 881	10.44 03	33.01 51	9.17 431		159	25 281	12.60 95	39.87 48	6.28 931
110	12 100	10.48 81	33.16 62	9.09 091		160	25 600	12.64 91	40.00 00	6.25 000
111	12 321	10.53 57	33.31 67	9.00 901		**161**	25 921	12.68 86	40.12 48	6.21 118
112	12 544	10.58 30	33.46 64	8.92 857		162	26 244	12.72 79	40.24 92	6.17 284
113	12 769	10.63 01	33.61 55	8.84 956		163	26 569	12.76 71	40.37 33	6.13 497
114	12 996	10.67 71	33.76 39	8.77 193		164	26 896	12.80 62	40.49 69	6.09 756
115	13 225	10.72 38	33.91 16	8.69 565		165	27 225	12.84 52	40.62 02	6.06 061
116	13 456	10.77 03	34.05 88	8.62 069		**166**	27 556	12.88 41	40.74 31	6.02 410
117	13 689	10.81 67	34.20 53	8.54 701		167	27 889	12.92 28	40.86 56	5.98 802
118	13 924	10.86 28	34.35 11	8.47 458		168	28 224	12.96 15	40.98 78	5.95 238
119	14 161	10.90 87	34.49 64	8.40 336		169	28 561	13.00 00	41.10 96	5.91 716
120	14 400	10.95 45	34.64 10	8.33 333		170	28 900	13.03 84	41.23 11	5.88 235
121	14 641	11.00 00	34.78 51	8.26 446		**171**	29 241	13.07 67	41.35 21	5.84 795
122	14 884	11.04 54	34.92 85	8.19 672		172	29 584	13.11 49	41.47 29	5.81 395
123	15 129	11.09 05	35.07 14	8.13 008		173	29 929	13.15 29	41.59 33	5.78 035
124	15 376	11.13 55	35.21 36	8.06 452		174	30 276	13.19 09	41.71 33	5.74 713
125	15 625	11.18 03	35.35 53	8.00 000		175	30 625	13.22 88	41.83 30	5.71 429
126	15 876	11.22 50	35.49 65	7.93 651		**176**	30 976	13.26 65	41.95 24	5.68 182
127	16 129	11.26 94	35.63 71	7.87 402		177	31 329	13.30 41	42.07 14	5.64 972
128	16 384	11.31 37	35.77 71	7.81 250		178	31 684	13.34 17	42.19 00	5.61 798
129	16 641	11.35 78	35.91 66	7.75 194		179	32 041	13.37 91	42.30 84	5.58 659
130	16 900	11.40 18	36.05 55	7.69 231		180	32 400	13.41 64	42.42 64	5.55 556
131	17 161	11.44 55	36.19 39	7.63 359		**181**	32 761	13.45 36	42.54 41	5.52 486
132	17 424	11.48 91	36.33 18	7.57 576		182	33 124	13.49 07	42.66 15	5.49 451
133	17 689	11.53 26	36.46 92	7.51 880		183	33 489	13.52 77	42.77 85	5.46 448
134	17 956	11.57 58	36.60 60	7.46 269		184	33 856	13.56 47	42.89 52	5.43 478
135	18 225	11.61 90	36.74 23	7.40 741		185	34 225	13.60 15	43.01 16	5.40 541
136	18 496	11.66 19	36.87 82	7.35 294		**186**	34 596	13.63 82	43.12 77	5.37 634
137	18 769	11.70 47	37.01 35	7.29 927		187	34 969	13.67 48	43.24 35	5.34 759
138	19 044	11.74 73	37.14 84	7.24 638		188	35 344	13.71 13	43.35 90	5.31 915
139	19 321	11.78 98	37.28 27	7.19 424		189	35 721	13.74 77	43.47 41	5.29 101
140	19 600	11.83 22	37.41 66	7.14 286		190	36 100	13.78 40	43.58 90	5.26 316
141	19 881	11.87 43	37.55 00	7.09 220		**191**	36 481	13.82 03	43.70 35	5.23 560
142	20 164	11.91 64	37.68 29	7.04 225		192	36 864	13.85 64	43.81 78	5.20 833
143	20 449	11.95 83	37.81 53	6.99 301		193	37 249	13.89 24	43.93 18	5.18 135
144	20 736	12.00 00	37.94 73	6.94 444		194	37 636	13.92 84	44.04 54	5.15 464
145	21 025	12.04 16	38.07 89	6.89 655		195	38 025	13.96 42	44.15 88	5.12 821
146	21 316	12.08 30	38.20 99	6.84 932		**196**	38 416	14.00 00	44.27 19	5.10 204
147	21 609	12.12 44	38.34 06	6.80 272		197	38 809	14.03 57	44.38 47	5.07 614
148	21 904	12.16 55	38.47 08	6.75 676		198	39 204	14.07 12	44.49 72	5.05 051
149	22 201	12.20 66	38.60 05	6.71 141		199	39 601	14.10 67	44.60 94	5.02 513
150	22 500	12.24 74	38.72 98	6.66 667		200	40 000	14.14 21	44.72 14	5.00 000
N	N²	√N	√10N	1000/N		N	N²	√N	√10N	1000/N

Table B-15. Squares, Square Roots, and Reciprocals (*Continued*)

N	N²	√N	√10N	1000/N	N	N²	√N	√10N	1000/N
200	40 000	14.14 21	44.72 14	5.00 000	**250**	62 500	15.81 14	50.00 00	4.00 000
201	40 401	14.17 74	44.83 30	4.97 512	251	63 001	15.84 30	50.09 99	3.98 406
202	40 804	14.21 27	44.94 44	4.95 050	252	63 504	15.87 45	50.19 96	3.96 825
203	41 209	14.24 78	45.05 55	4.92 611	253	64 009	15.90 60	50.29 91	3.95 257
204	41 616	14.28 29	45.16 64	4.90 196	254	64 516	15.93 74	50.39 84	3.93 701
205	42 025	14.31 78	45.27 69	4.87 805	255	65 025	15.96 87	50.49 75	3.92 157
206	42 436	14.35 27	45.38 72	4.85 437	**256**	65 536	16.00 00	50.59 64	3.90 625
207	42 849	14.38 75	45.49 73	4.83 092	257	66 049	16.03 12	50.69 52	3.89 105
208	43 264	14.42 22	45.60 70	4.80 769	258	66 564	16.06 24	50.79 37	3.87 597
209	43 681	14.45 68	45.71 65	4.78 469	259	67 081	16.09 35	50.89 20	3.86 100
210	44 100	14.49 14	45.82 58	4.76 190	260	67 600	16.12 45	50.99 02	3.84 615
211	44 521	14.52 58	45.93 47	4.73 934	**261**	68 121	16.15 55	51.08 82	3.83 142
212	44 944	14.56 02	46.04 35	4.71 698	262	68 644	16.18 64	51.18 59	3.81 679
213	45 369	14.59 45	46.15 19	4.69 484	263	69 169	16.21 73	51.28 35	3.80 228
214	45 796	14.62 87	46.26 01	4.67 290	264	69 696	16.24 81	51.38 09	3.78 788
215	46 225	14.66 29	46.36 81	4.65 116	265	70 225	16.27 88	51.47 82	3.77 358
216	46 656	14.69 69	46.47 58	4.62 963	**266**	70 756	16.30 95	51.57 52	3.75 940
217	47 089	14.73 09	46.58 33	4.60 829	267	71 289	16.34 01	51.67 20	3.74 532
218	47 524	14.76 48	46.69 05	4.58 716	268	71 824	16.37 07	51.76 87	3.73 134
219	47 961	14.79 86	46.79 74	4.56 621	269	72 361	16.40 12	51.86 52	3.71 747
220	48 400	14.83 24	46.90 42	4.54 545	270	72 900	16.43 17	51.96 15	3.70 370
221	48 841	14.86 61	47.01 06	4.52 489	**271**	73 441	16.46 21	52.05 77	3.69 004
222	49 284	14.89 97	47.11 69	4.50 450	272	73 984	16.49 24	52.15 36	3.67 647
223	49 729	14.93 32	47.22 29	4.48 430	273	74 529	16.52 27	52.24 94	3.66 300
224	50 176	14.96 66	47.32 86	4.46 429	274	75 076	16.55 29	52.34 50	3.64 964
225	50 625	15.00 00	47.43 42	4.44 444	275	75 625	16.58 31	52.44 04	3.63 636
226	51 076	15.03 33	47.53 95	4.42 478	**276**	76 176	16.61 32	52.53 57	3.62 319
227	51 529	15.06 65	47.64 45	4.40 529	277	76 729	16.64 33	52.63 08	3.61 011
228	51 984	15.09 97	47.74 93	4.38 596	278	77 284	16.67 33	52.72 57	3.59 712
229	52 441	15.13 27	47.85 39	4.36 681	279	77 841	16.70 33	52.82 05	3.58 423
230	52 900	15.16 58	47.95 83	4.34 783	280	78 400	16.73 32	52.91 50	3.57 143
231	53 361	15.19 87	48.06 25	4.32 900	**281**	78 961	16.76 31	53.00 94	3.55 872
232	53 824	15.23 15	48.16 64	4.31 034	282	79 524	16.79 29	53.10 37	3.54 610
233	54 289	15.26 43	48.27 01	4.29 185	283	80 089	16.82 26	53.19 77	3.53 357
234	54 756	15.29 71	48.37 35	4.27 350	284	80 656	16.85 23	53.29 17	3.52 113
235	55 225	15.32 97	48.47 68	4.25 532	285	81 225	16.88 19	53.38 54	3.50 877
236	55 696	15.36 23	48.57 98	4.23 729	**286**	81 796	16.91 15	53.47 90	3.49 650
237	56 169	15.39 48	48.68 26	4.21 941	287	82 369	16.94 11	53.57 24	3.48 432
238	56 644	15.42 72	48.78 52	4.20 168	288	82 944	16.97 06	53.66 56	3.47 222
239	57 121	15.45 96	48.88 76	4.18 410	289	83 521	17.00 00	53.75 87	3.46 021
240	57 600	15.49 19	48.98 98	4.16 667	290	84 100	17.02 94	53.85 16	3.44 828
241	58 081	15.52 42	49.09 18	4.14 938	**291**	84 681	17.05 87	53.94 44	3.43 643
242	58 564	15.55 63	49.19 35	4.13 223	292	85 264	17.08 80	54.03 70	3.42 466
243	59 049	15.58 85	49.29 50	4.11 523	293	85 849	17.11 72	54.12 95	3.41 297
244	59 536	15.62 05	49.39 64	4.09 836	294	86 436	17.14 64	54.22 18	3.40 136
245	60 025	15.65 25	49.49 75	4.08 163	295	87 025	17.17 56	54.31 39	3.38 983
246	60 516	15.68 44	49.59 84	4.06 504	**296**	87 616	17.20 47	54.40 59	3.37 838
247	61 009	15.71 62	49.69 91	4.04 858	297	88 209	17.23 37	54.49 77	3.36 700
248	61 504	15.74 80	49.79 96	4.03 226	298	88 804	17.26 27	54.58 94	3.35 570
249	62 001	15.77 97	49.89 99	4.01 606	299	89 401	17.29 16	54.68 09	3.34 448
250	62 500	15.81 14	50.00 00	4.00 000	300	90 000	17.32 05	54.77 23	3.33 333
N	N²	√N	√10N	1000/N	N	N²	√N	√10N	1000/N

Table B-15.   Squares, Square Roots, and Reciprocals (*Continued*)

N	N²	√N	√10N	1000/N	N	N²	√N	√10N	1000/N
300	90 000	17.32 05	54.77 23	3.33 333	**350**	122 500	18.70 83	59.16 08	2.85 714
301	90 601	17.34 94	54.86 35	3.32 226	351	123 201	18.73 50	59.24 53	2.84 900
302	91 204	17.37 81	54.95 45	3.31 126	352	123 904	18.76 17	59.32 96	2.84 091
303	91 809	17.40 69	55.04 54	3.30 033	353	124 609	18.78 83	59.41 38	2.83 286
304	92 416	17.43 56	55.13 62	3.28 947	354	125 316	18.81 49	59.49 79	2.82 486
305	93 025	17.46 42	55.22 68	3.27 869	355	126 025	18.84 14	59.58 19	2.81 690
306	93 636	17.49 29	55.31 73	3.26 797	**356**	126 736	18.86 80	59.66 57	2.80 899
307	94 249	17.52 14	55.40 76	3.25 733	357	127 449	18.89 44	59.74 95	2.80 112
308	94 864	17.54 99	55.49 77	3.24 675	358	128 164	18.92 09	59.83 31	2.79 330
309	95 481	17.57 84	55.58 78	3.23 625	359	128 881	18.94 73	59.91 66	2.78 552
310	96 100	17.60 68	55.67 76	3.22 581	360	129 600	18.97 37	60.00 00	2.77 778
311	96 721	17.63 52	55.76 74	3 21 543	**361**	130 321	19.00 00	60.08 33	2.77 008
312	97 344	17.66 35	55.85 70	3.20 513	362	131 044	19.02 63	60.16 64	2.76 243
313	97 969	17.69 18	55.94 64	3.19 489	363	131 769	19.05 26	60.24 95	2.75 482
314	98 596	17.72 00	56.03 57	3.18 471	364	132 496	19.07 88	60.33 24	2.74 725
315	99 225	17.74 82	56.12 49	3.17 460	365	133 225	19.10 50	60.41 52	2.73 973
316	99 856	17.77 64	56.21 39	3.16 456	**366**	133 956	19.13 11	60.49 79	2.73 224
317	100 489	17.80 45	56.30 28	3.15 457	367	134 689	19.15 72	60.58 05	2.72 480
318	101 124	17.83 26	56.39 15	3.14 465	368	135 424	19.18 33	60.66 30	2.71 739
319	101 761	17.86 06	56.48 01	3.13 480	369	136 161	19.20 94	60.74 54	2.71 003
320	102 400	17.88 85	56.56 85	3.12 500	370	136 900	19.23 54	60.82 76	2.70 270
321	103 041	17.91 65	56.65 69	3.11 526	**371**	137 641	19.26 14	60.90 98	2.69 542
322	103 684	17.94 44	56.74 50	3.10 559	372	138 384	19.28 73	60.99 18	2.68 817
323	104 329	17.97 22	56.83 31	3.09 598	373	139 129	19.31 32	61.07 37	2.68 097
324	104 976	18.00 00	55.92 10	3.08 642	374	139 876	19.33 91	61.15 55	2.67 380
325	105 625	18.02 78	57.00 88	3.07 692	375	140 625	19.36 49	61.23 72	2.66 667
326	106 276	18.05 55	57.09 64	3.06 748	**376**	141 376	19.39 07	61.31 88	2.65 957
327	106 929	18.08 31	57.18 39	3.05 810	377	142 129	19.41 65	61.40 03	2.65 252
328	107 584	18.11 08	57.27 13	3.04 878	378	142 884	19.44 22	61.48 17	2.64 550
329	108 241	18.13 84	57.35 85	3.03 951	379	143 641	19.46 79	61.56 30	2.63 852
330	108 900	18.16 59	57.44 56	3.03 030	380	144 400	19.49 36	61.64 41	2.63 158
331	109 561	18.19 34	57.53 26	3.02 115	**381**	145 161	19.51 92	61.72 52	2.62 467
332	110 224	18.22 09	57.61 94	3.01 205	382	145 924	19.54 48	61.80 61	2.61 780
333	110 889	18.24 83	57.70 62	3.00 300	383	146 689	19.57 04	61.88 70	2.61 097
334	111 556	18.27 57	57.79 27	2.99 401	384	147 456	19.59 59	61.96 77	2.60 417
335	112 225	18.30 30	57.87 92	2.98 507	385	148 225	19.62 14	62.04 84	2.59 740
336	112 896	18.33 03	57.96 55	2.97 619	**386**	148 996	19.64 69	62.12 89	2.59 067
337	113 569	18.35 76	58.05 17	2.96 736	387	149 769	19.67 23	62.20 93	2.58 398
338	114 244	18.38 48	58.13 78	2.95 858	388	150 544	19.69 77	62.28 96	2.57 732
339	114 921	18.41 20	58.22 37	2.94 985	389	151 321	19.72 31	62.36 99	2.57 069
340	115 600	18 43 91	58.30 95	2.94 118	390	152 100	19.74 84	62.45 00	2.56 410
341	116 281	18.46 62	58.39 52	2.93 255	**391**	152 881	19.77 37	62.53 00	2.55 754
342	116 964	18.49 32	58.48 08	2.92 398	392	153 664	19.79 90	62.60 99	2.55 102
343	117 649	18.52 03	58.56 62	2.91 545	393	154 449	19.82 42	62.68 97	2.54 453
344	118 336	18.54 72	58.65 15	2.90 698	394	155 236	19.84 94	62.76 94	2.53 807
345	119 025	18.57 42	58.73 67	2.89 855	395	156 025	19.87 46	62.84 90	2.53 165
346	119 716	18.60 11	58.82 18	2.89 017	**396**	156 816	19.89 97	62.92 85	2.52 525
347	120 409	18.62 79	58.90 67	2.88 184	397	157 609	19.92 49	63.00 79	2.51 889
348	121 104	18.65 48	58.99 15	2.87 356	398	158 404	19.94 99	63.08 72	2.51 256
349	121 801	18.68 15	59.07 62	2.86 533	399	159 201	19.97 50	63.16 64	2.50 627
350	122 500	18.70 83	59.16 08	2.85 714	400	160 000	20.00 00	63.24 56	2.50 000
N	N²	√N	√10N	1000/N	N	N²	√N	√10N	1000/N

Table B-15. Squares, Square Roots, and Reciprocals (*Continued*)

N	N²	√N	√10N	1000 /N	N	N²	√N	√10N	1000 /N
400	160 000	20.00 00	63.24 56	2.50 000	450	202 500	21.21 32	67.08 20	2.22 222
401	160 801	20.02 50	63.32 46	2.49 377	451	203 401	21.23 68	67.15 65	2.21 729
402	161 604	20.04 99	63.40 35	2.48 756	452	204 304	21.26 03	67.23 09	2.21 239
403	162 409	20.07 49	63.48 23	2.48 139	453	205 209	21.28 38	67.30 53	2.20 751
404	163 216	20.09 98	63.56 10	2.47 525	454	206 116	21.30 73	67.37 95	2.20 264
405	164 025	20.12 46	63.63 96	2.46 914	455	207 025	21.33 07	67.45 37	2.19 780
406	164 836	20.14 94	63.71 81	2.46 305	456	207 936	21.35 42	67.52 78	2.19 298
407	165 649	20.17 42	63.79 66	2.45 700	457	208 849	21.37 76	67.60 18	2.18 818
408	166 464	20.19 90	63.87 49	2.45 098	458	209 764	21.40 09	67.67 57	2.18 341
409	167 281	20.22 37	63.95 31	2.44 499	459	210 681	21.42 43	67.74 95	2.17 865
410	168 100	20.24 85	64.03 12	2.43 902	460	211 600	21.44 76	67.82 33	2.17 391
411	168 921	20.27 31	64.10 93	2.43 309	461	212 521	21.47 09	67.89 70	2.16 920
412	169 744	20.29 78	64.18 72	2.42 718	462	213 444	21.49 42	67.97 06	2.16 450
413	170 569	20.32 24	64.26 51	2.42 131	463	214 369	21.51 74	68.04 41	2.15 983
414	171 396	20.34 70	64.34 28	2.41 546	464	215 296	21.54 07	68.11 75	2.15 517
415	172 225	20.37 15	64.42 05	2.40 964	465	216 225	21.56 39	68.19 09	2.15 054
416	173 056	20.39 61	64.49 81	2.40 385	466	217 156	21.58 70	68.26 42	2.14 592
417	173 889	20.42 06	64.57 55	2.39 808	467	218 089	21.61 02	68.33 74	2.14 133
418	174 724	20.44 50	64.65 29	2.39 234	468	219 024	21.63 33	68.41 05	2.13 675
419	175 561	20.46 95	64.73 02	2.38 663	469	219 961	21.65 64	68.48 36	2.13 220
420	176 400	20.49 39	64.80 74	2.38 095	470	220 900	21.67 95	68.55 65	2.12 766
421	177 241	20.51 83	64.88 45	2.37 530	471	221 841	21.70 25	68.62 94	2.12 314
422	178 084	20.54 26	64.96 15	2.36 967	472	222 784	21.72 56	68.70 23	2.11 864
423	178 929	20.56 70	65.03 85	2.36 407	473	223 729	21.74 86	68.77 50	2.11 416
424	179 776	20.59 13	65.11 53	2.35 849	474	224 676	21.77 15	68.84 77	2.10 970
425	180 625	20.61 55	65.19 20	2.35 294	475	225 625	21.79 45	68.92 02	2.10 526
426	181 476	20.63 98	65.26 87	2.34 742	476	226 576	21.81 74	68.99 28	2.10 084
427	182 329	20.66 40	65.34 52	2.34 192	477	227 529	21.84 03	69.06 52	2.09 644
428	183 184	20.68 82	65.42 17	2.33 645	478	228 484	21.86 32	69.13 75	2.09 205
429	184 041	20.71 23	65.49 81	2.33 100	479	229 441	21.88 61	69.20 98	2.08 768
430	184 900	20.73 64	65.57 44	2.32 558	480	230 400	21.90 89	69.28 20	2.08 333
431	185 761	20.76 05	65.65 06	2.32 019	481	231 361	21.93 17	69.35 42	2.07 900
432	186 624	20.78 46	65.72 67	2.31 481	482	232 324	21.95 45	69.42 62	2.07 469
433	187 489	20.80 87	65.80 27	2.30 947	483	233 289	21.97 73	69.49 82	2.07 039
434	188 356	20.83 27	65.87 87	2.30 415	484	234 256	22.00 00	69.57 01	2.06 612
435	189 225	20.85 67	65.95 45	2.29 885	485	235 225	22.02 27	69.64 19	2.06 186
436	190 096	20.88 06	66.03 03	2.29 358	486	236 196	22.04 54	69.71 37	2.05 761
437	190 969	20.90 45	66.10 60	2.28 833	487	237 169	22.06 81	69.78 54	2.05 339
438	191 844	20.92 84	66.18 16	2.28 311	488	238 144	22.09 07	69.85 70	2.04 918
439	192 721	20.95 23	66.25 71	2.27 790	489	239 121	22.11 33	69.92 85	2.04 499
440	193 600	20.97 62	66.33 25	2.27 273	490	240 100	22.13 59	70.00 00	2.04 082
441	194 481	21.00 00	66.40 78	2.26 757	491	241 081	22.15 85	70.07 14	2.03 666
442	195 364	21.02 38	66.48 31	2.26 244	492	242 064	22.18 11	70.14 27	2.03 252
443	196 249	21.04 76	66.55 82	2.25 734	493	243 049	22.20 36	70.21 40	2.02 840
444	197 136	21.07 13	66.63 33	2.25 225	494	244 036	22.22 61	70.28 51	2.02 429
445	198 025	21.09 50	66.70 83	2.24 719	495	245 025	22.24 86	70.35 62	2.02 020
446	198 916	21.11 87	66.78 32	2.24 215	496	246 016	22.27 11	70.42 73	2.01 613
447	199 809	21.14 24	66.85 81	2.23 714	497	247 009	22.29 35	70.49 82	2.01 207
448	200 704	21.16 60	66.93 28	2.23 214	498	248 004	22.31 59	70.56 91	2.00 803
449	201 601	21.18 96	67.00 75	2.22 717	499	249 001	22.33 83	70.63 99	2.00 401
450	202 500	21.21 32	67.08 20	2.22 222	500	250 000	22.36 07	70.71 07	2.00 000
N	N²	√N	√10N	1000 /N	N	N²	√N	√10N	1000 /N

Table B-15. Squares, Square Roots, and Reciprocals (*Continued*)

N	N²	√N	√10N	1000/N	N	N²	√N	√10N	1000/N
500	250 000	22.36 07	70.71 07	2.00 000	**550**	302 500	23.45 21	74.16 20	1.81 818
501	251 001	22.38 30	70.78 14	1.99 601	551	303 601	23.47 34	74.22 94	1.81 488
502	252 004	22.40 54	70.85 20	1.99 203	552	304 704	23.49 47	74.29 67	1.81 159
503	253 009	22.42 77	70.92 25	1.98 807	553	305 809	23.51 60	74.36 40	1.80 832
504	254 016	22.44 99	70.99 30	1.98 413	554	306 916	23.53 72	74.43 12	1.80 505
505	255 025	22.47 22	71.06 34	1.98 020	555	308 025	23.55 84	74.49 83	1.80 180
506	256 036	22.49 44	71.13 37	1.97 628	**556**	309 136	23.57 97	74.56 54	1.79 856
507	257 049	22.51 67	71.20 39	1.97 239	557	310 249	23.60 08	74.63 24	1.79 533
508	258 064	22.53 89	71.27 41	1.96 850	558	311 364	23.62 20	74.69 94	1.79 211
509	259 081	22.56 10	71.34 42	1.96 464	559	312 481	23.64 32	74.76 63	1.78 891
510	260 100	22.58 32	71.41 43	1.96 078	560	313 600	23.66 43	74.83 31	1.78 571
511	261 121	22.60 53	71.48 43	1.95 695	**561**	314 721	23.68 54	74.89 99	1.78 253
512	262 144	22.62 74	71.55 42	1.95 312	562	315 844	23.70 65	74.96 67	1.77 936
513	263 169	22.64 95	71.62 40	1.94 932	563	316 969	23.72 76	75.03 33	1.77 620
514	264 196	22.67 16	71.69 38	1.94 553	564	318 096	23.74 87	75.09 99	1.77 305
515	265 225	22.69 36	71.76 35	1.94 175	565	319 225	23.76 97	75.16 65	1.76 991
516	266 256	22.71 56	71.83 31	1.93 798	**566**	320 356	23.79 08	75.23 30	1.76 678
517	267 289	22.73 76	71.90 27	1.93 424	567	521 489	23.81 18	75.29 94	1.76 367
518	268 324	22.75 96	71.97 22	1.93 050	568	322 624	23.83 28	75.36 58	1.76 056
519	269 361	22.78 16	72.04 17	1.92 678	569	323 761	23.85 37	75.43 21	1.75 747
520	270 400	22.80 35	72.11 10	1.92 308	570	324 900	23.87 47	75.49 83	1.75 439
521	271 441	22.82 54	72.18 03	1.91 939	**571**	326 041	23.89 56	75.56 45	1.75 131
522	272 484	22.84 73	72.24 96	1.91 571	572	327 184	23.91 65	75.63 07	1.74 825
523	273 529	22.86 92	72.31 87	1.91 205	573	328 329	23.93 74	75.69 68	1.74 520
524	274 576	22.89 10	72.38 78	1.90 840	574	329 476	23.95 83	75.76 28	1.74 216
525	275 625	22.91 29	72.45 69	1.90 476	575	330 625	23.97 92	75.82 88	1.73 913
526	276 676	22.93 47	72.52 59	1.90 114	**576**	331 776	24.00 00	75.89 47	1.73 611
527	277 729	22.95 65	72.59 48	1.89 753	577	332 929	24.02 08	75.96 05	1.73 310
528	278 784	22.97 83	72.66 36	1.89 394	578	334 084	24.04 16	76.02 63	1.73 010
529	279 841	23.00 00	72.73 24	1.89 036	579	335 241	24.06 24	76.09 20	1.72 712
530	280 900	23.02 17	72.80 11	1.88 679	580	336 400	24.08 32	76.15 77	1.72 414
531	281 961	23.04 34	72.86 97	1.88 324	**581**	337 561	24.10 39	76.22 34	1.72 117
532	283 024	23.06 51	72.93 83	1.87 970	582	338 724	24.12 47	76.28 89	1.71 821
533	284 089	23.08 68	73.00 68	1.87 617	583	339 889	24.14 54	76.35 44	1.71 527
534	285 156	23.10 84	73.07 53	1.87 266	584	341 056	24.16 61	76.41 99	1.71 233
535	286 225	23.13 01	73.14 37	1.86 916	585	342 225	24.18 68	76.48 53	1.70 940
536	287 296	23.15 17	73.21 20	1.86 567	**586**	343 396	24.20 74	76.55 06	1.70 648
537	288 369	23.17 33	73.28 03	1.86 220	587	344 569	24.22 81	76.61 59	1.70 358
538	289 444	23.19 48	73.34 85	1.85 874	588	345 744	24.24 87	76.68 12	1.70 068
539	290 521	23.21 64	73.41 66	1.85 529	589	346 921	24.26 93	76.74 63	1.69 779
540	291 600	23.23 79	73.48 47	1.85 185	590	348 100	24.28 99	76.81 15	1.69 492
541	292 681	23.25 94	73.55 27	1.84 843	**591**	349 281	24.31 05	76.87 65	1.69 205
542	293 764	23.28 09	73.62 06	1.84 502	592	350 464	24.33 11	76.94 15	1.68 919
543	294 849	23.30 24	73.68 85	1.84 162	593	351 649	24.35 16	77.00 65	1.68 634
544	295 936	23.32 38	73.75 64	1.83 824	594	352 836	24.37 21	77.07 14	1.68 350
545	297 025	23.34 52	73.82 41	1.83 486	595	354 025	24.39 26	77.13 62	1.68 067
546	298 116	23.36 66	73.89 18	1.83 150	**596**	355 216	24.41 31	77.20 10	1.67 785
547	299 209	23.38 80	73.95 94	1.82 815	597	356 409	24.43 36	77.26 58	1.67 504
548	300 304	23.40 94	74.02 70	1.82 482	598	357 604	24.45 40	77.33 05	1.67 224
549	301 401	23.43 07	74.09 45	1.82 149	599	358 801	24.47 45	77.39 51	1.66 945
550	302 500	23.45 21	74.16 20	1.81 818	600	360 000	24.49 49	77.45 97	1.66 667
N	N²	√N	√10N	1000/N	N	N²	√N	√10N	1000/N

Table B-15. Squares, Square Roots, and Reciprocals (*Continued*)

N	N²	√N	√10N	1000/N	N	N²	√N	√10N	1000/N
600	360 000	24.49 49	77.45 97	1.66 667	650	422 500	25.49 51	80.62 26	1.53 846
601	361 201	24.51 53	77.52 42	1.66 389	651	423 801	25.51 47	80.68 46	1.53 610
602	362 404	24.53 57	77.58 87	1.66 113	652	425 104	25.53 43	80.74 65	1.53 374
603	363 609	24.55 61	77.65 31	1.65 837	653	426 409	25.55 39	80.80 84	1.53 139
604	364 816	24.57 64	77.71 74	1.65 563	654	427 716	25.57 34	80.87 03	1.52 905
605	366 025	24.59 67	77.78 17	1.65 289	655	429 025	25.59 30	80.93 21	1.52 672
606	367 236	24.61 71	77.84 60	1.65 017	656	430 336	25.61 25	80.99 38	1.52 439
607	368 449	24.63 74	77.91 02	1.64 745	657	431 649	25.63 20	81.05 55	1.52 207
608	369 664	24.65 77	77.97 44	1.64 474	658	432 964	25.65 15	81.11 72	1.51 976
609	370 881	24.67 79	78.03 85	1.64 204	659	434 281	25.67 10	81.17 88	1.51 745
610	372 100	24.69 82	78.10 25	1.63 934	660	435 600	25.69 05	81.24 04	1.51 515
611	373 321	24.71 84	78.16 65	1.63 666	661	436 921	25.70 99	81.30 19	1.51 286
612	374 544	24.73 86	78.23 04	1.63 399	662	438 244	25.72 94	81.36 34	1.51 057
613	375 769	24.75 88	78.29 43	1.63 132	663	439 569	25.74 88	81.42 48	1.50 830
614	376 996	24.77 90	78.35 82	1.62 866	664	440 896	25.76 82	81.48 62	1.50 602
615	378 225	24.79 92	78.42 19	1.62 602	665	442 225	25.78 76	81.54 75	1.50 376
616	379 456	24.81 93	78.48 57	1.62 338	666	443 556	25.80 70	81.60 88	1.50 150
617	380 689	24.83 95	78.54 93	1.62 075	667	444 889	25.82 63	81.67 01	1.49 925
618	381 924	24.85 96	78.61 30	1.61 812	668	446 224	25.84 57	81.73 13	1.49 701
619	383 161	24.87 97	78.67 66	1.61 551	669	447 561	25.86 50	81.79 24	1.49 477
620	384 400	24.89 98	78.74 01	1.61 290	670	448 900	25.88 44	81.85 35	1.49 254
621	385 641	24.91 99	78.80 36	1.61 031	671	450 241	25.90 37	81.91 46	1.49 031
622	386 884	24.93 99	78.86 70	1.60 772	672	451 584	25.92 30	81.97 56	1.48 810
623	388 129	24.96 00	78.93 03	1.60 514	673	452 929	25.94 22	82.03 66	1.48 588
624	389 376	24.98 00	78.99 37	1.60 256	674	454 276	25.96 15	82.09 75	1.48 368
625	390 625	25.00 00	79.05 69	1.60 000	675	455 625	25.98 08	82.15 84	1.48 148
626	391 876	25.02 00	79.12 02	1.59 744	676	456 976	26.00 00	82.21 92	1.47 929
627	393 129	25.04 00	79.18 33	1.59 490	677	458 329	26.01 92	82.28 00	1.47 710
628	394 384	25.05 99	79.24 65	1.59 236	678	459 684	26.03 84	82.34 08	1.47 493
629	395 641	25.07 99	79.30 95	1.58 983	679	461 041	26.05 76	82.40 15	1.47 275
630	396 900	25.09 98	79.37 25	1.58 730	680	462 400	26.07 68	82.46 21	1.47 059
631	398 161	25.11 97	79.43 55	1.58 479	681	463 761	26.09 60	82.52 27	1.46 843
632	399 424	25.13 96	79.49 84	1.58 228	682	465 124	26.11 51	82.58 33	1.46 628
633	400 689	25.15 95	79.56 13	1.57 978	683	466 489	26.13 43	82.64 38	1.46 413
634	401 956	25.17 94	79.62 41	1.57 729	684	467 856	26.15 34	82.70 43	1.46 199
635	403 225	25.19 92	79.68 69	1.57 480	685	469 225	26.17 25	82.76 47	1.45 985
636	404 496	25.21 90	79.74 96	1.57 233	686	470 596	26.19 16	82.82 51	1.45 773
637	405 769	25.23 89	79.81 23	1.56 986	687	471 969	26.21 07	82.88 55	1.45 560
638	407 044	25.25 87	79.87 49	1.56 740	688	473 344	26.22 98	82.94 58	1.45 349
639	408 321	25.27 84	79.93 75	1.56 495	689	474 721	26.24 88	83.00 60	1.45 138
640	409 600	25.29 82	80.00 00	1.56 250	690	476 100	26.26 79	83.06 62	1.44 928
641	410 881	25.31 80	80.06 25	1.56 006	691	477 481	26.28 69	83.12 64	1.44 718
642	412 164	25.33 77	80.12 49	1.55 763	692	478 864	26.30 59	83.18 65	1.44 509
643	413 449	25.35 74	80.18 73	1.55 521	693	480 249	26.32 49	83.24 66	1.44 300
644	414 736	25.37 72	80.24 96	1.55 280	694	481 636	26.34 39	83.30 67	1.44 092
645	416 025	25.39 69	80.31 19	1.55 039	695	483 025	26.36 29	83.36 67	1.43 885
646	417 316	25.41 65	80.37 41	1.54 799	696	484 416	26.38 18	83.42 66	1.43 678
647	418 609	25.43 62	80.43 63	1.54 560	697	485 809	26.40 08	83.48 65	1.43 472
648	419 904	25.45 58	80.49 84	1.54 321	698	487 204	26.41 97	83.54 64	1.43 266
649	421 201	25.47 55	80.56 05	1.54 083	699	488 601	26.43 86	83.60 62	1.43 062
650	422 500	25.49 51	80.62 26	1.53 846	700	490 000	26.45 75	83.66 60	1.42 857
N	N²	√N	√10N	1000/N	N	N²	√N	√10N	1000/N

Table B-15.   Squares, Square Roots, and Reciprocals (*Continued*)

N	N²	√N	√10N	1000/N
700	490 000	26.45 75	83.66 60	1.42 857
701	491 401	26.47 64	83.72 57	1.42 653
702	492 804	26.49 53	83.78 54	1.42 45C
703	494 209	26.51 41	83.84 51	1.42 248
704	495 616	26.53 30	83.90 47	1.42 045
705	497 025	26.55 18	83.96 43	1.41 844
706	498 436	26.57 07	84.02 38	1.41 643
707	499 849	26.58 95	84.08 33	1.41 443
708	501 264	26.60 83	84.14 27	1.41 243
709	502 681	26.62 71	84.20 21	1.41 044
710	504 100	26.64 58	84.26 15	1.40 845
711	505 521	26.66 46	84.32 08	1.40 647
712	506 944	26.68 33	84.38 01	1.40 449
713	508 369	26.70 21	84.43 93	1.40 252
714	509 796	26.72 08	84.49 85	1.40 056
715	511 225	26.73 95	84.55 77	1.39 860
716	512 656	26.75 82	84.61 68	1·39 665
717	514 089	26.77 69	84.67 59	1.39 470
718	515 524	26.79 55	84.73 49	1.39 276
719	516 961	26.81 42	84.79 39	1.39 082
720	518 400	26.83 28	84.85 28	1.38 889
721	519 841	26.85 14	84.91 17	1.38 696
722	521 284	26.87 01	84.97 06	1.38 504
723	522 729	26.88 87	85.02 94	1.38 313
724	524 176	26.90 72	85.08 82	1.38 122
725	525 625	26.92 58	85.14 69	1.37 931
726	527 076	26.94 44	85.20 56	1.37 741
727	528 529	26.96 29	85.26 43	1.37 552
728	529 984	26.98 15	85.32 29	1.37 363
729	531 441	27.00 00	85.38 15	1.37 174
730	532 900	27.01 85	85.44 00	1.36 986
731	534 361	27.03 70	85.49 85	1.36 799
732	535 824	27.05 55	85.55 70	1.36 612
733	537 289	27.07 40	85.61 54	1.36 426
734	538 756	27.09 24	85.67 38	1.36 240
735	540 225	27.11 09	85.73 21	1.36 054
736	541 696	27.12 93	85.79 04	1.35 870
737	543 169	27.14 77	85.84 87	1.35 685
738	544 644	27.16 62	85.90 69	1.35 501
739	546 121	27.18 46	85.96 51	1.35 318
740	547 600	27.20 29	86.02 33	1.35 135
741	549 081	27.22 13	86.08 14	1.34 953
742	550 564	27.23 97	86.13 94	1.34 771
743	552 049	27.25 80	86.19 74	1.34 590
744	553 536	27.27 64	86.25 54	1.34 409
745	555 025	27.29 47	86.31 34	1.34 228
746	556 516	27.31 30	86.37 13	1.34 048
747	558 009	27.33 13	86.42 92	1.33 869
748	559 504	27.34 96	86.48 70	1.33 690
749	561 001	27.36 79	86.54 48	1.33 511
750	562 500	27.38 61	86.60 25	1.33 333
N	N²	√N	√10N	1000/N

N	N²	√N	√10N	1000/N
750	562 500	27.38 61	86.60 25	1.33 333
751	564 001	27.40 44	86.66 03	1.33 156
752	565 504	27.42 26	86.71 79	1.32 979
753	567 009	27.44 08	86.77 56	1.32 802
754	568 516	27.45 91	86.83 32	1.32 626
755	570 025	27.47 73	86.89 07	1.32 450
756	571 536	27.49 55	86.94 83	1.32 275
757	573 049	27.51 36	87.00 57	1.32 100
758	574 564	27.53 18	87.06 32	1.31 926
759	576 081	27.55 00	87.12 06	1.31 752
760	577 600	27.56 81	87.17 80	1.31 579
761	579 121	27.58 62	87.23 53	1.31 406
762	580 644	27.60 43	87.29 26	1.31 234
763	582 169	27.62 25	87.34 99	1.31 062
764	583 696	27.64 05	87.40 71	1.30 890
765	585 225	27.65 86	87.46 43	1.30 719
766	586 756	27.67 67	87.52 14	1.30 548
767	588 289	27.69 48	87.57 85	1.30 378
768	589 824	27.71 28	87.63 56	1.30 208
769	591 361	27.73 08	87.69 26	1.30 039
770	592 900	27.74 89	87.74 96	1.29 870
771	594 441	27.76 69	87.80 66	1.29 702
772	595 984	27.78 49	87.86 35	1.29 534
773	597 529	27.80 29	87.92 04	1.29 366
774	599 076	27.82 09	87.97 73	1.29 199
775	600 625	27.83 88	88.03 41	1.29 032
776	602 176	27.85 68	88.09 09	1.28 866
777	603 729	27.87 47	88.14 76	1.28 700
778	605 284	27.89 27	88.20 43	1.28 535
779	606 841	27.91 06	88.26 10	1.28 370
780	608 400	27.92 85	88.31 76	1.28 205
781	609 961	27.94 64	88.37 42	1.28 041
782	611 524	27.96 43	88.43 08	1.27 877
783	613 089	27.98 21	88.48 73	1.27 714
784	614 656	28.00 00	88.54 38	1.27 551
785	616 225	28.01 79	88.60 02	1.27 389
786	617 796	28.03 57	88.65 66	1.27 226
787	619 369	28.05 35	88.71 30	1.27 065
788	620 944	28.07 13	88.76 94	1.26 904
789	622 521	28.08 91	88.82 57	1.26 743
790	624 100	28.10 69	88.88 19	1.26 582
791	625 681	28.12 47	88.93 82	1.26 422
792	627 264	28.14 25	88.99 44	1.26 263
793	628 849	28.16 03	89.05 05	1.26 103
794	630 436	28.17 80	89.10 67	1.25 945
795	632 025	28.19 57	89.16 28	1.25 786
796	633 616	28.21 35	89.21 88	1.25 628
797	635 209	28.23 12	89.27 49	1.25 471
798	636 804	28.24 89	89.33 08	1.25 313
799	638 401	28.26 66	89.38 68	1.25 156
800	640 000	28.28 43	89.44 27	1.25 000
N	N²	√N	√10N	1000/N

Table B-15.   Squares, Square Roots, and Reciprocals *(Continued)*

N	N²	√N	√10N	1000 /N	N	N²	√N	√10N	1000 /N
800	640 000	28.28 43	89.44 27	1.25 000	**850**	722 500	29.15 48	92.19 54	1.17 647
801	641 601	28.30 19	89.49 86	1.24 844	851	724 201	29.17 19	92.24 97	1.17 509
802	643 204	28.31 96	89.55 45	1.24 688	852	725 904	29.18 90	92.30 38	1.17 371
803	644 809	28.33 73	89.61 03	1.24 533	853	727 609	29.20 62	92.35 80	1.17 233
804	646 416	28.35 49	89.66 60	1.24 378	854	729 316	29.22 33	92.41 21	1.17 096
805	648 025	28.37 25	89.72 18	1.24 224	855	731 025	29.24 04	92.46 62	1.16 959
806	649 636	28.39 01	89.77 75	1.24 069	**856**	732 736	29.25 75	92.52 03	1.16 822
807	651 249	28.40 77	89.83 32	1.23 916	857	734 449	29.27 46	92.57 43	1.16 686
808	652 864	28.42 53	89.88 88	1.23 762	858	736 164	29.29 16	92.62 83	1.16 550
809	654 481	28.44 29	89.94 44	1.23 609	859	737 881	29.30 87	92.68 23	1.16 414
810	656 100	28.46 05	90.00 00	1.23 457	860	739 600	29.32 58	92.73 62	1.16 279
811	657 721	28.47 81	90.05 55	1.23 305	**861**	741 321	29.34 28	92.79 01	1.16 144
812	659 344	28.49 56	90.11 10	1.23 153	862	743 044	29.35 98	92.84 40	1.16 009
813	660 969	28.51 32	90.16 65	1.23 001	863	744 769	29.37 69	92.89 78	1.15 875
814	662 596	28.53 07	90.22 19	1.22 850	864	746 496	29.39 39	92.95 16	1.15 741
815	664 225	28.54 82	90.27 74	1.22 699	865	748 225	29.41 09	93.00 54	1.15 607
816	665 856	28.56 57	90.33 27	1.22 549	**866**	749 956	29.42 79	93.05 91	1.15 473
817	667 489	28.58 32	90.38 81	1.22 399	867	751 689	29.44 49	93.11 28	1.15 340
818	669 124	28.60 07	90.44 34	1.22 249	868	753 424	29.46 18	93.16 65	1.15 207
819	670 761	28.61 82	90.49 86	1.22 100	869	755 161	29.47 88	93.22 02	1.15 075
820	672 400	28.63 56	90.55 39	1.21 951	870	756 900	29.49 58	93.27 38	1.14 943
821	674 041	28.65 31	90.60 91	1.21 803	**871**	758 641	29.51 27	93.32 74	1.14 811
822	675 684	28.67 05	90.66 42	1.21 655	872	760 384	29.52 96	93.38 09	1.14 679
823	677 329	28.68 80	90.71 93	1.21 507	873	762 129	29.54 66	93.43 45	1.14 548
824	678 976	28.70 54	90.77 44	1.21 359	874	763 876	29.56 35	93.48 80	1.14 416
825	680 625	28.72 28	90.82 95	1.21 212	875	765 625	29.58 04	93.54 14	1.14 286
826	682 276	28.74 02	90.88 45	1.21 065	**876**	767 376	29.59 73	93.59 49	1.14 155
827	683 929	28.75 76	90.93 95	1.20 919	877	769 129	29.61 42	93.64 83	1.14 025
828	685 584	28.77 50	90.99 45	1.20 773	878	770 884	29.63 11	93.70 17	1.13 895
829	687 241	28.79 24	91.04 94	1.20 627	879	772 641	29.64 79	93.75 50	1.13 766
830	688 900	28.80 97	91.10 43	1.20 482	880	774 400	29.66 48	93.80 83	1.13 636
831	690 561	28.82 71	91.15 92	1.20 337	**881**	776 161	29.68 16	93.86 16	1.13 507
832	692 224	28.84 44	91.21 40	1.20 192	882	777 924	29.69 85	93.91 49	1.13 379
833	693 889	28.86 17	91.26 88	1.20 048	883	779 689	29.71 53	93.96 81	1.13 250
834	695 556	28.87 91	91.32 36	1.19 904	884	781 456	29.73 21	94.02 13	1.13 122
835	697 225	28.89 64	91.37 83	1.19 760	885	783 225	29.74 89	94.07 44	1.12 994
836	698 896	28.91 37	91.43 30	1.19 617	**886**	784 996	29.76 58	94.12 76	1.12 867
837	700 569	28.93 10	91.48 77	1.19 474	887	786 769	29.78 25	94.18 07	1.12 740
838	702 244	28.94 82	91.54 23	1.19 332	888	788 544	29.79 93	94.23 38	1.12 613
839	703 921	28.96 55	91.59 69	1.19 190	889	790 321	29.81 61	94.28 68	1.12 486
840	705 600	28.98 28	91.65 15	1.19 048	890	792 100	29.83 29	94.33 98	1.12 360
841	707 281	29.00 00	91.70 61	1.18 906	**891**	793 881	29.84 96	94.39 28	1.12 233
842	708 964	29.01 72	91.76 06	1.18 765	892	795 664	29.86 64	94.44 58	1.12 108
843	710 649	29.03 45	91.81 50	1.18 624	893	797 449	29.88 31	94.49 87	1.11 982
844	712 336	29.05 17	91.86 95	1.18 483	894	799 236	29.89 98	94.55 16	1.11 857
845	714 025	29.06 89	91.92 39	1.18 343	895	801 025	29.91 66	94.60 44	1.11 732
846	715 716	29.08 61	91.97 83	1.18 203	**896**	802 816	29.93 33	94.65 73	1.11 607
847	717 409	29.10 33	92.03 26	1.18 064	897	804 609	29.95 00	94.71 01	1.11 483
848	719 104	29.12 04	92.08 69	1.17 925	898	806 404	29.96 66	94.76 29	1.11 359
849	720 801	29.13 76	92.14 12	1.17 786	899	808 201	29.98 33	94.81 56	1.11 235
850	722 500	29.15 48	92.19 54	1.17 647	900	810 000	30.00 00	94.86 83	1.11 111
N	N²	√N	√10N	1000 /N	N	N²	√N	√10N	1000 /N

Table B-15. Squares, Square Roots, and Reciprocals (*Continued*)

N	N²	√N	√10N	1000 /N	N	N²	√N	√10N	1000 /N
900	810 000	30.00 00	94.86 83	1.11 111	950	902 500	30.82 21	97.46 79	1.05 263
901	811 801	30.01 67	94.92 10	1.10 988	951	904 401	30.83 83	97.51 92	1.05 152
902	813 604	30.03 33	94.97 37	1.10 865	952	906 304	30.85 45	97.57 05	1.05 042
903	815 409	30.05 00	95.02 63	1.10 742	953	908 209	30.87 07	97.62 17	1.04 932
904	817 216	30.06 66	95.07 89	1.10 619	954	910 116	30.88 69	97.67 29	1.04 822
905	819 025	30.08 32	95.13 15	1.10 497	955	912 025	30.90 31	97.72 41	1.04 712
906	820 836	30.09 98	95.18 40	1.10 375	956	913 936	30.91 92	97.77 53	1.04 603
907	822 649	30.11 64	95.23 65	1.10 254	957	915 849	30.93 54	97.82 64	1.04 493
908	824 464	30.13 30	95.28 90	1.10 132	958	917 764	30.95 16	97.87 75	1.04 384
909	826 281	30.14 96	95.34 15	1.10 011	959	919 681	30.96 77	97.92 85	1.04 275
910	828 100	30.16 62	95.39 39	1.09 890	960	921 600	30.98 39	97.97 96	1.04 167
911	829 921	30.18 28	95.44 63	1.09 769	961	923 521	31.00 00	98.03 06	1.04 058
912	831 744	30.19 93	95.49 87	1.09 649	962	925 444	31.01 61	98.08 16	1.03 950
913	833 569	30.21 59	95.55 10	1.09 529	963	927 369	31.03 22	98.13 26	1.03 842
914	835 396	30.23 24	95.60 33	1.09 409	964	929 296	31.04 83	98.18 35	1.03 734
915	837 225	30.24 90	95.65 56	1.09 290	965	931 225	31.06 44	98.23 44	1.03 627
916	839 056	30.26 55	95.70 79	1.09 170	966	933 156	31.08 05	98.28 53	1.03 520
917	840 889	30.28 20	95.76 01	1 09 051	967	935 089	31.09 66	98.33 62	1.03 413
918	842 724	30.29 85	95.81 23	1.08 932	968	937 024	31.11 27	98.38 70	1.03 306
919	844 561	30.31 50	95.86 45	1.08 814	969	938 961	31.12 88	98.43 78	1.03 199
920	846 400	30.33 15	95.91 66	1.08 696	970	940 900	31.14 48	98.48 86	1.03 093
921	848 241	30.34 80	95.96 87	1.08 578	971	942 841	31.16 09	98.53 93	1.02 987
922	850 084	30.36 45	96.02 08	1.08 460	972	944 784	31.17 69	98.59 01	1.02 881
923	851 929	30.38 09	96.07 29	1.08 342	973	946 729	31.19 29	98.64 08	1.02 775
924	853 776	30.39 74	96.12 49	1.08 225	974	948 676	31.20 90	98.69 14	1.02 669
925	855 625	30.41 38	96.17 69	1.08 108	975	950 625	31.22 50	98.74 21	1.02 564
926	857 476	30.43 02	96.22 89	1.07 991	976	952 576	31.24 10	98.79 27	1.02 459
927	859 329	30.44 67	96.28 08	1.07 875	977	954 529	31.25 70	98.84 33	1.02 354
928	861 184	30.46 31	96.33 28	1.07 759	978	956 484	31.27 30	98.89 39	1.02 249
929	863 041	30.47 95	96.38 46	1.07 643	979	958 441	31.28 90	98.94 44	1.02 145
930	864 900	30.49 59	96.43 65	1.07 527	980	960 400	31.30 50	98.99 49	1.02 041
931	866 761	30.51 23	96.48 83	1.07 411	981	962 361	31.32 09	99.04 54	1.01 937
932	868 624	30.52 87	96.54 01	1.07 296	982	964 324	31.33 69	99.09 59	1.01 833
933	870 489	30.54 50	96.59 19	1.07 181	983	966 289	31.35 28	99.14 64	1.01 729
934	872 356	30.56 14	96.64 37	1.07 066	984	968 256	31.36 88	99.19 68	1.01 626
935	874 225	30.57 78	96.69 54	1.06 952	985	970 225	31.38 47	99.24 72	1.01 523
936	676 096	30.59 41	96.74 71	1.06 838	986	972 196	31.40 06	99.29 75	1.01 420
937	877 969	30.61 05	96.79 88	1.06 724	987	974 169	31.41 66	99.34 79	1.01 317
938	879 844	30.62 68	96.85 04	1.06 610	988	976 144	31.43 25	99.39 82	1.01 215
939	881 721	30.64 31	96.90 20	1.06 496	989	978 121	31.44 84	99.44 85	1.01 112
940	883 600	30.65 94	96.95 36	1.06 383	990	980 100	31.46 43	99.49 87	1.01 010
941	885 481	30.67 57	97.00 52	1.06 270	991	982 081	31.48 02	99.54 90	1.00 908
942	887 364	30.69 20	97.05 67	1.06 157	992	984 064	31.49 60	99.59 92	1.00 806
943	889 249	30.70 83	97.10 82	1.06 045	993	986 049	31.51 19	99.64 94	1.00 705
944	891 136	30.72 46	97.15 97	1.05 932	994	988 036	31.52 78	99.69 95	1.00 604
945	893 025	30.74 09	97.21 11	1.05 820	995	990 025	31.54 36	99.74 97	1.00 503
946	894 916	30.75 71	97.26 25	1.05 708	996	992 016	31.55 95	99.79 98	1.00 402
947	896 809	30.77 34	97.31 39	1.05 597	997	994 009	31.57 53	99.84 99	1.00 301
948	898 704	30.78 96	97.36 53	1.05 485	998	996 004	31.59 11	99.89 99	1.00 200
949	900 601	30.80 58	97.41 66	1.05 374	999	998 001	31.60 70	99.95 00	1.00 100
950	902 500	30.82 21	97.46 79	1.05 263	1000	1000 000	31.62 28	100.00 00	1.00 000
N	N²	√N	√10N	1000 /N	N	N²	√N	√10N	1000 /N

Table B-16. Table of Values for Computing Height of Normal Curve at z

(Table shows value of $e^{-(z^2/2\sigma^2)}$)

Z	.00	.01	.02	.03	.04	.05	.06	.07	.08	.09
0.0	1.00000	.99995	.99980	.99955	.99920	.99875	.99820	.99755	.99685	.99596
0.1	.99501	.99396	.99283	.99158	.99025	.98881	.98728	.98565	.98393	.98211
0.2	.98020	.97819	.97609	.97390	.97161	.96923	.96676	.96420	.96156	.95882
0.3	.95600	.95309	.95010	.94702	.94387	.94055	.93723	.93382	.93024	.92677
0.4	.92312	.91399	.91558	.91169	.90774	.90371	.89961	.89543	.89119	.88688
0.5	.88250	.87805	.87353	.86896	.86432	.85962	.85488	.85006	.84519	.84060
0.6	.83527	.83023	.83514	.82010	.81481	.80957	.80429	.79896	.79459	.78817
0.7	.78270	.77721	.77167	.76610	.76048	.75484	.74916	.74342	.73769	.73193
0.8	.72615	.72033	.71448	.70861	.70272	.69681	.69087	.68493	.67896	.67298
0.9	.66689	.66097	.65494	.64891	.64287	.63683	.63077	.62472	.61865	.61259
1.0	.60653	.60047	.59440	.58834	.58228	.57623	.57017	.56414	.55810	.55209
1.1	.54607	.54007	.53409	.52812	.52214	.51620	.51027	.50437	.49848	.49260
1.2	.48675	.48092	.47511	.46933	.46357	.45793	.45212	.44644	.44078	.43516
1.3	.42956	.42399	.41845	.41294	.40747	.40202	.39661	.39123	.38569	.38058
1.4	.37531	.37007	.36487	.35971	.35459	.34950	.34445	.33944	.33447	.32954
1.5	.32465	.31980	.31500	.31023	.30550	.30082	.29618	.29158	.28702	.28251
1.6	.27804	.27361	.26923	.26489	.26059	.25634	.25213	.24797	.24385	.23978
1.7	.23575	.23176	.22782	.22392	.22008	.21627	.21251	.20879	.20511	.20148
1.8	.19790	.19436	.19086	.18741	.18400	.18064	.17732	.17904	.17081	.16762
1.9	.16448	.16137	.15831	.15530	.15232	.14939	.14650	.14364	.14083	.13806
2.0	.13534	.13265	.13000	.12740	.12483	.12230	.11981	.11737	.11496	.11259
2.1	.11025	.10795	.10570	.10347	.10129	.09914	.09702	.09495	.09290	.09090
2.2	.08892	.08698	.08507	.08320	.08136	.07956	.07778	.07604	.07433	.07265
2.3	.07100	.06939	.06780	.06624	.06471	.06321	.06174	.06029	.05888	.05750
2.4	.05614	.05481	.05350	.05222	.05096	.04973	.04852	.04737	.04618	.04505
2.5	.04394	.04285	.04179	.04074	.03972	.03873	.03775	.03680	.03586	.03494
2.6	.03405	.03317	.03232	.03148	.03066	.02986	.02908	.02831	.02757	.02684
2.7	.02612	.02542	.02474	.02408	.02343	.02280	.02218	.02157	.02098	.02040
2.8	.01984	.01929	.01876	.01823	.01772	.01723	.01674	.01627	.01581	.01536
2.9	.01492	.01449	.01408	.01367	.01328	.01288	.01252	.01215	.01179	.01145
3.0	.01111									
4.0	.00034									

index